California Chronicle.

L. VI. SAN FRANCISCO, FRIDAY MORNING, JUNE 6, 1856.

Evening Bulletin.

VOL. III. SAN FRANCISCO, FRIDAY EVENING, OCTOBER 17, 1856. NO. 9.

Daily Alta California.

VOL. III. SAN FRANCISCO, TUESDAY MORNING, JANUARY 13, 1852. NO. 12.

Same illus. inside back cover.

THE SAN FRANCISCO DAILY HERALD.

IV. SAN FRANCISCO: SUNDAY MORNING, OCTOBER 2, 1853. NO. 123.

SACRAMENTO DAILY UNION.

WHOLE NO. 1492 SACRAMENTO, MONDAY MORNING, JANUARY 7, 1856. PRICE TEN CENTS.

SOUTHERN CALIFORNIAN.

INDEPENDENT WEEKLY PAPER, DEVOTED TO THE INTERESTS OF SOUTHERN CALIFORNIA, LITERATURE, THE MARKETS, &C. &C. &C.

L. 2. LOS ANGELES, WEDNESDAY MORNING, AUGUST 8, 1855. NO. 4.

THE FIREMAN'S JOURNAL
AND MILITARY GAZETTE.

VOL. III—NO. 2. SAN FRANCISCO, SATURDAY, APRIL 12, 1856. WHOLE NO. 54.

THE PACIFIC.

REV. J. W. DOUGLAS, PROPRIETOR.

"First Pure, then Peaceable without Partiality and without Hypocrisy."

VOL. I. SAN FRANCISCO, CALIFORNIA, FRIDAY, AUGUST 29, 1851. NO. 2.

SAN FRANCISCO DAILY EVENING NEWS.

OFFICE No. 35 COMMERCIAL STREET (LONG WHARF) CORNER OF FRONT STREET: SUBSCRIPTION PRICE 25 CENTS PER WEEK.

VOL. I.] SAN FRANCISCO: MONDAY EVENING, MAY 1, 1854. [NO. 155.

A HISTORY
OF CALIFORNIA NEWSPAPERS
1846-1858

Edward Gilbert and Edward C. Kemble
[FROM AN OLD DAGUERREOTYPE]

A HISTORY OF
CALIFORNIA NEWSPAPERS
1846 - 1858

by EDWARD C. KEMBLE

❁ ❁ ❁

Reprinted From the Supplement to the Sacramento Union *of December 25, 1858*

Edited and with a Foreword
by HELEN HARDING BRETNOR

THE TALISMAN PRESS
Los Gatos, California 1962

Library of Congress catalog card 61-10539

Contents

To my parents
for their faith
and to my husband
for his works

Foreword

by Helen Harding Bretnor

Edward Cleveland Kemble published ***The History of California Newspapers*** in the Sacramento ***Union*** of December 25, 1858. Newspaper publishing in California was then scarcely twelve years old, but its history was already an active, adventurous, and complicated one. Hundreds of papers had been started, and hundreds had already perished, their fortunes varying with those of the Gold Rush towns which gave them birth. Their history was in danger of perishing with them.

Kemble was singularly well qualified to write that history. He came to San Francisco—then still Yerba Buena—in 1846, at the age of seventeen, accompanying the town's first press. From the founding of the *California Star* in January of the following year, he was intimately connected with the newspapers of San Francisco and of Sacramento, and this experience helps to explain the almost paternal devotion with which he recorded the births and deaths of papers, the permutations and relationships of the wildly proliferating Press, and the fate of the many, many men concerned in it. This interest was constantly reflected in the newspapers with which he was associated; his ***History*** was a recapitulation and expansion of his continuing reports, based on the record of the files and the results of a questionnaire which he circulated among editors throughout the State. As he realized at the time, the period of individualistic journalism was fast coming to an end; the transcontinental telegraph would soon bring uniformity. He preserved the story of California's early Press while the material for it was still available. Slight emendations may still be made today, but the body of the work could not now be reproduced. For this record we owe him a debt of gratitude.

"The boy editor," as he was sometimes called in California, came by his interest naturally. Born in Troy, New York, on November 11, 1828, he was the son of John Cleveland Kemble, editor of the Troy *Budget* and a former New York State Senator. By 1845, young Kemble was a printer in New York City, working on the *Prophet,* weekly organ of the Latter Day Saints. In this capacity, though not himself a Mormon, he sailed on the *Brooklyn* early in February 1846 with the California-bound colony led by the paper's editor, Elder Samuel Brannan.

The expedition was recruited and equipped to be as nearly self-sustaining as possible; it was intended to form the nucleus of a settlement, perhaps an empire, in Mexican Alta California, for hard-pressed Mormons from the United States. "Nearly all the trades were represented," Kemble wrote twenty years later for the Sacramento *Union* of September 11, 1866, in what Hubert Howe Bancroft called "a very complete narrative of the whole matter, probably the best extant." Kemble continued his recollections:

> . . . a goodly assortment of all the implements and utensils of domestic industry, including some of the most recent improvements in husbandry, had been purchased with the company fund and stowed aboard the Brooklyn . . . They had a small library for use on board the ship . . . and as a crowning triumph of the genius of civilization which directed their efforts, they had taken on board with them a press, type and entire office material of the *Prophet* newspaper, two of the printers (mere boys) employed on the paper adhering to its fortunes and accompanying this first Yankee press on its mission to California.

Not only was the expedition equipped to print a newspaper on arrival, but before leaving New York enough of a start had been made—a masthead for the Yerba Buena *California Star* engraved and stereotyped, and a few lines set up and packed—to enable Kemble later to make a half-serious claim to precedence over the Monterey *Californian,* in date of planning if not of publication.

The voyage progressed with the usual dissatisfactions and discomforts, but without major disaster. Kemble recalled it as a better-behaved voyage than most, with no scandal, though perhaps some talk about the leader of the expedition, who soon deserted the company's rough fare for the captain's table. There were several deaths, and two births, a storm in the first days, and another off the coast of Chile which drove them back almost to the Horn. The captain, a timid soul, warned them that he did not expect the ship to survive the second tempest. He also expected a mutiny of the passengers, for no apparent reason, and had the crew prepare the ship's rusty arms against attack. Their first landing was at the island of Juan Fernandez, and a welcome week it was, with fishing and the exploration of scenes made familiar by the childhood reading of *Robinson Crusoe.* The next stop, on the twentieth of June, was at Honolulu, where a friendly reception made the Mormon passengers forget their suspicions of strangers, but where they learned the distressing news that the United States was at war with Mexico and that probably California was no longer available for a new empire. The rest of the voyage was occupied in military preparations to aid the American conquest if necessary, and in making a good impression on the captain.

On the 31st of July, 1846, the ship entered the Bay of San Francisco.

> As the strange ship sailed up to the entrance of the silent harbor curious eyes were watching from her crowded decks the slowly unfolding of scenes [sic] of this then foreign landscape. There

were anxious eyes, too, fixed on the fort ahead, and as the ship drew within range of her guns it was deemed prudent by the Captain and chief men aboard that all but the crew should retire under hatches. And so, in silence and apprehension, Fort Point was passed.

Coming back on deck, the newcomers gazed with wonder on the bold, bleak, treeless shores and the broad expanse of water stretching before them, disturbed only by the myriads of wild fowl. Rounding the point later known as Telegraph Hill, they found the cove already occupied by a Yankee man-of-war at anchor, and four or five battered hulks like their own, flaunting the colors they thought they had left behind.

On shore the United States flag was flying above a low red-tiled building, on an open square, the center of a stunted growth of dingy foreign-looking houses, scattered over the clear space that stretched back from the sandy beach. What an odd, uncouth town it was! and how its discordant features did smite and jar on the preconceived fancies of the Brooklyn passengers.

Whatever they expected to see, the very fact of their presence changed the balance of the picture, as had the arrival of the *Portsmouth.* Alta California was no longer Mexican; nor was it to be a Mormon empire.

The United States had taken over in California. In Monterey and in Yerba Buena, marines guarded plaza and custom-house; the posts of alcalde, or chief civil magistrate, were held by naval officers. Men of the Bear Flag were enlisted as volunteers in the United States Army; Commodore Stockton entered Los Angeles, and on August 17 proclaimed: "The Flag of the United States is now flying from every commanding position in the Territory, and California is entirely free from Mexican dominion."

Among American institutions, one of the first to be encouraged was that of the Press. Newspaper beginnings may have been small in California, but they were prompt to appear after the occupation. Even before the ***Brooklyn*** company could set up their press and print the *California Star* in Yerba Buena, the old Mexican government press in Monterey was being readied for action with the blessings of the United States Navy. This relationship between the Navy and the *Californian* was recognized by Kemble who, however, in his speculations perhaps did not give enough credit to Robert Baylor Semple as prime mover. Semple's part is indicated by a letter which exists in transcript in the Bancroft Library, copied from the Society of California Pioneers' archives before their destruction in the San Francisco earthquake and fire of 1906. It would seem worth printing the document in this connection. Addressing Captain Daingerfield Fauntleroy of the company of California Dragoons, Private Semple writes:

Monterey Aug 1846

Dear Sir

On my arrival here I found everything in a state of quiet, no news from the enemy and but little apprehention on the part of the officers here of any attack from them, but they are expecting information from the south daily Mr Price will hand you this and tell you all the news.

On examination I found a very good press and a sufficient quantity of type to print a paper, the size of this sheet [12½ by 8½ inches]. Capt. Mervin[e] offered me the use of them and his warm support in the publication of a paper. Parson Colton who is practiced in the chair Editorial is highly pleased and offers his talents and the warm support and approbation of the Comodore. Mr. Miner [George Minor, Lt., U.S.N., on the *Savannah*] offered me the upper room in the North end of the upper Barracks for an office to which I have removed all the printing materials. I have also got 40 reams of paper which will answer for a commencement and I am in hopes that in a short time we shall be able to enlarge the sheet. I should have gone out tomorrow according to promise but the Captn thought it unnecessary and advised me to write to you requesting a discharge. I regret exceedingly to ask for it, but as my object in leaving home, was to act where I cant [sic] be of the most service to my adopted country and being the only person here who understands the management of a newspaper. I feel it my duty to do so,

My opinion is coroborated by all the officers on the station, that a well conducted paper at this time would do more to conciliate the Natives and unite the foreigners residing in California than any other step which can be taken, and would have a powerful tendency to get things right at home. It will be the medium through which the movements of the energetic officers on this station will reach the people, not only of this country but our friends at home. It will set forth the immense resources of this country, and its commercial importance and will have a powerful influence in settling this country with an enlightened population.

With this view of the matter I feel that my duty impels me to ask for my discharge but permit me to assure you, that it is with feelings of regret, that I leave the company with which I have been so kindly and amicable associated. Should you differ from me in opinion, notify me by the first oportunity and you will find me at my post.

With my kinest feelings for your officers and the company
I remain With great Respect
Your Obt Servant
R. Semple

It is noted that Semple served in Monterey from July 15 to August 15, 1846, when he was "discharged by request to Edit Paper." The Monterey *Californian,* first newspaper in California, made its appearance on August 15.

The "very good press" found by Semple was the famous Ramage whose long and honorable history has been told by Kemble with affectionate respect and with more accuracy in detail than was observed by most of his successors. For three quarters of a century one writer after another told of the "Mexican war press" which had come the long way overland, finally reaching California with Zamorano. Modern scholarship, however, has shown Kemble to have been basically correct. In the *Quarterly News-letter* of the Book Club of California, June 1934, George L. Harding published his findings, based in part on research by Adele Ogden, in which he showed that the press had come from Boston on the *Lagoda,* arriving in June or July of 1834, shortly before Zamorano printed his "Aviso al Público."

It was invoiced in Boston on May 20, 1833, and the order could have been carried by Captain Thomas Shaw who sailed from San Diego for Boston on January 17, 1832, as supercargo of the ship *Pocahontas*. Thus Kemble was correct in outline, though mistaken as to date by two years. Harding gives a complete account of the early history of the press in his biography, *Don Agustín V. Zamorano, Statesman, Soldier, Craftsman, and California's First Printer,* (Los Angeles, The Zamorano Club, 1934) which he dedicated to "the memory of Edward C. Kemble, the first historian of California's pioneer press."

Beginning with Colton's statement in the *Californian,* quoted by Kemble and by most writers on the subject since then, much has been made of the lack of the letter "w" in the "spanish font, picked up here in a cloister." Semple may have been speaking optimistically when he called it "a sufficient quantity of type to print a paper," but the "w" was not entirely lacking, as a study of the files will show. The type, identified by Harding as being from the Boston Type and Stereotype Foundry, started as a good English alphabet, though it may have developed a Spanish accent from its long years in California.

While the *Californian* was making its appearance in Monterey, San Francisco's first press was being set up in temporary quarters above a grist mill. Here, job printing was done, and official notices and proclamations, but for some reason the New York-made masthead was not used until the issuance of "An Extra in Advance of the *California Star*" on October 24, 1846. A copy of this extra was seen by Douglas C. McMurtrie in the possession of Boutwell Dunlap before 1928, and was reported by Herbert Fahey in 1956 and by Robert Greenwood in 1961.

In the latter part of October, Frémont issued a call for volunteers in Monterey, and a manuscript notice was posted in the billiard rooms of the City Hotel and the Portsmouth House in Yerba Buena. The *Brooklyn* Mormons were urged in a patriotic appeal by their leaders to join—and, Kemble wrote later, "my good friend of those days was what the Methodists would call a powerful exhorter"—but only the young printer responded, though later on a few of the Mormons turned up in the battalion. Kemble's account of his adventures then, and other recollections of the days of 1846-1848, appeared as a series of letters to the Sacramento *Union* published at intervals during 1871-1873. It would be well worth reprinting, but is too long to allow more than an outline and brief excerpts here.

Early in November 1846, the Yerba Buena company of volunteers, consisting of Thomas Fallon as captain and Kemble as "high private," marched forth past the snares of bars and billiard parlors, cheered on by the populace. Kemble, as the rank and file, was in charge of the pack train consisting of one mule—which he seemed to find an army in itself. From the Plaza, they followed the sandy road to the Mission, battling the mule all the way. They lunched at the site of San Mateo, and at last reached Santa Clara at candlelight. In San Jose, the Yerba Buena company disbanded, "Big Fallon" to go on alone to Monterey, and Kemble to join a company under Captain B. K. Thompson. On November 20, he enlisted in Company G of Frémont's California Battalion for three months at $25 a month, receiving the rank of Quartermaster Sergeant, "(probably in recognition of his gallant service with the mule on the road from Yerba Buena) . . . His principal duty was to make out requisitions on the Battalion Quartermaster, which were never filled." There were thirty-five in the company, "rough border men, runaway sailors, negroes, etc."

The company of San Jose volunteers under Captain Thompson, encamped at San Juan, was joined by a company of mounted men from Sutter's Fort under Captain Burroughs. Leaving the San Jose men in camp to refresh their mounts, the two officers with a band of captured horses left for Monterey through the narrow gap in the Gabillan Mountains. Soon Thompson reappeared dramatically, with news of a party of Californians. Eager for battle, he rushed his men helter-skelter in a "ten-mile race" to Gomez' rancho, shedding equipment all the way. Four scouts had been cut off and surrounded by the Californians; a party of Walla Walla Indians with the Sacramentans was attempting a rescue, while the rest guarded the horses at Gomez' rancho. There was disagreement between the two officers: Thompson urged immediate attack; Burroughs felt it would be impractical, as the small, untrained band was responsible for the horses—and there were 200 Californians arrayed against them.

It was past meridian when our Indian allies came galloping back with word that the enemy were preparing to attack our party, and pretty soon we saw a body of horsemen move out from the oaks and form line of battle along the banks of the Salinas river, full two miles off. We could see even at this distance that they were splendidly mounted, and as the sun fell on their lance-heads their arms seemed to flash a proud defiance in our faces. Our men were drawn up to receive them, but they came no nigher. Our red-skins, bristling with feathers and grim with paint, were fierce for scalps and thirsty for the blood of the foe. They rushed out upon the plain, advancing within musket shot of the California line, brandished their arms and dared the threatened assault. Mounted on their little cayuse ponies, they would sometimes draw the better mounted enemy in squads after them . . . From these encounters the Indians would ride back to our position and survey our peaceful attitude with wonder and contempt. Another hour of indecision passed and Thompson could control himself no longer. He rode over to Burroughs and branded him with cowardice and demanded that the men should be led into action. Burroughs, stung by his reproaches but deadly pale and evidently weighed down with a presentiment of evil, ordered his company to take fresh horses and prepare for battle. Then followed another scene like that we had witnessed at the Mission in the morning. Few of our men had other animals besides those on which they were mounted; but they rode out into the plain with upraised arms and gallant front, and with cheers

> that must have been heard at the Salinas river.
>
> Drawn out in line of battle, the American volunteers that were about to engage the native forces in this the first and only fight of any consequence which occurred during the war in Northern California, numbered fifty-five. I am giving it more prominence, doubtless, than it deserves; but, for the reason just stated, and because important results hung upon it, and also because it has never been written up, to my recollection, let us be particular with what followed.

Kemble then proceeds to give details of the brave, unnecessary battle, in which three or four were killed on each side, including the reluctant Captain Burroughs, and as many more wounded. The Americans were left in posession of the field, but with a new respect for the gallant Californians. Kemble retained the memory of Captain Thompson, "the 'hell-roaring sorrel' . . . out in the plain, bare-headed, far in advance of our company, shaking his fist impotently at the retreating Californians." The amateur soldiers, however, sobered by the sight of blood, went about the business of preparing against renewed attack, while sending word to Frémont of the fight on the Salinas. Two anxious nights, with a day occupied in burial of the dead and care for the wounded, were followed by an alarm the next morning as a column of mounted men was seen approaching under a strange flag. As the company prepared for battle, they heard the strains of "Yankee Doodle" and realized that here was the eagerly awaited relief. Frémont, the hero of Kemble's youthful imagination, whose adventures had awakened his interest in the West, had arrived with his buckskin and blue-shirt battalion with their banner of an eagle painted on a square field of blue. The horses were saved, Frémont's march to the south could continue, and the Battle of Natividad passed into the limbo of history, almost unnoticed.

Kemble's opinion of Frémont underwent a drastic change during the "bloodless, bad weather, hungry-belly campaign" following the battle, and his account of the famous march of the California Battalion is full of vivid detail. As supplies disappeared, his comments became sharper.

> It was said to be Fremont's intention to baffle the enemy who were supposed to still hold possession of Santa Barbara, by a flank movement, crossing the mountains above the town while they watched for them by the main road, and so sweeping down along the sea shore, surprise them. This, to be sure, was about what we had been doing ever since the battalion marched southward, and if we had not surprised the enemy at any point we had been ourselves astonished, and I ought to add disgusted, more than once . . . The theory of Fremont's campaign was so absurd that it had dropped below criticism at our camp-fires. Every man, down to the Digger horse-thief Indians, knew that we were beating the air in our roundabout marches—that while we were wearing out our animals and exhausting the strength of our hardiest men by seeking out the roughest and most impracticable routes southward, in the vain hope of stealing a march on the foe—his well-mounted spies knew all about our movements and where we encamped every night. However, the surprise maggot in our leader's brain was about to hatch out again, and we lighted our camp-fires at St. Inez and killed the last of our lean beeves . . .

That was the last of comfort before Santa Barbara. The next day, December 24, they were ordered to cross the mountain, taking a disused trail too steep for cannon — but somehow they made it to the top where they camped in a gale of wind. Christmas Day found them drenched by sheets of rain, each one fighting his own way down the mountain, all discipline gone with all cheer. That night, Kemble

> found himself . . . at the foot of the hill of difficulty, bare-headed, sore-footed, with one leg of his trowsers slashed up to the thigh, *calcinero* fashion, but grimly holding on that gun. We lay down in the sheets of water which overspread the earth everywhere, and supperless and fireless shivered the long night away.

Most distressing to Kemble was the loss among the precious horses; a tidying-up expedition rescued the cannon but was too late for the animals — over one hundred horses and mules were counted, dying or dead, in the track of the battalion. There was a week in Santa Barbara for recovery; the unsurprised enemy had left. The battalion then continued on south, to find the war over; there was nothing to do but to sign the Capitulation at Cahuenga on January 13. Later, with his pay in his pocket, Kemble and a friend had a pleasant and leisurely ride back to Yerba Buena, arriving early in April.

❁ ❁ ❁

In the meantime, number one of the *California Star* had made its appearance on January 9, 1847, preceded by a *California Star—Extra* dated January 1 and addressed "To the Saints in England and America." This extra is known only through a reprint in the English *Millennial Star* of October 15, 1847; it contained news of the Mormon colony in California, a report on prices and advice on travel, and the announcement that publication of a newspaper "by the sanction of Colonel Freemont" would begin the following week. The extra may not have been widely circulated in California, or perhaps was forgotten by the time Kemble returned to Yerba Buena; at any rate, he does not mention it in his *History*.

The *California Star*, Samuel Brannan publisher, began with Elbert P. Jones as editor in "the absence of the gentleman employed as the permanent editor." Kemble suggests that Colonel William Henry Russell, orator of the day at the Stockton reception and ordnance officer of the California Battalion, was to have been permanent editor, though admitting that "he did not return to the post, if he was ever actually engaged as editor of the *Star.*" Swasey, in *The Early Days and Men of California,* assumed that Kemble was the intended editor, as he became in fact the practicing editor soon after his return from the south. Washington Allon Bartlett later claimed an editorial connection with San Francisco's first paper, which was categorically denied by Brannan.

Alcalde Bartlett, a naval lieutenant given to pomposity, at least supplied the goad; the town was under martial law, its easy routines interrupted by parades and curfews, and the new residents wanted a voice in municipal affairs. A major purpose in founding the *California Star* at that time was to provide this voice, which could reach the ears of the officers in charge.

The memory was still strong thirteen years later when Bartlett published a card in a New York newspaper, which contained the following statement:

> . . . having a large acquaintance among the gentlemen of the editorial fraternity—having been myself twenty-five years in the publishing service, and being actually proprietor and editor of journals on both sides of our continent—(having written the first editorial ever printed in the now famous city of San Francisco, and with my own hands, when Chief Magistrate there, pulled the press for the first printed sheet ever printed in that city) . . .

Brannan's response to this challenge, in a letter to the San Francisco *Alta California* of November 19, 1859, is pointed enough to be extremely interesting:

> I beg to differ with Mr. Bartlett's statement, and I send you a bound volume of the first paper ever printed in San Francisco, in which you will find the first editorial signed by E. P. Jones, Esq., who I employed as editor, and the prospectus signed by myself . . . I . . . set up all the type with the assistance of Mr. John Eager, a young man who came to this country with me. The establishment belonged to me, and Mr. Bartlett had no pecuniary interest in it whatever. I did the press-work on the paper, Mr. Eager and myself being the only practical printers in this place at that time, Mr. Kemble, whom I afterward employed as editor, being absent with Col. Freemont's battalion at Los Angeles. There was no other printing office in the place for Mr. Bartlett to be connected with, or ever had been, a fact which can be attested by a hundred witnesses now living in this country, if necessary. Mr. Bartlett might have come into the office while I was at work and

asked the privilege to pull the bar for one sheet, but I have no recollection of it, but if so, it could not have been the first sheet, for we were quite alone and it was after midnight when it was struck off, the balance furnished the next day . . . I make the above statement at the request of several gentlemen, who were in California in 1846, and not from any feeling of ill will towards Mr. Bartlett.

Respectfully yours,
S. BRANNAN

On November 21st, the *Union* ran a front-page account of Judge Bartlett's adventures in the California of 1846-7, putting him in no very favorable light. The emphasis was heavy on the ludicrous aspects of the "Vaquero General's" capture by the Californians and his relief from public office; no mention was made of his editorial activities. On the following day, the *Union* reprinted Brannan's denial. Kemble himself was by no means as polite as Brannan in his statements regarding the "Quarterdeck Alcalde," for whom he had no respect whatsoever.

Kemble, indeed, was no respecter either of pretense or bombast, and anything he construed as a departure from his own high standards of conduct aroused his indignation. In later years he could treat his youthful tilts with levity, but his ideals remained the same. His brief account, in the *History*, of the eviction of the irascible Jones, first editor of the *Star*, is amplified in one of the *Union* articles of 1873:

The publisher having been called out of the country had committed the oversight of his paper's interest to the writer hereof, bidding him exercise a sort of censorship over its columns. There came a fierce editorial to the office, red-hot from the forge of our Georgia Vulcan, and the youth in charge of the paper rejected it. There came a fiercer editor on the heels of the offending manuscript and demanded its insertion, which being again refused the editor declared his intention of taking charge of the office, and proceeded to take possession of the "first side," or half-printed sheets, of the forthcoming issue. Then there was quickly arranged without music a lively and engaging waltz around the floor of the printing office, to the utter consternation and discomforture of types, "forms," stools and everything that stood in the way. The dance began in the house and ended in the street, where the party of the first part suddenly concluded he had no use for the half-printed *Stars,* and wondered at the size of the edition which had been made to appear before his eyes during the little whirl around the office floor. He thought he would not be any longer its editor, and so the publisher's proxy, a youth who in early boyhood had learned "the trade" by printing on a home-made press, from type picked up from the sweeping of a country newspaper office, a little sheet called the *Comet,* assumed a place among the regular celestial bodies as the editor of the *Star.*

The *Star's* announcement of the editorial change, on April 17, 1847, gives no hint of the difficulty, unless one reads between the lines.

Dr. E. P. Jones having withdrawn from the Editorial Department of this paper, and Mr. Brannan, the Proprietor and Publisher of it, being temporarily absent, during his absence, or until he can be heard from and some permanent arrangement made, the publication of the Paper will be continued by the Subscribers, in whose charge the office was left by Mr. Brannan.—They will give the readers of the "Star" the current news of the day, and respectfully solicit contributions from those who feel an interest in sustaining a Press in the Town of San Francisco.

Edw. C. Kemble
John Eager

Dr. Jones then became a real estate operator, and by 1850 was reputed to be a millionaire. In 1873, Kemble could write of himself,

But that which was and still is the occasion of a just pride to the person who wrote the sophomorish editorials of the *Star,* was the uncompromising war that he waged against the Alcalde ring of that year. How many deeds of corner lots now worth millions of dollars could he have stuffed in his sleeve had he not been afflicted with the infirmity of getting on the reputable side of questions of common morality?

From mid-April through September, 1847, the *Cali-*

fornia Star continued with no editor listed. Kemble, however, would appear to have been the one responsible, and to have done a job satisfactory to the absent publisher, for on Brannan's return from Salt Lake City, the name of Edw. C. Kemble was elevated to the editorial box, where it stayed from October 2 until the end of the paper the following year.

That year of 1847, "The Peaceful Eve of the Riotous Golden Morn," as Kemble later called it, was nostalgically remembered by him. A census was taken by Edward Gilbert, then a lieutenant in Stevenson's regiment and later Kemble's partner on the *Alta*, which reported a population of 459 in San Francisco, of whom 273 could read and write; the *Star* claimed between three and four hundred subscribers, presumably not limited to local circulation. It was a "modest era of honest industry, legitimate enterprise and quiet social enjoyment," spiced in the two California newspapers by "local broils, Alcalde battles, editorial personalities and arrivals and departures of shipping." The weather was mild, the war of conquest was at an end, the disbanded volunteers were either settled upon farms or starting commercial enterprises. Solid settlers were coming through from Oregon, and the main hope for the development of the country lay in agriculture. Rumors of rich mineral deposits were rife, but tales of gold were the least of these. All these resources and prospects were described in the *Star's* special publication of April 1, 1848, prepared late in February, and sent east by courier.

It is no great wonder that Kemble missed what could have been the biggest story of his career—the gold discovery, one of the great dramatic news stories of all time—or that, considering the aftermath, he spent much of the rest of his life explaining his oversight. In common with many who knew California before the rush, he preferred the pastoral period with its promise of gradual development.

So it was that, early in March of 1848, hoping for an item about the acres Captain Sutter would sow in wheat that spring, Kemble watched the launch from New Helvetia, with its crew of Kanakas and Digger Indians, making her landing off the foot of Clay street, about a stone's throw from the beach at Montgomery street. The passengers were strangers and knew nothing of any use to the interviewer—nothing about the sowing, or how many hides would be sent down, or whether there would be many men returning to the States that year—and Kemble had almost given it up for a bad job when one of the men said he could show them something if they would come up to the store with him.

> And back to the store we all went. It is the strangest thing that I cannot remember this man's name. He had been in the employ of Captain Sutter, but had come down on business of his own. He was black-eyed, bushy bearded, lank and nervous, and chewed tobacco as a school girl chews gum—as though the lower jaw was run by clock-work. Standing at the counter, he took out a greasy purse, and out of that produced a little rag, which he carefully opened, disclosing a few thin flakes of a dull yellow metal. "That there," said he in an undertone, "is gold, and I know it, and know where it comes from, and there's a plenty more in the same place, certain and sure!"

Unfortunately, it was not convincing. The stranger was not in the least excited, and the city men set him down as acting a part. Other local people wandered in, and looked at the lusterless bits of metal. One said it was mica, another that it was fool's gold. After a while the group at the store broke up, and, if Kemble remembered aright, the *Star* went to press that night without an item concerning the gold mines. Not until the eighteenth of March was the discovery mentioned in the *Star*.

A month later, rumors had become persistent enough to persuade the editor to join the first party to visit the gold mines. Perhaps he felt the need of a vacation, and this made as good an excuse as any. None of the three travelers—Major P. B. Reading, George McKinstry, Jr., and Kemble—professed to believe in the mines, and certainly no one intended to take part in any such miserable fraud as they believed the pretended gold discoveries to be. In holiday mood the three embarked in Leidesdorff's schooner, the re-rigged hull of the little pioneer steamboat *Sitka*, and after some five to seven days among the windings of the Sacramento they reached Sutter's Fort. An unenlightening evening with the Captain persuaded them that he was more amused than convinced by Marshall's enthusiasm and was, in fact, more concerned over the fate of the mill than interested in any possibility of mineral wealth. To urge along the work of logging, Sutter consented to join the expedition to the mill, adding two of his favorite Indian "boys" to the party to look after the horses and make camp.

Along the way, Major Reading frequently rode out from the trail to break off bits of rock. Once or twice he thought he had found traces of silver, but no sign of gold was seen, though they crossed streams which later yielded fortunes. On the second morning they came to the camp at the mill, an untidy, temporary-looking bivouac, with the men sitting or sprawled on the ground near the unfinished mill and the flooded race.

> They hardly returned our greeting as we rode up. It was apparent from the first moment we came in sight we were unwelcome guests. We had not been slow to perceive in the words and looks that were exchanged before we came within hearing that the object of our visit was well understood and would receive no aid or encouragement from Marshall and his friends. We unsaddled our beasts, and while Captain Sutter and Marshall started off by themselves, the Major and the rest of the party endeavored to gain a little information respecting the gold discovery from the other lumbermen. Opening oysters with a wooden toothpick would have been an easy task compared to that job. One of the fellows "allowed" he didn't "go much on its being gold, anyway." Another guessed Marshall was a "little mite cracked" on the sub-

> ject. In answer to the direct question where the gold was found, the reply was, "Oh, anywhere along the race or down by the river, where you've a mind to try for it," which was true enough, as it afterwards appeared, but intended to be a very smart and evasive answer.

Since they had come so far, the Major proposed that they try their luck. Borrowing an Indian basket, they walked down to the nearest point of the mill-race. There the Major filled the basket with earth and began the operation of washing for gold, as they had heard it was done in the placer mines of southern California. It was very slow, and it produced no sign of color. The Major cheerily tried again, while the hot sun beat down on the breathless valley, and the others wandered off to find some shade. At lunch-time the lumbermen returned from their pretense of work, and various Indians dropped by to greet Captain Sutter.

> . . . and now from another quarter . . . approaches the sole representative of the mining interest in our party. He is greeted with a quiet "what success, Major?" and replies, "not enough to buy a drink" . . . There could be no reality in such gold discoveries as these. So we dropped the subject for the time being, and the editor of the *Star* noted on his memorandum book, as a subject for his next week's paper, the practical result of a test made of the gold-producing qualities of the soil at the alleged gold mines, and wrote over all, in emphatic character, "humbug."

For a month Kemble tried to preserve a stolid sanity in the face of the mounting gold fever, but at last even the *Star* had to admit that there was some truth behind the excitement. The *Californian,* which had moved to San Francisco in May of the year before, suspended publication after June 2, 1848; the *Star* reported this on the tenth, and then on the fourteenth announced that it was forced to do likewise, as printers, editor, and all joined the exodus to the mines. California was left without a newspaper.

It was not for long, however. On the fifteenth of July, and spasmodically thereafter until November 11, the *Californian* appeared under a changing array of publishers. Kemble, who had returned from the Feather River mines in September, bought the *Star* from Brannan, and then acquired the *Californian*, bringing out the combined *California Star and Californian* on November 18, 1848. One week after his twentieth birthday, having already been printer, editor, clerk of the Town Council, and miner, he was proprietor of the only newspaper in California.

Kemble as he was in the fall of 1848 was remembered by one "Santiago," reminiscing in the San Jose *Pioneer* of September 7, 1866:

> We see him now, through our mental vision, precisely as he then appeared. He was attired in a neatly fitting light-blue roundabout or jacket; his nether garment was of fine black cloth; his vest of similar texture and color. His cheeks were like a ripe peach, rosy and smooth as velvet; his eye sparkled and scintillated with tender emotion—it was black as coal; and his beautiful glossy hair, of similar hue, fell gracefully on either side of his tranquil brow. Your fair readers will think, doubtless, with us, that Edward C. Kemble, at the time we speak of, was a very handsome and good-looking young man . . . To sum up his character in a few words as we estimated it: he was a gentleman of strict integrity and moral worth—of the most tender susceptibilities—unassuming, generous, and magnanimous; and we will venture to say that he never wrote a word that would cause a blush to tinge the cheek of the most fastidious maiden, for his writings were always couched in elegant phraseology and of high moral tone.

Besides his youth and good looks, Kemble had a level enough head in practical matters. He realized that his growing newspaper and job-printing business was more than one man could handle in a Gold Rush which could no longer be denied. He was fortunate in persuading Edward Gilbert, a printer from his home town, to join him, and the two, with a brief series of third parties, transformed the two old papers into a new "Mother of Newspapers," the *Alta California*. This is not the place to write the history of the *Alta*; Kemble covers the early years, and its long and respected career, from 1849 to 1891, deserves a book in itself. The same may, of course, be said for the Sacramento *Union*, and he has adequately covered the other papers with which he was associated.

His friendship and close association with Gilbert were of great importance to Kemble's life and career, and consequently to the early history of journalism in California. Gilbert had come out in March 1847, as a first lieutenant in Company H of Stevenson's New York Volunteers. From 1848 on he took a prominent part in public affairs. He was a candidate for Alcalde, and seems to have acted as deputy Collector of Customs. He was a member of the Constitutional Convention, and was subsequently elected one of the two first Congressmen from California. That, of course, was after he had served as the *Alta's* "senior editor" for nearly a year.

Early in '49, it fell to Kemble's lot to establish the first newspaper in Sacramento, as a company project. This was the *Placer Times*. He returned to San Francisco for reasons of health in June, resumed his work on the *Alta*, and was otherwise active, for we find him as a member of the Immigrant Relief Committee in 1850, and in May of that year he was elected "4th Sergeant of the First California Guard."

In October, he went East, and before his departure was entertained at a grand supper given in his honor at Delmonico's in San Francisco by the editorial fraternity, and attended also by gentlemen of the press from Sacramento, Stockton, Marysville, and Sonora, as well as by other friends. There were thirteen "Regular" toasts, followed by "uncounted Volunteers," followed by songs and a poem on the occasion, followed by a speech by Kemble on the singularly appropriate subject of the history of journalism in California. The first toast is well worth reprinting here,

> To *Our Guest*, the father of the California Press—like the Sultan of Turkey, although in his youth, he sees about him a goodly number of heirs to the throne, with a child born unto him in his own Seraglio daily.

The party went on well into the small hours. And it is interesting to remember that the father of the California Press was twenty-two years old.

Kemble and Congressman Gilbert returned on May 20, 1851, having travelled by steamer and the Isthmus. At this point, the world must have appeared one of infinite promise to the partners. As newspapermen, they were firmly established, and at the local top of their profession in the midst of the soaring population and the multiplying riches of the new Golden State. Besides, professional boundaries were then far easier to cross than they are now, and success in one field was frequently only a stepping stone to greater achievements in another. Gilbert's prospects seemed particularly bright. Still only thirty-two, it appeared to those who knew him that he was destined for a career of national importance.

Frontier editing, however, had very real hazards. 1851 was a year of alarums and excursions. The *Alta,* burned out in the fire of June 22, suffered heavy financial damage but recovered sufficiently to play as important a role as ever in support of the first Vigilance Committee. Generally, it was a time of hot tempers and violent remedies. Sometimes editors were assaulted for their opinions. More rarely, they were murdered. Some felt bound to support their views and statements with their lives.

Gilbert was of this number. On August 2, 1852, he fought a duel with the Hon. James W. Denver, who—later to have the city of Denver, Colorado, named after him—was then State Senator from Klamath and Trinity

Counties. The quarrel began with a political statement in the *Alta*. Gilbert was the challenger, and the weapons were rifles at forty paces. The first exchange was without effect. Denver, an expert, deliberately fired aside; Gilbert, who could "barely hold his piece," missed. But either Gilbert or his second—perhaps because Gilbert had scoffed at bloodless duels in print—insisted on continuing. Denver then killed him.

Public opinion, naturally enough, was with the chivalrous and reluctant General Denver. Gilbert was dead, and was widely mourned in the State. His promising career was at an end. Now his only national role, ironically, was to be that of a victim and a memory when, in 1884, a distorted version of the encounter killed Denver's chances of getting the Democratic Presidential nomination and threw the choice to Grover Cleveland.

Kemble appears to have been almost literally stupefied. The *Alta* of August 3, already ruled in deep black for the death of Henry Clay, carried, in a few words, only the bare statement of the facts. "The deep gloom cast by this unfortunate and lamentable affair," it said, "forbids further reference." On August 4, the *Alta* had nothing to say on the subject. And on the 5th, the day of Gilbert's funeral, it did not appear. On the 6th, it reported the funeral and printed the oration on its page 3. A four-page paper, for news it simply re-ran page 2 of the issue of the 4th.

"Santiago's" view, written fourteen years later, may have reflected a certain nineteenth century romanticism, but if it exaggerated it at least did not fabricate out of whole cloth.

> Kemble and Gilbert—"Santiago" wrote—were devotedly attached to each other, and perhaps the untimely death of the latter was the greatest shock that the former ever received. When we met Kemble, a day or two after the death of poor Gilbert, he was dressed in deep mourning and wore a very, very sad look. We

never beheld him smile after that calamity, but our intercourse ceased very soon after.

Kemble's brief record of the ensuing year is one of new partnerships, disagreements, and misfortunes, attributed by him largely to the loss of Gilbert. It was, nevertheless, a year of continuing prosperity. In the fall of 1853—a date he himself misstates as 1852—after the "loss of an only near relative," he left on a year's journey to Europe and the Near East, which he reported in regular letters to the *Alta.* He was, he said, going to act as their correspondent in the Crimean War, but illness forced his return before he saw any fighting. When he came back, in November 1854, he found the paper insolvent. He sold it in January 1855—and only then was Gilbert's name taken off the masthead.

No one can say definitely that Kemble's attitude toward the newspaper game in California changed dramatically after Gilbert's death. However, his viewpoint, which had been fresh, direct, and aggressive, did seem to change. Though he remained an active editor for some years, we now seem to see the observer rather than the doer, the developing historian rather than the pure maker of history.

Perhaps indicative of this, too, was his departure for New York in the summer of 1855, to help organize, and serve as secretary of, a Committee on Pacific Coast Emigration. This group, composed largely of New York merchants and shippers trading with California, was the pioneer in its field, and its methods were afterwards applied in settling Kansas and other areas in the West. For the Committee, he edited a paper called *The Californian,* and he lectured on California's resources and opportunities throughout the eastern part of the country.

Kemble was also, of course, maturing—he was now, after all, in his middle twenties—and sometime after 1855 he assumed the responsibilities of marriage, to Cecilia Amanda Windsor. After his return to California in 1857, the project of writing the history must have started to take concrete form. There had been many evidences of this interest and of his appreciation of its significance, in his earlier work—in the columns of the papers with which he had been associated—and, as an excellent example, in his speech at Delmonico's in 1850.

The latter part of 1857 he spent on the San Francisco *California Chronicle*, resigning at the end of the year to become an editor of the Sacramento *Union*. It was during this period that he gathered the major part of the material for his *History*, sending out questionnaires to every—or almost every—newspaper in the state, and to men who either were or had been in the field. The questions would appear to have followed this form:

1. How many newspapers or periodicals have been published in ....?
2. What were their names and the names of the proprietors and editors?
3. When was such commenced, and how often and how long published?
4. What was the nationality and denomination of each, if political or religious?
5. What peculiar circumstances attended the origin or lives of either?

The response was very satisfactory, and Kemble made every effort to fill in occasional gaps from his own recollections and the files of the *Union* and other papers. The result was published in the special Christmas issue of the *Union* for 1858.

Immediate press comments were, by and large, highly favorable. The *Alta*, on December 27, wrote:

> HISTORY OF THE PRESS OF CALIFORNIA.—The *Sacramento Union* of the 25 inst., is published on a double sheet, with eight pages of matter, five of which are devoted to a history of the Press of California, the longest article we have ever seen in any paper, and a valuable contribution to the literature and history of the State.

A day later, the San Francisco *Times*, in a considerably longer comment, gave credit where credit was due despite the fact that the *History* appeared without a by-line:

> THE HISTORY OF NEWSPAPERS
>
> The Sacramento *Union* of Saturday publishes an interesting and lengthy article entitled "The History of California Newspapers," commencing from the earliest date of those journals and coming down to the present time. Everybody connected with the subject should preserve a copy of the paper . . . We presume this to be mainly if not wholly from the pen of Mr. E. C. Kemble, of the *Union*, the pioneer among the survivors of California editors, and who was for several years one of the proprietors of the Alta *California*. We can detect here and there some slight errors and omissions, but as a whole the work is an admirable performance and evinces great industry and careful research on the part of the writer.

And on January 1, 1859, the North San Juan (Nevada County) *Hydraulic Press* provided additional descriptive details for those who had no chance to read the original:

> HISTORY OF CALIFORNIA NEWSPAPERS.—Under this title the Sacramento *Union* of December 25th presented as a Christmas Gift to its readers an elaborate, complete, and interesting historical account of the newspaper press of this State, commencing with the year 1832, and coming down to the present day. This account appears in a double issue and occupies twenty-eight columns. Much of it is highly entertaining, and will hereafter possess a historical value, and in publishing it the proprietors of the *Union* have established another claim to their already deserved popularity . . .

Actually, someone on the *Hydraulic Press* staff must have forgotten to count a full page. There are *thirty-five* columns of very small type which, in the present edition, occupy 200 very respectable pages.

There were, of course, corrections and emendations from the reading public, and these themselves illustrate the magnitude of the task Kemble undertook and accomplished —the story of more than three hundred newspapers throughout the State, with their changes of identity and ownership, and of many times that number of individual editors, reporters, and publishers.

Some of these corrections, though of considerable interest in themselves, were used by those who offered them as springboards for pet subjects. The Reverend William Anderson Scott, for instance, pointed out that the *Pacific* was not, as Kemble stated, an official organ of the Presbyterian Church, and then delivered himself of several hundred words regarding a disputation of his own with its staff and with other coreligionists. The *Pacific,* pointing out that it had already attended to the correction of the error, then took issue with him in a pointed several-hundred-word rejoinder.

Two letters of correction, however, were important and interesting enough to be reprinted in their entirety. Douglas C. McMurtrie used them in his separate introduction to the 1927 edition of the *History,* and they cannot be omitted here. The first was from William L. Newell and appeared in the *Union* for March 4, 1859:

NEW YORK, Feb. 4, 1859.

In the "History of California Newspapers," published in the DAILY UNION, of December 25th, I find statements and insinuations made in reference to me, personally, which are not true. My friendly relations with each and all of the proprietors of the UNION are sufficient to warrant me in believing that you would not, knowingly, place me in a false position. I would, therefore, respectfully ask you to allow me to vindicate myself by publishing the following statement of facts in your valuable paper. Your compiler, speaking of the starting of the *Daily California Chronicle,* says:

"The type and material on which the Chronicle appeared, had been ordered by the proprietors of the *Alta California,* through Wm. L. Newell (one of the *Chronicle* company), who had solicited said order for a Boston firm of type makers, of which he was the agent, etc., . . . and when the type arrived refused to give it up to them."

The facts are these: The *Alta* required a new dress. The proprietors had neither credit nor money to order one themselves.

I said I would order one on my own credit and responsibility. I sent the order to John K. Rogers & Co., of Boston, who knew me personally. They filled the order for me and held me responsible, and no one else, for the payment for the same. They would not ship it in the name of the proprietors of the *Alta,* but did so in my name. I stated in my letter to John K. Rogers & Co., that I would remit in full by the first Pacific mail steamship that should sail after the arrival, in the harbor of San Francisco, of the vessel having on board the office. After I retired from the *Alta* establishment, and before the arrival of the vessel, I offered the invoice to the proprietors of the *Alta,* through their business man, D. A. McDermott, stating, in my offer that they should pay me the original cost and charges, with a fair commission added for the use of my credit or money, and for attending to the business. They kept me waiting without stating whether they intended to take the office or not, until the arrival of the vessel having on board the same. This offer remained open for two or three months. There appeared to be a desire to either throw the office on my hands, or get it, if possible, without paying for it. I stated distinctly and publicly, that I would start an opposition paper if they did not take the office and pay for it. The proprietors of the *Alta* were cognizant of these facts. On the arrival of the vessel containing the office, I wrote to E. Gilbert & Co., stating that the office had arrived, and that I was ready and willing to deliver it on the full payment to me for the same, with my commissions added thereto. I furthermore stated in this note that the offer would remain open for a stated number of days, and if they did not take it within the time specified, I should take it on my own account. The proprietors of the *Alta* failed to come down with the money, and at the expiration of the time (the day before the sailing of the steamer), I took the office myself and remitted for the same by the next day's steamer, as I had promised to do so in my letter to John K. Rogers' Co. By the terms proposed by me to the proprietors of the *Alta* the office would have cost them a little over $2,500. I sold it to Frank Soule & Co. for $3,000, and it was cheap at that price. Various attempts were made to get me to deliver a portion of the material to the proprietors of the *Alta,* hoping thereby to force the delivery of the whole without paying for the same. I refused to be caught in the trap.

Again your compiler says: "It may have been concerted between Newell and his associates, while in their old place, to withdraw from the *Alta,* and build up a new paper, which should overthrow it." So far as I am personally concerned, this insinuation is without foundation. Mr. Gray, one of the present proprietors of the UNION, is one of the parties referred to in the above sentence, and can state whether he was a party to, or cognizant of any such movement previous to leaving the *Alta* establishment. It must be that Mr. Gray did not see these statements before their publication, or he certainly would have corrected them, as he is, or was, familiar with most of the facts which I have stated. The person who gave the assumed information to your compiler either did, not know the circumstances of which he presumed to speak, and heard the mis-statements, or else he furnished it for the purpose of gratifying his malice by asserting what he knew to be false.

In justice to the memory of the lamented Gilbert, I would state that these transactions occurred after his death. The name of the firm, however, remained unchanged at the head of the *Alta.*

WM. L. NEWELL

The second letter, published in the same issue, was from James W. Simonton, who twenty years later was Kemble's chief in the New York office of the Associated Press:

EDITORS, UNION. In reading your highly interesting "History of California Journalism," published on the 25th of Dec., 1858, I discovered one or two errors in connection with my own name, which, though trivial, perhaps, you will permit me to correct.

The statement that I was a *partner* with Crane & Rice in the proprietorship of the San Francisco *Courier,* in 1851, is a mistake. In January of that year I became an associate editor of that journal; and having made preliminary arrangements for its entire transfer to me within a few months, I returned to the East in April, with the view of taking my family to California and establishing myself there. The fire of May, '51, which burned up the *Courier* establishment, made it impossible to carry out my purpose.

It is true that the journal which, through your energy and industry, directed by practical talent, has become an "institution," was started with the type taken to California by myself, but the enterprising gentlemen who purchased it for that purpose did not seek to obtain it "at a sacrifice," but paid its full value, together with cost of transportation *via* the Chagres river and Isthmus of Panama.

May I be permitted to add that my esteemed friend, Dr. J. F. Morse, with much too modest appreciation of his own abilities, was with difficulty prevailed upon to undertake the duties of the editorial chair, and for a fortnight, nearly, insisted that I should do so in his stead. Unfortunately for myself—but quite the reverse, possibly, for the journal whose "small beginning" we are noting—there were considerations of duty which compelled me to decline; and Dr. Morse, finally, consented to waive his personal comfort, silence the murmurings of his unwilling judgment, and assume the duties which he discharged so acceptably and with so much success.

Trusting that, in pursuance of a long cherished purpose, I shall speedily resume my home in California, and meet you again as a brother journalist, I am,

Very truly, yours,

JAMES W. SIMONTON.

These are illustrative. Though Kemble naturally made occasional errors, few of these were grave. The book was quoted and requoted through the years, by journalists, historians, and biographers, and usually it was quoted anonymously, as it was published. Not until 1927 was it reprinted in book form, in a small edition put out by Douglas C. McMurtrie under the imprint of the Plandome Press of New York, and then, unfortunately, Kemble's name was omitted from the title page. The introductory material promised was omitted also, and Kemble's connection with the book in its new incarnation only became obvious the following year when McMurtrie's introduction was published separately in the *Quarterly* of the California Historical Society.

A month before the history appeared in the *Union,* on November 25, Mrs. Kemble gave birth to a son in Sacramento, and two years later, on January 16, 1861, she had another child, the Edward Windsor Kemble who eventually became famous as a cartoonist for the New York *Herald* and *Sun,* for *Harper's Weekly* and other national magazines, and as illustrator of the first edition of *Huckleberry Finn.*

After the start of the Civil War, Kemble went east and served in the Federal Army as a Paymaster in the Department of Virginia, finally being brevetted lieutenant-colonel for meritorious conduct. He also, during this period, acted as war correspondent for the Sacramento *Union.* After the War, he was Inspector of Indian Affairs under President Grant, and then for years, besides working as assistant manager of the Associated Press office in New York (in charge of California and West Coast matters), he was telegraphic correspondent for the San Francisco *Call* and *Bulletin* and for the Sacramento *Record-Union.*

He died at Mott Haven, New York, on February 10, 1886, after a two-weeks illness, at the age of fifty-seven.

Kemble was by no means forgotten. Whenever he visited California during his lifetime, the Press of San Francisco and Sacramento took notice of the fact, printing interviews with him and recollections of his pioneering days. On the occasion of his death, it published the appropriate obituaries. There were some mentions of his name in the years that followed. But he was never really given the credit due to him, as a historian of California journalism, until much later. We have seen that the McMurtrie reprint came out in 1927, and its introduction not long afterwards. In 1934, George L. Harding dedicated his definitive study of the first press and printer of California, *Don Agustín V. Zamorano; Statesman, Soldier, Craftsman, and California's First Printer,* to "the memory of Edward C. Kemble, the first historian of California's pioneer press." Perhaps inspired by this tribute, in 1939 a tree was planted in his memory in Sacramento. Now, as I write, the California Historical Society is planning to set aside three rooms in its newly acquired Library building to house the "Kemble collection on American Printing and Publishing" as a memorial to him.

It is my hope that this edition, with its annotated indices, will serve as an added tribute to Kemble and to all the other early California journalists of whom he wrote, by making his work more readily available to those scholars and journalists today who are interested in our beginnings.

❁ ❁ ❁

Concerning this edition of Kemble's *History of California Newspapers,* I have left the body of the text (except for obvious typographical errors) as in the original, including his somewhat erratic use of italics in names of newspapers. In his sectional summaries, I have inserted the full name and place of publication of the newspapers, for easier reference. Where such information is necessary in the main text, or where there is a wide difference in date, I have used footnotes. Minor variations have not been noted in the text, but, wherever possible, have been corrected in the indices. Newspapers not listed by Kemble have also been added in footnotes, distinguished by an asterisk. In the Index of Newspapers, entries are under each contemporary place of publication, with references to other relationships. The scope of this work does not include the history of newspapers after Kemble's terminal date, December 25, 1858. Nor have I attempted to list all the variations of frequency in the country papers, or the multiplications of personnel and other details in the major journals. The latter deserve, and some have already received, full treatment in individual histories. The former have been covered in area studies, such as Muir Dawson's *History and Bibliography of Southern California Newspapers, 1851-1876* (Los Angeles, 1950), Barbara Eastman's manuscript notes in the Bancroft Library on Columbia newspapers, and Helen S. Giffen's *California Mining Town Newspapers, 1850-1880* (Van Nuys, 1954), and, most notably, in Chester Barrett Kennedy's 1949 doctoral dissertation for Stanford University, "Newspapers of the California Northern Mines, 1850-1860: a Record of Life, Letters and Culture." The bibliographical studies of Herbert Fahey, George L. Harding,

Douglas C. McMurtrie, Alexander Smith Taylor, and Henry Raup Wagner are too well known to need listing here.

Among the many who have helped in the preparation of this edition, I owe particular thanks to Anna C. Dart, Lucille La Bourdette, and L. Macleod, as well as to Mr. Abajian of the California Historical Society, Mrs. Giffen of the Society of California Pioneers, Mr. Ottley and Miss Meyer of the State Library's California Room, Mrs. Schroeder of the Mariposa Historical Society, and Mrs. Swartsfager of Grace Cathedral in San Francisco, and especially to my colleagues of the Bancroft Library. Dr. Chester B. Kennedy offered most generous cooperation, and the section on the Northern Mines is largely dependent on his work, which should be consulted for further details. This edition would not have been undertaken without the encouragement of Dale L. Morgan, and it could not have been completed without the faithful assistance of my husband, Reginald Bretnor. And throughout its preparation, it has owed much to the cooperation and personal interest of the publisher, Robert Greenwood.

HELEN HARDING BRETNOR

BERKELEY, CALIFORNIA
JUNE, 1962

San Francisco *Evening Picayune*
and San Francisco *Herald*
[FROM AN OLD DAGUERREOTYPE]

The Sonora *Herald*
[FROM AN OLD DAGUERREOTYPE]

Introduction

by Edward C. Kemble

Before undertaking a task so novel, and, to the majority of readers, of such questionable utility and interest as the compiling of a history of newspapers, it is very proper that we should offer a word of explanation. It is undoubtedly true that there is very little in the bare newspaper chronology of any State, the perusal of which can either amuse or edify those who are not now, or who have not been, in the profession. It is moreover true that the newspaper history of California, extensive and remarkable as it is in comparison, is neither old enough to delight the antiquarian nor sufficiently eventful to give it prominence in the general interest over similar histories of other States. And, lastly, it *is* a fact that newspapers in California have monopolized a larger share of public attention in the recital of incidents laudatory of their growth and development than their years, wisdom or influence entitle them to. But we meet the first of these objections by reminding our friends that one of the largest distinct classes in our reading community, and, of course, the most critical and exacting in their support of these public journals, is composed of persons who have been, in one way or another, in this country, directly concerned in the publication of newspapers. It will only be necessary to glance at the facts in connection with the press of San Francisco to substantiate this. The names of those who have been, at various times, personally interested in the journals of that city embrace over a thousand. This is more than a fifth of the present circulation of her leading morning newspaper. No country under the sun can show so large a proportion of what are termed "newspaper men," from their past or present connection with journals, to the number of newspaper readers as California. No society out of our State exhibits so great a degree of newspaper affinity and infatuation among its intelligent members—breaking down the barriers which, in other lands, render the sphere of the editor distinct, and mingling freely in the every day discourse and concerns of its organs. Ever since California became a State, this rare facility of intercourse between press and people has existed. The cause we suppose to be, simply, the sudden and great emergencies which, owing to her rapid growth, have arisen in political and social life, requiring the instant establishment of organs of public communication. With no previous training or aspirations for newspaper life, our citizens have been called from professional and mercantile pursuits to fill the chair of the editor. In this way all our intelligent classes have become familiarized with the newspaporial art, while at the same time, what, in other countries, is looked upon rather as a luxury, has become here a common convenience and necessity. And herein we find an answer to the second objection. Instead of monitors, censors and criterions, as in Eastern countries, our newspapers have been the simple organs of speech—the daily fitful utterance of communities. Our cities have broken out in newspapers. Every surge of popular excitement has been capped with a printed sheet. This ready use of ink and type has gendered their universal need. From our Cadmean sowing we have reaped a California harvest. It is doubtful if, as we have often been told, California owes her newspaper plenitude to the superior intelligence of the masses. The mortality among her public journals would seem to show conclusively that the ends for which most of them were established was subserviency to a passing interest; the fate of several of the leading journals of San Francisco, which in their day were the highest types of newspaper excellence in the State, shows that no considerations of a mere literary or intellectual character induced their support. The truth is patent that the motive with which a very large number of "newspaper enterprises" have been begun in this country has partaken of the transient and self-serving nature of most enterprises here, and has rarely been stimulated by a pure love of principle, or a deep and sincere attachment to State and party interests. We present these suggestions, unpleasant though they seem, in no spirit of deprecation. They represent, in part, the natural conditions of that rapid growth for which California is famous, and for which she has cause to be grateful, notwithstanding the temporary ills and inconveniences arising from such growth. It is the identity of her newspapers with each stage of her progress, each phase of her history, and each important change of the popular sentiment to which we look for the sustaining interest in these annals. In the lives of each of her public journals there is bound up somewhat of her political and social development. In the fickle character of our population, and the revolutions which have swept the path of our young State, they constitute not only the landmarks in her history, but the only faithful surviving tablets from which this history must be written. If this view is correct, may we not claim for our newspaper genealogy the dignity and interest of a State historical index? And though it comes upon half a dozen newspaper histories, compiled at different periods within the past ten years, and helps to swell the volume of memoirs, which, with a good deal of professional egotism, our journals are continually jogging the public memory, we cannot resist the conclusion that this species of narrative must be acceptable to the reader. According to the proposition we have laid down of the relations sustained by the newspaper in the community, and the sympathies which are reciprocally cultivated, such must be the fact. If there were not some broad foundation in public interest for these complacent allusions to its past history, we should not find them so frequent on the hundred tongues of the press. In regard, however, to the newspaper histories to which we alluded as having already gone forth, we will do no injustice if we simply remark that nothing like a connected narrative of the origin of our press and its progress in the establishment of newspapers in this country, with details of the separate fortunes of each, has ever been given to the public. Those sketches and compilations which have preceded us will be duly noticed in our concluding chapter.

The close of this year has been thought a proper time to compile the History of California Newspapers, because, with the end of 1858, will terminate the first decade of an established press in this country; and, beside, the material from which such a history must be drawn is rapidly passing away. The changes and vicissitudes incident to California life are scattering or destroying the records of our early journals, and their existence is fading from the memory of man. Few of the bound files or even loose copies of the pioneer newspapers remain. A year or two hence might obliterate every trace of many of them, and it is quite possible that even at this day the very names of some may be utterly forgotten. But we have still another motive for writing this history now. A new, and, we trust, a better era is dawning upon the press of California. Before the close of 1859, it is confidently believed an entire change in the newspaper intercourse of this country with the East will have taken place. The establishment of overland mail routes will, by that time, have put us in daily receipt of intelligence from the other side, and the extension of the telegraphic wire will give us hourly communication with our sister States, if not with the whole of Europe. California will then be no longer the remote, sequestered region, only valuable to the East for her mines of gold, and her newspapers will cease to borrow their tone and interest, almost exclusively, from the local events around them. They will become instead the mediums of thought and information between the people on the Pacific and those on the Atlantic. Besides elevating their sphere and enlarging their means of usefulness, the field which has been hitherto occupied by Eastern rivals will be wholly given up to them. The advantage accruing from this point alone is so important as to have arrested the thought of one of the greatest intellects of the age. W. H. Seward, in his remarks on the Pacific Telegraph Bill, thus points out the future of the press of California:

> "We on the Atlantic coast might, if anybody reasonably could, object to this communication, because, until it shall be made, the Atlantic press will be the vehicle of communication between this Atlantic region and the Pacific coast; but just so soon as you shall have established this telegraph, the New York press, the Boston press, the Philadelphia press, the Washington press, the Baltimore and New Orleans press will be dispensed with to a large degree, so far as they supply information to the Pacific coast, and the newspaper press of the Pacific coast will be an original, independent organ of communication, giving to the people of that coast information of all affairs on this side of the continent, and of all European affairs, just as early as we could enjoy it here, and, according to existing circumstances, three weeks or a month earlier than it would be obtained by mail."

In the preparation of the following statistics we have relied chiefly upon the statements of intelligent correspondents in the various localities in which newspapers have been printed. Our inquiries were addressed to them in the form of printed circulars in which blanks were reserved for replies, and categorical answers solicited. We were favored, in most instances, with very satisfactory answers, but where any doubt has existed in reference to names, dates, or circumstances, the files of the UNION and other papers have been searched for a solution of the difficulty. In this way we have succeeded in collecting, as we think, the data of nearly, if not quite every newspaper that has been published in California. If we have failed to make the compilation perfect, we still have the satisfaction of believing that it is as nearly complete as human industry and pains-taking can make it. In the arrangement of our historical notes, we shall follow the chronological order of newspaper beginnings—first, in the large cities; next, in the mines; and, lastly, in the agricultural and coast counties—that mode of proceeding agreeing exactly with the order in which journalism developed itself in this country. Commencing at Monterey we shall follow the press established there through its infancy up to its final change to San Francisco, taking up the voluminous newspaper history of that city also at its beginning, and writing it out to its last page, and so proceeding through the Sacramento, Stockton and Marysville histories in their order, but making each complete (as far as our means allow) as we go along. On the same genealogical plan we shall take up the history of the southern and northern mining press, tracing out each according to the dates in which the first papers were established in the several mining camps and towns. In each newspaper locality, as we are drawn to it, we shall finish its record up to the present time. And, following the mines, will come the northern agricultural and coast districts in the order of their newspaper opening, and then the southern agricultural and coast districts, which will finish the work. With the first part of our history, treating of the origin of the first California newspapers, as each is strongly blended with the peculiar lights and shadows of California social and political life in those early days, we shall dwell, with some minuteness, on their rise and progress. As we approach the later days of journalism in this country, merely a record of the newspaper enterprises will suffice. And now, having occupied considerable more space in an apology than we intended, if the reader has been propitiated towards our undertaking sufficiently to accompany us over the field, we shall remove twenty-six years from off his head, and place him (1832) in the little seaport of Monterey.[1]

[1]George L. Harding, on pages 191-196 of his *Don Agustin V. Zamorano, Statesman, Soldier, Craftsman, and California's First Printer* (Los Angeles, 1934), places the date somewhat later, documenting the arrival and first use of the Ramage press as being at some time between the dates of May 28 and July 28, 1834.

The Old Monterey War Press

In the Patent Office at Washington, preserved under a glass case, is an illustrious member of the family of printing presses, from which the newspapers of California are descended. The visitor is shown the old relic as a curious specimen of the art before the Revolution. But that which gives it its chief interest is the fact of its being the press at which that honored representative of "the craft," Benjamin Franklin, worked when a printer. It is probably the oldest printing press in America, though the same style, known as the Ramage press, has continued in use until within ten or fifteen years. The frame, platen, ribs, and part of the bed are of wood, the bed on which the type forms lie is of stone, and the screw, which is the mechanical principle by which the impression is taken, is of iron, and large enough to raise a building, to which the main uprights which support the press are of timber sufficiently thick for sills. This old Franklin machine, with its worm-eaten and well worn timbers is an exact counterpart of the press which, also furnished by the city of Boston, executed the first printing on the northwest shores of America; the press which gave to California the first newspaper, and on which was afterwards printed the first journals of the interior and the mines. We know not what relation its origin sustained to the Franklin press at Washington. They were probably never on speaking terms, having flourished at intervals doubtless wide apart. They may have come from separate manufactories. But the date at which our venerable California ancestor arrived on these shores, and the years and hard service which it had evidently seen before it left Boston, justify the presumption that it came into existence not far from the locality and era in which the Franklin press labored. That it was a member of the same extensive family is unquestionable.

This old press came to California about the year 1832. It is believed that it was contracted for in 1829 or '30. It was brought to these shores with a small quantity of old bourgeois type, two meager fonts of shaded title letter, and the necessary fixtures of a fourth rate country printing office, by Thomas Shaw, a Boston merchant. Its degree of completeness may be calculated from the amount paid for it by the contractor at Monterey, which was $460. The person to whom belongs the honor of first introducing printing on the northwest shores of the Pacific is Agustin V. Zamorano, former Secretary to Governor Echeandia. This gentleman contracted with Shaw to bring out from Boston a press and type, and the order was filled doubtless from the meanest and cheapest material in the market. We have before us a sample of some of the first printing executed with it. It shows the type to be about worn out, and the press to have given a very uneven impression. It was an actual printing press and fixtures however, and Zamorano was the first California printer. In 1825, when he came from Mexico as Echeandia's secretary he brought a small seal press and an alphabet sufficient for Government stamp purposes. Its utmost capacity was a hundred words, and we do not hear that it was applied to any other use than for official seals. When the Boston printing press arrived the office was set up at Monterey, and probably one of the first documents printed was a circular issued by

Zamorano announcing the establishment of the press and his readiness to serve the public. We are so fortunate as to have one of these cards of the first printer in our possession. It is dated Monterey, 1834, two years after the press arrived. As California was a pretty slow country in those days, the intervening time may have been occupied in setting up the office, perhaps in finding a type setter, or in instructing some one of the natives in the art, which is more likely. Perhaps, as printers have never been remarkable since the art was invented for a surplus of means, Zamorano may have found some difficulty in raising $460, and it must have been a small fortune in this country, where money was not then actually needed, after it was raised. But whether established earlier or not, the first evidence of its existence and of the readiness of the old press to serve its new and foreign masters is Zamorano's card, which we print, in order that those interested may compare the tariff of prices of the present day with those that existed twenty-four years ago. The circular appears on a half sheet, Spanish letter paper, yellowish with age, and is printed with very old bourgeois newspaper type, in which the capitals and small capitals form the only display lines. We translate Zamorano's card almost literally:

NOTICE TO THE PUBLIC.

At the Printing Office of the citizen Agustin V. Zamorano & Co., established in this Capital is offered to serve the public with the greatest exactness and care; receiving all kinds of writing under the rules established by the laws for the liberty of the press, subjecting the loose impressions to the following rates, and agreeing at more equitable prices with gentlemen who may wish to establish any periodical.

RATES FOR THE IMPRESSIONS.

Congratulation billets, per hundred, three dollars.
Invitation notes, and others similar, do. do., five dollars.
The eighth of a sheet of paper do. do., seven dollars.
The fourth do. do., eight dollars.

Half a sheet do. do., ten dollars.
One sheet do. do., twenty dollars.
The impression of more than 100 copies of said classes, 1 *peso, 4 reales, 6 granos el ciento.*

The impressions made on account of the Government of the Territory shall be taken with consideration for the equity of the prices.

The paper shall be paid for separately, according to its just value, or shall be furnished at the pleasure of gentlemen who wish their writings printed.

The character of the letter that shall be used is the same as that on which this impression is served.

MONTERREY, 1834.

——————

IMPRENTA DE ZAMORANO Y CA.

So much for Zamorano and the first printing office. His enterprise does not appear to have thrived well at Monterey, for in three years after the above date we hear of his press at Sonoma. This was the seat of the Northern Military Department of the Province, and the excursion of the types into that region was probably encouraged by the Comandante, General Vallejo. But the change, like most of the shifts to which printers are driven, appears to have been unaccompanied by a change of fortune for the better, at any rate we next find the press and type packed away at Monterey, where it remained until the invasion of the country by the Americans, and the establishment of the first Yankee newspaper in 1846. During the first peregrinations of the old Boston machine from Monterey to Sonoma and back, we hear of one José de la Rosa, who served in the capacity of printer.

One of the most curious documents preserved of the times in which the old press figured is a proclamation, issued by Governor Mariano Chico, who arrived from Mexico in 1836, with titles long enough to confound a courtier of the days of Louis XIV. His first salutation was a model of bombast and self-conceit. It complimented the Californians on their docility, and spoke of the gratitude they owed him for his sacrifice in leaving his wife and children in Mexico, and consenting to be their Governor. The following proclamation appears to have been printed. A copy found its way to the Sandwich Islands, and was published in the Honolulu papers long ago. We cannot better introduce it than in the language of one of the Hawaiian editors: "Fudge, thou Napoleon!" says he, "Fudge, thou Cæsar! Fudge, ye shades of heroes long entombed! Here is a proclamation all glorious, all magnificent! Read and tremble!"

The Citizen Colonel, Mariano Chico, etc., etc., to the Inhabitants of Upper California:

"Californians! Dire is the notice I have to give you—such as will fill you with vengeful consternation.

"Our exalted President, the conqueror of Tampico, the illustrious General Santa Ana, was taken prisoner by the insolent colonists in the Department of Texas, the 21st of April last. His fiery valor leading him to confide in fortune, carried him some distance in front of the army; that inconstant deity for this once abandoned him, and our country mourns the capture.

"The burning ardor of the veterans rose to its height, and they flew upon the robbers of their chief to snatch from them their prize and restore the nation to its new Ulysses; they will have already reached that pitch of glory, because who could resist the valor and might of Mexicans offended by a horde of mercenary adventurers! The nation, aghast at once, arose to rush in pursuit of the noble prisoner; when the sad disaster left the gate of the Capital the Congress and the Government displayed their powerful energies and placed in activity the immense resources of power and law, and, without doubt, the loss has been, ere this, repaired.

"The chastisement of a crime so execrable must have been exemplary; the black blood of the disgraced colony ought already to have washed out the injurious stains which momentarily chanced to fall on the reputation of the free Mexican.

"I desire at this moment to hasten, not with my companion in arms, to liberate the chief so dear to the republic, for they will already have returned him to their bosom and are paying him the homage of unbounded gratitude; but to hasten to manifest to my compatriots that to this remote country reach the emotions and feelings which that enthusiasm draws from all parts the nation's citizens to avenge her insults.

"I shall tell the world that Californians, beyond example patriotic and jealous of the national honor, are ready to swim the seas which separate them from their brothers, to join them if it were necessary to prolong the war until they have destroyed the last life of the insolent insulters of our dear country.

"Yes Californians. Thus I hear you offer, and with your oath write that of your fellow-citizen.

MARIANO CHICO.

Monterey, 24th July, 1836."

It is no wonder if a plain Yankee press and types accustomed to do honest service in the King's English should revolt at such fustian and verbiage as the above, and bring its owners no good fortune. We may imagine the old press to have felt a thrill of rapture through its rickety joints on being released from such barbarian usage and restored to the language and customs of its native land. We can fancy the wonder and delight with which the hidden and dusty old type opened their leaden eyes on the familiar faces of their countrymen, and the readiness with which they broke the thraldom of their fettered speech and turned out their sentences in bold, round English. How or by whom it was originally proposed to bring them forth out of their obscurity we are not advised. It is not unlikely that the idea of a newspaper at Monterey, after the capture of the port by the squadron, was first practically acted upon by Walter Colton, Chaplain of the frigate Congress. The first man employed to put the types and press in order, and afterwards as the first printer in the office, was Joseph Dockrill, one of the crew of that vessel. Com. Stockton gave him his discharge in order to facilitate the establishment of a newspaper. Colton was, no doubt, the active manager in the creation of the first paper, and may have only refrained from issuing it for want of a civilian to associate with him in the enterprise. He did not have to wait long. The Hour appears to have found its Man in Robert Semple, or Dr. Semple, as he was called, who arrived with the advance parties of the emigration of that Summer. Indeed, all circumstances seem to have worked most advantageously for the pioneer journal, enabling it to make its first appearance in just five weeks after the flag was hoisted and the country declared to be subject to the laws of the United States. Semple came to California by the Northern route, from one of the Western States, Illinois, probably, as he had a brother in Congress from that State. He was over six feet tall, lean, lank and good natured. It was a joke among the friends of the "tall Doctor" that he rode into Sutter's Fort from the journey across the Plains with his spurs strapped about the calves of his legs, the smallness of the mule he was riding and the length of his limbs admitting of no other arrangement. Semple was a man of considerable ability and enterprise, and warmly esteemed by those who knew his excellent qualities of heart. His ventures in this country did not prove fortunate, however. In politics he was a Democrat, though a warm admirer of Henry Clay. Among those who were instrumental in reconciling this country to a change of masters, and in opening its resources to settlement and cultivation, Semple took a prominent part, and deserves to be held in grateful remembrance among its ardent and devoted pioneers. Of his associate in the Monterey newspaper, Walter Colton, we can only speak from the record of his well earned distinction as a writer, and his meritorious services in the early history of the country. He was a zealous advocate of Christianity, and a man of varied and extensive acquirements. The style of his works, though florid, and his descriptions though exaggerated and bordering on romancing, have not detracted from their interest or popularity. He was the first American civil magistrate, besides the first editor in the country.

The *Californian,* as the first paper printed on the

Pacific coast between Oregon and the Equator was called, appeared on Saturday, the 15th of August, 1846. The size of the sheet was 11¾ by 10¼ inches, or a little larger than common foolscap. The paper used was the coarse Spanish article of that size, used both for writing and cigarito wrappers; in fact, the only paper in the country at that time. Owing to the width of the measure its pages were only two columns wide. The type was wretchedly old and worn, and destitute of "sorts," or particular letters; the press was probably stiff and rheumatic, and the ink thick, and applied with "balls." Colton, in his "Three Years in California," says of the type and press:

> "The press was old enough to be preserved as a curiosity; the mice had burrowed in the "balls;" there were no rules, no leads, and the types were rusty and all in pi; it was only by scouring that the letters could be made to show their faces; a sheet or two of tin was procured, and these, with a jack knife, were cut into rules and leads. Luckily, we found with the press the greater part of a keg of ink; and now came the great scratch for paper. None could be found except what is used to envelop the tobacco smoked by the natives. A coaster had a small supply of this on board, which we procured."

It may be judged the typographical appearance of the *Californian* was nothing to boast of under these circumstances. The publishing firm is announced as Colton & Semple; the terms of the paper, five dollars a year. The following is the "Prospectus" of the *Californian* and the salutatory with which it begins its first number. It might readily be taken for a declaration of independence on the part of the old press and type:

PROSPECTUS

This is the first paper ever published in California, and though issued upon a small sheet, is intended it shall contain matter that will be read with interest. The principles which will govern us in conducting it, can be set forth in a few words.

we shall maintain an entire and utter severance of all political connexion with Mexico. we renounce at once and forever all fealty to her laws, all obedience to her mandates.

we shall advocate an oblivion of all past political offences, and allow every man the privilege of entering this new era of events unembarrassed by any part he may have taken in previous revolutions.

We shall maintain freedom of speech and the press, and those great principles of religious toleration, which allows every man to worship God according to the dictates of his own conscience.

We shall advocate such a system of public instruction as will bring the means of a good practical education to every child in California.

We shall urge the immediate establishment of a well organized government, and a universal obedience to its laws.

we shall encourage imigration, and take special pains to point out to agricultural imigrants those sections of unoccupied lands, where the fertility of the soil will most amply repay the labors of the husbandman.

we shall encourage domestic manufactures and the mechanic arts as sources of private wealth, individual comfort, and indispensable to the public prosperity.

we shall urge the organization of interior defences sufficient to protect the property of citizens from the depredations of the wild indians.

we shall advocate a territorial relation of California to the United States, til the number of her inhabitants is such that she can be admitted a member of that glorious confederacy.

we shall support the present measures of the commander in chief of fhe [sic] American squadron on our coast, so far as they conduce to the public tranquility, the organization of a free representative government and our alliance with the United States.

we shall advocate the lowest rate of duties on foreign imports, and favor an exemption of the necessaries of life, even from these duties.

We shall go for *California—for all her interests, social, civil and religious*—encouraging every thing that promotes these, resisting every thing that can do them harm.

This press shall be free and independent; unawed by power and untrammeled by party. The use of its columns shall be denied to none, who have suggestions to make, promotive of the public weal.

we shall lay before our readers the freshest domestic intelligence and *t*he [sic] earliest foreign news.

we commence our publication upon a verry [sic] small sheet, but its dimentions [sic] shall be enlarged as soon as the requisite moterials [sic] can be obtained.

This prospectus occupies very nearly one column of the *Californian* and is followed by a sample of the "freshest domestic intelligence and earliest foreign news." This is the Declaration of War with Mexico and the Acts of the Congress of the United States, authorizing the raising of troops and appropriating ten millions of dollars to prosecute the war. It is "news" just three months old, and it occupies the remainder of the first page of the *Californian.* The first inside column gives the prospectus and some news scraps in Spanish; the second, local and country items and the following apologetical paragraph, giving an insight into the labor of printing a paper "under difficulties:"

"We are not fond of making apologies, but at present beg leave to inform our readers that the materials on which the Californian is printed, was found in the public buildings here, and have been used for the Spanish language, and in deed has been much injured by neglect. Many of the letters have been wasted or mislaid, and the whole very much out of order, so that, in fact, we have made our first number almost from chaos."

In this and a number of other paragraphs, the English grammar appears to have been most "injured by neglect." But allowance should be made for the off-hand fashion in which the materials of this first paper were thrown together. The first editorial suggestion in the *Californian* is the establishment of a mail through the country. "It would require but a single route," says the editor, "as the principal population is on the coast." The chief editorial in the paper is on the establishment of a Colonial Government in California. It desires a convention of citizens, adoption of a constitution, and the election of a delegate "who should proceed at once to the Capitol of the United States, present his credentials to Congress at the next session, claim a formal recognition of the territory of California and a seat in that honorable body." The remainder of the paper is filled with items in English and Spanish, a few extracts from Eastern papers, an account of the first battle fought between the Americans and Californians, and notices of the movements of the squadron. Only one advertisement, besides an official notice, appears in this little sheet. This is the card of a translator.[2] The official advertisement is from the Civil Magistrate's office, prohibiting the sale of liquors in Monterey. The matter of the *Californian* is all set in one kind of type, and the columns are unrelieved by rules or dash lines; this was the specimen number of this pioneer newspaper.

The next and succeeding numbers of the *Californian* show slight improvements in the typography and arrangement of its columns. That which most detracts from the mechanical success of this sheet, and presents the oddest blemish, is the want of particular letters, as "W," for instance. The following explanation of the cause of this deficiency we take from the editor's own hand, transferring its peculiarities of type and composition to our columns, mistakes and all:

> "Our Alphabet.—Our type is a spanish font, picked up here in a cloister, and has no W's in it, as there is none in the spanish alphabet. I have sent to the Sandwich Islands for the letter, in the meantime we must use two V's. Our paper at present is that used for wrapping cigars: in due time we will have something better, our object is to establise a press in California, and this we shall in all probability be able to accomplish. The absence of my partner for the last three months, and my buties as Alcaldd here have deprived our little papes of some of those attentions which I hope it will hereafter receive.
>
> "WALTER COLTON."

Dr. Semple was probably absent laying out the new town of Benicia, in which he had taken a proprietor's

[2]W. E. P. Hartnell.

interest. Sometimes the letter "V" ran out in setting up the paper. In the emergency thus occasioned, "W" would be spelled with two "U's." "THE NEUU MINISTRY" is the heading of an article. A very destructive gale had visited "Key UUEst." In his notices to correspondents the editor informs "VVandering VVillie" that he is declined. In one of his numbers the editor appears to have given offense to some one. What, then, did he do? Did he refuse to retract, or oblige the offended party to wait a whole week before the *amende honorable* could appear? He did neither; but, on being shown that he must recede, went straight to the office, ordered the press to be stopped, and in the remainder of the edition which had not been worked appeared the following substituted article which we copy *verbatim et literatim:*

> "In my anxiety for information in relation to tovvn lots, I vvas induced to publish in the first papers printed, of the present number, a small article vvhich seems to convey a different idea from vvhat vvas intended. And as an Editor I am determined never to make remarks vvhich bear upon the personal feelings of any. I have therefore substituted this article.
>
> "R. SEMPLE."

The Monterey editors appear to have not alone suffered from want of information on topics discussed, and a perverted use of the alphabet in spelling out their meaning, but, also, from want of knowledge of the construction of Spanish proper names. We read of the Toolárey valley, of Napper valley, and of Yerbabuno, meaning Yerba Buena, the present site of San Francisco. The suggestion for the establishment of a mail not being heeded by the authorities, one of the editors advertises for proposals to carry the mail between Monterey and San Francisco. In a subsequent number is a paragraph headed:

> "MAILS.—It is most devoutly to be wished that, as peace has been restored to the country that some one who has the POWER will use some means to open a communication through the country.

It is a *melancholy sight* for a poor editor to look over the packages of *eight weeks* of his little paper and see no possible means of sending them to his subscribers, and as little encouragement to subscribers to be two months at a time without their paper."

What would the country subscribers of the WEEKLY UNION think on receiving their papers two months old? In a subsequent number the editor announces that he has made arrangements for the distribution of his papers by means of agents at the different settlements, and that the said agents will act in the general capacity of Post-masters for all wishing to send letters to the editor "or any other person." Semple thus discourseth further of his own prospects and those of the town:

"Monterey is improving rapidly. Several American families have settled here, which is quite an acquisition to our society. The houses are all occupied. For ourself, being under the necessity of giving up the room we formerly had in the Governor's house to make room for the portion of Col. Stevenson's regiment stationed here, we were obliged to use a very slightly built shed on the corner of Dr. Stockes' yard. A small paper, a press and a small house, but rather a *lengthy* editor."

We make a few extracts from the *Californian* of February, 1847, to show the state of the country:

"We are pleased to see that the business of our country is attracting some attention abroad. Our friends Ward & Smith, of Yerba Buena, have received a large consignment of goods from the Sandwich Islands, which they offer at moderate prices."

"SCHOOL BOOKS.—A friend of ours, who is on his return to the United States, has a number of school books and some miscellaneous works, English reviews, etc., which he would sell, if immediately applied to."

The difficulty in the way of establishing an English school was the want of books.

"Our late American papers contain little else than heated *party politics*. We hope it may be long before such a state of things shall occur in California. The new tariff [of 1846] will, at least, not be a subject of quarrel here; for every move toward free trade will be an advantage to the country."

Ten years' experience as a gold producing State have somewhat changed the aspect of things in the latter respect.

"Previous to the hoisting of the American flag, the commonest prints and ordinary white cottons were sold by the piece to the farmer for about 18 to 25 dollars (60 to 80 cents per yard); cloths, 8 to 16 dollars yer yard; blankets, 6 to 8 dollars each; the most ordinary chewing tobacco, 75 cents to one dollar per lb.; coffee, 37 to 50 cents per lb.; sugar, salt, pepper and all manner of groceries in the same proportion. Farming utensils were so enormously high that but few farmers were able even to buy a plough, and therefore used a forked pole to root up their land, not plough it. Since the United States have taken possession of the country the self same articles have been reduced by the same merchants to about one-half and many articles to less than half, while beef, flour, potatoes, and in fact all the products of the country have held their own, and some greatly increased in price."

"California Law.—A man came into the Alcalde's office the other day bringing with him a paper from another Alcalde, stating that the bearer had been convicted of horse stealing, and wished to have a new hearing before the Chief Magistrate."

On the 24th of April the name of Colton is dropped from the firm, and the *Californian* appears "published every Thursday by Robt. Semple." The advertising patronage of the paper had been very inconsiderable thus far, though the rates had been fixed at "New York prices." We count only seven advertisements, besides the official proclamation and notices, in the number of April 24th. The largest and most conspicuous of them is for the new city of Francisca (afterwards Benicia), of which the editor is part proprietor. J. F. Romie advertises excellent fresh water from his well, "which he offers to the inhabitants of Monterey at the rate of two reals per week for each family." T. H. Green (whose exposure under his real name, Paul Geddes, afterwards in San Francisco created so much sensation) advertises dry goods, groceries and hardware.

Jas. Watson "keeps constantly on hand a large assortment of merchandise." Crane has opened a restaurant. Milton Little (still remaining, perhaps now the oldest merchant in Monterey) has just received a stock of goods "from the Islands." These are the principal business advertisements. They must have contributed to pay but a very small proportion of the editor's expenses. But some months before this, it is evident, Semple had made up his mind that he was in the wrong locality for business. On the 6th of May, the *Californian* appears for the last time in Monterey. There is no notice given of the intended change, and after it was made there was some complaint on the part of a few of the townspeople, that their long editor had walked off with a press and type not belonging to him, but a part of the public property at Monterey. These charges may have had no foundation, and in any event Semple was probably as much entitled to the material as the town; but he appears not to have stood long upon the order of his going after resolving to take his departure. His office was put on board a sailing vessel, his printer going with it. When the venerable old mill, with its square, heavy uprights and cross beams was again erected and the impression adjusted, it announced that the publication of the *Californian* would henceforth be continued at San Francisco.

At this point the narration of the original Californian newspaper enterprise ends, but it would be incomplete without a few words upon the spirit or genius of the undertaking. Both, Colton and Semple, the pioneers of the art on these shores, are dead. We may say without impropriety, however, that the mission of their journal was a very circumscribed and partial one, incapable of influence or of doing much wide spread good. From first to last it was a timid, obsequious flatterer of the naval authorities in the country, never once raising its voice in disapprobation of their acts, though some of them were totally subversive of the rights of our citizens, and dictated in a spirit of petty despotism or by a consciousness of power, rather than by a desire for the public good. These matters are of small consequence now, but in looking back over the file of the first public journal, we are struck by the dissimilarity in tone and spirit between it and the press of to-day. For example, how would a pretext like the following, taken from an editorial in the *Californian,* sound from one of our journals at the present time:

> "If our friends, who have more spleen in their composition than we have, will show us that an exposé of any officer, from the Governor to the Deputy Constable, can be a benefit to the quiet and happiness of the people, we shall not shrink from the responsibility. They should always remember that our columns are open to them, not for personal attacks or private quarrels, but for any suggestions promotive of the public good."

This was written in reply to a charge made against the *Californian* of a want of independence, it being "afraid to publish the faults of men in power." "To expose them," further says the editor, "could have been productive of no good and only served to widen the breach between the officers and the people, and had a tendency to destroy the confidence of the natives in the capacity of Americans to support such a Government as they boast of." What a monstrous confession to come from the lips of the conductor of a public journal!

Since the removal of the *Californian* but one newspaper has appeared in Monterey, and this only for a short time. The climate of the old Capital seems unfavorable for that species of enterprise. Monterey is situated below the isothermal plane of newspaper life in California. Little towns of half its size in the mountains will support their weekly or tri-weekly paper. The press is a sort of lichen, thriving well among the rocks, and delighting in a hardy growth. In old times it was the custom (and it may be continued to the present day for aught we know) for all Monterey to fall asleep every afternoon between two and three o'clock, and enjoy a *siesta* of two or three hours. We can imagine that such habits in a community would not be conducive to newspaper health. However, nine years "after the events related in the foregoing chapter," Monterey conceived and bore another newspaper.

The Monterey *Sentinel* appeared on the 2d of June, 1855. The materials of the paper were procured from Sacramento UNION office. It was edited and published by J. McElroy, and intended for a weekly paper, independent in politics. After one year of trial, not meeting with adequate support, the paper was removed,[3] as its predecessor had been, showing that the atmosphere of that part of the coast is decidedly deleterious, though not fatal to newspapers. It causes not their death but their removal.

[3]To Santa Cruz, as the *Pacific Sentinel,* June 13, 1856.

Newspapers in San Francisco

We began the history of the old wooden press of Monterey at Boston. Our narrative of the original newspaper enterprise at San Francisco will start out from New York. Up to this time we have proceeded in our history as though the honors of the first California newspaper were settled on our Monterey ancestor beyond dispute. The fame of its mechanical execution undoubtedly reposes with the ashes of the old descendant of Franklin. But in whose iron arms was locked the first secret of such an enterprise? When and by whom was the first idea of a newspaper in California conceived? The settlement of these questions seems to be necessary to the final apportionment of honors. The project of a newspaper on the shores of San Francisco Bay was born in New York, in December, 1845. The purpose was not only formed, but the details partly carried out, before January 1st of the succeeding year. The type and press were selected, the furniture of an office put up, and the name of the unrisen orb chosen, engraved and stereotyped. There were, in fact, type lines set up and packed with the material to be used in the printing of the first California journal. In an exact chronology of events connected with the enterprise and its mechanical developments we cannot, therefore, lose sight of the fact that the first types in a California newspaper were set in New York, in December, 1845. The office in which the material was assorted and prepared was that of a Mormon paper. Its owners and shippers were the company of Mormons who emigrated to these shores in the Brooklyn, which left New York February 5, 1846. The idea of connecting a newspaper with the expedition was evolved by its leader, Samuel Brannan, who was a printer, and for several months had been the publisher of the Mormon journal referred to. It is not known if the original intention was to print an organ of that sect on this coast; it is more likely that a secular paper was intended. The title chosen for this herald of civilization was the *California Star.* The vessel having on board the first colony bound for the North Pacific, and the pioneer newspaper of California, arrived at San Francisco July 31st. The material of the office were removed to the second story or loft of an old grist mill and store house, situated on the north side of Clay street, between Kearny and Montgomery streets. Here, some time during September, the press was set up and a number of jobs executed. The chief office of the press was to print the official notices and proclamations of the naval authorities; also, the blank deeds and other official forms of Alcalde Bartlett. One of the jobs remembered to have been done on the press at this time was the printing of the order of ceremonies for a grand reception given to Commodore Stockton, October 5th. The material used for the impression was blue satin. The honors of the occasion were contrived by some of Stockton's friends and parasites in the Navy. It is amusing to read the programme of the display. The Chief Marshall was Frank Ward; then came the band of music from the same frigate on which the hero's broad pennant was flying; then followed an escort of marines (from the U. S. ship Portsmouth), and then, successively, according to the programme: "Capt. John B. Montgomery and suite; Civil Magistracy of the District (Lieut. Bartlett prime mover of the ceremonies), and the Orator of the Day (Col. W. H. Russell); foreign

Consuls; Capt. John B. Paty, Senior Captain of the Hawaiian Navy; Lieut. Commanding Rudacoff, Russian Navy, and Lieut. Commanding Bennet, French Navy; Committee of Arrangements, captains of ships in port, officers of the late Government, strangers of distinction and citizens of the town." Copies of the above programme were distributed in the streets, and sought for with great avidity by the citizens and "strangers of distinction," as specimens of the first public printing in the town of Yerba Buena. A few weeks subsequent to this grand parade a vessel arrived in the harbor, bringing General Taylor's official report of the battles of the 8th and 9th of May. Then was issued the first news sheet in what is now the City of San Francisco. The official dispatches were printed in full on a half-sheet of the paper subsequently used for the *Star*. The engraved head of the paper was used at the top of the page, and this herald of its advent was offered in the streets as: "An extra in advance of the *California Star*." It was sold for "one real per copy." The date of this publication was about the first of November.

The regular issue of the *California Star* was commenced January 9th, 1847. The press and material had meanwhile been removed to an *adobe* building erected by the printers and some of the Mormon joint stock company then recently organized. The typos took a part in the mixing of the clay and the moulding of the *adobes,* with the rest. The house was situated in the rear of a frame building occupied by Samuel Brannan and family, just behind the old *adobe* Custom House (destroyed by fire in 1851), on the Plaza. The present Hall of Records occupies the same lot. The printing office consisted of one small hand-press, Hoe & Co.'s make, its appropriate furniture and a considerable amount of well worn brevier and minion type. The greatest deficiency was in job letter. The paper was brought from the East, nearly a two years supply, it was estimated. The size of the sheet on which the *Star* was printed was thirteen by eighteen inches. Its typographical appearance was very fair. The first number announced in the imprint that the *Star* was devoted to the liberties and interests of the people of California. It was to be published weekly by Samuel Brannan, and edited by E. P. Jones. The terms were six dollars per annum in advance; two copies ten dollars. Advertisements: one square (ten lines), two insertions, $3, and $1 for every additional insertion. The pages of the *Star* were of three columns each. The first issue contained as "outside" news, under a display line heading in the style of the New York *Herald*, "Later from the Army—Progress of the War—Matamoras taken without Opposition—Mexican Soldiers Deserting in Great Numbers." Then followed the extract: "The electric telegraph at Jersey City communicates the following important and interesting intelligence from the seat of war: From the New Orleans *Delta*, May 29th." This was the latest date from the East, when the first number of the pioneer journal in San Francisco was put to press (January 9th) seven months and eleven days old. The first editor commenced his career with the following salutatory:

> "To the Public.—The anxiety of the proprietor to commence the publication of his paper at the present time—the absence of the gentleman employed as the permanent editor, and my own convictions of the propriety and necessity of commencing it without further delay, have induced me temporarily to take charge of the editorial department of the *California Star*. As the conductor of a public journal I shall be governed solely by what I believe to be the interest of the people of California. Having no interest but in common with them, every possible means will be employed to ascertain their wishes, and the influence of the *Star* will be exerted in carrying them out. While on the editorial tripod, all private pique, personal feeling and jealousy will be laid aside. It will be my constant effort to make the *Star* useful and interesting. Its columns will be at all times open to the public for the discussion of all subjects of general interest. E. P. JONES."

Jones, or Dr. Jones, as he was more familiarly known,

was a thin, green-spectacled, billious-looking personage who came into the country with the Fall immigration of the year before. He emigrated, it is believed, from Tennessee, where he had practiced law. He was a man of very fair abilities, and his editorials are written with a good deal of nervous energy and a sort of uncouth felicity of thought and expression. But a good reputation as a lawyer or an editor was evidently not so precious in his eyes as a notoriety for sharpness and low, vulgar cunning. Unconsciously, in his introductory above given, he spoke a severer truth of himself than most editors would be willing to declare, in promising that while in the editorial chair "private pique, personal feeling and jealousy will be laid aside." With him they *were* only *laid aside*. But his vices frequently got the better of his intention. Jones, as he professes, was only temporarily engaged as editor. The person to whom he refers as the "gentleman employed as permanent editor" was, no doubt, W. H. Russell, then absent in the south, on the staff of Colonel Fremont. Russell, however, did not return to the post, if he was ever actually engaged as editor of the *Star*. There is yet another allusion in the editor's salutatory which should be noticed, viz: "The proprietor's anxiety" and his (the editor's) "own convictions" on the subject of starting the paper just at that period. It seems, that under First Alcalde Bartlett, a lieutenant in the navy, as the civil magistrate, and Captain J. B. Hull, of the United States sloop-of-war Warren, Commander of the Northern District, the little community of Americans at Yerba Buena were sorely oppressed, and their patience a good deal tried by ridiculous and ofttimes wantonly unjust decisions of law, by harsh and unnecessary municipal regulations, and by such general acts of petty despotism as individuals educated to rule men as though they were machines, are very apt to inflict upon all with whom they are brought in contact as the representatives of authority. Among the inconveniences to which the citizens were subject, was that of being driven backwards and forwards between their dwellings and barracks during the day, and out of the streets in the evening, as part of a system of militia police established by Commander Hull, who, taking counsel of his fears, had put the whole town under martial law. The necessity of reaching the ear of the Commander-in-Chief in some popular way, and moving a repeal of some of these burdensome laws, was one of the reasons influencing the proprietor in his choice of the time to commence the publication of the *Star*. From the tenor of the leading editorials in the *Star*, for the first three or four numbers, we should judge that the want of some medium of public opinion was strikingly manifest. In his second issue the editor claims the privilege of free speech, and quotes sections of the Constitution providing for the freedom of the press. The topic of the day was the need of wholesome laws for the conquered province. The want of a school in Yerba Buena enlists the sympathy of the editor, who offers half of a fifty-vara lot and fifty dollars as his donation, to help establish such an institution. An article on water lots and pre-emption laws contains the following paragraph:

"The Alcaldes never had, and have not now, the power of granting titles to any portion of the beach in front of this place; neither had the former Governors of this country. By the general laws of Mexico the beach land in front of all seaport towns was reserved for the use of the people generally, and could not be disposed of in any manner by the authorities of the town or province. We understand, however, that one of the former Governors did issue titles to two or three persons for one hundred varas square each on the beach. Being convinced that these titles are entirely worthless, and that it will be so decreed by the Courts hereafter to be established here, we advise the holders not to put any permanent or valuable improvements upon them at present."

The first advertisements received by the *Star* were lawyer's cards, a significant prelude to the overshadowing evil that has since rested on San Francisco. The editor appears to be troubled with long communications, the common complaint of the newspaper fraternity. More courteous than some of his brethren, he does not turn them off with an intimation that the writers cannot get back even their manuscript, but suggests that if they are anxious for their publication they "can easily send them to the Islands, where several papers are now published, or to the United States, where there is a newspaper in almost every village." He appears to have early arrived at a full appreciation of the dignity of his position, and the importance of supporting the same by exhibiting the magnitude of his newspaper enterprise. The *Star*, of June 21st, says of itself:

> "It is the only independent paper, and the only paper of a respectable size and typographical appearance now published on the whole coast of the Pacific, from the northern boundary of Mexico to the frozen regions of the north. We have the only office in all California in which a decent looking paper can be published, and we intend to add to it as the country grows!"

One would think such a determination might have been arrived at in a better temper and with less invidious boasting. But the *Star* editor and publisher had been wounded in a sensitive part of the malignity of its Monterey contemporary. Here is what the *Californian* had said on viewing the first copies of its San Francisco rival:

> "THE PRESS—We have received the first two numbers of a new paper just commenced at Yerba Buena. It is issued upon a small but very neat sheet, at six dollars per annum. It is published and owned by S. Brannan, the leader of the Mormons, who was brought up by Joe Smith himself, and is consequently well qualified to unfold and impress the tenets of his sect."

In the next number, the editor of the *Star* returns upon his assailant, as follows:

> "☞ We have received two late numbers of the *Californian*, a dim, dirty little paper printed at Monterey, on the worn out material of one of the old California war presses. It is published

and edited by Walter Colton and Robt. Semple, the one a lying sycophant and the other an overgrown lickspittle. At the top of one of the papers we find the words, 'please exchange.' This would be considered, in almost any other country, a barefaced attempt to swindle us. We would consider it so now, were it not for the peculiar situation of the country, which induces us to do a great deal of good for others in order to enable them to do a little good. We did think of charging the men of the *Californian* five dollars and seventy-five cents 'to boot' between papers, but as it seems to be their disposition to 'hump' themselves in future, while on the editorial tripod, we have concluded to give our paper to them this year so as to afford them some insight into the manner in which a Republican newspaper should be conducted."

Jones' model appears to have been copied by San Francisco papers of a later day. It might be well enough to place a stone here to mark the era when professional courtesy, personal good will and generous motives of business rivalry ceased between California publishers, and their intercourse began to be characterized by those petty jealousies, mean detractions and secret hostilities which have continued, with rare intervals and exceptions, to the present day. The disagreement between the two pioneer journals was never reconciled while each maintained a separate existence. The same number of the *Star* which contains the retort upon the Monterey paper, furnished the editor's report of a public meeting held at Yerba Buena. Jones has had some tolerably successful imitators of his editorial style among his brethren of the present day, but we have seen no reporter who could combine the extraordinary impudence, personal offense and sublime conceit manifest in the following essay. We print the report, entire, that our readers may have the specimen to keep as a sample of early newspaper reporting in California:

PUBLIC MEETING.—A large and respectable public meeting of the citizens of Yerba Buena, was held on Monday evening last, on the corner of the Portsmouth Square, opposite the Portsmouth House, for the purpose of taking into consideration a proper disposition of the public beach lands in front of the town. Mr. W. S. Clark was called to the chair, and Hugh Reed, Esq., appointed Secretary. In answer to a call from a number of citizens we explained the object of the meeting, and offered the following resolution:

Resolved, That we will use every effort to induce the Governor and Council to divide the beach lands in front of the town into convenient business lots, and to sell them for the benefit of the town, or the Territorial Government.

We made a few remarks in support of the resolution, in which we alluded to the attempt of a few designing individuals to appropriate the whole of this valuable property to their use for purposes of speculation. When we concluded, PARSON Dunleavy rose and commenced a heated personal attack upon us. He did not touch the subject before the people, and wound up with an attempt to break up the meeting in a row. We replied in a speech of about an hour's length, knocking the BARK from him at every word. In our concluding remarks, we told him that we were sorry that he had put himself forward as the mouth piece of a NASTY LITTLE CLIQUE. He attempted to reply, but was hissed down. Geo. Hyde, Esq., then rose and inquired whether he was included among the "nasty little clique." We remarked that he knew probably better than we did, and if the cap fit that he might wear it. Several persons in the meeting said at the same time, that they did not know whether the clique was nasty or not, but they knew Mr. Hyde was a d——d dirty fellow. Mr. Hyde inquired the names of the persons who made these remarks—one name was given, whereupon he expressed himself satisfied. After some further discussion, the resolution was passed almost unanimously, notwithstanding the strenuous effort on the part of W. A. Bartlett, Dunleavy, and George Hyde, who made repeated attempts to break up the meeting.

We have been compelled to report the proceedings of the meeting ourself, in consequence of the absence of the MAN WITH THE CLARET COAT.

In another place he accuses Commodore Stockton of having set aside the salutary state of things inaugurated by Commodore Sloat, and of having been, since his landing on the coast, "puffing and blowing around the country like a stranded grampus, cracking himself up as the greatest case out." This kind of newspaper talk opened the eyes of some of the quiet civilians in the town of Yerba Buena, and caused a gentle rustling of the plumes of the Navy. In April, Dr. Jones retired from the "tripod," as he delighted to call the chair editorial, and his place was filled by one of the printers in the office, a mere lad, who came out in the Brooklyn with Saml. Brannan, though not one of the Mormons. The exchange was not effected without hard words, and even blows, as most revolutions are accomplished, and it took place while the publisher was absent. The printer's name was Kemble; he had served under Fremont during the Winter, and on the disbanding of the rifle battalion at Los Angeles, he returned North, arriving at San Francisco in the beginning of April. Brannan was then preparing to make a journey across the mountains to meet the Mormons at Salt Lake. Before leaving he provided for a sort of censorship over Jones' articles, fearing that the latter might take advantage of his absence to make the paper a vehicle of personal abuse and improper discussion. Its publication and general welfare was therefore left with Kemble and his fellow printer, J. Eager, who afterwards joined the Salt Lake Mormons. Brannan had not been gone a week before the printers had occasion, first, for mild remonstrance, and then for resistance to the intemperate course and language of the editor of the *Star* in its columns. This audacious interference on the part of typo and ink-ball made the "tripod" reel with consternation and rage. On assuring himself that the publisher had actually set a gauge for the adjustment of editorials to his columns, like type to a measure, Jones threw up the editorship, with a tremendous explosion of wrath and the other raw material of his editorials, and ended by demanding possession of the edition of that week's paper, the outside of which had been put to press, with his name in the imprint as editor. The demand was resisted, and editor Jones becoming belligerent, was summarily ejected from the office. Nobody was much hurt, but the scene was highly ludicrous, and rendered laughable by the victor, after the conflict and while the editor was sopping one of his eyes, presenting him with the shattered remnant of his green spectacles. Jones quit editing from that time, and applying himself, with great shrewdness and foresight to real estate operations, in the Fall of 1849 or '50 he was able to leave San Francisco for his old home in the Southern States, with, it was estimated, nearly a million of dollars. He died, however, very soon after reaching the Atlantic States, and his widow erected a costly monument over his grave.

The maiden editorials of the new editor of the *Star* were highly sophomoric. His ideas were perpetually getting twisted up in the length and labyrinthine wanderings of his words. He was very anxious to keep within hailing distance, at least, of truth, decency and common sense, and under his management the *Star* prospered very well. It had between three and four hundred subscribers, and may be said, with these and its advertisements, to have paid expenses. The total population of San Francisco in August, 1847, was four hundred and fifty-nine souls. The proportion of white inhabitants was three hundred and seventy-five, of which number two hundred and twenty-eight were born in the United States. The number of native Californians in the town was only thirty-eight.

In January of the following year, the *Star* concluded its first volume, and entered upon its second in an enlarged form. The sheet now measured eighteen by twenty-two and a-half inches, or about the size of its cotemporary, the *Californian*, which had then been established in San Francisco about nine months. No changes occurred in the managerial department of the *Star*, meanwhile. On the 1st of April, the proprietors issued an extra sheet, made up for circulation in the United States, and dispatched a mail overland, by the way of Independence, containing two or three thousand of this the first Eastern edition of

California papers. On the 25th of March, the first flush of gold excitement is visible in the *Star*. The paragraph reads as follows:

> "So great is the quantity of gold taken from the mine, recently found at New Helvetia, that it has become an article of traffic in that vicinity."

The inaccuracies of this brief statement show how meager was the information and indifferent the public mind at a distance on the subject of the gold discoveries of that Spring. There had been two or three previous notices of the finding of gold on the American river, but none of them attracted attention. On the arrival of the authenticated reports of the "existence of a valuable mine on a tract owned by J. A. Sutter," the editor of the *Star* set out to visit the place and accompanied Sutter on his second visit to his "Placer." They spent several hours at the memorable sawmill, but found only a few grains of gold. This was in the month of April. On his return, May 6th, the editor barely alludes to the gold mine. There was certainly nothing elicited during his visit which could serve as the basis for a popular excitement, and so, a few weeks after, when the tide began to set in that direction, the editor, like good Mrs. Partington, with her broom, attempted to check the rising waves. He was probably honest, both in believing and declaring the "reputed wealth of that section of country, thirty miles in extent, all sham," for the sober truth had been magnified so many hundred times, and was so much out of proportion, that it was not recognizable under any form or coloring. The most prodigious stories were in circulation. Unable to sift the real grains from the mass of chaff by any process which reason or the experience of other countries could suggest, and conscious that most of those who went to the mines had really taken the bulk of these stories as the true measure of their value, the editor probably thought he was doing his duty by riding a tilt against the aggregated rumors, as Don Quixote charged the windmills. He gave the popular infection the name of the "gold fever." Of the mine itself he thought it would probably be traced as far south as San Fernando Mission, where gold had been known to exist for a number of years. "Though," he says, "our best information respecting the gold, and the quantities in which it is gathered, varies greatly from many reports current, yet it is placed beyond question that no richer mines of gold have ever been discovered upon the face of the continent." By the next number of the *Star,* the subject has become of sufficient magnitude to demand a leader. Next week the *Californian* is suspended, and the *Star* holds "an inquest" over the body. June 10th.—"The excitement and enthusiasm of gold washing continues—increases." The *Star* proceeds to give the first printed account, according to its best information of the exact condition and prospects of the gold mines. This description, and the fact that the *Star* had first ridiculed the excitement, confirmed the reports which had been already received in Oregon and the Sandwich Islands, and set the tide of emigration flowing hither from neighboring countries. This was the last act of the paper before it was carried away with the rising flood. The following week the printer of the *Star,* T. H. Rolfe, now one of the conductors of the Nevada *Democrat,* gave notice that his place would be vacant the coming Saturday. Yates, also a printer, and still in San Francisco, was a compositor on the *Star* at the time, and intimated a similar intention of trying his luck at picking up gold. It only then remained to follow the example of the *Californian,* and issue a slip announcing the suspension of the *Star*. This was done on the 14th of June. "In fewer words," says the editor, "than are usually employed in the announcements of similar events, we appear before the remnant of a reading community with the material or immaterial information that we have stopped the paper—

that its publication ceased with the last regular issue." After detailing the circumstances which have brought about the discontinuance, he speaks confidently of being able to resume the paper again. "On the approach of Autumn we shall again appear to announce the *Star* revived. Upon renewing its publication, if there should be a call for the measure, we will add to it and present a larger sheet than is at this time published on the Pacific Coast. Should we renew earlier than the time specified above, due notice will be given. We have done. Let our word of parting be, *Hasta luego.*" And taking this light-hearted leave of his readers, the editor, in company with his printer, set their faces toward the mines.

The golden hegira makes the first great epoch in the history of the San Francisco press. And at this point we turn to bring up the narrative of the *Star's* cotemporary.

The *Californian,* which was domiciled at San Francisco in May, 1847, was first published in an adobe house, on the hill fronting what is now Stockton street, and between Jackson and Pacific streets. It was the private residence of Don Nathan Spear, situated on a one hundred vara lot, and the *Californian* office was overshadowed in the rear by a huge wind mill, the first and only one in the place. The first appearance of the new comer in its new home was on the 22d of May. It came out on a sheet 18 by 22 inches in size—more than double its former dimensions—and presented a very respectable appearance, although its columns were 3½ inches wide, occupying three to a page, and its typographical accuracy was not remarkable. The *Californian* was in its ninth month when it was removed, but, with a facility common to newspapers in their early periods of existence, it made the change in its locality and dimensions the occasion for opening a new volume. In his introductory to the new volume the editor assigns as his reason for leaving Monterey, "not that he disliked the place or the people," but he had been so fortunate as to secure a valuable landed interest on the Bay of San Francisco, on which we are laying out a town." He therefore (he says) desired to be as near his interest as possible. The motto of the *Californian* was "Measures, not Men;" which, seeing that the editor was over six feet four inches in height, was not inappropriate. But the chief measure to which the new paper in San Francisco devoted itself was the building up of the rival city of Benicia, the landed interest to which the editor adverts above. This interest appears to have increased so much in value that his removal to San Francisco did not bring him quite near enough to his possessions. Accordingly, on the 17th of July, we find Dr. Semple's valedictory, announcing the sale of the *Californian* to B. R. Buckelew, a citizen of San Francisco, who had arrived the Fall before and established himself in the business of watch-making. Buckelew took up the reins editorial, but, like many poor fellows before and since, who have dreamed of the soft lining of an editor's chair, a few weeks of experience appears to have satisfied him, and, on the 8th of September, the name of Robert Gordon appeared as editor. Like Buckelew (who still retained his proprietary interest), the new editor was a novice in the profession, but he was a finished scholar and a graceful writer. His editorials were of a very much higher order of literary composition than had as yet appeared in California journalism. His connection with the paper lasted only until the end of the year, when Buckelew reappears upon the platform and announces: "We again assume control of our devoted paper." Gordon's engagement seems to have been terminated by that gentleman's taking what is called "French leave." Buckelew now remained sole editor until March, when he was joined by J. D. Hoppe. During this time the only peculiarity in the conduct of the paper was its suspicious leaning on the side of a very corrupt clique who had managed to get a voice in the Town Council, and were operating in real estate in the quarter of San Francisco known as Clark's Point, by the filling of lots, grading of streets and construction of a wharf, at the expense of the town, in that direction. The office, dwelling house, and most of the town lots of the *Californian* proprietor, being situated on Clark's Point, gave strength to the suspicions we have named. It may have been for reasons similar to those of the original proprietor, viz: that he was not near enough his interest, that, on the 10th of May, Buckelew withdrew altogether from the *Californian*, and became afterwards noted for his extensive engagements in the buying and selling of real estate. But, whatever the reason, at the date above mentioned a change in the owner and editorship of the paper took place, and we next find it under the editorial supervision of H. L. Sheldon, a printer, with J. D. Hoppe & Co., publishers, and Joseph Dockrill—the first American, to our knowledge, who had set types in the English language in California—as the mechanical overseer. This was the last change in the condition of the *Californian* in the Spring of 1848, before that memorable change which so altered the relations of printer and proprietor that the latter only subsisted at the will or pleasure of the former. Even while the elements of the new proprietary were settling into their places, the tides of this rapidly advancing change were rising high and higher in the columns of the journal. On the 29th of May the *Californian* was "beached," along with almost every species of art and industrial enterprise in existence at the time. A slip was issued from the office, addressed "To our readers," bidding them rather a mournful farewell. We submit a specimen of its leave taking:

> "The majority of our subscribers and many of our advertising patrons have closed their doors and places of business, and left town, and we have received one order after another conveying the *pleasant* request that 'the printer will please stop my paper' or 'my advertisement, as I am about leaving for the Sacramento.' We have also received information that very many of our sub-

scribers in various parts of the country have left their usual places of abode and gone to the gold region, showing that this fever (to which the cholera is a mere bungler in the way of depopulating towns) is not confined to San Francisco alone. We really do not believe that for the last ten days anything in the shape of a newspaper has received five minutes' attention from any one of our citizens. This, it must be allowed, is decidedly encouraging. The whole country, from San Francisco to Los Angeles, and from the sea shore to the base of the Sierra Nevadas, resounds with the sordid cry of '*gold*, GOLD, GOLD!' while the field is left half planted, the house half built, and everything neglected but the manufacture of shovels and pickaxes, and the means of transportation to the spot where one man obtained $128 worth of the real stuff in one day's washing, and the average for all concerned is $20 per diem; for such, in fact, are the reports which have reached us, and from apparently reliable sources."

"On account of which state of affairs," continues the editor, "we are reduced to the necessity of suspending *paper* payments." The *Californian* is not, however, announced as "extinct," but only "discontinued." "Whenever the people shall resume their reading faculties it will be recommenced." The mortuary with which this promise is accompanied is profaned by the eager advances of the destroyer, gold. Dickson & Hay offer "a liberal price" for Sacramento gold. Buckelew delivers an essay on the difference of the weights by which gold and grosser substances are weighed, and offers to adjust scales and weights to the Troy standard. Gold, gold, gold, rings through the circular announcing the decease of the *Californian*, like a volley fired over its grave.

California was now in the thickest shades of a newspaperless night. The *Star* survived the original pioneer, as we have shown, but two weeks. It had faded in the glories of the golden dawn, but not without a promise and a sign of re-appearing. Its mourners, if there were any, grieved, therefore, not as those without hope. As for its predecessor to the tomb, it remained "discontinued" until the middle of the Summer, when it proved that it was not extinct by rising, like the prophet of old in his grave at the touch of kindred nature—the receipt of great news. Its first resurrection was on the 15th of July, when the news to the 17th of March from the old world, of the revolution in France and abdication of Louis Phillippe, and other "highly important foreign intelligence" called it forth. Rumors of peace between the United States and Mexico had also reached it in its unquiet grave, and may have lent a quickening effect. It was a whole month before the *Californian* again revisited the glimpses of its former patrons. But by this time the rumors of peace were confirmed, and the object of its return was to spread before the public the "glorious news" of "the ratification of the treaty of peace," and "end of the war." The news was published on the 14th of August. Its receipt was the occasion of general rejoicing in San Francisco. The town was illuminated for the second time in its American history, and the excitement rose to a high pitch among all classes.

The *Californian* was raised this time by B. F. Foster, a printer. It was now given forth in its columns that it would continue to appear occasionally during the temporary suspension of business. The next week it appeared again, informing its readers that business had, in a measure, resumed its wonted course, and intimating that they might expect a weekly publication while it lasted. An encouraging amount of advertising patronage the week after confirmed the publishers in their intention, and the paper now made regular Saturday issues under the same business firm who had discontinued it. On the 7th of October, Hoppe retired from the establishment, and a new co-partnership was formed, consisting of H. L. Sheldon, B. F. Foster and W. E. Weaver, all printers. Sheldon was still editor. He announced in the initial number under the new management, that it was "their fixed determination to establish a lasting character for their journal, which shall render it, in years to come, the standard paper of the Pacific coast." How many times since, in the legion of journals which have sprung into life and died in this country, has this vain boast been repeated! The new firm held together one month. On the 11th of November, the *Californian* came out as usual, only without the name of an editor, proprietor or business manager about its columns. Turning to the leader we find an intimation that the paper has been abandoned by master and mate. A new hand is at the bellows. No specific arrangement is set forth for its continuance, but it *is* "to be continued." "Unless a mine explode directly beneath our feet," says the hopeful new comer, "the present attempt of the press to take a permanent stand in California will succeed." On next publication day, the readers of the *Californian* are told, they shall know more of the new proprietor and his designs. This was the last number of the *Californian* as a separate journal. On its next appearance it was merged into its former rival, the *Star,* of whose short history, conjointly with that of the pioneer journal after their fortunes were united, we come now to speak.

The *Star and Californian* was issued from the office of the combined establishments on Portsmouth Square, November 18th, 1848. By the aid of their united material, a very neat paper was presented. The editor and publisher was E. C. Kemble, former editor of the *Star*. Kemble came down from the mines in the latter part of September. Possessing himself of the material of the *Star,* for which he paid Brannan eight hundred dollars, he proposed to the *Californian* publishers to unite their office with his and give to the rising city and country one good paper. The owners of the *Californian* would doubtless have accepted the proposal, had not the debts of their establishment weighed so heavily upon their minds as to crush out hope, energy and courage. They owed Buckelew for nearly the whole of their material, their notes were rapidly maturing, and their present receipts and future profits based on an ordinary estimate of newspaper success, were not adequate to the old demands falling due. Sheldon & Weaver offered their interests to Foster for a release of the debts of the concern. Foster was prevailed on to accept the offer, and close with the proposition made by Kemble. The two former proprietors took passage in a vessel bound for the Sandwich Islands. On the morning after the vessel sailed, Kemble's partner was missing. Relying as much upon his practical acquaintance with the art to overcome the difficulties arising from the want of printers, as upon his authority over the *Californian* material, the absence of Foster was as unfortunate as it was unaccountable. Already the principal creditor and a clique of town, Government and real estate speculators stood ready to pounce upon the material, when a letter from Foster was found in the office containing a transfer of all his interests to his new partner. The writer had sailed in company with his late associates for the Sandwich Islands. The new proprietor was left alone with both establishments and their debts on his hands. Luckily, a printer was found after beating the town and suburbs. A small building was secured and the material of the two offices removed to the center from the extreme ends of the place. On next publication day the *Californian* appeared united with the *California Star*. A good deal had been accomplished in one week. The publisher announced the resumption of the *California Star*, as per promise, "after a suspension of nearly five months." It was re-commenced at the number and volume where it had broken off. The publisher agreed, however, to send the paper to the subscribers of the *Californian*, as well as those of the *Star*, to the expiration of the terms for which they had paid. The sheet was the same size as the former *Star*. The introductory contained a hint of enlargement, and also of future editorial improvement. The new paper entered zealously into the discussion of immediate plans for a civil organization throughout the Territory. It was well supported, and its prospects began to look encouraging. The need of assistance in the editorial and mechanical departments was manifest to no one so much as to the proprietor. The little one story tenement occupied as office, publication room, and lodging place for the editor and printer (in the rear of which they cooked their meals in camp style), was too small for the growing business of the establishment. Job work was the principal source of revenue, though a very respectable amount of advertising patronage came to the new paper. The absence of job type was a sore inconvenience. Handbills and posters had to be set in the type on which the paper was printed, with only two kinds of letter for "display lines." The majority of jobs were bills advertising the departure of vessels, for fifty of which, on a half foolscap sheet, the printers received sixteen and twenty dollars. Advertisements were charged at the rate of two dollars for one insertion of fifteen lines. About the middle of December indications of still another change in the fortunes of the single California newspaper began to appear in the columns of the *Star and Californian.* The leader of Dec. 16th is indited by a masterly and experienced hand.[4] The next number announces the close of the publication under the joint names of the old papers, and a new arrangement, new journal, new name and new partners, more suited to the altered circumstances of the country, to begin with the new year. The same paper contains the first notice of the "new town of Sacramento." But the most cheering signs of progress which were set in the sky when the old pioneer journals of the Territory were laid in the grave—the most hopeful rays which illumined their closing pages, and seemed to smile upon their labors and hallow their reform, were the tidings coming in from all parts of the country of great gatherings by the people in favor of a civil organization. They were the signal fires

[4]Edward C. Gilbert.

of the approaching political revolution, the beacon lights in the path of the new State.

The *Alta California*, the Mother of Newspapers, child of the union of the old Monterey pioneer, and the San Francisco maiden press—its lineage extending back through half a dozen civil revolutions on which the fortunes of this country hung; claiming some sort of kindred with the press of Franklin's city, and on its maternal side numbering among its ancestors one of the wives of Joe Smith—"the *Alta*," as it is popularly known, began its career on the 4th of January, 1849. Its immediate origin, after what has been said above of the marriage of the two papers, is very soon told. The publisher of the *Star and Californian* before his return from the mines, meditating plans for the resuscitation of his journal in San Francisco, had selected in his mind as a desirable person to engage with him in the enterprise an officer in Stevenson's New York regiment, who was a practical printer and an accomplished writer. He had, therefore, no sooner gathered the printing material of the city under one roof and re-commenced the issue of his paper, than overtures were made by him to the person mentioned tendering a one-half interest in the establishment. He was invited to join with him on an equal footing, paying no more for his interest than the assumption of half its debts. The offer was accepted; but, unfortunately, as it afterwards turned out, with the condition that a third partner, an intimate friend, should be added, and the shares be held in three equal parts. The original proprietor reluctantly acquiesced in this arrangement, but lived to hear from his first mentioned associate a manful acknowledgment that he had counseled badly. The difficulties in which the third share involved the firm, from its inadequate representation, and in some of the changes through which it passed, from the ruinous unfitness of the holder, can hardly be computed by thousands of dollars. The evil consequences of the first ill-advised step clung to the fortunes of the *Alta* under its original management, with singular tenacity, down to the latest day. The names of the first proprietors of the *Alta California* were E. Gilbert, E. C. Kemble, and G. C. Hubbard—all practical printers, and natives of one district in Northern New York. The name of the *Alta California* was proposed by Gilbert, who had also suggested the expediency of discontinuing the old papers, and starting an entirely new one. The dimensions of the sheet on which the first half of volume one appeared were 18½ by 22¾ inches, a trifle larger than the old *Star;* but smaller type were used, and the appearance of its columns otherwise improved. The leading editorials were written by Gilbert. The following extracts from the salutatory are examples, not only of the literary style of the senior editor of the *Alta*, but also of the spirit which animated the new publication, and the policy to which it was committed:

"This press will be independent of all parties, cliques, and persons. The cause which it will assert is the cause of California—the interests which it will endeavor to advance are the interests of California, and the rights which it will lend its aid to establish and preserve are the rights of the citizens of California. In doing this, it is believed that this paper will not be controlled by unworthy or sordid motives; that it will not be swerved by sectional or local jealousies; and that however much it may err in judgment, it will never degrade itself by becoming a channel through which prejudice or envy may vent its personalities or sarcasms.

"The unenviable position which this sheet at present ocucupies, of being the only paper printed in California, renders it imperatively necessary, were there no higher considerations, that it should be independent and fair. The publishers are fully sensible that unless such be its course it can accomplish but little in any cause, and nothing in a country so peculiarly situated as this. It behooves them, therefore, to carefully guide and guard its course—to see that it rises above all time-serving, expedient, available and personal considerations, and looks alone to the best interests and good of the greatest number. That it will do this the publishers firmly believe."

The *Alta California* remained true to its independent

convictions, although its publishers were all Democrats, and in the political changes which now took place in the territory and in the organization of parties they did not want tempting offers and inducements to conform the practice of their newspaper to their political faith as individuals. It entered earnestly into the work of forming a Provisional Government, and as zealously into the reform of municipal matters in San Francisco. The stand taken by the paper against the high-handed acts of the military authorities and the town officers appointed and sustained by Gen. Smith and Col. Mason, was warmly seconded by the people, and it would be difficult to conceive of closer knit sympathies between the public and a newspaper than those enjoyed by the *Alta California* in 1849. It was emphatically the people's organ, and its crowded business columns gave token of their hearty admiration. On the 22d March it was obliged to suspend two weeks for want of printing paper. When it next came out the steamer Panama was making ready to sail the next day (April 10th), and in compliment to the news which filled its columns, it gave its edition to the public as the *Alta California,* FOR THE STEAMER, thus setting the custom of a Steamer Paper, so diligently observed by the San Francisco press to this day. The price of subscription was now increased from $6 to $12 per annum, and its business was such as to make the issue of a Supplement necessary. On the 24th of May the retirement of G. C. Hubbard from the firm is announced. Hubbard sold his interest to T. R. Per Lee, a former brother officer in Stevenson's New York Regiment, and soon after returned to the East. The price paid for his share of the concern was $5,000. Per Lee retained his interest only a few months, his partners purchasing of him. The style of the firm was changed, after Hubbard's retirement, to E. Gilbert & Co. On the 2d July the *Alta* was enlarged to a sheet of 19½ by 27 inches dimensions, and printed on new type. At the election ordered by Gen. Riley for Delegates to a Constitutional Convention, Gilbert was chosen one of the Delegates from the District of San Francisco, by a larger majority than either of his confederates. While discharging his duties in this capacity at Monterey, he also filled the office of a reporter and the columns of the *Alta* presented a very full and satisfactory account of the Convention proceedings. The large paper began to overrun with advertisements, and a supplement was again necessary. The issue of October 11 contains two supplements, one giving a portion of the Convention proceedings, the other containing eight columns of advertisements, in addition to nearly fourteen and a half columns in the regular sheet. The want of more material, in addition to the small office recently received from the East, and which had been ordered by the old *Californian* began to be sensibly felt, especially after the establishment of the *Pacific News*, with a fine job office. Accordingly, on the arrival of the ship Apollo with a large assortment of newspaper and job material, in charge of R. C. Moore and J. B. Ormiston, printers from the New York *Sun* office, they were immediately waited upon, and negotiations commenced by the *Alta* proprietors, to obtain possession of the material. The result was the admission of Moore and Ormiston as partners. Their connection commenced on the 15th of October. In the Fall election of this year, under the new State Constitution, Mr. Gilbert was elected to a seat in the Lower House of Congress. During the campaign the *Alta* maintained its strict neutrality both in respect of party and person. December 10th the first tri-weekly publication commenced from the press of the *Alta,* the weekly running on as before. The dimensions of the new issue were those of the first weekly publication—the old super-royal size. About this time, in anticipation of the departure of Gilbert for Washington, J. E. Durivage was employed as an assistant editor, on a salary of $6,000 per annum. The typographical appearance of the tri-weekly was greatly admired, and its editorials were sprightly and popular. But three times a week was a limping gait, wholly unsuited to the pace of the city. The owners of the *Alta California* saw the demand for a daily, and they resolved to be the first in the field; but just then they were unprepared. A month later their resolve was quickened by the announcement that a daily was to be started on a specified day, by some young printers then in the city. The receipt of a prospectus of the *Daily Journal of Commerce* confirmed the news along with their intentions. On the 22d of January, 1850, the tri-weekly issue of the *Alta California* was changed to a daily, forestalling the *Journal* only a day. The second volume of the weekly was commenced on the 5th of January. On the 4th of May the buildings of the *Alta California* were destroyed in the second great conflagration which swept San Francisco. Most of the material was saved, although the proprietors sustained considerable personal loss, besides that of the large building occupied as the printing office. A few weeks previous to the fire, Moore and Ormiston disposed of their interest to Durivage. Their retirement was strongly opposed by the resident partners, and was altogether an unfortunate proceeding. They received for their joint interest (one-third) about $25,000 in cash. Nearly the whole of this large sum was paid directly out of the funds of the concern, and the share transferred to Durivage. Moore and Ormiston almost immediately returned to New York. In June, Edward Conner became connected with the paper. Conner was formerly a mail clerk in the New York *Herald* office, and coming to California, was made agent for the sale of one of Hoe's single cylinder "machine presses." This was the first steam press brought to California. One had been ordered for the *Alta,* but months, it was thought, would elapse before it could be received. The large and increasing edition of the paper was printed with great labor on a hand-press. In the brisk competition that had set in, it was highly desirable that the machine press should become the property of the *Alta*, and of no other establishment. It so happened that at the same time the proprietors of the *Alta* set their hearts upon the press, the affections of its owner centered on a partnership and name in the concern. This turn of affairs was very awkward. The senior associate was absent, and many other reasons forbade the forming of this new partnership. As no other terms could be elicited, and the demand for the press seemed to increase with each day's issue of the *Alta*, Conner was admitted to the ownership of a sixth of the paper. On the 4th of July steam was first applied to printing on the shores of the Pacific, and the edition of the *Alta California* of the next day carried out the impression it had made. The press used, however, was not the one brought into the country and into the office by Mr. Conner, but one of Taylor & Co.'s manufacture, which arrived from New York soon after. In October Kemble went East on business with his partner in Washington, and to pass the Winter in his native State. His place as editor was supplied by Frank Soulé, at a similar salary to that formerly paid Durivage. The paper, which had now reached dimensions of 26x40 inches, was further enlarged during the Winter of 1850. In May, the next year, the two original proprietors returned. The *Alta California*, at this time was one of the most profitable and, at the same time, most expensively managed newspapers in America. Its receipts could not have been less than $15,000 per month. The publishing firm still remained E. Gilbert & Co. The office of the paper was one of the most complete establishments in the United States, containing, besides large assortments of book and job type, two or three steam presses. The cost of the brick building was not far from $30,000. Its editorial apartments were even luxurious in their fitting up. On the 22d of June all these fair tokens of prosperity were reduced to an unsightly heap of ruins, and the ashes of what had been a most valuable and flourishing newspaper property were strewn upon the afternoon gale. The conflagration of the above date was a fatal blow to the *Alta*. It never fully recovered from the loss sustained, and the necessary heavy expenses incurred in supplying the place of the material from the San Francisco market. Only the type forms of the paper had been saved, but the *Alta* made its appearance next day. It was reduced to a sheet of eighteen by twenty-two inches, but before the end of July it had, step by step, regained its former size of twenty-eight by forty-two. Before the rainy season set in, the office was again comfortably housed in the building erected for the purpose, now occupied as the Hall of Records, in Portsmouth Square. The fire was succeeded by changes in the editorial department. Soulé's term having expired, Gilbert resumed his place as senior editor. Durivage retired from the paper, disposing of his interest to his senior partners. Conner was absent on a visit to the East when the fire occurred. In the Vigilance movement of this year the *Alta*, true to its original instincts, took the side of the people against bad laws and corrupt officials. It was at this time as popular and influential as it had ever been. Its convictions carried even greater weight than in times gone by, particularly on questions of State and National politics. Maintaining its original independence of party, it was essentially Democratic in its adherence to State and popular rights, and in its opposition to the cabals of section and party here and in Washington. Its opinions uttered at this time would have made it a bold, outspoken enemy of the Lecompton scheme, and a devoted friend to the State against the sectional partialities of the Administration. It held this position through the Spring and Summer of 1852. In August of that year Mr. Gilbert fell in a duel with J. W. Denver, a victim to the miserably false sense of honor, which in the state of public sentiment then existing, placed the resorter to the dueling code between two fatal extremes of opinion; one requiring the adjustment of personal differences on the field, and the other ridiculing the practice, chiefly on account of the usually bloodless termination. Gilbert was seduced into the duel through convictions, and a temperament which forbade his shrinking from responsibilities which the first imposed, and lost his life from sensibility to the ridicule to which the second and equally vicious class of opinions exposed him. The offense for which he was goaded into compliance with the absurdly styled "chivalrous" sentiment, was a little paragraph lampooning Governor Bigler and his tricks of office. It is unnecessary to speak of the circumstances of this affair in the present connection further than to say that Gilbert's independence as an editor, and the obnoxious course of his journal to the party of which Bigler was the head, joined to his mistaken views of personal honor and duty as a man and citizen, cost the State a valuable life. In the light of the higher principle involved, his death was a sacrifice to the liberty of speech and of the press, unmixed with license and untainted by base or immoral motive.

The loss of its senior editor was the severest blow the *Alta* had yet sustained. Besides the injury inflicted on its columns, the settlement of the estate was a perplexing and difficult matter. New partnerships had to be formed, although the business was still conducted in the name of E. Gilbert & Co. The want of practical and suitable managers in the departments heretofore overlooked by the senior proprietors, occasioned numberless disasters, and made foes in and out of the concern. The *Alta* remained prosperous, however, throughout the years 1852-3, though subject to many vicissitudes and editorial changes. Among the mishaps which occurred in '52 was the failure of its supplies of printing paper, and the reduction of the sheet to a number of foolscap pages, after exhausting all the wrapping and colored paper in the market. In early times, as high as $50 per ream had been paid for paper. In the Fall of 1852, the loss of an only near relative took Kemble to Europe. He was absent one year, and returned to find the establishment insolvent. During his absence it had been edited successively by A. C. Russell, C. A. Washburn, J. S. Hittell and E. G. Buffum. During Washburn's connection with it, the *Alta* departed from its hitherto inviolate neutrality to sustain the claims of Mr. Broderick. This offended many of the merchants of the city, and had a very injurious effect on the advertising business of the paper. It was also the means of bringing about a personal collision between Washburn and Washington, editor of the *Times and Transcript,* in which the former was wounded. In January, '55, the *Alta* was sold to the "Alta California Printing and Publishing Company," composed of Annis Merrill, Rev. S. D. Simonds, of the Methodist Episcopal Church and the compositors in the office. C. A. Washburn was the editor, and subsequently Mr. Simonds was associated with him. They tried the experiment of publishing a religious and anti-slavery daily, but it did not succeed. On the 1st of May, the name of the proprietory firm was withdrawn; on the 29th of September, the name of William F. Herrick appeared as proprietor; on the 8th of October, Pickering, Fitch & Co. became the owners, and April 4th, 1856, R. C. Moore & Co. bought it. Moore was formerly a partner in the firm of E. Gilbert & Co. Previous to that time it had been very poor property; its circulation was at one time reduced to only eight hundred; it did not even pay wages to the compositors, and it was, for a considerable time, on the verge of dying out. After Pickering, Fitch & Co. got it, it improved in business and value, but was still not profitable property. In the revolution which followed the death of Jas. King, May, '56, the *Alta* was the only one of the three leading morning papers which justified the action of the people. The consequence was an almost instantaneous revolution in its prospects. The principal business patronage of both the other journals was straightway transferred to the columns of the *Alta.* Since then the *Alta* has been a profitable and prosperous institution, with a much larger patronage than any of its morning rivals. On the 2d of December, 1856, it was sold by R. C. Moore & Co. to F. MacCrellish & Co., who still own it. Mr. Buffum was the chief editor from April, '56 till November, '57, since which latter date W. B. Farwell has been the senior editor. Here, with a few words on the dispersion of its former editors and proprietors, we leave the history of the existing pioneer journal to take up the threads of other San Francisco papers which have been multiplying with almost incredible speed along our way. To begin with Kemble, the oldest proprietor, after the dissolution of E. Gilbert & Co., under the auspices of the emigration movement in 1855 he began the publication of a California journal in New York city, for the purpose of disseminating information from that point throughout the East concerning the resources of the State. The plans of facilitating emigration having failed in San Francisco, the *Californian* was abandoned. Its editor is now connected with the press of Sacramento. Hubbard went to the West, established a paper, and in a Winter journey, in 1850, from one point to another, was frozen to death. Per Lee is, or was recently, a civil magistrate in Santa Cruz. Moore is in San Francisco and Ormiston in New York. Durivage went East in 1851, and has since been both editor and actor by turns; he is now, we believe, permanently on the stage. Conner, after starting the *True Californian,* whose history will be duly recorded, retired from a connection with the press of the State, and in the Spring of 1857 sailed for Valparaiso to establish a printing office and newspaper there. We are not advised if he succeeded, or whether he still remains in Chile. Soulé has gone to Australia. Buffum to Europe, where he was at last accounts. Washburn was, not long since, publishing a paper in Chicago, Illinois. Russell is in the Marysville *Express.* Hittell is still in the *Alta*; and this, we believe, closes the list of its principal managers and editors.

From following the history of the pioneer journal up to this time, we return to take up in successive periods the lives of other San Francisco newspapers. It will not be necessary—nor is it, indeed, possible—for us to give their separate histories with as much attention to details as we have done in the early narrative of the *Alta California.* Most of the actors in the enterprises which immediately followed it have passed from the stage, and, without much labor and expense, materials for so connected an account could not be gathered. The *Alta* is, moreover, a fair type of the fortunes of the old California newspapers—we might almost say of the early Californians. From its early identification with the popular history of the State, it has become something of a monument among our political institutions, and its files contain the only complete transcript of California past life and events to be found in the State—the only material from which the future historian will be able to collate a reliable and unbroken volume. In retracing our steps to the good old days of '49, newspapers rise almost as thickly around us as those famous turbaned monuments of "the faithful" at Scutari. Our path lies through a literary graveyard. But emerging from this Valley of Death, strangest among the marvels of our journey, the first to press upon our notice from the spirit world of newspapers is the apparition of one which seems to have been like the Scottish hero, "untimely ripped" from the web of the future. As the first California newspaper was conceived in New York, and the pioneer newssheet of San Francisco issued several months before it had "a local habitation and a name," so now we have the parallel prodigy, from the days of '49, of one of the first cotemporaries of the *Alta,* having been born several thousand miles away, and having an existence several months in advance of its actual appearance on this planet. According to the testimony of this fore existent spirit, the *Pacific Courier* was a *Courier* of the Atlantic, alive eight or nine months before the publication of any such newspaper was known. This testimony is among the printed records of the time, and if it have any weight must contest with the *Pacific News* the honor of being the second paper in San Francisco, dating from 1849. But we shall consider its claims in due season. The paper last mentioned was the foremost on the ground in substance, at any rate, if not in spirit, and is, therefore entitled to our first attention.

The *Pacific News* was commenced tri-weekly on the 25th day of August, 1849, by Faulkner & Leland. Faulkner had previously published a Democratic paper in Norwich, Connecticut, and his associate, was a townsman of the same place, and has since become one of the proprietors of the Metropolitan Hotel, New York. On the tidings of the gold discoveries being confirmed, Faulkner packed up the material of his newspaper office and started for California. The *News* was first issued as a tri-weekly independent paper, but with a decided leaning to politics, and a highly favorable opinion of the talents of T. Butler King, and certain other pioneer demagogues who were spying out the land in the new El Dorado. It was issued on a sheet of the same size as the tri-weekly *Alta California,* and having a superior job office, for a short time it had the great bulk of the job printing, and literally "coined money." Warren Leland very early sold out, receiving about thirty thousand dollars for his interest. He returned to the East almost immediately, and was afterward succeeded in the *News* by one of his brothers, who likewise disposed of his interest advantageously. A sketch, published in one of the New York Sunday papers not long afterwards, gave the life and portrait of the first Leland as the "founder of the first newspaper in San Francisco." In the Winter of 1849, the *News* was purchased by Winchester, Skillman & Co. Jonas or "General" Winchester is well known as a publisher some years ago, in Ann street, New York. It was under the management of this firm that it became (January 31st, 1850) a Democratic organ, the first that was printed in the State. In the Spring of this year, F. C. Ewer, now of the Episcopal clergy in San Francisco, was editor of the *News*. The paper suffered severely in the great fire of that year, and was compelled to suspend a couple of weeks from the loss of material. It was not very successful after this, suffering once or twice more from fire, and in 1851 was discontinued.

The year 1850 commenced with two newspapers in San Francisco, one in Sacramento, and with half a dozen preparing to take the field. Material was on the ground for one or two at San Francisco and one at San José, and more was expected "around the Horn." Prospectuses for two were before the public, and editors, publishers, and printers, looking out for openings were arriving in every steamer. The first to enter the field with a sheet bearing the semblance of a newspaper were some enterprising Frenchmen.

Le Californien was the title of a curious looking print, which made its appearance on the 21st of January. It declared its ambassadorship as an organ of the French interests, and of course was printed in that language. It was a sheet of foolscap size, and was *lithographed,* on account of the impossibility of procuring French accented type. The names of those concerned in getting up the *Californien* are not given, nor are we aware whether it issued more than one number.

On the 23d of January appeared the third paper and the second daily journal in San Francisco.

The *Journal of Commerce* was started on the above date, by Washington Bartlett, who had brought a newspaper office from Florida. He had issued the prospectus early in this month, while the *Alta* and the *News* were tri-weekly papers, announcing that he would publish a daily paper to be called the *Journal of Commerce*, on the 22d of January. It happened, however, that his paper did not appear until the next day, while the *Alta* appeared on the 22d, and announcing that it would become a daily thereafter, as it did, claimed the honor of being the first daily in the city. The *Journal* was burned out in the great fire of May 4th, 1850, and again on the 14th of June; after the latter fire its publication was suspended for six weeks, until the 25th of July, when it again appeared, and existed till the 1st of February, 1851, when it finally died.

On the 1st of June (same year) the daily San Francisco *Herald* was started by Foy, Nugent & Co. John Nugent and Edmund Randolph were the editors. The paper was a success from the beginning. In July Nugent became the sole proprietor, paying, if rumor be true, about $15,000 to John E. Foy for his interest. The money was supposed to have been furnished by Folsom, Howard and other wealthy real estate owners. Nugent was a bold, caustic writer, and a bitter and relentless enemy, rushed with all his soul into the political quarrels of the time, and made himself a reputation at once. In March, 1851, William Walker, the associate editor of the *Herald*—since then the renowned fillibuster—wrote some articles about the Courts of the city, and he spoke of Levi Parsons, Judge of the District Court, in no favorable terms. This the Judge construed to be such a contempt as the law would punish, and he accordingly had Mr. Walker arrested and imprisoned. The affair created a great sensation; a large indignation meeting was held on the Plaza to approve the course of the editor and condemn that of the Judge, and after the meeting had adjourned the crowd went to the prison to cheer the prisoner. He was soon after released under *habeas corpus* from the Superior Court. Mr. Walker was succeeded, the next year, by Mr. Hamilton. During the Fall, the *Herald,* like many of the other journals of the State, suffered much for the want of printing paper, and was often printed on wrapping paper, blue, brown or yellow, as it could be had. The paper became, however, a good commercial journal. It was about this time that the auctioneers of the city formed a combination and gave their advertisements to the *Herald* exclusively. As they did a vast amount of business, and advertised largely, their preference for the *Herald,* secured its success. This advertising sustained it in after years, when the fortunes of California newspapers began to crumble, and when fears were entertained by the friends of the *Herald* for the solvency of that journal. Nugent remained its editor, however, and the paper continued independent, but noted for its partisan zeal in behalf of its friends and its malignant bitterness towards its enemies. Mr. Hamilton died in the Spring of 1853, and A. J. Moulder, who had previously occupied a place on the staff of the *Herald,* became associate editor. The acrid political articles with which the *Herald* abounded during the time of its prosperity led to bitter animosities, two of which ended in duels between Mr. Nugent and members of the City Council, whose course he had condemned. The first duel was with Alderman Cotter, in the Summer of 1852. The Alderman was unharmed; the editor received a compound fracture of the thigh bone. The wound was a very dangerous one but it healed, leaving the leg apparently as good as ever. The quarrel was caused by some remarks in the Council about Nugent by Cotter, who was very indignant at the charge made in the *Herald* that the purchase of the Jenny Lind Theater for a City Hall was a fraud. The second duel was with Thomas Hayes, in the Summer of 1853. Mr. H. had done his utmost to have the city give her title to the lands in the city to the persons in possession of them, and Nugent spoke in no complimentary terms of him and his scheme.

Hayes published a long card in the *Whig*, of June 8th, in which he recited a number of alleged misdeeds of Nugent, adding a number of insulting epithets, the whole being avowedly intended for the purpose of provoking a challenge. The editor challenged him, and the result was a second wound, this time from a rifle shot, which made a compound fracture of Nugent's arm. From this, also, he recovered. In 1855 Moulder was elected Controller of the city. Nugent withdrew all but his name from the paper, which still continued to thrive, dependent mainly, however, on the auctioneers' printing.

On the 14th of May, San Francisco was thrown into a great convulsion by the murder of James King of Wm., editor of the *Evening Bulletin.* The whole people raged with excitement. They organized an association for the purpose of administering justice and purging the city of evil doers, and they took possession of the government. This revolution exercised a powerful influence upon the press of the city. The day before the murder the five morning papers, the *Chronicle, Herald, Town Talk, Alta* and *Globe,* had value and influence, and were prosperous in the order as they are here mentioned. The *Chronicle* was the popular paper, with the largest circulation; the *Herald* had the auctioneers' advertisements; and the *Alta* and the *Globe* were living along from hand to mouth. The day after the murder all this was changed; the *Chronicle* and *Herald* having spoken of the homicide without denouncing it as a murder, and having taken ground against the reorganization of the Vigilance Committee, fell at once from popular grace, and the greater portion of their patronage was transferred at once to the *Alta,* which chimed in with the tone of the popular excitement. The course of the *Herald* was attributed to a feud existing between its editor and the murdered man. The Front street merchants were indignant that private enmity, perhaps sheer envy, should control the action of one of the guardians of their press.

As they are the chief props of the auctioneer league, they had only to give notice to the latter that they would not patronize any man who should advertise in the *Herald.* This settled the question both as to interest and principle in holding longer to their business covenant with the *Herald.* Though it is proper to add that most of the auctioneers were indignant as the jobbers, and willingly withdrew from that paper. All classes of business men followed suit. The copies of the paper on Front street were collected and burned. The dissatisfied advertisers and subscribers formed a string at the door, and waited their turns to get at the book so that they could write down, "Stop my paper," or "Take out my advertisements." The next day the *Herald* was reduced from being a sheet 28 by 42 inches to be less than one-fourth the size. There was a strong probability that it would soon die. But it did not die. Had the opposition manifested a less violent spirit, it is thought probable the *Herald* might as in times past, have sided with the people. But the loss of business steeped the soul of its editor in gall, and he became a hater of Vigilance Committees. He fought the popular movement with all his might. Some of the ablest articles were written by eminent lawyers. The *Herald* now began to consort with the Democratic party. In the Presidential campaign of 1856 it advocated Buchanan, and has continued a party paper since. The *Herald* has now grown up to be a large paper again, but it has neither the patronage, the influence, nor the profits which it commanded of old. Nugent ceased to write regularly for the paper when the Vigilance excitement subsided, and it has been since edited by M. G. Upton. The name of the old editor still flies at the head of the columns, though Nugent himself holds a Federal appointment on Puget Sound.

The *California Courier,* by James M. Crane & F. W. Rice, came into actual existence on the 1st of July, 1850. This is the journal which seems to have had a sort of spiritual existence before it was tabernacled in ink and paper—to have been a thing of shadows before it was one of types. In the Fall of 1849, copies of a letter sheet printed document were circulated in San Francisco under the head of the *Pacific Courier—Extra.* It contained the following electrifying intelligence:

> "The undersigned has commenced the publication of a newspaper of the above name, in San Francisco, California, and takes this course to announce his object to the public at large. As yet no editor of whom any portion of the people of the United States have a knowledge for being both capable and trustworthy, has commenced a journal of high character in this distant but interesting part of the Union."

The "interesting" announcement, of which this is an extract, was signed by "Jas. M. Crane, Esquire, Editor and Proprietor," and backed up by a list of about fifty names, headed by President Taylor, and including T. B. King and other well known Whig politicians. These were followed by a number of "Notices of the Press," showing, in a highly flattering manner, the opinion in which Crane and his enterprise was held, chiefly by the Whig press of the South. The appearance of this "extra," with its list of indorsers, caused considerable fluttering in the camps of those journals already in the field. The *Alta* and *News* found themselves suddenly thrust out of existence or into disgrace, and only one "capable and trustworthy" paper published in San Francisco, and this a journal which, up to that hour, they had never heard of. Considering the respectability of the indorsers, such an announcement as that of the *Pacific Courier Extra* was well calculated to startle them. Nor is it possible now to account for the honors which loaded the premature statement and flourish of intentions contained in the *Extra* except on the supposition that they were forged. The facts of the *Pacific,* afterwards, *California Courier,* are about as follows: Previous to 1849, Crane had been a letter writer in Washington, and being an ardent supporter of Fillmore's Administration, he induced a number of zealous Whigs to supply him with the means for starting a newspaper in San Francisco to advocate Whig principles. He purchased material for publishing a good paper, but he was unfortunate in shipping it on the old steamer Chesapeake, which spent a whole year on the voyage to California. Crane, meanwhile, had issued his prospectus, under the head of *Pacific Courier*, Extra, as though the paper were already started, and followed it to San Francisco. Here he remained several months waiting for the material, with great impatience. At last it came, and the *Courier* was commenced. It was not very successful. The editors did not agree very well together; and it sometimes happened that when one had gone out of town, the other would disavow editorial articles published by his associate the previous day. In '51, James W. Simonton became a partner and associate editor, with Crane and Rice. The *Courier* died in January, '52, P. P. Hull and L. R. Lull having become its proprietors a few days before it expired. Death did not, however, terminate its career. As it had existed before it was born, so now it lingered after it was dead. On the 1st of February, 1854, after two years sleeping in the tomb and when almost its name had faded from the recollection of man, the *Courier* burst the fetters of the grave and returned to the haunts of the living again. Crane had galvanized it into life. It had the same size, title, and general appearance as the first. But it did not last long. The stamp of death was on its brow. Again it died and was buried. It has never been resurrected since, but probably "still lives" in some nook or corner of the spirit world, ready to step forth at the summons of its master, and achieve another victory over death. Crane was in Washington last Winter endeavoring to procure the official recognition of his claims as delegate from Carson Valley

Territory.[5]

The *Evening Picayune*, the first evening paper on the Pacific coast, was commenced on the 3d of August, 1850, by (Dr. J. H.) Gihon & Co., proprietors, and P. A. Brinsmade, editor, and W. W. Shepard, associate editor. The establishment was burned out by the May fire of '51; and Shepard and Brinsmade started the *Morning Post* a couple of weeks after. The *Picayune* was revived by other parties, A. C. Russell and C. S. Biden having editorial charge of it during most of the latter period of its existence. Isaiah C. Woods was part owner of it in the beginning of '52. In March of that year it expired; George O'Doherty being the owner of it at the time. The *Picayune* contained several columns in French, edited by M. Derbec, who afterwards established the *Echo du Pacifique.*

The *Watchman* is the title of the first religious paper commenced in this country. It was started in the beginning of 1850, although the prospectus was published in the Summer of 1849; Rev. Albert Williams, of the Presbyterian clergy, was the editor. The paper was of course intended as an organ of that Church. It was issued weekly, but did not last long.

The *California Illustrated Times*, also started in 1850, was the first pictorial sheet published on the Pacific coast. It was printed at the *Alta California* office, and its publishers were Thomas Armstrong & Co., Englishmen. The engravings were much above those seen in ordinary American pictorials, rather superior, we should think, to the average style of cuts in some of our magazines of the present day. The *Times* appeared first on the 1st of September, 1850, but was not long continued. The principal writer for the *Times* was Carleton.

---

[5]The *California Daily Record** is reported for this period by the Fort Worth Public Library, which has Vol. I, No. 91, dated October 12, 1850.

La Gazette Républicaine, Hoogs & Anselm, publishers, was the title of a French tri-weekly paper, started in August of this year. It was not, we believe, the first attempt to start a French paper in San Francisco; but, like the first, it was unsuccessful.

The daily *Public Balance* was established Dec. 8th, 1850, by Benj. R. Buckelew and Eugene Casserly, under the firm of Casserly & Co. Buckelew, then a prominent man in California, is uneducated, but shrewd and enterprising, and was then very wealthy. He is the same man whose connection with the *Californian* of 1848 we have already noticed. He had become greatly offended at the *Alta* on account of the refusal of that paper to puff him and his undertakings; so he declared his intention to break it down by establishing a superior rival. Early in '50 he entered into an agreement with M. T. O'Connor, that the latter should go to New York, purchase the material for a first class daily paper, and then establish and edit it, Buckelew to furnish the money. He furnished O'Connor with money or credit to the amount of $20,000 or more, with which the latter purchased a press, type, etc., in New York, and shipped them to San Francisco. Before they arrived, however, the two quarreled, and Buckelew took Casserly for his partner. These two quarreled likewise, in a few days after the publication of the paper was commenced. Buckelew insisted upon inserting editorial articles which Casserly disliked, and they separated. On the 2d of January, '51, Casserly commenced the publication of a second *Public Balance,* which was printed so as to resemble the first one very closely. Buckelew had an injunction issued to restrain Casserly from using the name of his paper. The first injunction did not avail; nor did the second—and many were used, until at last Casserly was compelled to change the title of his journal, and he adopted that of the *Daily Balance*. The two papers kept up a continual quarrel with each other. Both were 24 by 36 inches in size; both were sold at the low price of five cents per number, or twenty-five cents a week; Casserly afterwards changed the name of his paper to the *Standard*; and both died in the latter part of '51. For Buckelew, the experiment of publishing a newspaper proved in no wise profitable; general rumor said it cost him upwards of $30,000.

This closes the chapter of the newspapers of 1850, with the exception of the notice of a publication called the *Illustrated Guide*, which we find in the *Alta California*, of December, 1850. It calls the new *Illustrated* an excellent design, and says that it is published by Berford & Co., but we find no further notice of the affair.

We now proceed to sketch rapidly the lives of those of the succeeding year.

The *Hombre*, a weekly satirical paper, of quarto size, was commenced by Dr. William Rabe, in April, 1851, but soon abandoned.

On the 24th of May the daily *Morning Post* was started, by Shepard & Co., and it died on the 14th of November of the same year. W. W. Shepard and P. A. Brinsmade were the editors. The *Post* was Whig in politics, and was the only active opponent in the State of the Vigilance Committee of '51.

The *Pacific Evening Star* was commenced in June, by Sutherland, Rust & White. Its existence was brief.

The *Sunday Dispatch*, a weekly, after the style of the New York paper of the same name, was also started in July. Only a few numbers were published.

On the 1st of August the weekly *Pacific* was started, as an organ of the Congregationalist Church; and it still exists, the oldest and most prosperous religious paper on the coast. J. W. Douglass was its first editor, and he was succeeded by I. H. Brayton, who still holds the position nominally, though now absent on a visit to the Atlantic States. The editorial labor is at present done by S. V.

Blakeslee, associate editor, and several Congregational and Presbyterian clergymen of the city. The *Pacific* has always been a high toned and well managed paper. It is considered as an organ of the Presbyterian as well as the Congregationalist Church.

During the year '51 a weekly paper, styled the *Christian Observer*, was established, as an organ of the Methodist Church South, but it soon expired. The Rev. Dr. Boring was its editor.

The *Clarion*, a weekly paper, owned and edited by Mortimer J. Smith, lived and died in the Summer of this year.

From a catalogue of the papers of 1851, we pass to those of '52.

On the 15th of January, 1852, the *Western American*, a daily newspaper, was established by Charles E. Pickett. Notwithstanding his "liberality," declaring himself "a disciple of Epicurus in philosophy, of Jesus Christ in morals, and of Thomas Jefferson in politics," thus trying to suit all tastes, his enterprise soon failed, and the *Western American* died.

On the 17th of February, 1852, the publication of the *San Francisco Shipping List and Prices Current* was commenced by S. O. Johnson & Co. On the 17th of March, *Sloat's San Francisco Prices Current and Shipping List* was commenced by L. W. Sloat. On the 5th of April, the title of Johnson's paper was changed to the *San Francisco Prices Current and Shipping List*, and not long afterwards the "San Francisco" was dropped. The *Prices Current and Shipping List* still exists as a weekly commercial paper. It is now owned by G. K. Fitch & Co.

In March, George O. Doherty, then proprietor of the *Evening Picayune*, started a daily morning paper called the *Times*. It lived but a short time, and died with the *Picayune*.

The *Evening Journal* was established on the 25th of May, by Pinkham, Gee & Co., and proved a profitable enterprise. It was edited, at first, by Washington Bartlett, but experienced many changes in its editorial as well as in its proprietary department. The paper leaned towards Whiggery and Anti-Slavery, and was at one time looked upon as a Whig organ. In 1853 R. K. Browne was its editor. In 1855, H. K. W. Clarke being its proprietor and C. A. Washburn editor, it became an organ of the Republican party, and so continued till it expired, in the beginning of '56.[6]

The *San Francisco Daily Whig* was started by Hull, Matthewson & Co., publishers, with F. M. Pixley and L. R. Lull editors. It was the organ of the Whig party, and derived great profit, during more than a year, from the public printing of the city. W. B. Farwell, W. V. Wells and J. D. Whelpley became connected with its editorial department during the period of its prosperity. In March, '53, its name was changed to the *San Francisco Daily Whig and Commercial Advertiser,* and in the ensuing September the *Whig* part of the name was dropped, the Democrats having carried the city. In the Spring of '54, the *Advertiser* became an organ of the Broderick faction of the Democracy, William Walker, the fillibuster, being its editor at the time. On the 27th of September it sank to rise no more.

The first permanent French paper in San Francisco, the *Echo du Pacifique,* was established on the 1st of June by M. Derbec, editor and proprietor, which position he has held up to the present time, being now the oldest newspaper proprietor in San Francisco. The fourth page of the *Echo* was printed in Spanish under the title of *El Eco del Pacífico,* until January, '56, when a separate paper was started under that title. The French *Echo* was a tri-weekly till the 1st of January, '56, when it was

[6]On June 21, 1852, the only number of the *Sun** appeared; reported by the *Alta California* of June 22 and 28, 1852.

changed to a daily. It is now one of the largest papers in the city, being 28x42 in size.

As the Presidential campaign approached, it became necessary to have newspaper organs to the music of which the voters might march to the polls. The first of these was the *Daily Staats Zeitung,* a German paper established by Jacob Haehnlen, proprietor, with Karl Krug, editor. In the Fall of '53 it became independent in politics, and its name was changed to the *Freie Presse.* It finally died about the beginning of '54.

In the month of June, of this year, the *Daily Times and Transcript,* then an organ of the Democratic party, was removed from Sacramento to San Francisco, to be at the chief center of population and influence. Fitch and Pickering were the proprietors, and Pickering was editor. About the beginning of '54, Edwin Bell purchased it, and B. F. Washington became the editor, and under his management it was a leading paper. It died in the Fall of '55, its good will and material going back to the *Alta California,* which had given it life in the first place.

The *Bugle* was an organ of the Whig party during the campaign, published by the State Central Committee, and edited by A. C. Russell.

It was sometime during this year that a small paper, called *Satan's Bassoon,* was started by A. M. Kenaday, for a freak. It did not last long.

The *Golden Era,* a weekly, literary, Sunday newspaper, was started on the 19th of December, 1852, by R. M. Daggett and J. McD. Foard, editors and proprietors. A number of similar papers have been started in the State, but this is the only one which has proved permanent. It has now a quarto form, and has a large circulation among the miners, to whose tastes it is more especially adapted. Robert F. Greeley is its present chief editor.

On the 15th of February, 1853, the *Curiosity Shop,* a humorous, weekly, illustrated paper, was issued in a small quarto shape. It lasted but a few weeks.

In April, the *California Temperance Organ,* a weekly paper, was started by the Sons of Temperance. The paper continued to exist till May 11th, 1854, when its name was changed to the *Star of the West,* but only one number was published under the new name.

On the 6th of May, the *Weekly Catholic Standard,* an organ of the Catholic Church was established. It existed about a year. During the greater portion of its existence it was published by William Hamill.

On the 19th of May, the *Daily Sun* was issued. It began as a little sheet, about eight by fourteen inches in size, and was circulated gratuitously, to advertise the job office of F. A. Bonnard. It contained a few little items and funny paragraphs; and the publisher, seeing that there was a demand for it, enlarged it, and charged twenty-five cents per week. Its circulation increased rapidly, and in the Fall had become more extensive than that of any other paper in the State. It changed owners and editors a number of times. R. B. Quayle and J. C. Cremony were its editors during '54. J. E. Lawrence was owner about the end of that year. Subsequently, A. S. Gould and W. Bausman became the proprietors. In the Summer of '55, the paper, previously independent, became an organ of the Democratic party. When the Vigilance tocsin struck, the *Sun* wavered in its choice for a day or two, but at last came out against the Committee with all the venom, malignancy, and abuse, that the wrath of man could devise. During the campaign of '56, it was edited by C. H. Hempstead, since appointed Superintendent of the Mint. During '57, it was edited by J. C. Cremony, and in the Fall of that year it died.

In June, the *Weekly California Christian Advocate,* an organ of the Methodist Episcopal Church, was established. It still exists, and has a large circulation. Rev. S. D. Simonds was its editor for about three years after its establishment. Its present editor is Rev. E. Thomas.

On the 16th of June, *The Present and the Future,* a daily paper, was established by Dr. E. Theller, who was editor and proprietor. One-half of the paper was in French, under the title of *Le Présent et L'Avenir,* the editorial labor of which was performed by M. Lachapelle. On the 1st of August, the name of the paper was changed to the *Public Ledger,* and the French department dropped; but the *Ledger* did not prosper, and finally died on the 1st of March, 1854.

On the approach of the September election, a small German paper, printed in Roman type, was started by J. A. Reichart and Dr. V. Loehr, under the title of the *California Demokrat,* as an organ of the Democratic party. It still exists, Dr. Loehr being the editor, but since the middle of '56 it has been independent, and friendly to the Vigilance Committee.[7]

In October, the *Messager,* a tri-weekly paper, was established by L. Albin, proprietor—M. Lachapelle, editor. The *Messager* continued to exist until the last day of March, 1856.

The *Daily Evening News* was started on the 1st of November, by C. Bartlett and F. W. Pinkham, the editors being Julian and Washington Bartlett. The *News* was a sprightly paper, and prospered for a time, but was killed, early in '56, by the competition of the *Bulletin.* On the 21st of January it absorbed the *Daily Evening Picayune,* and changed its name to the *Evening News and Evening Picayune.*

The *Daily California Chronicle,* a journal destined to occupy a prominent place in the press of the State for a time, was started on the 21st of November, by Frank Soulé & Co. Soulé had been formerly connected with the *Alta,* as had, also, most of the other publishers, who were

---

[7]*California Chronik** is listed by Gregory as Sunday edition of *California Demokrat,* 1852 to date.

printers. The type and material on which the *Chronicle* appeared had been ordered by the proprietors of the *Alta California*, through Wm. L. Newell (one of the *Chronicle* company), who had solicited such order for a Boston firm of type makers, of which he was the agent. Newell had been retained in the office of the *Alta California*, as foreman, since 1849, but becoming dissatisfied with the publishers he abandoned his situation, and, when the new type arrived, refused to give it up to them. In the meantime, the old hands of the *Alta*, most of whom had grown comparatively rich from the concern, hearing that they were to be discharged and their places given to printers hired and brought out from New York, united with Newell. It may have been concerted between Newell and his associates, while in their old place, to withdraw from the *Alta* and build up a newspaper which should overthrow it. At all events, this is what we find them attempting to do, the *California Chronicle* being an exact imitation of the pioneer journal, adopting its general tone, and seeking to ingratiate itself with the same classes of the community. It published a large amount of matter, and gradually gained in favor until in the Fall of 1855 it had a larger circulation than any other large paper in the city. At this time James Nisbet and John S. Hittell were associate editors. During the Winter of 1855 and 1856, the *Bulletin* gained rapidly in influence, and, by frequent attacks on the *Chronicle* and Mr. Soulé, did it some injury. But the paper continued to flourish and to have a large circulation until the 14th of May, when King was shot. Mr. Soulé opposed the re-organization of the Vigilance Committee, and did not denounce the shooting as a murder, but referred to it as a homicide, in which both parties might be equally to blame. That day the paper was visited by the vengeance of an indignant community, by the withdrawal of numerous subscribers and advertisers. The next day the *Chronicle* endeavored to remedy its error by declaring in favor of the Vigilance Committee, but it was too late; popular favor could not be conciliated in that way, notwithstanding that the paper continued to advocate the cause of Vigilanceism from that time forward. During the Summer it became the organ of the Republican party, Soulé withdrawing from the editorship. By this time most of the shares were owned by Newell, he having bought from the printers in the days of the *Chronicle's* prosperity. During the Presidential canvass the paper was edited by various persons. The defeat of the party sank the fortunes of the *Chronicle* still lower, and in the Summer of 1857 Newell sold the concern, which had once been estimated as the most valuable newspaper property in the city, worth forty or fifty thousand dollars, for about five thousand dollars, to a joint stock company of Republicans. During the State election of that year the *Chronicle* was edited by J. H. Purdy and others. From September to the end of 1857 the leading articles were written by E. C. Kemble. Its circulation and business was small, and it was very much neglected by the trustees and managing men, and during the Winter barely maintained itself. In the Spring of 1858 the *Chronicle* breathed its last.

In the latter part of 1853 A. C. Russell commenced the publication of a new daily *Evening Picayune.* It did not succeed, and on the 21st of January was absorbed by the *Evening News.*

On the 16th of January the weekly *California Farmer,* an agricultural paper, was started by J. L. L. F. Warren. It still exists.

On the 27th of January the first number of the *Pioneer,* a monthly magazine, octavo in size, of sixty-four pages, appeared, Lecount & Strong being the publishers, and F. C. Ewer editor. It existed nearly two years, dying in the Fall of 1855. It was a well conducted magazine, and contained many interesting articles.

On the 15th of March a weekly quarto paper, which

aspired to a literary character, was started by M. A. M. Taylor and "Dr. J. F. Morse," under the title of the *Bon Ton Critic.* Its career was cut short by the arrest of Dr. Morse for grand larceny, and his sentence to imprisonment in the State edifice at San Quentin.

Early in the year 1854,[8] J. H. Purdy commenced the publication of a weekly Democratic journal called the *Pacific Statesman,* which lasted about a year.

On the 17th of March the *Wide West,* a weekly Sunday literary newspaper, was established by Bonestell & Williston, the latter acting as editor. It changed hands several times, being at one time published by W. W. Kurtz & Co., and subsequently, by E. G. Jefferis & Co. It was a good paper of its class, but it had too many competitors to thrive, and after a long existence with little profit to its owners, it died in July, 1858, during the Fraser river exodus. At the time of its death J. E. Lawrence was its editor and part owner, and E. G. Jefferis, publisher.

On the 28th of April the *Golden Hill News,* a weekly lithographed paper, published in Chinese characters and language, was established by Howard & Hudson. It did not live long.

An illustrated humorous paper called *Young America on the Pacific,* was started in April, R. E. Doyle being the chief editor. Like others of the same clan, its life was short.

In July[9] the weekly *Police Gazette* was established by J. H. Dunn. He was murdered a few weeks afterwards by a printer employed in his office, and the *Gazette* did not appear again.

In the beginning of August the daily *Journal of Commerce* was started by E. J. C. Kewen, as a Whig organ. After the election it was sold to Theodore M. Bosworth & Co., upon whose hands it soon died.

---

[8]March 30, 1853. It continued to September 2, 1853, if not longer.
[9]April? Dunn was killed in May, 1854.

During this month also, *La Crónica,* a Spanish newspaper, was issued by J. Joffre and J. T. Lafuente. Its fourth page was printed in Italian, under the title *La Cronica Italiana.* The Italian department was given up at the end of a couple of months. The *Crónica* was sustained until October, 1855.

In September H. Davison commenced the publication of the *Weekly Leader.* It was independent in religion and politics, and had no strongly marked characteristics of any kind. It did not exist long.

Two weekly advertising papers were commenced in October—the *California Mail* and the *Pathfinder.* The latter was devoted to advertising exclusively; the former contained some literary articles from the pen and scissors of R. F. Greeley. Both had a brief existence.

The daily German *Abend Zeitung* (Evening Gazette) was established on the 25th of September, 1854, by A. J. Lafontaine and J. Behrens, the latter acting as editor. The paper had no very peculiar character, and lived only three months.

On the 12th of November the daily *Town Talk,* paper 15 by 19 inches, was started by William H. Mantz & Co., at the price of one bit per week; the first experiment of publishing a newspaper in California at so low a price. It was a sprightly paper, and soon grew to have a very large circulation. In 1855 it was sold to P. P. Hull & Co., under whose care it continued to thrive. The *Town Talk* chimed in with the popular cry during the Vigilante Committee excitement, and gained considerably in patronage and influence; so that it was soon enlarged, and its price increased to two bits per week. It has changed owners and editors several times during the last two years. Its name, also, has been changed to the *Times,* and its present proprietors are Towne & Bacon; W. V. Wells being its editor.

During the month of November the *Pacific Recorder,* an organ of the Baptist Church, was established, but soon died.

A paper called the *Water Fount,* an advocate of hydropathy, was published in New York, though purporting to be issued in San Francisco, where its main circulation was; and an illustrated weekly called the *Uncle Sam,* purporting to be published in San Francisco, and printed in Boston, and sent out by every mail.

During this year several little French papers were started, of which no copies are to be found, and of which the dates are not preserved in any record. To avoid omitting any of them we shall here mention all the defunct French papers of the city, with the name of the editor and the term of its existence. Nearly all belong either to 1854 or 1855:

1. Messager, daily, Lachapelle; 3 years.
2. Patriote, daily; Toubin; 3 months.
3. Courrier de la Californie, daily; Vesian; 6 weeks.
4. La Presse, daily; Gandonniere; 1 day.
5. Gazette Républicaine, tri-weekly.
6. Le Français, tri-weekly; Thiele; 1 month.
7. Colibri, semi-weekly; Toubin; 2 months.
8. Mineur, semi-weekly; Thiele; 1 month.
9. Spectateur, weekly; Thiele; 6 months.
10. Passe-Partout, weekly; Chemin; 3 months.
11. Revue Californienne, weekly; Toubin; 1 month.
12. Revue Californienne, weekly; L'hériter; 3 weeks.
13. Tam-Tam, weekly; De France; 1 week.

There were French departments in the *Star, Picayune, Evening Post, Whig, Present and Future,* and *Globe.*

The *Masonic Record* is the name of a paper, notices of whose existence we find in July of this year.

On the 4th of January, 1855, the *Oriental,* a newspaper printed partly in English and partly in Chinese, was established by the Rev. William Speer, a Presbyterian clergyman, who had been a missionary in China, and understood the tongue. Mr. Lee Kan, a Chinaman, was his associate editor. The paper was religious in its character, and existed two years. It was published thrice a week in Chinese, and one of its issues in each week had one page of English. Its size was twenty-one by twenty-eight inches. It expired in the beginning of '57.

In February, William Miller published No. 1 of the San Francisco *Medical Journal*, announced as a monthly periodical, devoted to medicine and surgery. No second number was issued.

The Daily San Francisco *Journal*, a German morning paper, was founded in the beginning of '55, by Ruehl & Co., Julius Froebel being the editor. Mr. F. made his paper a very valuable and instructive one—really one of the best in the city in its editorial department. About the beginning of '56, Mr. Froebel left, and Julius Korn took editorial charge. The paper died in the Fall of '57.

A weekly German illustrated humorous paper, called the *Criticus*, was commenced in the Spring of '55, by Silversmith & Taffia. In September it was changed into an English publication, and it died in November.

The *Fireman's Journal*, a weekly paper, devoted to the interest of the Fire Department in San Francisco, was started on the 7th of April, by C. M. Chase & Co., proprietors; Marcus D. Boruck, editor. Its size at first was twelve by eighteen, and now is twenty-five by thirty-eight.

The *Daily Citizen* was established on the 25th of May,[10] by W. B. Farwell, as an organ of the American or Know Nothing party, Farwell and Buffum being the editors. The *Citizen* died on the 10th of October next ensuing, or rather was transferred to Sacramento, the Americans having control of the State Government.

In August, a small daily Spanish paper, called the *Sud Americano*, was established by Lafuente, Leguizamont & Elespura. It lived but a few weeks.

---

[10]Reported by the San Francisco *Alta California* on May 16, 1855. Continued by the second *State Tribune* of Sacramento.

A daily German campaign paper, called the *Deutscher Democrat*, was published during August, by Wagner & Gelbrecht.

The *Weekly Cosmopolitan* was published during the Summer and Fall of '55, by R. F. Ryan. It was literary, Irish-American, and anti-Know Nothing in character.

The *Daily Evening Bulletin* was started on the 8th of October, by C. O. Gerberding & Co., proprietors, with James King, of William, as editor. King came to California in the Fall or Winter of 1848, and was for a time connected with the firm of Hensley, Reading & Co., first at Sutter's Fort, and afterwards, as bankers on I and Second streets, in this city, under the name of Hensley, Merrill & King. He was next heard of as a partner in a banking house in San Francisco, and afterwards conducting business in his own name. Reverses overtook him, and he entered the banking house of Adams & Co., and had charge of their business until the memorable financial explosion of '55. His connection with the banking houses of San Francisco, had given him a clue to those secrets on which he afterwards founded the popularity of his journal. When Adams & Co. failed, embittered by his misfortunes, and honestly desirous, no doubt, to rid the community of some of the knaves and rogues who were occupying high places, he found congenial employment in attacking several well known bankers, lawyers, and politicians, through the *Bulletin*, turning against them, with telling effect, the knowledge acquired during his banking experience, and startling every body, not less with facts than with the personal fearlessness of his assaults. His first attacks were against the political banking house of Palmer, Cook & Co., and I. C. Woods, the managing partner of the bankrupt house of Adams & Co., and others connected with the management of its assets. In the angry and suspicious mood of the community, sore from its recent injuries at the hands of the bankers, the advent of such a champion as

King was hailed with pleasure. Thus sustained, the *Bulletin* increased the range of its batteries, and extended its fire to the shoulder-strikers, ballot-box stuffers, and political vagabonds generally, in the city. He wrote with a vigorous pen, and was well informed in the affairs of those whom he attacked. His paper "took" like fire runs. In six months, the daily edition had grown to the before unexampled circulation (for California) of seven thousand copies. It became a power in the State; King was the idol of a large portion of his readers. About the 10th of May, '56, he saw fit to make a newspaper attack on J. P. Casey, an ex-convict from the State Prison of New York, and a professional ballot-box stuffer; and on the 14th ensuing, Casey shot King down in the open street, in broad daylight. King died; the Vigilance Committee took possession of the city; the whole State sympathized with the movement; and the *Bulletin* being the chief organ of the Committee, was in demand everywhere. Before King was shot, James Nisbet had been employed as associate editor of the paper; after he died, the name of Nisbet, as responsible editor, was hoisted for a week; and at the end of that time, Thomas S. King became the editor, and still continues to hold the position. As the excitement about the Vigilance Committee died away, the circulation of the *Bulletin* fell off, but it is still large. The present editorial staff of the paper is composed of Thomas S. King, James Nisbet, C. Julien Bartlett, and Theodore H. Hittell. It is a common assertion, that King cannot write such editorials as appear in the *Bulletin,* and that he is merely the "ostensible" editor. This, however, is an error. He is a fluent and forcible writer, and usually writes the first editorial. Nisbet makes up the news, selects miscellaneous matter, reads the proof of all the editorial articles, makes any suggestions to the writers that may occur to him, and takes charge of all letters and communications. Bartlett ordinarily writes the second editorial, attends to State politics, and gets up miscellaneous paragraphs. T. H. Hittell takes care of the legal and local news.

On the 31st of October, soon after the death of the *Citizen,* Alexander Bell started the *Daily American,* an organ of the American party. It lived about three months. Edward Pollock, since dead, was the editor.

Le Phare (French for Lighthouse) is a daily French newspaper, now 18 by 24 inches in size. It was started as a semi-weekly, 12 by 20 inches in size, 22d July, 1855, and was soon afterwards enlarged and changed to a daily. P. Heitzeberg, A. H. Rapp and W. M. Hinton are the editors and proprietors. The *Phare* is republican and hostile to Napoleon and his Administration.

The *Western Standard* was the name of a weekly paper started in 1855, under the auspices of G. Q. Cannon, who was alike publisher and editor. It was discontinued in the Summer of 1857. It was distinguished for an ardent advocacy of the peculiar doctrines of the Latter Day Saints, which it was ready to discuss and defend in season and out of season. Quite many were the wars which it waged with the secular and religious press concerning the polygamic faith, the designs of Brigham Young towards the United States Government, and the general institutions of Mormondom. When the Mormon trump was sounded, calling the faithful to the City of the Saints in 1857, the *Standard* was discontinued, and the editor rejoined his brethren in that memorable locality.

During the Spring of '55, a weekly law journal[11] was started by M. G. Upton, E. A. Pollard, and W. N. Walton. It existed a couple of months. It was an octavo pamphlet of about 24 pages.[12]

On the 24th of December the *Weekly Sunday Times* was established by James P. Casey, who afterwards killed

---

[11]San Francisco *Law Review.*

[12]In the Fall, a steamer paper called the *Pacific Whalemen's List** ran from October at least through December 19.

King, and was afterwards hanged by the Vigilance Committee. Casey was nominally the editor as well as proprietor of the *Times,* but John C. Cremony was the real editor. The *Times* died with Casey.

On the 22d of January, 1856, the *Eco del Pacífico,* a daily Spanish paper, was started by M. Derbec. It still exists. Messrs. Herrera & Blanch are the present editors.

In March an illustrated weekly paper called the *Sunday Varieties,* was started by Wm. Mulligan. It still lives, James W. Walsh being the editor and proprietor. It is decidedly disreputable in character.[13]

On the 26th of May the *Daily True Californian* was established by Edward Conner, C. J. Bartlett, Washington Bartlett and W. H. Rhodes, the latter being the chief editor. The paper was an advocate of the Vigilance movement, but otherwise was independent. It was 28 by 42 inches in size, that is, of the largest class, and occupied a prominent place for a few months in the press of the city, but it died during the Fall.

In May the *Weekly Legal Intelligencer* was started by Whitton, Towne & Co., with A. W. Harcombe as editor. It was abandoned in the same month.

The *Phoenix* was an independent weekly paper, published by H. Davison. It was inaugurated in 1856, lived a few months and died in the same year. It was independent in tone, literary and humorous in its aspirations, and occasionally indulged in cuts to give point and significance to its miscellaneous articles.

The *Daily Globe* was established on the 13th of March, 1856, by Moody & Co. It was intended to be an organ of the Democratic party, but it adopted the side of the Vigilance Committee in May, and remained faithful to it till the Spring of 1857, when J. C. Duncan became the editor,

[13]On April 28 appeared the first number of *La Semaine Littèraire,** edited by Dr. Toubin, (*Alta California,* April 29, 1856).

who made it an organ of the Administration, and an enemy of the Committee. On the 16th of August, 1858, the name of the paper was changed to the *National,* and G. W. Guthrie became the proprietor, with G. P. Johnston as editor. Next month, Johnston challenged, and wounded in a duel, W. I. Ferguson, a State Senator from Sacramento, and on his death, which occurred in October, withdrew from the paper. About ten days afterwards the name of George Washington appeared in its columns as editor.

On the 19th of June, the first number of the *Mercantile Gazette and Shipping Register* was issued on a letter sheet. It was continued semi-monthly till April, 1857, when it was changed to a weekly paper 22 by 34 inches in size. It is exclusively commercial, and is owned and edited by Theodore M. Bosworth.

Hutchings' Illustrated California Magazine, a monthly octavo of 48 pages, was started in July, and sooned attained a very large circulation. It still exists; Hutchings & Rosenfield, proprietors. J. M. Hutchings, editor.

Early in August, the *Daily Evening Post* was founded by J. H. Udell & Co., to advocate the cause of Republicanism during the Presidential campaign. On the 7th of October, the *California Evening Pathfinder* was issued by J. B. Brown and F. F. Fargo; and soon after the two papers were united, under the title of the *Post and Pathfinder.*

The *Fillmore Ranger,* an organ of the American party, was published during October.

About this time the *Daily Evening Star,* the *Weekly Young America* and the *Eagle of Freedom* were started, nominally edited by boys, and intended for their perusal.[14] The last named paper was Republican in politics. Each of the above named papers, commencing with the *Post,*

[14]The *Boy's Journal** was reported by the *Alta California* of November 15, 1856.

finished its career the same year.

In September, a weekly organ of the Jewish faith, called the *Voice of Israel,* was started. It lived about six months.[15]

In November, H. Davison, who had formerly published the *Leader,* made an experiment with an *Evening Times,* but it did not succeed.

The *Daily Morning Call* was established on the 1st of December by an association of practical printers. It was only twelve by twenty inches in size, independent in politics, and aiming to make itself the organ of the mechanics. It was managed with prudence and economy, and contained at times articles of considerable ability. It sold at the low price of one bit per week. The editing was mostly done by the proprietors the first year of its publication. After that time Wm. H. Newell wrote for it for several months; and then E. A. Rockwell became editor, and now occupies that position. The present size of the paper is sixteen by twenty-four inches. It has a large circulation.

The first paper which arose in San Francisco in 1857 was the *Weekly Gleaner,* a small quarto of sixteen pages, established as an organ of the Hebrew Church by the Rev. J. Eckman. It still exists.[16]

In April of this year appeared the *California Register,* a Republican paper, the prospectus for which was issued in Sacramento, where it was first intended the *Register* should be published. Parker H. French was editor and publisher. The same cause which doubtless prevented its location here, viz: want of a printer, terminated its existence with its fourth number. It was intended to be a morning daily paper, and was about the size of the *Sacramento Bee.*

---

[15]From September 17 to November 12, 1856, Gregory lists the *Star of Empire,** with a page in German as *Der Deutsche Republikaner.**

[16]The *California Family Visitor,** a weekly Victorian miscellany, was advertised by Julius Eckman in the San Francisco directory of 1858.

Early in the year, the *Weekly Mirror of the Times* was founded by some colored men, as an advocate of the interests of the Africans of the State. It died early in '58. It was edited by Jonas H. Townsend.[17]

In July, the *Weekly Spirit of the Times*, a sporting newspaper, somewhat after the style of the New York *Spirit of the Times*, was started by a company of printers. It is now edited by H. E. Highton.

About midsummer, H. J. Labatt commenced the publication of the decisions of the District Courts of the State, in the form of monthly pamphlets, of forty-eight pages each. The *District Court Reports* died during the Fraser fever of '58.

In the Summer, the *Daily Evening Ledger* was started by Porter & Co., the printing being done in the *Globe* office. Soon after the establishment of the *Ledger*, it was sold to E. Pollock, who edited it until it died, which was within a few days.

Sometime in the Summer,[18] also, Edward Marriott commenced the *News-Letter*, a semi-monthly summary of the fortnight's news, published just before the departure of the Panama steamers. It is defunct.[19]

The *Daily Evening Plaindealer* was started on the 17th of October, by A. M. Heslep. It professed great honesty, but was imbued with too much of the personal spleen and bitterness of its publisher to succeed. It died in December.

In November, 1857, the *Daily Evening Argus* was established by Raphal Schoyer, with Dr. E. A. Theller as editor. The proprietor expected to get the printing of the auctioneers, but failed, and the paper did likewise in a few

---

[17]*California Free Press*,* published by Joseph Weed & Co., first issue reported by the *Alta California* of June 28, 1857, appears to have been the next paper started that year.

[18]June 20, 1856. It survived in one form or another, to 1928.

[19]On July 23, 1857, the *Alta California* announced the coming publication on August 8 of the *Settler's Free Press*.*

months after it was started. Shortly before it died an attempt was made to issue a morning as well as an evening edition, but this only hastened its death.

About the end of the year, the *Weekly Pacific Methodist,* the organ of the Methodist Church South, edited by the Rev. O. P. Fitzgerald, was moved from Stockton to San Francisco, and still exists.

On the 1st of January, 1858, the *Pacific Medical Journal,* a monthly octavo pamphlet of forty pages, was established by Drs. J. B. Trask and David Wooster. It still exists.[20]

During the same month the first number of a weekly paper, called the *Examiner and Inquirer,* was issued by S. L. Brittingham. That number exhibited but little character, and had no successor.

On the 6th of March, the *Weekly Monitor,* an organ of the Catholic Church, was established by Marks, Thomas & Co. It was suspended on the 3d of July, in consequence of the Fraser river exodus, and was resumed the 16th of October.

In the last week of February a pair who called themselves Mr. and Mrs. Weekes arrived in San Francisco from New Orleans, and immediately the lady announced that she would establish a weekly newspaper to be called the *Athenaeum,* which should contain contributions from a number of the most famous English authors, and should be a literary periodical of the first rank in its kind. A fortnight later the first number was issued, and it was a pretty fair paper (that the matter was stolen was not then known). With it as a sample, she drummed through San Francisco, Sacramento and Stockton, and got a number of subscribers to pay a year's subscription of $5 in advance.

[20]The San Francisco directory for 1858 also listed a French literary weekly, the *Bibliothèque Populaire,** edited by L. Albin, who died on February 6, 1858.

After three numbers of the *Athenaeum* had appeared,[21] Mr. and Mrs. Weekes disappeared mysteriously, and it was soon after discovered that they had gone to Australia. That was the death of the *Athenaeum.*

In May, Mrs. A. M. Shultz and F. M. Day commenced the publication of the *Hesperian,* a semi-monthly literary paper of sixteen quarto pages. It still exists, Mrs. Day being now the sole editor.

On the 1st of October, the *Daily Evening Telegram,* 14x20 inches in size, was established by W. H. Mantz & Co. It is now published by W. H. Hinton & Co., Mantz, editor. It is independent in politics, and is sold for one bit per week.[22]

On the 3rd of October, J. C. Duncan commenced the publication of the *Weekly California Home Journal,* a family Sunday paper. It is still in existence.

The *California Culturist,* a monthly magazine of forty-eight pages, devoted to the interests of agriculture, was established on the 15th of June, by Wadsworth and Turrell, Wadsworth being the editor. It is now owned by Towne & Bacon.

The *Daily Evening Republican* was published as a campaign paper for the last two weeks in August, by Wheelock and Hoffman, the former being the editor.[23]

The *Illustrated Pacific News* is the name of a new weekly which made its appearance the first week in December. H. Davison is the editor, proprietor and printer thereof.

On the 23d December, 1858, the first number of a weekly

---

[21]The paper ran from March 2 to the Weekes' departure on April 14, 1858.

[22]On the 27th of September, the *Alta California* announced the forthcoming *Daily Evening Telegraph** by H. Davison & Co., the first issue to appear on October 15.

[23]In November the *Overland Mail Letter** made its appearance, to be tri-weekly (*Alta California,* November 15, 1858).

paper, called *The Telegraph Hill,* was issued. It was printed on only one side of a sheet, 16 by 24 inches in size. The name of F. N. Smith appears as editor. The paper has no strong characteristic, and does not appear as the advocate of any interest or doctrine.

Thus we have gone through the long list of the periodicals started in San Francisco within the last eleven years. They number 132 in all, and the united number of their proprietors, editors and reporters is more than a thousand. No city in the world can boast a newspaper press so great in its development, so singular in its character, so wonderful in its fortunes. The papers have been printed in six different languages, have represented nine different nationalities, have devoted themselves to the interests of religion, politics, morals, law, medicine, literature, commerce, agriculture, news and slander; have preached eight different forms of religion, and have been the organs of seven distinct political parties. Most of these papers expired within a twelve-month after they were started, and only twenty-six survive. The *Alta* and the *Herald* are the only papers in the city which date from 1850, and both have been on the verge of the newspaper grave. Not an editor or proprietor connected with the press in 1850, is to be found now in the same position. And what has become of them all? Let us mention the fate of a few of the editors and reporters. Gilbert's fate we have already mentioned; also that of King and Dunn, at the hands of assassins. Nugent, Washburn, Loehr and Rapp have been wounded in duels, and Russell dangerously wounded with a knife—all for articles they had written. Lafuente and Walton have been sent to Penitentiaries, the former for homicide and the latter for larceny. Washington is Collector; Hempstead, Mint Superintendent; Moulder, State Superintendent of Public Instruction; Johnston, Clerk of the United States Circuit Court; Nugent, United States Commissioner to Fraser river; and Korn, Port

Warden. Ewer has taken to the pulpit, and Durivage and Pillet to the stage. Hull married Lola Montez, and Walker made himself world-famous by fillibustering in Lower California and Nicaragua. Soulé went last Summer to Australia, Conner went to Chile, Moran to Mexico, Rice to Panama, Froebel to Germany, Lachapelle to France, Williston to Victoria; a score of others are scattered about in different States and Territories of the Union, and an unknown number are engaged in mining, farming and trading in California. Not one can be said to have become rich from the profits of their newspapers.

The few papers and periodicals which now exist in San Francisco, are as follows. The dailies are usually sold by the week, the weeklies by the piece or by the year:

DAILIES

The Daily Alta California, 32 by 46; 7 days; 50 cents.
The Daily Herald, 25 by 38; 7 days; 50 cents.
The Daily National, 28 by 42; 6 days; 37 cents.
The Daily Times, 22 by 32; 6 days; 25 cents.
The Daily Morning Call, 18 by 24; 6 days; 12 cents.
The Daily Echo du Pacifique, 28 by 42; 6 days; 50 cents.
The Phare, 24 by 36; 6 days; 25 cents.
The California Democrat, 24 by 36; 6 days; 50 cents.
The Eco del Pacífico, 26 by 40; 6 days; 37 cents.
The Daily Evening Bulletin, 28 by 42; 6 days; 37 cents.
The Evening Telegram, 14 by 20; 6 days; 12 cents.
Lyceum Gazette, 16 by 24; 6 days—gratis.

WEEKLIES.

The Golden Era, 32 by 46; 12 cents.
The California Home Journal, 28 by 42; 12 cents.
The Pacific, 24 by 36; 12 cents.
The Christian Advocate, 28 by 42; 12 cents.
The Monitor, 28 by 42; 12 cents.
The Gleaner, 24 by 32; 12 cents.
The Mercantile Gazette, 26 by 40; 12 cents.

The Prices Current and Shipping List, 26 by 40; 12 cents.
The Fireman's Journal, 26 by 40; 12 cents.
The Spirit of the Times, 28 by 40; 12 cents.
The California Farmer, 28 by 42; 12 cents.
The Weekly Alta California, 12 cents.
The Weekly Bulletin, 12 cents.
The Weekly Herald, 12 cents.
The Weekly Times, 10 cents.
The Weekly Echo du Pacifique, 12 cents.
The Weekly Illustrated Pacific News.

SEMI-MONTHLY

The Steamer Alta California, each 25 cents.
The Steamer Herald, each 25 cents.
The Steamer Bulletin, each 25 cents.
The Hesperian, each 12 cents.

MONTHLIES

Hutchings' California Magazine, each 25 cents.
The California Culturist, each 25 cents.
The Pacific Medical Journal, each 25 cents.
The Weekly Telegraph Hill.

The *Weekly Alta, Herald, Bulletin, Times* and *Echo,* and the Steamer *Alta, Herald* and *Bulletin,* are mere reprints of the matter published in the dailies of the same name, the weeklies being intended for circulation in the country on this Coast, and the Steamer for circulation in the Atlantic States and Europe.

Newspapers In Sacramento

On viewing the long list of failures in San Francisco, and seeing how unprofitable the business has been to some of her very respectable citizens, driving them out of the country, and into penitentiaries and public offices, or worse than all, off upon false errands of honor, to be killed or maimed like gladiators, still for the popular amusement, and perceiving, withal, what poor property the majority of the surviving journals are, one feels almost tempted to congratulate Sacramento, on the proportionately fewer untimely newspaper deaths she has had to mourn, and the comparative immunity her citizens have enjoyed from newspaper bankruptcies. And though the number of journals is no greater now than it was eight years ago, the numerical deficiency as compared with her seaport neighbor, is more than compensated by the stability her press has attained. It is, moreover, probable that the circulation of the Sacramento press is considerably greater in the ratio of her population, than that of the San Francisco journals. But it must not be inferred from what we have said, that our newspaper history is a smooth, unbroken narrative. It has had its periods of expansion as well as its contraction and centralization; its sudden changes, high prosperity, beggarly adversity, good and evil births, marriages, divorces, deaths, funerals, and mourners. Our newspaper chronology is no barren tree, as we shall find.

There is a tradition still remembered by some of the native Californians, of the existence of a marvellous spring[24] somewhere on or near the site occupied by San Francisco, which years ago was deemed to possess such remarkable virtues, that devoted wives, returning from drinking its waters forgot even the barrenness of the scene of their pilgrimage, and ever after blessed the fertilizing properties of the well, along with the good domestic Saint who had consecrated it to their uses. The fruitfulness of the parent newspaper tree in that city, suggests the possibility of its roots having found the soil moistened by the marvellous flow. Undoubtedly, it transmitted its virtues to the press of other chief cities in the State, when it furnished slips from which have sprung their oldest newspapers. And thus we discover in the history of a Sacramento journal, the same remarkable fecundity, only under less favorable circumstances for development, than in San Francisco.

The first newspaper in Sacramento, was a scion from the *Alta California.* Its transfer and growth were cotemporaneous with the origin of the city. It had its rise in the necessities of a shrewd, active, liberal, and far-sighted little community gathered about Sutter's Fort, in the winter of 1848. They had planned a large city, and "laid off" the lots, right and left from the high ground about the Fort, extending down to the river's bank. Undismayed by the storms of winter, which had cut off communication and put a stop to trade with the mines, or by the rise of waters, which threatened to convert commercial sites into mill privileges, and leave the line of their water front as undefined as that of San Francisco, our city ancestors getting together around the hearth of one and another, discussed their Spring projects, and drew into their designs those characteristic figures, typical of American genius, and prominent in our vignettes, a steamboat and a news-

[24]El Polín, at the Presidio of San Francisco.

paper press. One of their number, on a recent visit to San Francisco, had gathered from one of the proprietors of the *Alta California,* then just commenced, that their interests required a good correspondent, (very difficult to get in those days) or a local newspaper established nearer the mines. But who should start such a sheet, and wherewithal should it be kept alive? The shrewdest and foremost merchant at Sutter's Fort, and now one of the wealthiest men in the State,[25] had from friendship to one of the proprietors[26] of the *Alta California,* discouraged his setting out in the chimerical design of founding a newspaper in San Francisco. What infatuation, therefore, to try such an experiment elsewhere, in the unsettled state of the country? However, the *Alta California* was a success, and reasoning from that, perhaps a press at Sutter's Fort might be supported. The Fort merchants resolved to secure the printer against loss as nearly as they could, and endeavor to get the *Alta* publishers to establish a branch of their concern at the new city of Sacramento. An instrument in the form of a covenant was signed, and a few hundred dollars subscribed by the merchants to assist in the enterprise. The paper was forwarded to the publishers of the *Alta* with the prayer of old, to "come over and help us." In the list of subscriptions was one of nine town lots, to be selected by the founder of the press, and deeded by Sutter. The *Alta* proprietors consulted, but only one was strongly in favor of trying the experiment. When every other objection had been got over, there still remained the primary one of scarcity of material. At length, from the beggarly fonts and worn out stuff tucked away in little heaps of "pi," an office was patched up. The old California Ramage press was voted for the excursion, and its weary old joints again taken down and sen-

[25]Samuel Brannan.

[26]Edward C. Kemble.

tenced for transportation. A few reams of Spanish foolscap were sent with the boxes of type and press, on board one of the launches running as regular packets to Sacramento. The name of this vessel, if we remember rightly, was *Dice me Nana*, (says my mamma) and it was not long since that we were furnished by the late T. O. Larkin, with an amusing scrap of history showing the derivation of the name, which may not be out of place here. It was the second vessel built on this part of the coast, and probably the first California vessel to ascend the waters of the Sacramento. Her builder's name was John Davis, an early resident of the place now known as San Francisco. His heirs still own valuable property on the public Plaza there. The name was taken from the lips of a little Spanish girl, who had been made by her mother an adept in the art of borrowing. Her visits to the neighbors, invariably had as a prelude, *"Dice me nana,"* (says my mamma) will you lend her this or that article, "*por un remedio,*" (for a remedy) which excuse of a remedy was applied indiscriminately by a little girl to whatever she wished to borrow; she had been taught to say "for a remedy," in applying for medicine and food, and not been told when to lay it aside. So *Dice me nana* became historical, and not less so from its service, as the vessel which transported the first printing press north of San Francisco, in this State.

About the 20th of March, the pioneer craft and her pioneer cargo arrived at the landing of the embryo city. The time consumed in that memorable voyage from San Francisco to Sacramento, was eight days, or twenty-four times longer than the period of a trip in the present day, and forty-eight times longer than the period in which we hope to see the same journey performed by land, in some future day not distant. One of the proprietors of the *Alta California* had accompanied the material as far as the prospective town of Webster, laid off eight or ten miles below Sutterville, where he abandoned the vessel, and in company with one or two others, set out to walk the rest of the distance to Sutter's Fort. It was late in the evening when the party, without any further adventure than a thorough sousing overboard, from a canoe, in attempting to cross the "lake" at Sutterville, arrived at the Fort. But late as it was, the arrival of the press was celebrated that night with oysters and champagne, in one of the old rooms within the adobe walls. Arrangements were at once made for the setting up of "the mighty engine," and as the business of the future city was all at the Fort, and that site eminently favored for the building of a city that should laugh at the disasters of the flood, it was decided to establish the newspaper there. But before that could be done, an office must be built. Lumber was selling at $500 per M. There were no shingles—but worst of all there was no carpenter. Here were bricks to be made, and almost without mud and straw. The services of a *quasi* joiner were secured at last, however, and between the printer and his help, the house, a little one story cabin, with a cotton roof and no ceiling, was put up. It stood about two hundred yards distant from the northeast corner bastion, and not far from what is now the corner of Twenty-eighth and K streets. Into this thin shell, through which the rays of the sun shot like fiery lances, the material of the paper was removed, and on the 28th of April, 1849, appeared the first number of the pioneer journal of Sacramento, and the interior of the State.

The *Placer Times,* was a little sheet, thirteen by eighteen inches in size, of which specimens are preserved by a few of our old residents as a great curiosity. The head was carved from a piece of wood with a jack-knife, and the face of some of the type were made by the use of the same instrument to conform to the printer's demand for assorted letters. The letter O, minus its right cheek, readily slid into the place of the third character of the alphabet, but the attempt to turn up the tail of the Q, so as to form a G, was a ridiculous failure. These, however, were trifling difficulties, compared with the labors imposed upon the publisher, by actual deficiency of the machinery of an office. It was not so grievous a burden to set the type for his little sheet, but when he brought his type forms to the press to be worked off, and found it necessary on account of the warping effect of the sun's rays, to plane down the wooden "platen" with a jack-plane, in order to make it sufficiently level to give an even impression, and on inspecting his inking apparatus, found the glue and molasses roller which had been moulded in the morning, and buried to keep it away from the heat, also overcome by the amorous embraces of the atmosphere, and spreading its liquid sweetness far around. When these and similar little incidents occurred, as they did, weekly, to shake the confidence of the *Times* publisher, already pretty well shaken under a debilitating attack of chills and fever, it is not to be wondered at, if he felt at times discouraged. However, the *Times* continued to be published weekly, on Saturdays, during the months of May and June, when the increasing illness of the editor compelled him to abandon his post, and return to the cooler climate of San Francisco, the common resort of invalids in those days. He had arranged to have one of his associates in the *Alta California* take his place, but this person not arriving in time, some of the citizens took the matter in hand, and got out a paper for the week in which the exchange was being effected. On the 28th of June, the publishing firm of the *Placer Times* was changed from E. C. Kemble & Co., to T. R. Per Lee & Co., the partners still being the owners and editors of the *Alta California.* Per Lee was wholly unacquainted with the business of a newspaper office, and only remained a fortnight in his new charge. He left the *Times* in the care of a former printer in the New York *Tribune* office, J. H. Giles, and returned below to sell out his interest in the two establishments to his remaining partners. Giles was ratified in his position, and continued as the agent of E. Gilbert & Co., to edit and publish the *Times* throughout the remainder of the year 1849, and until April of 1850, when he was succeeded in the editorship by J. E. Lawrence, and at the end of another month or two returned to his Atlantic home with a snug competency, one of the very few newspaper publishers who have taken a fortune with them out of the State.

At the risk of prolonging this narrative beyond its sustaining point of interest, we make a short summary of the features of this era in newspaper publication. In the fourth number of the *Times,* (May 19) appears the annexed invitation:

> "We have introduced into our columns to-day, much more selected matter than we design doing during the present size of our paper. * * We will be pleased to hear from the different gold diggings, the result of the labor, the news current, etc. Until we can employ regular correspondents, we will compensate the services of any who may undertake to perform the light task of an occasional contributor, *by supplying them with batches of Late State papers, and all other readable matter* received at this office; such being much sought after, is probably the only reward we can name that would be listened to, and we hope by the arrangement to secure a good deal of valuable information to our readers. The real signature must accompany each communication."

In the beginning of July, the building and office of the *Times* was removed to Front street, on a lot leased by Sam Brannan. It may here be proper to mention, that the voluntary offer of nine lots made by the proprietors of Sacramento, to the founders of the first newspaper, was never of any benefit to the *Times* publishers. Although the offer had been made without conditions, and the publishers were to be left free to choose the lots, when a selection came to be made, Sutter's agent (Burnett) restricted the choice to the property about the Fort, and would not allow any of the lots near the river, which were the only ones of any considerable value, to be taken. In this way, while some of the chief merchants and real estate owners were pocketing large profits from transfers, exchanges, and bonuses exacted by the proprietors from the city, the men who, at considerable personal sacrifice, had contributed to build up the fortunes of Sacramento, by establishment of the press here, were defrauded out of the small contribution subscribed by Sutter, and the first of that long series of wrongs, denominated "cheating the printer," inaugurated north of the Bay. It may have been this ingratitude which nerved the printer of the *Times* to demand "equal and exact justice" in defining his position (July 25) as follows:

> "Numerous requests are sent to us to notice gratuitously, new undertakings and enterprises, we respectfully decline doing so. Proceedings of meetings, editorial business notices, and marriages and deaths, must be paid for. Printers in the States may amuse themselves by laboring for nothing to advance various interests—*here,* it is out of the question."

The *Times* man could probably afford to be thus explicit with his patrons. We find in a succeeding number, the following amusing and good-natured complaint of a mishap, which put the *Times* out of joint for one week, also, a threat which must sound like the height of audacity to some of the advertising sheets in San Francisco:

> "We dislike these cards apologetic, but we think our readers will excuse the delay in the issue of the present number, when we tell them that about one-half of the types prepared for it were very innocently upset by a gentleman last week. *Moral:* If you have any sympathy with suffering humanity, (mercury 112° in the shade) be careful how you knock around in the printing office.
>
> "By the way, our advertisers have got the start of us to-day. A few of them will have to stand aside next week, as we may have something to say."

Printers are not ungrateful, nor publics always ungenerous, as the following paragraph in next week's number shows:

"We take the occasion to offer our acknowledgments for the liberal and generous encouragement extended to this establishment by a number of gentlemen, particularly those who have insisted upon paying more for services rendered for them than we asked them."

This paragraph having the appearance of the finest irony was an honest acknowledgment, and appears in connection with a notice of the *Times'* prospects. In the same article, the editor promises to have his paper carried to his subscribers after that date. It had been the custom, it seems, for his readers to call at the office. He thus contradicts a rumor that "outside parties" had control of his columns:

"As a general thing, the editorials have not been *written at all,* but hastily composed *from the case,* 'amid the noise and confusion' of this bustling locality, and with a half dozen asking where the Post Office is, and is the steamer in? etc. Not a line will appear in the columns of the *Times* written by other persons, unless paid for at the rate of three dollars for every twelve lines."

From this rule, even the productions of the muse were not excepted. A column of poetry, one verse beginning with

"I've been roaming, I've been roaming.
Where men have strange courts and rules,"

illustrates the truth of *that* part of the discourse, at least, by advertising rules at the top and bottom of the column, and the usual sign, * 1t, signifying, paid for one time, at the end of the last stanzas. During this time, the paper continued weekly, at ten dollars per annum, and was of the original dimensions. In November, (1849) the *Times* was enlarged to its former size, and soon after removed to Second street, between K and L. It had been once removed previously, and this was the third ambulation of the building and office. One corner of the *little shanty* was used during the winter of 1849, by the late J. E. Birch, as the office for his pioneer line of stages in this State. Among the business notices of the paper (Dec. 29) was one signed by the editor, advertising money, entrusted to him by others, to loan in sums of $1000 and $5000.

On the 22nd of April, the *Times* appeared tri-weekly, under the editorial management of J. E. Lawrence. It was two or three weeks behind its neighbor of the *Transcript,* which was started as a tri-weekly. But the prestige lost by this circumstance was recovered June 5th, 1850, by the appearance of the *Times* as the first daily paper in Sacramento. It still retained the size of the tri-weekly, eighteen by twenty-two inches. No other change now occurred until the Fall of this year. On the 8th of October 1850, the *Times* establishment, including newspaper and job offices, good will, the building, and two lots, passed out of the hands of its original proprietors. It was purchased by L. Pickering, J. E. Lawrence, and L. Aldrich, for $16,000. Eight thousand dollars for the building and material, and the balance for the real estate. A short time after the purchase, Pickering and Lawrence bought also the interest of Aldrich. The neutrality of the paper did not suffer by the change, although its editorials began to evince a deeper interest in the movements of parties, then just forming, and in the action of the Democratic party in particular, than was consistent with a journal professing to stand aloof from such matters. During the Squatter riots in August, the *Times* "drew the sword and threw away the scabbard," in defense of the real estate owners, but in the hands of its new owners, it appeared disposed to shape its course differently, with regard to the "Squatter question." It continued through the winter without change in the managerial department, and in June of 1851, annexed the *Transcript* to it, under an arrangement which can be best stated after we have brought up the history of that journal. The last number of the *Times,* in its single or bachelor state, was issued June 15th.

The Sacramento *Transcript,* the second newspaper in Sacramento, was established on the 1st of April, 1850. It appeared as a tri-weekly, the size of the *Times,* and is entitled to the merit of being the first press in the interior whose issues broke in upon the long seven days' newspaper silence, though the *Times* followed as a tri-weekly during the same month. There were six proprietors of the *Transcript*, G. K. Fitch, S. C. Upham, J. M. Julian, H. S. Warren, Theodore Russell, and F. C. Ewer. The style of the firm was, Fitch, Upham & Co. G. K. Fitch and F. C. Ewer, were the editors. All the proprietors, save two, were practical printers. The material with which the paper was started was brought to this State by Fitch, who, if we mistake not, was concerned in the printing of the Panama *Star*. The paper presented a handsome appearance, and was edited with much care and ability, evidently taking as a model the Boston *Transcript.* It affected a high order of literary taste, and contained a large amount of editorial. The *Transcript* was deemed good property by the craft, several fifth interests being sold for $5,000 during the Summer of 1850. One of the proprietors, S. C. Upham, sold his fifth interest to G. C. Weld, for $10,000, shortly after the *Transcript* was started. A Mr. Grove who also purchased an interest, paid Fitch $6,000 for it. On the 10th of August, the *Transcript* appeared in mourning for the death of Weld, who had only a few weeks before joined the paper. Both the *Transcript* and *Times* were enlarged in July, 1850. Of course there was much rivalry and not a little ill-feeling between the two journals. The last comer was started as an independent sheet. In the Fall of this year the community, having been stirred up meantime pretty extensively by the politicians who were arriving on every steamer, began to choose sides according to their party predelictions in their old homes, and to extend the lines of party organization throughout the State. The papers began to look on which side to jump, and among them, the *Transcript* evinced a leaning towards party doctrines. No public profession was made, however, until December, when the *Transcript* hoisted Democratic colors, and became the first organ of that party in the State north of San Francisco. The consideration which seems to have led to this step was the prospect of obtaining the State Printing; and in this it was successful, the principal manager of the *Transcript,* Fitch, stepping in for that coveted morsel of party patronage. The *Transcript,* in making known its political preference, however, claims that all the editors and proprietors are Democrats. It continued to advocate the doctrines of its chosen party, under its original name and management, until June, 1851, when a fusion took place, which gave to the public, in lieu of the two original journals of Sacramento, a joint publication, due notice of which we must hold a few moments in reserve, as it was a separate newspaper; and there are other enterprises which claim each their historical niche above the new combined organ of Democracy.

Settlers' and Miners' Tribune, was the third paper in Sacramento. It was brought into the field by the Squatter Association of Sacramento, as the champion of their asserted rights. The first number appeared on the 30th of October, 1850. The principal editor was Dr. C. L. Robinson, well remembered for his part in the Squatter riots of that time, and subsequently as the Free State Governor of Kansas. The associate editors were J. McClatchy and L. M. Booth. The types used in the *Tribune* were brought from Maine, by Cyrus Rowe. The size of the sheet was about that of the *Times.* It was published six times a week, and of course defended, with all its might, the interests of the Squatter community, cementing them with stout Democratic mortar. John Bigler was one of its favorites. The cholera considerably interfered with the prospects of the new organ, but we are told its circulation was about 800 copies daily. The *Tribune* was continued only about four weeks as a daily paper, the precise date of its stoppage being forgotten. After the daily was discontinued the weekly went on, but about the 8th week from commencement, this, too, vanished and was heard of no more.

The Sacramento *Index* is the first of the journals of an opposite political faith to the Democracy, that was started north of San Francisco. The *Index* began the volume on the 23d of December, 1850. The publishers were Lynch, Davison & Rolfe, practical printers, the editors J. W. Winans and H. B. Livingston. It was printed at the office of the *Times* and issued as an evening paper, the first of the afternoon class of newspapers out of San Francisco. In size it was nearly that of the morning papers during the Summer of 1850, and its appearance was very neat and printer-like. The *Index* was the second exponent of the doctrines of the old Whig party, published in the State, and in its support of that party, as well as in the character and tone of its editorials on general subjects, it was remarkable for its vigor and high literary ability. Most of the inside matter was original. In the municipal elections of that year, it made a gallant fight for its party and principles. During the Winter of 1850-51, a gambler was arrested for shooting a citizen, and afterwards taken by the populace and hung. The *Index* condemned the action of the people and was very severe against mob violence and lynch law. The community, however, generally sustained the hanging, and the opposition of the *Index* cost it the popularity which it had begun to achieve. Our citizens did not carry their resentment so far as to force their tradesmen to withdraw their patronage from the paper, but their disapprobation was, no doubt, sensibly felt by the *Index,* for shortly after it was discontinued. Previous to its stoppage, however, it changed its publication hour from evening to morning. Its last number appeared March 17th.

THE DAILY UNION. — On the 19th March, 1851, appeared the first number of the DAILY UNION. This paper originated with four practical printers, previously compositors in the office of the *Transcript,* and the design of its publication was conceived as early as April or May, 1850, nearly a year before the first number was issued. The names of the parties who were actively concerned in bringing forward the design were C. L. Hansicker, J. Court and W. J. Keating. Disappointed in getting material in the country, in June, 1850, Keating was sent to New York to purchase a press and types. He was furnished with $2,700 in gold dust, besides money to pay his expenses, and, on arriving in New York, made two or three hundred dollars clear from the sale of his dust. A newspaper office was bought of James Connor & Sons, the type founders, and shipped on board a steamer bound around Cape Horn for San Francisco. But some delay occurring from the seizure of the vessel, the type was transshipped on board the Sea Serpent, a sailing vessel. Other delays occurred, and, at the end of the year, the material not arriving, the parties began to look about for another press and type with which to commence their enterprise. In the beginning of 1851, J. W. Simonton, late the Utah special correspondent of the New York *Times,* arrived with a printing office, with which he designed to establish a Whig paper in the country. Finding the field pretty well occupied by the *Courier,*[27] in San Francisco, and the *Index,* here, he offered to sell the material at a sacrifice. By this time the vessel, with the New York office, was within a few weeks of becoming due at San Francisco; but while the projectors of the new paper wavered, a strike occurred among the hands on the *Transcript,* and it was resolved to begin this journal at once. In these

[27] *California Courier.*

days, compositors were receiving two dollars per thousand "ems," and it was the attempted reduction of the rate to one dollar and fifty cents, or 25 per cent., on the part of the *Transcript* publishers, which caused the strike. Simonton's office was immediately purchased, and on the 19th of March, as aforesaid, two days after the *Index* suspended, the DAILY UNION was begun. The original movers of the enterprise, in starting it, found it necessary to connect six others with them, all practical printers like themselves. The names of the parties concerned were as follows: A. Clark, A. C. Cook, E. G. Jefferis, F. H. Harmon, C. L. Hansicker, S. H. Dosh, J. Court, W. J. Keating and W. K. Davison, the names of the three latter not appearing with the others at the head of the column. The title of the firm was C. L. Hansicker & Co. The editor of the UNION was J. F. Morse, whose letters to the New Orleans *Delta,* and well known literary attainments, had early attracted the attention of the proprietors to him. He had, in fact, been engaged from the first, and, as the final arrangements were being consummated, exerted himself considerably among the citizens of Sacramento to procure a favorable reception for the new paper. The name UNION was adopted, says the editor, in the first number, "as a befitting symbol by which to indicate the nature of the arrangement in which we are engaging. By a union of practical journeymen printers, whose industry has endowed them with adequate resources, we have been secured ample means for publishing a journal which we hope to make of utility, and interesting to the community in which it is printed." Another reason given was that the title was suggestive of the principle by which the love of our old homes is kept alive, and our interests, as a great people, bound together. The sentiments of the UNION are thus stated:

"Whilst in politics our paper will be neutral and independent, yet in every question of Commerce, Climate, Trade, Manufacture, Mining, Agriculture, or in any conceivable issue in which the interests of our State, County or City are involved, we shall always be found unequivocally and uncompromisingly a Sacramento friend of California."

The sheet on which the first fifty-two numbers of the UNION were printed was 23 by 34 inches in size, of good quality, and the typographical appearance of the sheet was fair—some of the type, however, being a larger letter than is usual on daily papers. It contained twenty-four columns of matter, eleven of which were transient reading, and the remainder advertisements, State Laws, Prices Current, etc. The terms of subscription and advertising are not given, but the chief feature in the UNION'S economy was the price of single copies of the paper, which was placed at the low figure of *five cents,* making it the cheapest paper in the State at that time. The publication office was on the same site now occupied by the UNION building. The daily edition for the first week was about five hundred. This number increased by July to about eight hundred.

According to the plan laid down in the commencement of this newspaper bibliography, we have sketched the origin of our journal with a degree of minuteness which we shall hardly be expected to follow, but which may be excused for the sake of the historical interest attached to these early beginnings in California journalism. From its commencement the UNION steadily increased in circulation and business. On the 29th of March it issued its first steamer paper. The mechanical work was nearly all done by the proprietors, and of course a great saving effected on what they would have been compelled to pay for hired labor. In this way newspapers have been started and sustained in California almost without capital; and only on this plan has it been possible to avoid the heavy current expenses of their publication, and keep within the requirements of the Typographical Association rules. Its position in respect of parties, then in the first flush of successful organization, was the only source of difference with the UNION publishers. At that time the Whig party held in check the movements of the Democracy. The city, just entering upon an exciting municipal election, was believed to be Whig by a considerable majority, and the sympathies of the editor, a majority of the proprietors, and best friends of the UNION were with the Whig party. On the 29th April, the UNION made its party choice, and hoisted Whig colors. In doing so, however, it reserved a wide degree of latitude in its partisan career, and proposed to defend Whig measures and men only "when their character conformed to the name." With this change of position, there was a proprietory change; S. H. Dosh selling out his interest to his partners. He received $600 for his share. His retirement was followed in June by that of Harmon, who sold for about the same amount. On the 23rd of this month the paper was enlarged to about its present size, and the new type ordered from New York the year before, and which arrived in May, was now introduced. On the 1st January, 1852, the UNION commenced its second volume under very encouraging auspices. During the first year the paper had paid expenses, and now stood free from debt. With the new volume there were changes in the proprietorship, and the name of H. B. Livingston, who had been connected with the paper for several months before, appears at the head of the columns as associate editor. The style of the publishing firm was now E. G. Jefferis & Co., Hansicker having sold out, receiving $2,000 for his interest. At the end of January Court also withdrew, selling his interest to W. W. Kurtz for about $2,100. On the 10th of this month the paper began to print a regular weekly edition, single copies twenty-five cents. February 13th, Cook sold to H. W. Larkin, and on the 3d of April following, Davison to P. Morrill. There were now of the original proprietors only Jefferis, Keating and Clark remaining. The paper was considered well established, and notwithstanding the depression in business, caused by the flood of this Spring, its prospects were second to no journal in the State. In May, Dr. Morse retired from the editorship of the UNION, and was succeeded by A. C. Russell, who occupied the chair until August. On the 20th of this month his connection ceased, and L. Upson became editor. During a short retirement, in the Fall of 1853, John A. Collins took his place. The proprietors adopted in '52 the London journal system of disconnecting the names of individuals with the columns of the paper, and of making it the embodiment of whatever views were editorially expressed instead of identifying them with persons. This policy has always been retained in the UNION since the retirement of its first editor, and has since been adopted into other journals in the State. On the 2d November, 1852, the office was totally destroyed in the great fire which swept the city, the proprietors saving only a small press and type sufficient to print their paper foolscap size. It made its appearance the second morning after the fire, and soon regained its former dimensions. A new brick building was also erected, and a larger stock of material than ever added to their establishment. The paper entered upon its third volume with a large circulation. Besides its daily, weekly and steamer editions, it also printed a PICTORIAL UNION semi-annually. On the 16th May, 1853, the third and last change in the publication firm took place. Jefferis and Kurtz sold their interests to Larkin, Morrill, Keating and J. Anthony. The latter had been connected with the business management of the paper since November, 1851. After the dissolution of the old firm the business was conducted under the name and style of James Anthony & Co., which it has retained to the present day. On the 5th of June, '53, Keating sold to Morrill, Larkin, Anthony and Clark. During the previous Summer, Clark started on a voyage to the Society islands, and never was heard from again. The vessel in which he sailed, the Martha, was afterwards reported to have been lost on one of the islands of the South Pacific. His interest was sold in December, '53, and purchased by the firm. At this time the estimated value of the UNION was $25,000. On the 20th July, 1853, steam was introduced to run the presses of the establishment, being its first application to a newspaper office outside of San Francisco. But one change in the proprietory interests of the UNION has occurred since 1853. In May, 1858, P. Morrill sold his one-third share to J. Gray. The proprietors now are, H. W. Larkin, J. Anthony, J. Gray. With respect to the political sentiments of the paper, the following extract from the fifth anniversary number of the UNION (March, 1856) will perhaps as well explain its attitude on questions of State and National policy as anything we can give:

> "While the Whig party maintained its organization, its measures and men met in the UNION a firm, constant unflagging, if not able advocate. But the UNION was never, in the true sense of the term, a party organ; it never expects or aspires to become the *organ* of any party—believing such a position to be incompatible with that independent station a paper should occupy if it desires to benefit the public. In its future course it will struggle to maintain the same character towards parties which has heretofore marked its career. It has never hesitated to approve what it considered right in any party, or to condemn the acts of the party with which it was identified, whenever it believed them wrong. From this line of action it will not deviate in the future."

The UNION sustained the action of the Vigilance Committee of 1856. On the 17th of November, 1858, the UNION issued a double sheet daily, the first publication of the kind in the State, and the largest double sheet daily in the United States. It had before that, on every arrival of an Eastern mail steamer, issued regularly a fourteen column supplement. The new double sheet contains fifty-six columns. It is issued whenever a press of news requires it.

Democratic State Journal.—The *California Statesman,* which expired in this city on the 24th of last June, terminated a course of political journalism and a series of newspaper changes which have hardly had their equal in the history of any city of similar age. No more striking illustration of the vicissitudes and varied fortunes of a partisan press was ever exhibited. With the demise of the *Statesman* finally ended the struggles of the oldest Democratic Administration paper in the State, the name *Statesman* being the last shift to which the old *Democratic State Journal* resorted in its efforts to preserve unbroken the line of Administration organry, which it had founded in 1852. On the 5th of February of that year, the *Democratic State Journal* made its first appearance, with the names of V. E. Geiger & Co. as publishers, J. W. Gish being the business manager. Its editorials were written by Geiger and Washington, the latter present Collector of the port of San Francisco; Geiger is Indian Agent at the Nome Lackee Reservation. It took the field with the *Placer Times and Transcript,* and divided with that paper the support of the Democratic party. It was early committed to the support of John Bigler in his political aspirations, and for a while held such even faith with its neighbor of the *Times* that it became apparent one or the other must give way or pitch the tone of its Democracy a note higher or lower. The *Times and Transcript* was the advocate of Gwin, and the preference had doubtless given a peculiar cast to its editorials, more acceptable at that time to the Chivalry wing of the party in San Francisco than here; and so it did not despise a tender of $6,000 from the *Journal* proprietors, conditioned on its removal to San Francisco. In the Fall of the same year Gish retired, and the paper was continued by Geiger and Washington. In November, '52, the entire material and office were consumed in the great fire. The ensuing Spring, Washington seems to have found the individual and party preferences of the *Times and Transcript* more in consonance with his own sentiments, and to have followed after it, taking the position of editor in chief. Meanwhile B. B. Redding, who had previously joined the *State Journal,* had taken a desk in the editorial department, and after Washington's retirement was announced as one of the managers. On the 30th of July the *Journal,* which since the fall of the preceding year had been obliged to hold its way against a rival more formidable than was the *Times and Transcript,* entered into a coalition with the *Californian,* by which, though it retained its name, in substance and worldly goods it was transferred to the proprietors of the latter sheet. Redding was a party in the purchase, and the name and style of the new firm was Redding, Johnson & Co., composed of B. B. Redding, P. C. Johnson, S. J. May and J. McClatchy. The *Journal* was sold for $15,000. It was continued by the new firm without change until April of the following year, 1854, when Johnson sold his interest to Snowden, and two months later May sold to Redding & Snowden. Hitherto, under the new management, the editorials had been written by Redding, McClatchy and May. In the fall of this year William Walker commenced writing for the paper. Walker, it is needless to remind our readers, is the same who had already fillibustered Sonora, and subsequently reaped a harvest, if not of honors, of bloodshed in Nicaragua. The price at which the editorial labors of the embryo chieftain were retained was about $250 per month. His editorials, though not remarkable for depth of reasoning, were not wanting in vigor, and his style was polished, and his satire keen. About the time of his commencement in the *Journal* (October), McClatchy retired, disposing of his interest to D. J. Thomas. Walker's engagement only lasted until the following February, when he set about raising his first Nicaraguan expedition. On his leaving the *Journal* McClatchy resumed the position of editor, continuing a month, when John White became principal editor. In 1856 Snowden sold his interest to Redding & Thomas, under whose names and management, with White as chief editor, it continued until the month of June, 1857, when, borne down by the weight of its private calamities and party neglect, it ceased, and was sold under attachment to the printers in the office. Its publication was suspended for a period of four weeks, when it was resumed, with the names of Henry Shipley & Co. as publishers. It was conducted by the new firm, embracing most of the printers in the office, with Shipley, and afterwards R. Rust, as editor, until the Spring of this year, when it made its last proprietory change as the *Journal.* On the 24th of April the co-partnership was dissolved, the interests of most of the hands being purchased by P. W. S. Rayle. S. W. Ravely was announced as publisher, and so continued until the end of the month, when the flickering light of the *Democratic State Journal* fairly went out, and upon its venerable ruins sprang up a new candidate for public and party favor. At one time during the first few years of the *State Journal,* it published a column of French, the only issue in an European foreign tongue ever given from the press of this city. It opposed the Vigilance Committee in 1856.

Placer Times and Transcript.—On the 16th of June, 1851, the two pioneer journals whose separate history we have followed above were united under one name. The size of the paper was an inch larger each way than the SACRAMENTO UNION at present. The State printing, which G. K. Fitch then held, was the basis of the coalition of the two papers. Under the arrangement, Fitch retained a one half interest in the printing, and Pickering & Lawrence were jointly owners of the other half. The editors of the new sheet, which espoused the political faith of the former *Transcript,* were Pickering, Fitch & Lawrence. During the Summer and Winter of 1851 nothing of greater interest occurred in the married life of the paper than marks the intercourse of a political organ with the world and its own kin. Between the *Times and Transcript* and the *State Journal* there was, as we have remarked, a great degree of jealousy and rivalry. At length the career of the old journal suddenly ended in this city, by the removal of the establishment to San Francisco in the manner hitherto related. The *Times and Transcript* made its farewell bow to the Sacramento public in June, 1852, just a year from the time it was united.[28]

California Statesman.—The first paper of this name printed in Sacramento was commenced on the 13th of November, 1854, by J. W. Gish & Co. It was Democratic in politics, and the especial advocate of the reëlection of Gwin to the United States Senate by the Legislature of that Winter. The principal editor was Henry Meredith. The *Statesman* was the organ of what may be considered the straight-out Democracy of that period, its cotemporary, the *State Journal,* occupying for the first time in its career, the dubious ground of a Broderick supporter, denominated then, as now, factional. But the *Statesman,* in its support of Gwin, it would seem had "reasons more relevant" than mere party considerations. Though it hardly survived the session of the Legislature, it lived long enough to demonstrate the error of the principle which had called it into existence as a party sheet. On the 1st of March, Gish and Woodward filed a complaint in the District Court, alleging that the publication of the *Statesman* had been undertaken on an agreement of Gwin and Hardenbergh to pay $2,500 for the maintenance of Gwin's claim in the Senatorial contest. Gwin also promised to take the Government printing away from the Empire county *Argus* and give it to the *Statesman,* when he got

[28]In July and August, 1851, a semi-monthly *News-Letter** was published by A. C. Morse (San Francisco *Alta California,* July 15, 1851.)

back to Washington. The complainants laid their damages at $20,000, but the suit was dismissed, the Court deciding that a contract or agreement such as that alleged, was contrary to public policy. On the day the complaint was filed, Hardenbergh commenced suit against Presley Dunlap, to recover possession of the *Statesman.*

The Californian, of which we have partially sketched the history in conjunction with that of the *State Journal,* was commenced on the 17th of November, 1852, as a Settler Democratic morning paper. The destruction of nearly the whole city by fire in the fall of that year, left the new comer without a roof to shelter its head, a difficulty which was only obviated by one of the proprietors bringing into the city from his ranch, two miles distant, a rude kitchen, which was set up and occupied as a printing and publication office for the paper, and a hotel for one or two of the proprietors. These were at first known under the firm of E. Williamson & Co., with McClatchy and Thomas editors. The paper was about super-royal size. In April, 1853, S. J. May bought a one-fourth interest, and became one of the editors, Thomas retiring. No other changes of note occurred until the 30th of July, when the fusion with the *Democratic State Journal,* noticed above, took place.

Pacific Banner, O. C. Wheeler and E. J. Willis, editors, T. Alter publisher, was commenced about the month of August, 1852, and published once a week, with a slight interruption caused by the burning of its office, for one year. It was an organ of the Baptist denomination, and the first religious paper in the city. The publishers sank about $3,000 in their enterprise.

The *California Farmer and Journal of Useful Sciences* was the title under which the San Francisco weekly agricultural paper, the *Farmer,* was commenced January 9th, 1854. The prospectus announced that it would be published both in San Francisco and Sacramento; but it did not make its appearance in this city as a local publication until next year. The original publishers were Warren & Son and J. K. Phillips & Co.; J. F. Morse, editor. Morse continued his connection only one month. In May, 1855, the *Farmer* was removed to this city, along with the office of the Agricultural Society; but it only remained about fourteen months, returning to San Francisco in July, 1856.

Illustrated Historical Sketches of California, with a Minute History of Sacramento Valley, was the title of a monthly magazine, edited by J. F. Morse, and assisted by S. Colville, the first number of which appeared March 10th, 1854. Its mechanical execution and the interest of its editorial matter were highly commended. It only appeared once, owing to the bad management of the person who superintended its affairs.

Sacramento Daily Democrat.—This paper was almost a republication of the Benicia *Vedette,* being printed on the same material, which was moved up here for the purpose, and edited by R. C. Mathewson, who had conducted that journal up to the time of its death. The publishers were J. M. Shepard & Co., and the first number was issued March 13th, 1854. Its politics are expressed by its title. The *Democrat* only existed a few months, scarcely seeing a hundred issues.

Pacific Recorder, a semi-monthly journal of very neat appearance, designed to be issued simultaneously at San Francisco and Sacramento, as an exponent of the doctrines of the Baptist Church, made its first appearance July 15th, 1854, edited by E. J. Willis, formerly of the *Pacific Banner.* It was published semi-monthly until about the month of July, 1855, and from that time carried on weekly until March of the following year.

California State Almanac and Annual Register. A publication by this title was issued from the *State Journal* office in December, 1854, containing the usual statistical matter of almanacs. It was a neatly printed pamphlet, and was sold at 50 cents per copy.

State Tribune [Nos. 1 and 2]—On the 8th of June, 1855, appeared the first number of a daily morning paper under the above name, edited by Parker H. French and S. J. May. It professed independence in politics, but inclined to Democratic doctrines, with a yearning for the tenets of the new American sect. French was proprietor until September, when he sold to May, and left the State to join the "army of liberators" in Nicaragua. On the 1st of August J. M. Estell became editor, and the *Tribune* entered the campaign against John Bigler and the Democracy with a bitterness and effectiveness of opposition which won for it a leading place among the American or Know Nothing journals of the State. French, returning from Nicaragua in October, purchased back an interest in the *Tribune,* but appears not to have arranged for the payment, and went to San Francisco without the transfer being regularly made to him. Here, however, he sold his interest, or a part of it, to Farwell, Monson & Valentine, printers of that city, who came up and got possession of the material by attachment, on the 13th of October.

On the 16th of October, two *State Tribunes* made their appearance, to the confusion and political scandal of the town. May & Co., late proprietors of the original paper, had obtained the material of the old *Statesman,* and every morning saw a repetition of the scenes familiar to the admirers of the Comedy of Errors. The San Francisco Antipholus was mainly distinguishable from its namesake of this city by the style of the publication firm, that being Farwell & Co., while this was May & Co. Both were alike ardent in protesting their soundness on American issues; neither differed greatly from the other in style and ability, and each was equally violent in its outpourings of wrath and bile against the other. This warfare lasted for about two weeks. On the 30th of October, the Farwell *Tribune* succumbed, and the next day the other came out under the proprietorship of James Allen & Co., still as an American sheet, in which faith it lived until June 1st of the following year, when this "last of the *Tribunes*" also disappeared. Its place was filled the next day by a new American journal, which bore a name denoting its political creed.

The *Water Fount and Home Journal*, by Alex. Montgomery & Co. The prospectus for this, the first temperance journal in our city, was issued in San Francisco, and promised the simultaneous appearance of a weekly paper of the above title in San Francisco and Sacramento, about the 1st of June, 1855. On the 16th of May, the publication was commenced in San Francisco, but without its Sacramento counterpart. It was a sheet about the size of the UNION, of respectable appearance, and edited by A. Montgomery. It was continued weekly in that city until August, and then suspended. On the 15th of December following, its publication was renewed in this city. The *Water Fount and Home Journal* was the official organ of the Grand Division of the Sons of Temperance. Its Sacramento career lasted nine months.

The *Spirit of the Age*, the name of an afternoon paper, launched into this breathing world, December 6th, 1855, was conducted by G. H. Baker and J. A. Mitchell, the former as editor. It was "neutral in politics, and independent in everything," addressing itself with some vigor to the exposition of several local evils, gambling among the rest. Its circulation was from ten to twelve hundred. In June, '56, its name was changed to the *Sacramento Age*, and the sheet was enlarged. About this time Baker withdrew, and the publishing firm became H. A. Appleton & Co. J. S. Robb, formerly of the Stockton *Journal*, was engaged as editor, and Marvin, formerly of the Sonora *Herald*, succeeded J. R. Atkins, in the local department. About the month of August or September, Robb died, and W. Wright became editor of the Age. The paper only lasted until the beginning of 1857. Previous to the Fall election of 1856, the *Age* was sold to the American or Know Nothing party, and advocated their cause during the Fall canvass.

The *Daily Evening Times,* by A. Badlam & Co., was the name and firm of a little advertising sheet, printed daily and distributed gratuitously among business men, in the winter of 1855. It was only ten by eighteen inches in size, and derived its support from a few advertisements which were inserted on most any terms. The publishers displayed considerable ingenuity in getting their little sheet out, inventing and making a press, composed entirely of wood, for the purpose. Their type was a gift from the old *Statesman* office, and had been used before to print a sheet of the same species as the *Times,* in Amador county. So that it may be said of this diminutive specimen, that in one respect, at least, it was distinguished above all other California newspapers, and this was its cheapness. The type being set by one of the parties concerned in getting it out, and other labors similarly economized between them, its daily expenses are estimated to have been about a dollar per day. Commencing December 24th, with a circulation of two hundred, it reached seven hundred by March of the next year, when it was discontinued.

The California American.—This was the successor of the last *State Tribune,* and a candidate for the patronage of the new State rulers in 1856. It began this life June 2d of that year, the day after the *Tribune* died. Its proprietors were Jas. Allen, J. R. Ridge and S. J. May, Allen being chief editor until January, 1857, when Ridge assumed head management. It was not successful, notwithstanding one of the proprietors held the office of State Printer and during the first six months is said to have sunk over $15,000. It died in February, 1857.

City Item, a daily morning paper which came into existence on the 11th of December, 1856, was published by

C. Babb & W. H. Harvey. It was an independent sheet, of small size, furnished at 12½ cents per week, and had a circulation of about 1,000 copies. Its editor was Paschal Coggins. It was continued about seven months.

Daily Times, Republican, from August 15th, 1856 to January 24th, 1857. The *Times* was a well printed sheet, about 24 by 36 inches in size and edited with ability. It was published daily, Mondays excepted, by C. Cole & Co.; C. Cole, principal editor. It was very active during the Presidential election on the side of Frémont. In November it changed from a morning to an evening paper. It was printed under a joint stock arrangement and sent abroad a considerable weekly edition.

The Chinese News.—It is a little singular that the only paper ever printed in a foreign language in our city should have been a Chinese publication, particularly when we remember the considerable German and French elements in our population. The *News* was a sheet of respectable size and appearance, commenced in December, 1856, by Ze Too Yune, *alias* Hung Tai, a very intelligent native of the Flowery Land residing in our city. It was published not quite two years, first as a daily, next tri-weekly and afterwards irregularly—sometimes once a week and then once a month. It sold at twenty-five cents per week, and had 200 circulation. It was Young Hyson in politics. Too Yune proposes to revive it.

Temperance Mirror.—A quarto-monthly of this name was commenced January, 1857, O. B. Turrell, printer and publisher, and W. B. Taylor, editor. The first number appeared in this city; the second was published at San Francisco. It was continued in that city during February and March. The *Mirror* announced as its cause, Temperance and Good Morals.[29]

---

[29]The San Francisco *Alta California* of January 14, 1857, reported a new Sacramento paper, called *My Paper** and edited and published by "My Self."

The Sacramento Daily Bee.—After long groping in the newspaper charnel-house, it is pleasant to come upon the steps of a living and breathing acquaintance. The *Bee* is the only surviving member, beside the UNION, of the pretty large newspaper family whose remains we have been exploring. It was commenced by an association of practical printers, after the manner in which this journal was first started, on the 3d of February, 1857. It was a morning paper, independent in politics, and edited by J. R. Ridge and S. J. May. On the 6th of April, it was changed to an evening paper. During the summer of '57, Ridge retired, and his place was filled by J. McClatchy. The present proprietors are, F. S. Thomson, L. P. Davis, and W. H. Tobey, under the firm of W. H. Tobey & Co. A few days since, we had the pleasure of congratulating the *Bee*, on an enlargement of its dimensions. It exhibits otherwise tokens of prosperity, and may be said to be one of the few paying newspapers in the State.[30]

The *Star of the Pacific*, a quarto monthly religious paper, commenced in Marysville, May 15th, 1857, was removed to this city after its third number, and published until near the end of the year. It was then suspended, but revived again in May, 1858, at which time it appeared in a change of dress, and somewhat reduced in dimensions. Its publisher and editor, was A. C. Edmonds, a Universalist clergyman, who has been engaged in other publications in our State.[31]

The *Daily State Sentinel*, the second Republican paper in Sacramento, was established July 27th, 1857, by J. R. Atkins & Co. It was a morning paper, of neat though

---

[30]On April 3, 1857, the Republican *Anti-Office-Seeker** appeared, planning to issue four or five numbers. The first two are in the Bancroft Library.

[31]In June (announced for the 3rd, reported on the 17th) the first number of the *California Republican** was issued by McClatchy & Taylor. (San Francisco *Alta California*, May 24, June 17, 1857)

small size, and its editorials were written by several different persons, under the general editorship of Atkins. About the 25th of October, the latter withdrew, and the paper was continued by C. D. Hossack & Co., and edited by C. A. Sumner until its discontinuance, which happened about the beginning of 1858. The circulation of the *Sentinel,* before the election, was about eight hundred.

The *Eye Glass* was the name of a sheet, in pamphlet form, consisting of eight pages, published and edited by C. A. Sumner. The first and only number appeared on Saturday, August 22d, 1857. Its vocation, according to its own giving forth, was the inspecting of matters literary and artificial, with anecdotal notices of the eminent and lowly. This vocation was pretty well followed, if we may judge of the specimens exhibited in the number referred to, and which is now extant.

The Covenant and Odd Fellow's Magazine.— This was a monthly magazine, of 32 pages, whose No. 1, vol. 1, dates August 31, 1857. J. D. Tilson, was publisher, and A. C. Edmonds, editor. Only ten numbers were published. In religious belief, the *Covenant* inclined to Universalist doctrines.[32]

The Temperance Register.—H. Davison & Co. "Literature and Temperance." A monthly periodical, with the above title, was started in this city, September, 1857, led a brief but erratic life. It appeared first in a quarto form, as a monthly. Next month (October) it divided, like Biela's comet, and appeared in separate parts, semi-monthly, each part half the size of the monthly issue. The last number in October, was so full of advertisements that the editor complained of want of space for original matter. Its next change, reasoning from this circumstance, should have been to a weekly. On the appearance of its fourth

[32]The San Francisco *Alta California* of August 25, 1857, reported the arrival of the Sacramento *Sign and Grip,** an I.O.O.F. paper.

number, however, it had gone back to a monthly. The issue of December 12th, is the last we are able to find.

The Herald of the Morning.—The title of a literary Sunday publication, J. McDonald & Co., proprietors. The first number was issued December 20, 1857. One of its devotions was at the shrine of Spiritism, that being an object among others to the discussion of which it was devoted. C. B. McDonald, was literary editor, until the second number, when his name was withdrawn. It departed this life with the fourth number.

The Phoenix.—Though scarcely deserving a name among our public prints, the sheet being a vehicle for the malignant abuse and indecency of a private individual,—may be mentioned as a part of the typographia of our city. It was vended by E. McGowan, from about the Fall of 1857, until the Summer of '58. A few months previous to its discontinuance, it was called the *Ubiquitous.*

The Watch Dog.—A semi-monthly sheet appeared about the 1st of January, 1858. J. Mortimer Smith, editor. It appeared to have been littered in the same kennel with the *Phoenix,* baying in deep-mouthed sympathy with it. The *Watch Dog* starved in about two months.

The Sacramento *Visitor,* visited us for the first time on the 26th of March, 1858, and was introduced by P. Coggins, editor, and Brown, Ingham & Co., publishers. It was a brief but agreeable guest, terminating its visit about the first of June.

The Sacramento Mercury.—A Democratic Administration paper, by this name, was published last summer,[33] by H. S. Foushee, and edited by W. S. Long, the first number appearing March 28th (Palm Sunday). But the co-incidence of its birth was no presage of victory, for before it had completed half a volume, it had run its course. The *Mercury* was about the size of the present

[33]Following the *Age*.

Bee. In the latter part of its career, A. Montgomery was associated in its editorial management. The *Mercury* took its heavenward flight the 12th of October.

The California Statesman (No. 2.)—This was the last earthly tabernacle into which the spirit of the old *Democratic State Journal* passed, before bidding the scene of its long labor a final adieu. The *Statesman* was commenced about the 1st of May, 1858. S. W. Ravely, was publisher, and A. C. Russell, editor. The paper did not succeed, notwithstanding its price of subscription was reduced to twenty-five cents per week. On the 24th of June, the baffled spirit of the old organ took its flight.

The Californian.—The second paper of that name in Sacramento, was a small neutral sheet, edited by D. J. Thomas, and started July 9th, 1858. It was "in session" one week.

The Baptist Circular.—A third Baptist paper was started in this city in August last, and is now in existence. The *Baptist Circular* was published once a month, or as often as funds were received sufficient to defray the expenses of each number in advance, by Rev. J. L. Shuck. Under this novel arrangement, the *Circular* appears to succeed very well, and is now announced as permanently established.

The *Morning Star,* a Democratic sheet, of Administration preferences, arose on the 2d of November. It is a small, though neat publication, issued daily, Mondays excepted. Published by McClure & Co., and edited by A. Montgomery. It is the last comer to this cold world. Like its predecessor, the *Mercury,* it began its career on Sunday.

We have thus the names of forty distinct newspapers, published at different times in the city, only four of which are now in existence, viz.:—SACRAMENTO DAILY UNION; *Daily Bee;* the *Morning Star;* and *Baptist Circular;* the last, published monthly.

Of the above number, twenty-five have been daily papers, one was commenced as a tri-weekly, and one as a semi-weekly; seven have been weekly, four monthly, and one was started as an annual. Twenty have professed politics, five religion, three temperance, one odd-fellowship, one squatter's rights, one agriculture, two literature, one pictures, (besides the semi-annual PICTORIAL UNION), one scurrility, and one statistics. Five have been independent, and one has been printed in Chinese. Of the political papers, nine were different shades of Democracy, two were Whig, three American, or Know-Nothing, and two Republican. Three of the five religious papers belonged to the Baptist persuasion, and the remaining two were Universalist. Concerned in the publication of the above papers, we can count the names of one hundred and thirty persons, though there were others whose names are not known. About seventy-five persons have appeared as editors of the above papers, and what is a little singular in the life of California editors, not one of them has ever been called upon to leave his post and fight a duel, or take serious part in a street fight, on account of articles he or others may have written in our papers. Beyond a few personal encounters, limited to a battery of fists and sticks, and the productions of deadly weapons, without using them, there have been in our city none of those savage altercations which usually mark the intercourse of editors in new States, similarly situated to our own, and from which San Francisco, with her cooler climate, larger and older society and metropolitan restraints, has not altogether escaped. Nearly all who have been prominently connected with the Sacramento press are alive, though widely scattered, and occupying, in some instances, widely different positions. Giles, of the Placer *Times,* is married and settled in Massachusetts. Lawrence, sits at the receipt of Customs, in San Francisco. Pickering is, or was not long since, in Europe. Fitch, of the old *Transcript,* is in

San Francisco. Ewer, is also there, a minister of the gospel. Robinson, of the Settler's *Tribune,* was the famous free State Governor of Kansas, in the troubles of 1855 and '56. Washington is Collector at San Francisco. Geiger, is Indian Agent. Walker, has taken and lost Nicaragua, and is preparing to take it again. Two of the original founders of the UNION are in this city. Its original editor is in the successful practice of his old profession, Medicine, in Sacramento, and thus the changes have run from grave to gay, from lively to severe, since our newspaper history begun. But while the large proportion of those who were identified with it, have failed to make one cent from their connection, oftener losing all they had made in something else, we can remember four or five who have returned to the East very comfortably off in this world's goods, from the share they have taken in the fortunes of newspapers in Sacramento.

Newspapers In Stockton

From Sacramento the next stride of the Press was to Stockton. This was the second city of 1849, and the oldest but one or two of the sites which were chosen for American towns after the occupation of the country by our people. Before the gold was discovered, C. M. Weber, an old resident of the San José Valley, had directed his attention to the selection of a place for the building up of a town in the San Joaquin Valley, and, if we are not greatly deceived, a town survey was made in that quarter. We find notices in the California papers of 1848 of a settlement having been founded in the valley, not far from what is at present the city of Stockton. Before this, however, and undoubtedly the first to "locate" in that region were some of the "Brooklyn Mormons," who erected a settlement on the Stanislaus in 1846. Stockton was first brought regularly into the market, for the sale of her town lots, in June, 1849. On the 16th March, 1850, the first newspaper was started in the place.

The Stockton ***Times*** was one of the progeny of the *Alta,* and the third paper in California printed on the old Boston wooden press of 1832. In January, 1850, H. H. Radcliffe, an Englishman by birth, applied to the publishers of the *Alta* for material on which to print a paper at Stockton. The only spare press in their establishment at the time was the old wooden one which had just been carefully brought down from Sacramento. The owners disliked to let this go, intending, as they said, to preserve it as an heirloom in their establishment. On condition that they should have the privilege of re-purchasing it when other machinery could be procured to take its place, the venerable relic was suffered to depart on its last journey from San Francisco. With it they sold a part of the old type of the former *Star and Californian* office. Out of these rude materials were constructed the first number of the *Times,* the pioneer journal of the San Joaquin Valley. It was issued on a sheet about the size of the original *Placer Times* (foolscap), and bore a strong family resemblance to the old newspapers of the country. The publishers' names were H. H. Radcliffe and John White. The *Times* filled a vacancy long complained of by the San Francisco editors, supplying them with news from a part of the mines from which they could only hear, prior to its establishment, through private advices. It became a prime medium of communication with the Southern Mines. It advocated no particular political faith, but was devoted to the advancement of the interests of this section of country. Its original title was *Stockton Times and Tuolumne City Intelligencer*—the latter portion apparently having been added in view of an anticipated rivalry, which it was then somewhat feared would result in favor of Tuolumne City over Stockton. The Stockton paper saw the usual ups and downs which fell to the lot of the original journals. In August it was enlarged and otherwise improved. A few days after it was compelled to come out on a half sheet, "on account of the illness of the compositor." We have not a file, or even stray copies of the *Times,* and therefore cannot follow it through its vicissitudes. The *Times* was discontinued on the 27th of April, 1851, the material, press, etc., having been purchased by George Kerr, and destroyed, a few days after, in the great fire, May 6th, 1851. From this disaster the old press, however, escaped, having gone on its last mission of enlightenment as the pioneer into the Southern Mines.

Stockton Journal.—The first number of the Stockton *Journal* was issued as a weekly on or about the 18th of June, 1850, by Bartlett & Robb, the office having been purchased, and supported in its infancy, by private subscription. Its editor, John S. Robb, was formerly of St. Louis, where he was well known. Its publication was continued until August 1st, 1851, when Samuel Knight became a partner in the firm of John S. Robb & Co., by whom the paper was published (Robb continuing the editor) until November 5th of the same year. The paper then came into the possession of John Tabor and Orin F. Jackson, by whom it was conducted until the withdrawal of Jackson, on the 17th of February, 1852. From this date to the 22d of June, 1854, the paper was published by John Tabor, Robert Wilson being its editor. On the 22d of June, 1854, a difficulty occurred between Tabor, of the *Journal,* and Joseph Mansfield, of the *Republican,* which resulted in the death of the latter. From this date Tabor's connection with the paper ceased. The fatal affair grew out of an article that appeared in the *Journal.* Mansfield accosted Tabor upon the street, and after some exchange of words, Tabor drew a Derringer pistol from his pocket and fired upon Mansfield, being within three or four feet of him. Mansfield lingered until three o'clock, and then expired. A Coroner's Jury returned a verdict in accordance with the above circumstances. Tabor, in the meantime, was taken into custody by the Sheriff, and remained in prison seven months prior to his trial, which took place in the District Court, January term, 1855. He was found guilty of murder, and sentenced to be hung on the 16th of March following. Through the great exertions of his friends, in the circulation of petitions for his pardon, which reached nearly every part of the State, and also to his native State of Texas, he was pardoned on the 8th of March, 1855, by Gov. Bigler. The *Journal,* from the date of the death of Mansfield, passed into the hands of Samuel Knight and B. W. Owens, and was edited by T. C. Osborn, until a sale of the office was effected, Henry A. Crabb and William Biven being the purchasers, by whom the material was afterwards employed in the publication of the *Argus.* Tabor went to Nicaragua and took part in Walker's operations there. We perceive by late Eastern news that he is still associated with the designs of the fillibuster hero, and proposes taking a press with him on the next invasion of Nicaragua by Americans.

San Joaquin Republican.—This paper was first issued May 14th, 1851, under the proprietorship of George Kerr, who continued in its publication until August 23d, 1853, when Joseph Mansfield and William Biven became part proprietors in the establishment, and the business was continued under the firm of George Kerr & Co. until January 23d, 1854, at which time Kerr and Biven withdrew, and the publication was continued by Jos. Mansfield, H. C. Patrick, J. B. Kennedy and J. M. Conley, under the firm of Mansfield, Patrick & Co. On the 22d of June, 1854, Mansfield was killed by John Tabor (then proprietor and editor of the Stockton *Journal*), after which time the paper was conducted by H. C. Patrick, J. B. Kennedy, J. M. Conley and P. L. Shoaff, under the firm of H. C. Patrick & Co. The firm was again changed on the 7th of January, 1855, and C.A. Hutchinson became a partner, under the name and style of J. M. Conley & Co., which partnership was continued until December 23d, 1857, when J. M. Conley and H. C. Patrick became sole proprietors, and have since conducted the publication of the paper. The *Republican* was issued from its commencement as a semi-weekly, until June 14th, 1853, and from that date as a tri-weekly, until December 29th, 1853, since which time it has appeared daily. Its political course has been Democratic, sustaining the Administration from its first issue. Its original editor was John White, who continued as such until September 1st, 1854, when A. C. Bradford occupied that position until August 7th, 1855; since which time the paper has passed through the editorial charge of E. R. Campbell, A. C. Baine, A. J. De Prefontaine, and A. C. Russell. The paper, at the present time, is under the editorial control of F. L. Sargent.

Stockton Daily Evening Post.—This paper was first issued on the 2d of January, 1854, under the proprietorship of Wm. Biven, and editorial control of William and Rasey Biven. Its politics were Democratic. Its publication was continued, with a very handsome subscription list, until the establishment of the *Argus,* when it was discontinued, but shortly after issued under the latter name.

Stockton Daily Item, an evening paper, published by an association of printers, under the firm of C. H. Howe & Co. First number issued on the 4th of January, 1855, and the paper discontinued its publication on the 3d of March of the same year. The paper was originally designed as an organ of local burlesque, through which course it attained a large city circulation.

Stockton Daily Gazette, an evening paper, and a campaign organ of the Republican party, was first issued on the 8th of October, 1856, and edited by John F. Damon. The publication was continued until the 5th of November, when its existence terminated with the hopes, that year, of the party whose principles it had defended.

Stockton Daily Argus.—This paper was originally published by William Biven and Henry A. Crabb, under the editorial control of the latter. Its first number was issued on the 7th of June, 1854. The political course of the paper was Whig, and was edited, during short periods, while it advocated Whig principles, by A. G. Stakes and A. C. Russell. After a temporary change as a weekly, it was re-issued as a daily on the 7th of March, 1855, and was edited and conducted by William Biven, sole proprietor, by whom its course of politics was changed to the advocacy of the American party—the first paper in the State as an organ of that party. Since the demise of the American party in this State, the political course of the *Argus* has been favorable to Democratic principles as understood and advocated by S. A. Douglas.

The Pacific Methodist.—This paper was established by the Annual Conference of the M. E. Church, South, which assembled in Sacramento in November, 1856, and its publication, weekly, ordered to be made in Stockton. Its first number was issued in San Francisco, in the latter part of November of that year, and was published regularly thereafter in this city during the Conference year, under the direction of a Publishing Committee. Rev. O. Fisher was appointed its editor, to whose untiring exertions the paper is greatly indebted for its present position. The press and material were removed to San Francisco shortly after the close of the Conference year, where it has since been published under the editorial management of Rev. O. P. Fitzgerald.

Weekly Stockton Democrat.—The first number of this paper was issued on the 6th of December, 1857, under the proprietorship of William Biven and editorial control of Rasey Biven. Its politics were Administration Democracy, which it continued to advocate until the 15th of August, when its political course was changed to that of the Democracy as advocated by Stephen A. Douglas, and the paper came under the editorial control of William Biven. A rapid circulation was attained by the *Democrat* from its first number.

It appears from the above minutes that the whole number of papers that have been started in Stockton, since 1849, is nine—of which three, two dailies and one weekly, remain. Concerned in the publication and editorship of them we can count the names of thirty-two persons. Two of the papers have been independent in politics, two Administration, one Whig, American and Democratic by turns; two Douglas Democrats, one Republican, one religious, and one burlesque. Though brief, the annals of the Stockton press show no exception to the general fortunes of newspapers in California. It has seen its good and evil days; peaceful scenes and scenes of bloodshed, disaster and crime. Its early founders are passed away, and there have been changes in the separate management of the journals along every step of their way. The new Overland Mail routes which lie up the valley of the San Joaquin (one of them terminating at Stockton), should open to the newspapers now established there visions of increased usefulness and prosperity, perhaps call others into the field. It may easily happen that, during the coming Spring, the Overland news will be disseminated from that point, the stages not being able to cross the San Joaquin in the season of floods. This will afford the Stockton journals an opportunity to prove their enterprise, and take the lead of their cotemporaries, oftentimes, in spreading the news through the mines.

Newspapers In Marysville

The *Alta California,* of July 1st, 1850, has a notice, under the head of new papers, of two fresh enterprises, begun at each of the two northern and southern mining centers. One of these is the pioneer journal of the mines, established three days afterwards, at Sonora; the second is a project which had been commenced almost at the same time for the erection of the first press at Marysville. Advertisements of both plans appear, almost simultaneously, in the San Francisco journals, but a month elapsed after the Sonora paper was issued before Marysville took her place in the line. In justice to the enterprise of the former city, we should assign it a place in our history immediately following the Stockton press. But to complete the classification of the Cities of the Plains, before following journaldom into the mountains, we make this slight departure from our chronological order. Marysville has been second only to Sacramento in the respectability of her press and the value of newspaper property, notwithstanding she did not start in newspaper life until two journals had been established in Stockton. The changes and reverses which have fallen to the lot of her publishers are even greater than those through which our Stockton neighbors have passed. And it is a source of regret that we have not been able to compile a more circumstantial narrative of the origin and career of the

Marysville newspapers. We have been kindly supplied with the outlines of their history, including the names of the editors and proprietors and the important dates in their publication. These, with a few recollections of the early beginnings in newspaperdom, must serve us in the construction of our Marysville chapter.

The Marysville *Herald* entered the lists as the pioneer journal of the City of the Buttes, on the 6th of August, 1850. The *Herald* first sounded its parley in the name of R. H. Taylor, a merchant, in San Francisco, in 1849-'50. Taylor saw an opening for a newspaper at Marysville, early in the Summer, and, as soon as he could negotiate for a press and type, entered the field. The *Herald* was commenced, semi-weekly, a small but neat sheet, and was edited with sprightliness and good taste. It grew in popularity, eschewed politics, and by October was ready to take on a third day or tri-weekly issue, *only* the editor said he must have more advertisements to fill up with. In the Spring of '51, S. C. Massett became connected with it, as part proprietor and itemizer. Following Massett the subjoined persons were successively proprietors: L. W. Ransom, D. J. Marrener, W. W. Smith, O. P. Stidger, J. Allen, L. R. Lull. The names of those who have been principal editors of the *Herald* since Taylor laid down "the shears" are J. Allen and L. R. Lull. The *Herald* early abandoned its neutrality, and, during its seven years and a-half of existence, passed through the several political changes of Whig, Know Nothing, Republican and "Stars and Stripes." During the Vigilance revolution of 1856, it sustained the action of the Committee. On the 1st of January, 1858, the *Herald* blew its last summons and departed.

The *California Express* was established by R. Rust & Co., November 3d, 1851. Its proprietors from the beginning to the present time have been L. Gee, W. T. Giles,

R. Rust, T. Mitchell, J. McElroy, A. Brady, L. Laird, G. W. Bloor, G. I. Foster, M. D. Carr, L. Magruder, S. Addington, J. Laird, W. F. Hicks, the four last named being the present proprietors. Its editors from the commencement have been R. Rust, J. R. Ridge, A. C. Russell (present editor.) The *Express* is the oldest living paper in Marysville, and though started neutral in politics, was very early attached to the Democratic faith, in which it has since remained. In 1856 it opposed the action of the Vigilance Committee.

Daily Inquirer.—Commenced November 1, 1855, a Democratic sheet. Its proprietors were J. De Mott & Co., and afterward O. O. Ball. Its editors at different times were G. C. Gorham, W. N. Walton, W. H. Mantz, Buckelew & Coulp. The *Inquirer* tried the virtue of Simon Suggs' motto, "Its good to be shifty in a new country," veering round to opposite points in the political compass during its short career. For awhile it was neutral, then it took on Know-Nothingism, and finally went back to Democracy, in which hope it died December, 1857.

The *Weekly Spiritualist,* an advocate of the school of A. J. Davis' Harmonial Philosophy, was begun in February, and discontinued in May, 1857. It was published and edited by L. W. Ransom.

Star of the Pacific, a Universalist paper, commenced in March,[34] and suspended (removed[35]) July 1st, 1857; A. C. Edmonds, editor and proprietor.

Daily News, the title of a journal commenced January 9th, and continued until August 9th, 1858, was presided over editorially by J. Allen, with the following persons successively proprietors: A. S. Randall, S. B. Christian, J. F. Whittaker, J. Allen, W. Boulware, J. O. Heatley. The *News* was neutral in politics.

---

[34]i.e. May, 1857.

[35]To Sacramento.

National Democrat—the last acquisition to the newspaper ranks of Marysville—was commenced August 12th of the present year, and is still published. It is a Douglas Democratic sheet, and its proprietors are: A. S. Randall, S. B. Christian, J. F. Whittaker, James Allen, W. Boulware, J. O. Heatley, G. W. Bloor. The editor of the *Democrat* is J. R. Ridge.

Our Marysville newspaper account sums up as follows: Seven newspapers, five of which have been daily and two weekly; three Democratic, one Whig, one neutral, one Universalist, one Spiritualist. With them we have the names of thirty-two proprietors and twelve editors, nearly all of whom are still living, and many of them still in Marysville. Taylor has turned lawyer, and is practicing at Downieville; Massett is lecturing in the East; Rust is in the State Department. The existing Marysville papers are the *California Express* and the *National Democrat.*

Sonora and the Southern Mines

Sonora has the honor of having given birth to the first newspaper published in the mines of California. This would be something of a distinction in itself, but she is also deserving the credit of having, like a good mother, succeeded in "raising" her first offspring, a merit of which but few of the towns in our State can boast. The origin of her first newspaper is made historical from the initial number appearing on the 4th of July, and from its having been printed on the press and some of the type, perhaps, with which the old *Californian* was published—the identical wooden press imported from Boston in 1832. We have traced the history of this aged relic from Sacramento back to San Francisco, and thence to Stockton, where it performed service in the office of the first printer. In the Spring of 1850 Radcliffe, of the *Stockton Times,* disposed of the original material of his office to Marvin & White, of Sonora. He does not appear to have fully given up his interest in the old establishment, but to have been associated with the new enterprise, as we find his name announced in the advertisement of the Sonora paper, in connection with Marvin & White. Sonora was almost unknown outside of the little community of the Southern mines, when this advertisement of a newspaper in that region appeared.

The *Sonora Herald* commenced its career on the 4th of

July, 1850[36]; John White and John G. Marvin editors and proprietors. The first seven numbers were printed on foolscap, and were sold at fifty cents a copy. Its career and changes have been as follows: After reaching its twelfth number, John White's interest was transferred to J. R. Reynolds, extensively known as the ex-Judge of the First Instance. He continued half proprietor for two weeks, then transferred his interest to Dr. Haley, who sold to Dr. L. C. Gunn, after a short suspension of publication. The fifteenth, sixteenth and seventeenth numbers were issued by Judge Marvin and Dr. Gunn. In the eighteenth number Judge Marvin retired, and E. L. Christman succeeded him. The *Herald* continued to be issued by Christman & Gunn until the fortieth number, when Dr. Gunn became the sole proprietor. Under his auspices it continued till May 22d, 1852, when Walter Murray and James O'Sullivan succeeded him. On the 19th of February, 1853, O'Sullivan sold to Murray. On the 1st of August, 1853, Murray sold back to Gunn. In April, 1854, the *Herald* was sold to O'Sullivan and Alexander Murray, a brother of the former proprietor. In September, A. Murray sold to O'Sullivan, and the latter remained the sole proprietor till after the election in 1855, when E. A. Rockwell was announced as editor and proprietor. Rockwell retired in August, 1856, and O'Sullivan again became proprietor, conjointly with Matthew Kearney. They are still the proprietors. The several proprietors, with the exception of J. R. Reynolds, Alex. Murray and Mr. Kearney, have also been the editors. Of the proprietors of the *Sonora Herald,* White was an Englishman; Walter Murray and Alexander Murray, also Englishmen; O'Sullivan and Kearney were Irish-

[36]First number printed in Stockton *Times* office for distribution in Sonora. Steamer edition, June 1, 1853, listed by New York Historical Society.

men; Marvin, Reynolds, Christman, Gunn and Rockwell were natives of the United States. The paper was independent until August, 1853, when it became Democratic, and continued so until the Fall of 1855, when, under Rockwell, it became the organ of the American party. In the Fall of 1856, it resumed its character as independent, and has so continued to the present time. The *Herald* has always been a weekly paper, except for a few weeks in the Summer of 1856, when it was published daily. The *Sonora Herald* was the first paper in California to advocate a title in fee simple to the mineral lands. It commenced as far back as 1850, when Gunn was its editor. During the editorial career of this gentleman, an article condemning fillibustering having excited the ire of one of the Nicaraguan adventurers, he was personally assaulted by the latter, though not much injured. This was in the Winter of 1854, and society has somewhat improved in our mountain towns since then.

The Sonora *Mountain Whig,* a weekly paper, and, as its name denotes, attached to the old Whig party, was published during the summer of 1852, by J. W. Dunn. It was only carried on five weeks. The *Whig* was the only exponent of the principles of that party ever published in Sonora or the southern mines.

The *Union Democrat,* an Administration paper, A. N. Francisco proprietor, was commenced at Sonora July 1, 1854, and is still continued. Through the political changes and vicissitudes of the past four years, it has clung to the Administration. It has always been a weekly print. In 1855, C. Donavan was engaged in the editorial department; in 1856, Otis Greenwood. The present editorial assistant is N. P. Turner.

MOKELUMNE HILL.

The next paper in the southern mines was started at Mokelumne Hill, Calaveras county.

The *Calaveras Chronicle* was commenced October 9, 1851, by H. Hamilton, J. J. Ayers and H. A. De Courcey, the latter occupying the chair of editor. It was begun, and always has been, a weekly paper, Democratic in politics. De Courcey was formerly connected with the Nevada *Journal,* and remained editor during 1851 and 1852, when Hamilton took his place. In the Spring of 1852, De Courcey received a ball through his body in a duel with one Carter, opposite this city, but survived the wound. He is now dead, however. Hamilton continued to conduct the paper through the years 1852-'3-'4-'5, when George L. Shuler took the chair, and carried it into 1857. We find the names of J. O'Meara and J. N. Bingay connected with the *Chronicle* as editors, during a part of this time. In 1857, John Shannon became proprietor and editor of the paper, which position he still occupies. The *Chronicle* office was destroyed by fire on the 20th August, 1854, but the press was saved. No other paper in the English language has been published at Mokelumne Hill. There has been established since, however, the California *Staats Zeitung,* a weekly German paper, published and edited by A. Wagner. It was commenced about the middle of October. It still lives.

Quamkeag Coyote, the title—nothing more can we find[37]—of a literary humorous sheet, of which the first number was issued in May, 1854, "from somewhere near Mokelumne Hill." The names which stood for its editors were Parthenon Slimface and Peter Noodles.

COLUMBIA.

The Columbia *Star* was the next orb that threw its light into the southern mines. It was an ill-omened sheet, however, being born out of time, and the light it cast was meteoric and lurid. Its coming seemed a fit presage to

[37]Reported in San Francisco *Alta California,* June 8, 1854.

the disaster which actually befell the press in that section shortly after; just as, in old times, comets were regarded as harbingers of destruction. The *Star* arose in Columbia, Tuolumne county, October 25, 1851. The press and materials used were those with which the Sonora *Herald* had been started, the same which had printed the Stockton *Times,* and before it the Placer *Times,* and the *Californian,* at San Francisco and at Monterey. This was the old wooden press of Ben Franklin's city, the Father of Newspapers on the Pacific. We have reached the last stage of its long life of usefulness, and must deal circumstantially with the events which terminated its career. In October, Dr. Gunn, of the Sonora *Herald,* sold the Ramage press and some of the old type to G. W. Gore, of Columbia, for the purpose of commencing a paper in that town. The material was removed and the publication commenced on the date above given. A balance of three hundred and seventy dollars remained unpaid, however, for which Gunn sued and attached the press and type. It was sold under execution, and bought by some person bidding for Gunn, for three hundred and ten dollars. After the sale, the press was left standing upon the sidewalk, it being difficult to get a cart the same afternoon to remove it to Sonora, which is but a few miles distant. That night the press was removed into the middle of the street and an act of vandal ruffianism committed which will always be a reproach to the town of Columbia. Either led or instigated by Gore, his companions and sympathizers kindled a fire under the aged relic and destroyed in a few moments what, even in barbarian countries, would have been held in veneration a lifetime, if only as an unmeaning curiosity. A greater outrage never desecrated the name of an American town, or disgraced American citizenship, and the only possible palliation that can be suggested is the very meagre one that the incendiaries may not have known the age and historical value of the old press. There were those in Columbia who evidently attached an archeological interest to the first issue of the press in that town, for we read that an ounce was paid for the first copy of the *Star* that was printed. What a misfortune that these could not have interposed to prevent the destroying of a relic whose history would have been more curious than that of any similar article, perhaps, now in existence. As an heirloom of the art on these shores, its value would have been almost priceless. The destruction of the old press took place on the night of the 13th[38] November. The Sonora *Herald* of the following week, commenting on the occurrence uses the following language:

> "We sent, yesterday, for the charred and half-consumed timber which constituted the frame, and brought it to our office, in front of which it is now deposited, for examination by all who feel interested in the relic. It shall be duly labelled and preserved, not only to show what it once was, and in memory of its past services, but also to show to the better members of society, who are fast emigrating to California, how different has been the character of some of the settlers. The appearance of the press alone, as it now stands, forms a chapter in the history of the State; and whenever a State museum may be established, it shall be placed in it."

Unfortunately for the good intentions of the editor, Sonora has been swept five or six times by conflagrations, and as we do not hear that the remains of the press are still preserved, there is every reason to believe the charred timbers of the Columbia incendiarism have not escaped a second burning, and that they have long since mingled their ashes with those of the town whose fortunes they may have helped to originate, in the printing of the first mining newspaper. As for the Columbia *Star,* it only blinked twice, and was then lost in the glare of the heathenish conflagration it had kindled.

---

[38]November 12, 1851.

The Columbia *Gazette* was the second paper in Columbia. It appeared in October, 1852, just a year from the date of the occurrence above mentioned. The editor and proprietor was T. A. Falconer. It was commenced as a weekly neutral paper, but soon turned Democratic, and has since continued a defender of that faith. In November, 1855, it changed from weekly to semi-weekly,[39] but in the following summer it returned to its former periodic issue. Falconer continued editor of the *Gazette* until the close of the first year, when J. C. Duchow took his place. The latter was joined in the proprietorship by P. M. Lancey.[40] It was well managed by the new firm, until November, 1855, when T. N. Cazneau assumed control. His career ended in July of the following year, when Duchow again leased it for six months. From this period to the Winter and Spring of 1858, it passed through several changes, when J. W. Oliver took charge of its columns for a couple of months, during which time its hand was against the Administration. It was the first weekly Democratic paper to come out for Douglas. Oliver was succeeded by G. R. Parburt, who, on taking the helm, put the *Gazette* on the tack of the Administration, which, however, proved to be a short tack, for in a few weeks the paper died.

The Columbia *Clipper* was established by Heckendorn, Gist & Wilson, in May, 1854. It was an organ of the American party, and published weekly, J. Heckendorn, editor. We are unacquainted with the incidents of its career. It remained unchanged in politics until its close, which was in May, 1857.[41]

The *Columbian* started June, 1856, Oliver & Wilson,

---

[39]As Columbia *Gazette & Southern Mines Advertiser.*

[40]T. M. Yancey.

[41]June? 1856. With Columbia *Gazette,* issued *Clipper & Gazette, Extra,* July 11, 15, 22, 1854, following fire of July 10.

proprietors; J. W. Oliver, editor. The course of this paper, though an independent sheet, was adverse to the Administration, and favorable to the election of Fillmore to the Presidency. It was well sustained, having, it is said, over a thousand circulation—the largest attained by any paper in the Southern mines. It was only continued a year, however, expiring in May, 1857.[42]

Tuolumne Courier, the name of the fifth paper published in Columbia, was commenced in June, 1857, by Duchow & Urmy. The latter continued his interest only a few months. Like its predecessors of the Columbia press, it was commenced as a weekly. It was issued from the material and office of the *Columbian.* In politics, the *Courier* claims to be independent, though supporting the present Administration. Its present proprietors are Duchow & Brother, and E. Boden; J. C. Duchow, editor.

Columbia News, is the sixth and last paper commenced in this flourishing part of Tuolumne. The *News* was only commenced last August. Its editor and proprietor is D. Youcham. It is published weekly, and supports the Administration Democracy.

JACKSON.

The path of early journalism in the southern mines leads us now into Amador county, where, after the foundation had been laid for the press in Columbia, the next newspaper made its appearance. Momus appears to have presided over the birth of the first journal in this section, and not to have withdrawn his favors in the subsequent history of the press. As very frequently happens, his choice for a mask for his inclinations fell upon the solemn bird of Minerva, and accordingly the first newspaper presentation is under that head.

The *Owl,* we learn, was published fitfully during the

---

[42]June 21, 1856 - June 6, 1857.

years 1853-4, in the town of Jackson. Its editor and publisher was Charles Boynton. It was a small owl, but, like the one that called forth the Paddy's admiration, it kept up a powerful thinking, and its owlish jokes were very clever and pointed. It afforded much amusement to the Amadorians, relieving the long night which preceded the dawn of regularly established newspapers, with local squibs and *bon mots,* and only taking its flight when the morning of the press had fairly risen.

The Jackson *Amador Sentinel* was commenced January 1st, 1854, the editor and publisher, Charles Boynton, was the same who had been concerned in the *Owl.* The first measure to which the *Sentinel* addressed itself was the division of Calaveras county. In the Summer of 1855 Boynton sold the paper to O. D. Avaline, and went to the Atlantic States, where he published the La Salle (Ill.) *Press,* and has since died. The *Sentinel* still goes on.

The *Bell* was the sonorous name of the second humorous sheet printed in Amador. It was issued from the *Sentinel* office in August, 1855. Like its predecessor, it was printed for fun and burlesque. It rang forth but two merry peals, however, expiring, maybe, from its own mirth, with the second number.

The *Democratic Standard* was a campaign paper printed in the Fall of 1856. It was edited and published by Homer King, from the *Sentinel* office. The *Standard* continued three months from August 6th. It was not a profitable enterprise.

The Amador *Weekly Ledger* was commenced at Volcano, Oct. 27th, 1855, as an independent sheet, by T. A. Springer and E. B. Daingerfield. In April, 1857, it was removed to Jackson, where it is still published. In the meantime (July, 1856), it had abandoned its neutrality and hoisted Democratic colors, but it has never supported the Administration on the Kansas question, and in the last election took sides with the anti-Administration party but did not support McKibben and Dudley. T. A. Springer is now sole editor and proprietor.

The *Students' Banner* was a little publication which appeared once, on the eve of a public school exhibition at Jackson, and probably in aid of the fete, March 30th, of the present year, G. O. Ash and N. C. Briggs publishers.

The *Independent,* edited and published by J. H. Dennis, was the seventh and last paper started in Jackson. It was a political campaign paper, half the size of the *Sentinel,* and devoted to the interests of an independent ticket in the last Fall election. It was only continued five weeks from the 5th of August.

Before going out of Amador we must not forget to notice a little paper called the *Prospector,*[43] printed on a copying press, and distributed gratis along the line of the Empire Ditch Company. It was only 7x10 inches in size, worked on a handful of type, and appears to have had for its object merely the killing of time. Its proprietors, printers and editorial staff were the officers of the Ditch Company (M. B. Clark, A. Badlam and W. J. Wallace), who, growing weary of indolently "sitting at the receipt of customs," first tried the excitement of starting a store, next opened a bowling alley, and still, like Sir Charles Coldstream, dreadfully bored, took a newspaper. The *Prospector* was commenced in May, 1854, and published weekly about a year. Its advertisements paid expenses, and it was very popular among the miners.[44]

---

[43]Quincy *Prospector;* first fifteen numbers published from March 3 to November 17, 1855, in Quincy, Amador County, near Ione; 12½ cents a number; may have lasted nearly a year.

[44]Lancha Plana *Amador Dispatch**, September 10, 1858 to date, was later published in Jackson.

VOLCANO.

See Amador *Weekly Ledger* above.[45]

MARIPOSA.

In Mariposa, since 1854, there have been four newspapers published.

The first was the Mariposa *Chronicle,* commenced in January, 1854, by W. T. Whitacre and A. L. Gould. It was afterwards edited by John C. Hooper. The *Chronicle* was intended for a neutral paper. It only lived until March of the following year.

The Mariposa *Gazette* was also designed for an independent sheet. It started in July, 1855, and it still continues. Last Fall the *Gazette* hoisted the Democratic flag. The original publisher of the paper and the present editor and proprietor is L. A. Holmes. The editor of the *Gazette* is called, in his section of the country, the Nimrod of the Mountains. The friend to whom we are indebted for our notes of the Mariposa press sends us a sketch of the habits and appearance of the mighty hunter of that region, which we are permitted to insert here for the benefit of the readers at a distance who do not know how a Californian mountain editor looks. After commending the *Gazette* man as a jolly, rollicking fellow, who bags more quail, turkeys, and grizzlies than any one else, who uses but little cold water for any purpose, and "no other cosmetic than a compound of gunpowder and *aguadiente,*" he introduces the annexed sketch from a local paper:

"In the early part of last week, on the trail leading from this town to Millerton, might have been seen, one evening, emerging from a thicket, where he had taken shelter from the scorching rays of the sun in the middle of the day, *a solitary horseman!* It was a frightful apparition to encounter in that dreary and lonesome

[45]Jackson. This may have been the Volcano *Observer* announced by the San Francisco *Alta California* of October 1, 1855.

trail. The horse was a counterpart to Rosinante. Exceedingly thin in flesh, but one eye, with a neck and head like a tilt-hammer—his legs covered with windgalls and spavins. Being wind-broken, he puffed like a little engine, and what added to his untoward appearance, the coyotes had eaten all the hair off his tail. It was ludicrous to hear him in his efforts to drive away the flies, thumping with his stump tail upon his lank and hollow sounding ribs. The rider was a pursy fellow, not unlike the picture of Santa Claus. He wore a gray sack coat, with capacious pockets on the sides, from each of which the muzzle of a pistol protruded of a glassy appearance, and in which a cork was inserted to prevent a premature discharge. Hanging on the pummel of his saddle, in a dilapidated white silk handkerchief, was his wardrobe, consisting of a bosom and collar, a hickory shirt and a Pike county fowling piece, and snugly wrapped up in a half sheet of the Mariposa *Gazette,* was a handful of parched corn and a bologna sausage. A dingy-looking note-book, in which were numerous hieroglyphics, done in pencil, denoted that the stranger belonged to the editorial fraternity."

The Mariposa *Star* rose in June, 1858; a weekly paper like the other Mariposa journals. Its editors and publishers are J. W. Ross and James Lawrence. Democratic in politics.

SAN ANDREAS.

In Calaveras county, to which point we are again led in the order of newspaper excursions, besides the paper at Mokelumne Hill, two have been commenced at San Andreas.[46]

The San Andreas *Independent,* owned by Armor Clayes & Kooser, and edited by B. P. Kooser up to the 18th of September of this year, was started on the 24th of September, 1856, was a weekly paper, and is still published. As its name indicates, it is untrammeled by party politics, and finds its most congenial occupation in the development of the resources of the county and the

[46]San Andreas *Times** announced by San Francisco *Alta California,* December 17, 1855.

advancement of social and intellectual refinement. It is edited by S. Seabough.

The *Calaveras Union,* printed at San Andreas from October 11th, 1856, to the 8th of November following, was an American campaign paper, published weekly, and edited by A. C. Lewis.

MURPHY'S.

At Murphy's, in Calaveras county, the following papers have been printed, both during the past year:

The *Big Tree Bulletin* a little sheet commenced May 4th,[47] at the Big Trees, and afterwards removed to Murphy's, was more curious than useful, being printed, while its home was among the giant arbor vitæs, on one of the stumps of these forest wonders. Its editor and proprietor was J. Heckendorn. It appeared semi-weekly, and was about the size of a foolscap sheet. At the twelfth number it was removed, and took the additional name of Murphy's *Advertiser.* It was only issued once at this place.

The *Semi-Weekly News,* D. Youcham and J. Palache, editors and publishers, was another small sheet, the first number of which appeared on the 21st of July. It died at the end of the fourth week. It was independent in all things, even to the means of support. Its subscriptions for the month of its existence amounting to twenty-six dollars, and its *receipts to ten!*

HORNITOS.

The Mariposa *Democrat,* published in Hornitos, was moved from Mariposa in July last, where it had been published since July, 1856. Its original proprietors were D. B. Milne and W. Baer. It is now conducted by W. Godfrey. Its name is an index of its politics.

---

[47]April 30 - July 3, 1858.

❁ ❁ ❁

From the above data it will be seen that the number of newspaper localities in the Southern mines has been ten, inclusive of the stump of the Big Tree; the whole number of papers published, twenty-nine, one of which has been published daily, two semi-weekly, twenty-two weekly, and three or four occasionally, or accidentally. Seven were commenced Democratic, one Whig, about fifteen independent and neutral, two American, eight humorous and one educational. Those papers which survive, and their politics, are as follows: Sonora *Herald,* independent; Sonora *Union Democrat* and Mokelumne Hill *Calaveras Chronicle,* Democratic; Mokelumne Hill *California Staats Zeitung,* Dem.; Columbia *News,* independent; Jackson *Amador Sentinel,* Volcano *Amador Weekly Ledger,* Mariposa *Gazette,* Mariposa *Star* and Hornitos *Mariposa Democrat,* Democratic: San Andreas *Independent,* independent. Eleven in all—eight Democratic, three independent.[48]

[48]In addition, the Columbia *Tuolumne Courier,* independent, and the Lancha Plana *Amador Dispatch.*

Nevada and the Northern Mines

Nevada, in Nevada county, was the first city in the Northern mines at which the press was located. Though not the oldest settlement in the Northern gold regions, it was, in 1850, and has since been, one of the most prosperous. It has had two permanent papers.

The first is the *Nevada Journal,* which was started in April, 1851, by Warren B. Ewer, who was its first editor. He was succeeded in the proprietorship by Alban & De Courcey; the latter gentleman, editor. Then Alban & Sargent became proprietors, the latter assuming the editorship. Sargent & Budd next succeeded as proprietors, the former continuing editor. Then came the firm of Budd & Skelton, the former editor. Sargent & Skelton came next as proprietors; Sargent, editor. Then N. P. Brown came into the firm, which was known by the name of Sargent & Co. Sargent retired in 1855, and the firm became composed of E. G. Waite, N. P. Brown, H. M. Fuller and Jno. P. Skelton; Waite, editor; who continued in the business until the great fire of 1856, when Fuller and Skelton retired, and Sargent again came into the firm; remaining, however, but three months, since which time the concern has been owned and carried on by Brown & Waite. The *Journal* was a weekly paper for a time after its establishment, when it became a semi-weekly for about six months; then it became a weekly again, and has so remained ever since. In politics the *Journal* was a Whig paper up to July, 1855, when it began the advocacy of American principles under its present editor. Since the contest of 1856 closed, the *Journal* has hoisted no ticket at the head of its columns, but advocated the American side pretty strongly in '57, and the popular sovereignty, or Douglas side in '58. In the fire of July 19th, 1856, the *Journal* establishment was entirely destroyed, but was started again in two weeks, or with the loss of but two issues.

The *Young America* was a weekly paper started in September, 1853, by R. A. Davidge, who was its editor. It continued under that name about a year,[49] when Niles Searls became the ostensible editor. The name was changed about the same time to *Nevada Democrat,* by which it has been known ever since. I. J. Rolfe & Co. became proprietors about the same time. With the substitution of A. P. Church for George Russell and Wm. Pierson,[50] the firm has remained the same till the present. Henry Shipley became editor in the Summer of 1855, but ceased about the 1st of January following, and was succeeded by W. F. Anderson, who retired from the tripod early in the Summer of 1857; since which T. H. Rolfe has been the editor. Rolfe was a printer on one of the Oregon papers in 1847, and was, the year following, connected in the mechanical department of the *California Star,* in San Francisco. The *Democrat* has been what its name denotes in politics from its commencement. During the split in the Democratic party in 1854 it espoused neither side. In 1858 it took the Douglas side, and has advocated, up to the present time, those principles, and is now claimed to be a popular sovereignty organ. The *Democrat* office was also demolished by the fire in

[49]September 14, 1853 - January 25, 1854.

[50]Pearson, William B.

1856, but was re-issued again with a loss of four issues.

A Directory of Nevada, Grass Valley and Rough and Ready was gotten up and published on the 1st of January, 1856, by N. P. Brown and J. K. Dallison, which contained a historical sketch of Nevada county, by A. A. Sargent.

Four short-lived papers made their appearance in '54 and '55. The *Coyote*[51] barked but once. It was issued from the *Journal* office, by Col. A. W. Potter, and was intended for a *funny* sheet.

During the Winter of 1855, John S. Foster issued from the *Democrat* office a religious and temperance paper called the *Miner's Spy-Glass.* It died after two issues. Simultaneously with the issue of the *Spy-Glass* came a paper from the *Journal* office, by "an association of brethren," published semi-occasionally, when they felt like it, another funny sheet, called the *Miner's Spectacles.* John Patterson, Brown and Skelton composed the association. The *Spectacles* soon became the *Muggins Mirror,* which lived just long enough to see the *Spy Glass* give up the ghost, when it quietly departed forever.

DOWNIEVILLE.

Downieville, Sierra county, was the next station of a Northern Mines' newspaper.

The *Mountain Echo,* W. T. Giles, editor and proprietor, was the name of the first Downieville paper, started in the Spring of 1851.[52] It was published weekly, and supported the Democratic party. In the Spring of 1853, Oscar O. Ball succeeded Giles, and the *Echo* became a neutral sheet. Next Summer its name was changed to *The Citizen.*[53] During the Winter of 1852-'3, the pre-

---

[51]September 30, 1854.

[52]June 19, 1852.

[53]*Sierra Citizen,* February 11, 1854.

vailing scarcity of printing paper in the country threw the Downieville press on its resources, and compelled it to adopt all manner of expedients to get along. It was for a time printed on sheets of coarse wrapping paper, pasted together, as many as four, sometimes, in a copy. J. C. Langton purchased the *Citizen* and Calvin McDonald became editor in 1855. During this and the succeeding year it continued independent. The next change of proprietors put the concern in the hands of A. Helm and H. Hickok, under whom, October, '56, E. R. Campbell assumed editorial control. In 1857 J. C. Langton became editor and publisher, and was assisted the next year by Wash. Wright. In the Fall campaign of 1857 the *Citizen* was Democratic, but in the month after election it went back to its first love, and became "independent in all things." This lasted until the next election (1858), when it again took the field as a Democratic paper. In October, 1852, King, Ham and Wright became the publishers of the *Citizen*. Its first editor, Giles, who brought the press into the valley, superintending its descent down the hillside on "skids," is now publishing a Douglas paper in Illinois.

The *Bugle* was the name of a Whig campaign paper published weekly in Downieville during the Fall of 1852, W. S. Spear, editor. It was printed on the old *Echo* press.[54]

The *Old Oaken Bucket* was a weekly temperance paper, advocating a prohibition liquor law for California; published and edited by Geo. E. Tallmadge and C. B. McDonald. It was commenced on the 4th of July, 1855,

[54]The Downieville *Herald** was announced, by way of the Sacramento *Union,* in the *Mountain Echo* of December 11, 1852; it was quoted by the Marysville *Herald* of September 27, 1853. Chester Barrett Kennedy, "Newspapers of the California Northern Mines, 1850-1860: a record of the life, letters and culture." Thesis, Ph.D., Stanford, 1949. p. 541-2.

and died in the Fall of the same year.

The *Sierra Democrat* was commenced by John Platt, proprietor, and W. Campbell, editor, June 21st, 1856, at Forest City. It was published weekly for one year at that place, when it was removed, and its second volume begun at Downieville, with Platt and Forbes publishers. January 1st, 1858, the *Democrat* office and most of its material were destroyed by fire. The regular issue was kept up by means of slips, containing legal advertisements, printed at the *Mountain Messenger* office. In supplying the place of the press and stock that was destroyed, the owners of the *Democrat* had to pay $400 for transporting it from Sacramento to Downieville, on account of the snow. September 5th, 1857, W. J. Forbes commenced as editor, and has held the post ever since. The *Democrat* is a supporter of Douglas.

COLOMA.

Coloma, El Dorado county, the old site of Sutter's Mill—the memorable spot where gold was first discovered—was without a newspaper until the Summer of 1851. Before Placerville became a formidable rival, Coloma was the chief town of the rich mining region surrounding it. But the removal of the county seat, and the bitter, prolonged contest which followed, has resulted disastrously to the prospects of Coloma. This is the only place where newspapers have been published in which we have found difficulty in procuring information of the local press. A friend residing in El Dorado county has, however, furnished us a statement of the Coloma newspaper history, which we insert:

The *El Dorado News,* a Whig paper, was established July 19th, 1851, by Springer & Harmon. These gentlemen subsequently removed it to Placerville, sometime in 1852.[55]

---

[55]December 6, 1851.

The *Miners' Advocate,* a Democratic sheet, edited and published by Gelwicks, Garfielde & Conness, was established in the Summer of 1852.[56] In November 1853, it was sold and removed to Diamond Springs.

The *Empire County Argus* was started in November, 1853, under the management of Gelwicks & Co.; the publishers disagreed politically, and Gelwicks withdrew from the concern, leaving it under the management of Fuller. Subsequently, the paper passed through many changes, and was alternately edited by Fuller, Woods, Forbes, and probably others. In the Spring of 1857, it was removed to Placerville by H. F. Smith. The *Argus,* through all its vicissitudes, claimed to be Democratic, and was always a staunch supporter of Senator Broderick.

The next, and last Coloma paper, was the *True Republican,* established in October, 1857, by Wheelock & Kies, and, afterwards, R. Cole was added as a partner and editor. This firm dissolved some time last Spring, and has since been ostensibly under the management of George O. Kies. The name of this paper is indicative of its political sentiments. It was a thorough advocate of Republican doctrines until last Winter, when it espoused the cause of Douglas. The *Republican* started at Coloma at a very inauspicious period, and has been gradually dying ever since its birth. All the Coloma papers have been weeklies.

PLACERVILLE.

Placerville, El Dorado county, was the next place visited by the press. Between this sprightly city and Coloma there has existed for several years, an uncompromising rivalry, growing out of the change of County Seat and other questions of local precedence. Since August, 1851, there have been published in Placerville eleven political papers, in the following order:

The *El Dorado News,* a Whig paper, edited and pub-

[56]Sept. 25. Reported in San Francisco *Alta California,* Sept. 28, 1852.

lished by F. H. Harmon and T. A. Springer. The *News* was removed from Coloma to Placerville, December 6th, 1851, and continued until May, 1853.[57]

The *Placerville Appeal,* a Democratic paper, published by Wm. S. Fleming & Co., was established March, 1853, and was continued for six weeks.[58]

The *El Dorado Republican,* Whig ("Miner and Settler"), edited and published by T. A. Springer and R. Cole, continued from June, 1853, until it finally merged into the *Mountain Democrat,* in February, 1854.[59]

Placerville Herald, a Democratic campaigner, by F. A. Bee and W. Wadsworth, established in April, 1853, and discontinued in November of the same year.[60]

The *Mountain Democrat,* by D. W. Gelwicks & Co., established by a company of Democrats February 17th, 1854; since edited and published by Gelwicks and W. A. January up to the present time.

Placerville American, Know Nothing, edited and published from July, 1855, till the Autumn of 1856, by Wadsworth & Childs, afterwards, until November, 1857, by Harvy & Childs. It was then sold to Barstow & Park, and edited by Cole and Dietz for a few months, when it finally failed.[61]

El Dorado Republican, by W. Wadsworth a campaign paper, established before the election of 1857 and continued about five weeks.

Empire County (Weekly) *Argus,* Democratic. This paper was removed from Coloma to Placerville in August, 1857, by H. F. Smith, who edited and published it

---

[57]Name changed to *El Dorado Republican.* San Francisco *Alta California,* June 15, 1853.

[58]Subsidiary of *El Dorado News.* Kennedy, p. 520.

[59]Ceased publication; plant sold to *Mountain Democrat* February 17, 1854. *ibid.* p. 521-2.

[60]Press sold to Coloma *Empire County Argus. ibid.* p. 521.

[61]Kennedy also lists the Placerville *El Dorado County Times**, a weekly running for six issues from September to November, 1856.

until the following October, when it was changed to a tri-weekly. All the above papers were weekly.

Tri-Weekly Argus, Democratic, published by Smith & Co., established in October, 1857, discontinued in February, 1858.

Tri-Weekly Index, Democrat, published by Langari & Phelps. This paper was only a change of the *Tri-Weekly Argus;* was established February 13th, 1858, and continued until its forty-eighth issue, when it was again changed to the *Tri-Weekly Register.*

Tri-Weekly Register, Democrat, edited and published by H. A. Moses, established in June, 1858, and discontinued in the following September, after the general election. The type and press are still remaining in the office, and it is said the publication will shortly be resumed. The above list comprises all the papers that have been published in Placerville, though it may not be entirely free from chronological inaccuracies. Besides the editors whose names appear, there were other writers whose hands were known in the community in which they lived, but which it would be improper even if it were possible to make public.

SHASTA.

The next migration of the Northern mining press was almost to the head of the Sacramento Valley. Shasta, for some time "at the head of ox team navigation," as the papers were wont to say in ridicule of the new river cities, which, in 1850, claimed the highest navigable points, is the chief city of Shasta county, and situated on the Sacramento about 175 miles above our city. Three papers have been published there since 1852.

The Shasta *Courier* is the oldest, and was commenced March 12th, 1852, by S. H. Dosh, J. C. Hinckley, and A. Skillman. It was at first independent in politics, but in October, '55, it became a Democratic paper. In the fire of November 28th, 1852, the *Courier* building and nearly all of the printing material of the office were consumed, which occasioned a cessation in its publication of precisely four months. On the 14th of June, 1853, when the entire town was burned, the office building was again consumed, but all of the material was saved. The Saturday following the *Courier* made its appearance on a half-sheet. It has been published regularly since. Skillman & Dosh are its present proprietors, Hinckley having disposed of his interest to them some years ago.

The Shasta *Republican* was commenced October 20th, 1855, as a Know Nothing or American sheet. Its publishers were J. C. Hinckley and H. C. Moffitt, who continue to own and edit it. The *Republican* remained a supporter of the American party while it had a national existence. During the agitation of the Kansas question, it advocated the Lecompton policy, and now sustains the measures of President Buchanan. Both of the above papers still publish weekly.

Shasta *Vigilante,* G. K. Godfrey, publisher, commenced June 15th, 1856, and published one month. This paper was the Vigilance sentiment of 1856, chrystalized. It started soon after the excitement at San Francisco. It was to be the organ of the freedom of the press, liberty of speech, purity of elections, political and moral reformation, enterprise and progression, and to promote the happiness of the miner and settler, and the true glory and prosperity of California. These high and worthy aspirations were quenched, probably, in the reactionary flow of popular sentiment.

AUBURN.

The first newspaper in Placer county appeared in Auburn, in September, 1852.

The *Placer Herald* was started by R. Rust and T. Mitchell, September 11th, 1852. It took neutral ground at the commencement of its career, but it is now Administration Democrat. It has always been a weekly; its present editor and proprietor is C. H. Mitchell.

Placer Democrat was the name of a paper commenced in Auburn in April, 1854, Lynch & Sherman, editors and proprietors. In personal politics it favored the views of the present United States Senator, Broderick; keeping time with the music of the Democratic party. It failed after six months' weekly time-keeping.

The Auburn *Whig* (afterwards *Placer Press*) was commenced October 18th, 1854, M. E. Mills, editor, and C. Winkley and A. L. Stinson, proprietors. It was continued weekly eight months, when it followed the fate of most Whig journals in later days, and that of the glorious old party on whose departing path it had loitered.

The *Placer Press* is the name of the remaining journal published in Auburn. It took this name June 1st, 1855, and with it espoused the fortunes of the American party. It has passed through several editorial and political changes, and is now closely identified with the interests of the Douglas Democrats. Joseph W. Scobey, editor; Smith & Co., proprietors.

YREKA.

From Shasta to Yreka, Siskiyou county, the distance is over a hundred miles, still northward, and over a rugged, mountainous district traveled by mules and pack trains. The press had no sooner become established in Shasta than fresh fields, still higher up in the path of adventure, lured it further on. With the same celerity that the miner packs and shoulders his tools and blankets for a new start, in the Spring of 1853 a printing office was loaded on some mules and carried over the mountains to Yreka. At this period freight to this town was fifty cents a pound, and this was the actual cost per pound of transporting the first newspaper material to Yreka.[62]

The *Mountain Herald* was encouraged in its mission by the zeal of some of the citizens of Yreka, who, for the purpose of having a newspaper in their town, became security for the sum ($1,500) with which the *Herald* was started. This sum was borrowed and paid back by the owners of the paper from its profits, as the *Herald* soon became a prosperous concern. The paper made its first appearance June 11th, 1853. In the Winter of 1854 a large press and fine lot of material was added to the establishment. The paper continued independent from the beginning, and was published weekly by C. N. Thornbury, W. D. Slade, H. S. Van Choate; Thornbury conducting its columns. These parties retained it until the Spring of 1855, when an opposition being threatened by the American or Know-Nothing part of the community, they sold the *Herald* to J. W. A'Neal, H. G. Ferris, D. D. Colton, and J. Tyson. The new management resolved to make a total change in the character of their enterprise, and dropped the name of the paper to begin with.

The Yreka *Union* was the title preferred by A'Neal & Co. for their journal, which was announced at first as an independent sheet; but it is said it had already been pledged to support the American party. Before it had been long published, A'Neal withdrew from it, and shortly after brought suit in the District Court against his late partners for breach of contract in failing to make the *Union* an American organ. J. Tyson & Co. now made the *Union* a Democratic paper, which it has remained since, under the editorial management of a half dozen different persons. The case of A'Neal against his partners was lost through disagreement of jury. The *Union* is now pub-

[62]The San Francisco *Alta California* of September 27, 1852 announced the Yreka *Northern Herald*,* to be started by the Messrs. Thornbury and Mendenhall.

lished by Tyson & Brown, weekly.

The Siskiyou Chronicle.—This paper began life in June, 1856, as the organ of the American party, advocating the election of Fillmore. Its first publishers were J. W. A'Neal, S. P. Fair, and J. W. Brown; but A'Neal afterwards sold his interest to W. I. Mayfield, and the firm became Mayfield & Co. The office was subsequently leased to Thornbury & Glascock, whose lease expired not long since. It is now edited by J. W. Oliver, and published by Mayfield & Co. After the death of the American party it assumed an independent tone, which it has maintained ever since.

The Ladies' Budget—A neat little sheet of this name was published in Yreka, under the superintendence of the fair members of one of the churches, and for the benefit of their Society. It only numbered two editions; but the intelligence, refinement, and progress which called it into life is a pleasant commentary on the state of society in this mountain town, almost on the borders of the State. The *Budget* is remembered for its earnest inquiry respecting the regalia of the *E Clampsus* [sic] *Vitus* brotherhood.

GRASS VALLEY.

Grass Valley, Nevada county, contains a printing office from which have been published at different times since 1853 four newspapers and one monthly mining journal. This newspaper fecundity has been caused by the restless endeavors of the press and type to adapt themselves to the wants of the community and the interests of the proprietors. Its various issues have been but one paper under three different names; two political persuasions, four changes of proprietary interest, and we know not how many editors.[63]

[63]In addition, Kennedy lists the *Campaign Tribune,** probably one month in the summer of 1855, reported by the Grass Valley *Telegraph*

The Grass Valley *Telegraph* was the name primarily adopted. This was when the press was established Sept. 22, 1853. J. Wing Oliver was editor, and W. B. Ewer & Boardman, proprietors. It was neutral in politics and remained so, issuing weekly, until the Presidential campaign of 1856, when the Republicans obtained possession of the office, and in place of the *Telegraph* was published

The Grass Valley *Intelligencer,* E. R. Budd editor and proprietor. The types continued to talk Republican during the fall of the Fremont contest, and at its conclusion, with a facility which types and lawyers' tongues alone possess, they returned to speaking the truth from a different, and at length from a directly opposite quarter. Their next change being a return to their old neutral habits and name,

The Grass Valley *Telegraph,* when it resumed its publication after the death of the *Intelligencer;* was published and edited by W. B. Ewer. It continued, as before, neutral, and on the 31st July again stepped out to make room for

The *Nevada National,* a Democratic sheet, edited by G. B. Roberts, which has continued a weekly print like the others, up to the present time. It is now edited by R. Shoemaker, Roberts having retired in the Summer of 1858.

The *Mining Journal,* the only one in the State, was a quarto monthly publication, which commenced at Grass Valley in the month of July, 1856,[64] and has been published with considerable regularity most of the time since. It is now suspended, but we understand it will shortly be

of August 7, 1855, and the *Republican Banner,** reported by the Nevada *Journal* of August 22, 1856, which may have been superceded by the *Intelligencer.*

[64]Grass Valley *California Mining Journal,* February, 1856 to July, 1858. First copy reported by San Francisco *Alta California* March, 29, 1856.

resumed, devoted as before to mining interests. It was chiefly made up of the mining articles in the *Telegraph*, and was published by the same editor, W. B. Ewer.

BIDWELL.

Bidwell's Bar, the first mining settlement on Feather river, became the locality of the first newspaper in Butte county, November, 1853.

The *Weekly Butte Record*, as it was called, was commenced on the 12th of that month by C. W. Styles, L. P. Hall (known among printers as "Long Primer Hall") and H. A. De Courcey. Hall was editor. In politics it was Democratic, and has continued in this faith to the present time. Soon after it was started, De Courcey and Hall quarreled and finally fought, which was the cause of the former going to jail for a short time. On the 28th of January, 1854, the *Record* passed into the hands of its present proprietor, J. De Mott. It was published as a weekly paper at Bidwell, until June 28th, 1856, when it was removed to Oroville, where we shall duly follow it after disposing of the claims of some of the newspaper towns which have precedence of Oroville. There is now no paper published in Bidwell.

GIBSONVILLE.

Is a town in Sierra county, whilom the seat of a newspaper, which was established in 1854.

The Gibsonville *Trumpet* blew its first blast May 3d, 1854.[65] It retained its name until the expiration of five or six months, during which it was published semi-monthly, when it became the *Mountain Messenger*, and was issued weekly. At the end of sixteen months it was removed to

[65]This may have been the *Trumpet's* last blast; Gregory follows these dates, preceding it by the *Herald*, but it was reported by the San Francisco *Alta California* Nov. 23, 1853, as the Gibsonville *Trumpet*. Kennedy does not list the *Herald*.

La Porte, where it is still published. The first few numbers of the *Trumpet* were *printed* in Marysville, the matter for which was written at Gibsonville, and forwarded from thence, by express, and returned to printed form, ready for distribution to those desiring copies. A press and material were soon procured and taken by teams within a few miles of its destination, at which point the snow prevented the teams from proceeding, and the whole was laid by the roadside until the next day, when the Gibsonville boys turned out almost *en masse,* and with sleds and their backs, dragged and packed the material to the place designed for its reception.

DIAMOND SPRINGS.

Diamond Springs, in El Dorado county, was a mining settlement of so much promise in 1854 as to induce the establishment of a printing press. Thither, accordingly, was removed the material of a Coloma press, and in September[66] of the year named, a weekly journal of fair proportions and good appearance made its bow to the public.

The *Miners' Advocate* was published by F. A. Snyder during September. In October he died, and the paper was purchased by Wm. S. Fleming and C. B. Lawton. During the Winter Fleming disposed of his interest, and the *Advocate* was conducted by Lawton and P. C. Johnson until the Spring of 1855, when it was removed to Folsom, Sacramento county. The *Advocate* was published daily a short time at Diamond Springs, but this was a losing operation. It was Democratic.[67]

GEORGETOWN.

Georgetown, El Dorado county, was the next place visited by the newspaper press. There has been but one

---

[66]October, 1853. San Francisco *Alta California,* October 9, 1853.

[67]Diamond Springs *El Dorado County Journal,** (w) Jan. 1-29, 1856, L. Bradley, reported by New York Historical Society. Kennedy gives closing date of February 17, 1856. San Francisco *Alta California,* December 17, 1855, says it is to be Know-Nothing.

journal published here.

The Georgetown *News*, J. Wing Oliver, proprietor and editor, was first issued on October 19th, 1854. On February 1st 1855, John Platt, Jr., became proprietor, but Oliver continued to edit it until May 24th, 1855, when J. G. McCallum became editor and co-proprietor with Platt; and from his connection with it it became the organ of the American party. It was originally published as a Whig paper. McCallum withdrew from it on the 11th of October, 1855. It was afterwards published by Platt & Shaw, and edited by the latter until the 22d of May, 1856, when it ceased to exist. It was then removed by Platt to Forest City, Sierra county, and published as a Democratic paper.[68]

WEAVERVILLE.

Weaverville, Trinity county, claims the next oldest newspaper history, though the order we have laid down for tracing out the growth of the press carries us a long journey from the scene of the last enterprise, and plants our feet again in the mountainous region at the head of the Sacramento. Three papers have been published at Weaverville, as follows:

The *Trinity Times,* first issued, December, 1854; proprietors, E. A. Rowe and Cutter; editor, E. Trask. The *Times* was a weekly sheet, and at first neutral; it shortly after changed to Know Nothing, and before it had completed a year and a half of its existence it became Democratic. Trask was succeeded in the editorship by E. A. Rowe, J. C. Crowninshield, C. E. Williams, E. Pollock, W. S. Smart, J. G. Howard, and J. Comny, in the order named. Its career was far from successful.

The *Weaverville Democrat;* proprietors, H. J. Howe and M. T. Crawford; editor, H. J. Howe; was commenced

---

[68]Forest City *Sierra Democrat.*

sometime in August, 1855, and published every Saturday for six months. It was Democratic in politics. The object of the *Democrat*, as related to us was to kill off the *Times*, in which, having succeeded, it quietly succumbed. The press and material were sold to Seaman & Gordon, with which they commenced the

Trinity Journal.—This paper first appeared February, 1856, and has been published every week since. It claims to be independent in everything. Proprietor, D. E. Gordon; Calvin B. McDonald, editor.

OROVILLE.

At Oroville, the county seat of Butte county, ten or fifteen miles from Bidwell, whose newspaper history we have already given, the first journal was established on the 10th September, 1855. At this time the county seat was at Bidwell; and between the local press of the two places there followed a sharp and exciting struggle as to which should have the seat of government. At last Oroville absorbed the trade of Bidwell, and the public officers followed, together with nearly all of the population and some of the buildings. The Bidwell press went along with the rest, and, after locating in the new place, revenged itself by crowding its Oroville adversary out of the field.

The *North Californian* was the title of the Oroville journal. It was published originally by C. G. Lincoln and S. L. Snyder. Lincoln subsequently became sole owner, and continued its editor during its existence. The *North Californian* was published weekly until the Spring of 1857, when it became a daily sheet, and so continued until August 10th of the same year, when it was issued as a tri-weekly. In the county seat war the paper exhibited a good deal of energy. Lincoln sold to Smith & Co., in April, 1858, who changed the name of the paper to the *Morning Advertiser*. The *North Californian* was a neutral paper until the Presidential canvass of 1857, when it became

Republican.

The Butte *Record,* whose birth and early education we have already mentioned, was removed from Bidwell to Oroville, in July, 1856, and on the 14th of that month it was issued as a daily, on a sheet of small size. It continued to appear every day (Sunday excepted) until last Fall, when (10th of September) it changed back again to a weekly publication. From February 2d, 1858, to September, it was issued tri-weekly. The politics of the paper remained unchanged. G. H. Crosette and H. H. Mighels are editors of the *Record.*

The *Butte County Democrat,* a Democratic paper, whose object appears to have been chiefly connected with the local politics of Butte county, was commenced August 11th, 1857, and continued until the day after the Fall election. It was issued tri-weekly, from the *North Californian* office, and edited by G. W. Kretzinger.

Morning Advertiser.—We have mentioned this paper in the notice of the *North Californian,* and it may be said to be a part of its history. Its publishers, Smith & Co., were printers, and in its editorial conduct, though the writers were not known, it manifested uprightness and ability. The proprietors refusing to insert an article on the Sunday Law, but publishing it as a communication, the writer who had furnished its principal editorials withdrew. The *Advertiser* did not long survive his withdrawal. The last number appeared June 11th, 1858. The *Advertiser* was a weekly paper, neutral in politics.

IOWA HILL.

Iowa Hill, in Placer county, was represented by a newspaper for two years, commencing with the same date at which the press was established in Oroville. We have a very meager outline of its career.

The Iowa Hill *News* was born September, 1855. Its publishers were Miller & Olmstead, who continued it for about three months, when the firm became Olmstead & Co. It was independent during that period of its existence, but it was changed by the new proprietors to a Democratic sheet. In November, 1857, the *News* was removed to North San Juan.[69]

QUINCY.

But one paper is published in Quincy, Plumas county. It was commenced under the title of *Old Mountaineer*, the first number of which was issued late in September, 1855. The founder was J. K. Lovejoy, afterwards associated with McElwain in its publication. The *Old Mountaineer* was an American organ when started. About the last of July, 1857, its publication ceased, the material having passed into the hands of other parties. Immediately, out of the contents of the office and subscription book was reconstructed a new local advocate of Plumas county interests, of opposite politics, however, and a different name.

The Plumas *Argus* is the name of the paper now issued at Quincy, published weekly, as was its predecessor. It was started at the date above mentioned (July, 1857), by J. H. McNabb and J. C. Lewis, by whom it is still continued. The *Argus* has always been Democratic, and it is said to be the first paper in the State which raised the name of Douglas for the next President.

The *Fillmore Banner* was an American campaign paper, published during the contest of 1856. L.[70] Caulkins was the editor.

Plumas *Democrat*, another campaign paper, but of antagonistic principles to the above, was edited by E. T. Hogan and J. S. Ward, during the 1856 struggle. Neither of these sheets survived the day of election. In the fall of 1856 the Republicans and Democrats hired each three columns in the *Old Mountaineer*, in which to set forth or

[69]As North San Juan *Star*, November 18, 1857.

[70]Silas Caulkins.

defend their party sentiments. The *Mountaineer* thus became a threefold organ, preaching Americanism along with the other party doctrines.

LA PORTE.

We have given a sketch of the history of the paper published at this place under its original name, the *Trumpet,* when it was published at Gibsonville.

The *Mountain Messenger* removed to La Porte in the fall of 1855, was at first neutral in politics, afterwards American, and then again neutral. The proprietors have been A. Helm, W. F. Myers, J. K. Lovejoy, W. S. Head & A. L. Smith, who also edited their paper, and have been followed or assisted by A. J. Howe, S. F. Seabury, W. L. Parvin, John Charlton and W. S. Byrne, the present editor.

FOLSOM.

Our rambles in the path of the newspapers bring us back to Sacramento county, where the interior press was started in 1849. In the interval which elapsed before a newspaper was commenced out of Sacramento, in this county, nearly every part of the mines, north and south, and the settlements in the upper and lower valleys of the State had called into existence a local press. Precisely seven years had elapsed when our newspaper chart showed the addition of another Sacramento town. The reason for this, is, that in the progress of its settlement all parts of the county have been brought within such frequent communication from Sacramento, and its newspaper wants, however varied, so thoroughly supplied from the capital, that no field has remained which a county press could advantageously occupy. At length a combination of local and mining interests seemed to offer inducement for a press at Folsom, near the northeastern boundary of the county, and here the next newspaper was started, on material which the miners supplied.[71]

The *Granite Journal* began life on the 8th of March, 1856. It was printed on the press and types which had last produced the *Miners' Advocate,* at Diamond Springs, whose wanderings we have traced from still another part of El Dorado. The *Journal* was published and edited by L. Bradley, who was assisted by S. Seabough. It was commenced as a weekly neutral paper, but on the approach of the last Presidential contest, took side with the American party. In October of the same year it was sold to the Republican party, and edited by G. H. Baker until the 25th of December, when its publication ceased.

The Folsom *Dispatch* was founded on the material of the *Journal,* April 4th of the next year. When commenced it was independent in politics but latterly it has taken ground with the Administration. Carpenter & Wellington were the original proprietors of the *Dispatch,* but subsequently Carpenter retired, and Wellington continued the publication until June 14th, 1858, when W. Ewing took the chair editorial, which he still occupies. W. M. Penry & Co. are the publishers. The *Dispatch,* like the *Journal,* is weekly.[72]

FOREST CITY.

The *Sierra Democrat* was published at this place for one year, commencing June, 1856, before its removal to Downieville, where it is now continued. Its origin and history are duly mentioned in our notes on the Downieville and Georgetown, El Dorado, press, from which latter place it was taken to Forest City. The *Democrat* has been some-

---

[71]The Granite Hill *Miners' Exposé,** edited by Mr. Baker, was reported by the San Francisco *Alta California,* of February 14, 1856. Kennedy suggests it was in manuscript, and one issue only.

[72]Folsom *Mooney's Folsom and Placerville Express,** weekly, December 1858 to September 1860? when it moved to San Francisco. Listed by Kennedy.

thing of a traveler.

NORTH SAN JUAN.

North San Juan is a mining and trading locality of considerable enterprise and importance, in Nevada county.

The *Pioneer* was the name given by an association of its citizens to an occasional publication which appeared in 1856, commencing in July.[73] Its object was the intelligent one of creating an interest and want in the community for a regular local journal. In this it succeeded, inducing a press already established at Iowa Hill to migrate to and take up its abode in San Juan.

The *North San Juan Star* was the new title adopted by the publishers of the Iowa Hill *News*, in transfering their establishment to the new scene of labor and commencing the San Juan paper. The proprietors of the *Star* were J. P. Olmstead and T. J. Waters—Olmstead, editor. It was commenced in November, 1857, and was published weekly until August 14, 1858. We are told it was well supported but lacked the requisite energy. But whatever the cause, it passed from the hands of the original proprietors to those of the firm of Avery & Waters, who closed up the old concern and began a new paper.

The *Hydraulic Press* is the name adopted by the purchasers of the *Star*. It was first issued Aug. 21st, and has been since published weekly. The editor is B. P. Avery. Both the above papers were neutral in politics and religion.

YANKEE JIM'S.

Yankee Jim's, in Placer county, has had two newspapers, one of which is continued to the present time.

The *Mountain Courier*, published and edited by Parker

---

[73]B. P. Avery, in the North San Juan *Hydraulic Press* of January 1, 1859, said that it was a manuscript paper "published" by an association of *one*, from March to July 4, 1856.

and Groves, was commenced December 17th, 1856. It was published weekly, and in politics was neutral and independent. It only lasted eleven weeks, failing for want of capital, and, it is said, proper management. The creditors became uneasy and closed up the establishment.

The *Placer Courier* was started with the old stock of the *Mountain Courier*, on the 4th of July, 1857. It was published and edited by E. B. Boust, until November 20th, when R. J. Steele became editor. Like its predecessor, it is neutral in politics. It is a weekly sheet.

❁ ❁ ❁

This completes a list of twenty-one newspaper localities in the Northern Mines, in which have been printed, in all, sixty-five journals, counting those in each locality as distinct publications. We have also counted separately those papers which appeared under new names and auspices. Of the above number three were published daily at some period in their lives, four were tri-weekly, one semi-weekly, and fifty-one were started weekly, one was semi-monthly, one monthly, and four were published irregularly. In politics, twenty-one were commenced as Democratic sheets, seven as Whig papers, six as American and three Republican; two were religion, one temperance, one was devoted to mining and two to humor; twenty were independent in politics. The papers which now exist in the Northern Mines may be thus classified: Nevada *Journal* (Ind.); Nevada *Democrat*; Downieville *Sierra Citizen* (Dem.); Downieville *Sierra Democrat; Mountain Messenger,* La Porte (Ind.); Coloma *True Republican* (Repub.); *Mountain Democrat*, Placerville; Shasta *Courier* (Dem.); Shasta *Republican* (Dem.); *Placer Herald*, Auburn (Dem.); Auburn *Placer Press* (Dem.); Yreka *Union* (Dem.); Yreka *Siskiyou Chronicle* (Ind.) *Nevada National*, Grass Valley (Dem.); Weaverville *Trinity Journal* (Ind.); *Butte Record,* Oroville (Dem.); *Plumas Argus,*

Quincy (Dem.); Folsom *Dispatch* (Dem.); North San Juan *Hydraulic Press* (Ind.). Making nineteen papers, in all, now published in the Northern Mines, of which fourteen profess Democracy, one is Republican, and four are independent.

Northern Agricultural and Coast Counties

Among the things not to be forgotten in the California Winter of 1849, is the session of the first Legislature at San José. Could a press have been set up at the quondam capital on the assembling of that body, and a type and ink impression have been taken of the daily scenes within and around the legislative halls, not only would the material it would have furnished richly freighted the columns of a daily newspaper, but we should have had preserved to this date one of the most remarkable chapters in the political history of a State that ever was written. Instead of which we have only a few meager notes to draw from; and, outside of the uncertain memories of men, such is the barrenness of the record, that citizens dwelling in San José are not able to furnish us with simple facts relating to prominent events of that time. Among these events was the endeavor to establish a State official paper at that place during the Winter of the first Legislature. When the time shall come for writing the history of this country, the person upon whom this task shall devolve will sadly feel the omission of the press from the first State capital, and the want of such assistance as our newspapers, and our newspapers alone, can furnish of every other epoch and phase, and almost every other locality of the chief events in our country's growth. As we have said before, our journals have been the flower and expansion of the times in each of the epochs of this country—nearly every era and event culminating in a newspaper. The most important of the few exceptions is the Winter of 1849 at San José.

The attempt to establish a paper to which we have referred was rather the promise of one, which promise may or may not have been made for keeping. Its authors were certain political speculators who came in with the Fall flood of Eastern adventurers in 1849. Before the first Legislature met, a scheme presented itself to the individuals referred to by which the State printing might be obtained. To carry it out the establishment of a press at the Capital was deemed necessary; and before the month for convening of the Legislature drew nigh, one of the parties was dispatched to the East after a printing office. In the meantime, it was given out that a paper, to be called the *Statesman,* was shortly to be established at San José. The publishers of the embryo journal were announced to be Marcy, Robb & Robinson. The Legislature assembled on the 15th December. Notices of the proposed issue of the *Statesman* appeared in the journals in existence. On the strength of these and other promises H. H. Robinson was elected State Printer on the 10th of January, under a law passed for creating the office. On the 5th February J. S. Robb returned to San Francisco with two presses and material for a printing office; but the *Statesman* was never started. A falling out is said to have occurred between Robinson and his partners, which may have been the cause of the failure. The first Legislature passed without a newspaper at the seat of Government, or a competent newspaper correspondent there to daguerreotype its proceedings for the San Francisco press. When it convened again the field was occupied.

The *California State Journal* was the pioneer sheet at San José. It was published by J. B. Devoe, and made its first appearance on the 14th December, 1850. It was commenced as a semi-weekly, but, during the session of the

Legislature, changed to a weekly[74] publication. We have not been able to hear of full files of this journal in existence. From the columns of its exchange cotemporaries we infer that it finished its course shortly before the adjournment of the Legislature in the Spring of 1851.

The San José *Daily Argus* was the next to take up its residence near the halls of the Legislature and watch the doings of that ever susceptible and suspicionable convocation. Its first issue dates January 6th, 1851, the day of the assembling of the Legislature. Its publishers and editors were C. M. Blake & Co., and as they state in their introductory, their sheet was "Democratic to the core." The *Argus* was the first daily paper outside of San Francisco and Sacramento, and the last, we believe, that has ever been published at San José. Extravagant must have been the anticipations which led to its establishment at all. On the 14th of February, it closed its hundred eyes, as a daily, and only opened them once a week. The precise date of its final disappearance is lost, though it probably did not long survive the adjournment of the Legislature and the departure of its cotemporary, the *State Journal.*

The San José *Weekly Visitor,* published by Damon, Emerson & Jones, succeeded the *Argus,* making its first visit on the 21st of June, 1851. The paper was published with considerable regularity through the Fall and Winter of that year. Sometime in the succeeding Summer, Damon withdrew, and Emerson & Jones changed the name of the *Visitor* to the

Santa Clara Register.—We are informed that about twenty numbers of the *Register* appeared, under the management of Emerson, Jones & Parks. On the 1st of November, 1853, the office was sold to F. B. Murdoch, who entered the field with still another new title for the San José paper:

---

[74]Daily in January, later semi-weekly?

San Jose Telegraph.—This was the prefix to the title of *Register*, under which the new paper appeared, November 3d, 1853—F. B. Murdoch, publisher and editor. After a time the *Register* was dropped, and the publication has since been continued regularly by the original proprietor. It is Republican in politics.

The San José *Tribune* was commenced in June or July, 1854, as a semi-weekly print, by W. S. Letcher, who afterwards sold to Givens George,[75] who became editor and proprietor. In 1855 it changed to weekly, and was Know Nothing in politics. It has since become Administration Democratic.

BENICIA.

This place may claim the honor of being the first site for an American town in California which enlisted the services of a newspaper. Its origin may almost be said to have been co-eval with that of the first newspaper. It was founded in part by Semple (the editor of the Monterey *Californian*), the columns of which paper, after its removal to San Francisco, were for a time devoted to the building up of a commercial city on Carquinez Straits. The first knowledge of the existence of such a project was derived from the *Californian* shortly after it was established at Monterey. The site was probably selected about the time that paper was started. Semple gave up Monterey, and finally gave up his newspaper at San Francisco to be nearer the scene of his labor. His zeal and industry were worthy of better results. Benicia is one of those singular instances of mistaken locality which defy the powers of Government, wealth or industry to change their destiny. Its history proves the impossibility of forcing trade and settlement into a place, against the popular will. The "City of Magnificent Expectations,"

---

[75]Givens George was reported as publisher by the San Francisco *Alta California* of July 6, 1854, which said the paper appeared to be Whiggish.

as it was styled in 1850, has had only three newspapers, and of these not one remains in the place at this time. In October, 1850, material was purchased in San Francisco, with which to start a paper at Benicia. It was shortly afterwards sold, we believe, for less than cost. One of the San Francisco papers noticing the proposition to start a paper at the city on the Straits, suggested the name of "Benicia Grand Bellows and Carquinez Gas Works," as an appropriate title. Another attempt was made next Spring, and this time succeeded. We have only brief notes of the Benicia press.[76]

The *California Gazette* began about the 20th of March, 1851. St. Clair, Pinkham & Co. were the publishers. It was carried on weekly through the year, but we have not been able to learn when it expired.

Benicia Vedette.—This was the second guardian of the liberties of the people at the Carquinez metropolis. It took its post on the 18th of September, 1853. The editor and publisher was R. C. Matthewson, formerly connected with *The Balance,* at San Francisco and afterwards with the *Democrat,* in this city. The *Vedette* was a soldier in the Democratic ranks, and appeared weekly. In February or March, 1854, it rode off duty and had no successor until the Fall of the next year.

The *Solano County Herald,* published by McGeorge & Cellers, was first issued on the 5th of November, 1855, and still continues to be the local paper of Solano county. It is now located at Suisun, is Democratic in politics, and is published weekly by Hooton & Co.

Benicia Sentinel.—This is the name under which the local paper of Martinez (Contra Costa *Gazette*), printed across the Straits from Benicia, is circulated in the latter place. It purports to be published weekly, by Bonnard & Co.

---

[76]The Sacramento *Transcript* of Sept. 27, 1850 reported one issue of the Benicia *Courier.**

SONOMA.

Sonoma is put down in our first chapter on the movements of the original press in this country, among the towns which were illumined by its presence. How long it remained, or what part it bore in facilitating the intercourse of society or the Government at that place, we have not the means of knowing. That no periodical was issued, either at Sonoma or elsewhere, from the old War press, is very evident. The first American newspaper in the ancient town appeared in 1852.

The Sonoma *Bulletin* was a small sheet published on the 12th of June, 1852, and continued for three years, by A. J. Cox. It was neutral in politics, according to our best recollection, and its discontinuance was caused by the removal of the county seat from Sonoma.[77]

The Sonoma *Blunderbuss* was the title of a small sheet of pugnacious tendencies which opened fire about the 1st of August, 1855. It soon exploded.

OAKLAND.

Three newspapers have been published in Oakland, Alameda county, beginning with 1854; but each is now extinct, owing to the overshadowing circulation of the Metropolitan press on the opposite shores of the bay. The San Francisco papers are furnished, morning and evening, almost from one end to the other of the bay settlements in Alameda county.

The *Alameda County Express* was the first paper printed in Oakland, and the first on the eastern shores of San Francisco Bay. It commenced March 18th, 1854, and was published weekly by Bonnard & Co. Its editor was J. R. Dunglison. It lasted nine months and two weeks,

[77]A "seven-by-nine sheet" was published in Vallejo by Messrs. Cox & Eaton, the *Bulletin,** as reported in the San Francisco *Alta California* of November 25, 1855; its discontinuance was reported on December 17, 1855.

receiving a rather limited support. It was neutral in politics.[78]

The *Contra Costa* commenced September 22d, 1854. It was printed at the *Evening Journal* office, San Francisco, and edited by Mrs. S. M. Clarke, an estimable lady and accomplished writer. The *Contra Costa* was intended to do service as a ladies' paper, as well as in the drudgery of a general news organ. It was edited with much ability, but only lasted about one year, the editor's ill-health, as well as the limited sphere of support compelling her to retire from the field she occupied so well. Mrs. Clarke now resides in San Leandro, and, we are pained to add, is slowly passing away under the ravages of her disease.

The Oakland *Herald,* H. Davison, publisher and editor, commenced January 1st, 1855, was a neutral weekly sheet, published eight months.

The *Leader,* mentioned among the San Francisco papers of 1855, was advertised as a joint product of Oakland and San Francisco.

CRESCENT CITY.

Our newspaporial muse is, fortunately, not a woman in petticoats, or she would find her garments an incumbrance in keeping pace with the events we have undertaken to follow. Another long geographical stride becomes necessary to reach the chronological point at which the next newspaper appears. Crescent City is the seaport and principal town of Del Norte, one of most northern counties of the State. It is also the only newspaper site of the county, and the second one on the California coast above San Francisco. It is situated about the same distance from the northern boundary that San Diego is from the southern line of the State. It curiously happens that both extremes

---

[78]The San Francisco *Alta California* of September 12, 1854 reported that the *Alameda County Express* had changed its name to the *Contra Costa.*

of our coast line are watched over by a *Herald* press.

The Crescent City *Herald,* the only paper published in Del Norte county, was commenced June 11th, 1854, by F. B. Y. Zechtig[79] and U. B. Freaner. In December, 1854, G. H. Gubler[80] took the place of Zechtig, and the paper was conducted by Gubler and Freaner. In June, 1856, Gubler died, and his interest was purchased by T. S. Pomeroy, the present editor. Since that time it has been published by Pomeroy and Freaner. One of the firm informs us that "it has always been a weekly, and, when steamers do not arrive, it is a *weakly* sure enough." Concerning the politics and prospects of the paper, in reply to a question addressed the same good-humored individual, he advises us that the *Herald* ignores all political and religious denominations, "is independent as a wood-sawyer's clerk; went in for making money, in which, I am sorry to say, it made a shocking failure." The *Herald* is not the first paper in California that has failed from the same cause.

UNION.

At Union, in Humboldt county, on the bay of the same name, is printed the second northern coast paper.

The Humboldt *Times* was commenced in the Summer of 1854, not long after the Crescent City paper was started. Its first proprietor and editor was E. D. Coleman. In 1856 we find the name of Vandyke and Wiley at the head of its columns. Its present proprietor is A. Wiley. It was commenced as a weekly neutral sheet. The place of publication was changed from Union to Eureka recently.

The *Northern Californian* made its first appearance, December 15th, S. G. Whipple, editor and proprietor.

PETALUMA.

At the thriving village of Petaluma, in Sonoma county,

---

[79]B. Y. Fechtig.

[80]G. H. Grubler.

is published the *Sonoma County Journal*, which commenced its career, August 18th, 1855. It was first called the *Petaluma Weekly Journal and Sonoma County Advertiser*—T. L. Thompson, proprietor and editor. In May, 1856, it was purchased by H. L. Weston, who still conducts it. It is published weekly, and is independent.

NAPA.

Two weekly papers are published in Napa City, of which we have the following meager notes:

Napa County Reporter—commenced July, 1856; still published; Montgomery & Co., publishers; R. J. Montgomery, editor; independent in politics.

Napa City Herald—commenced June, 1858; still published; editor and proprietor, until November, J. D. Lillard; present editor, T. J. Tucker. The *Herald* is Administration Democrat in politics.[81]

SAN LEANDRO.

This is now the only newspaper town in Alameda county, and the proprietors of the journal published there have a difficult task to maintain their footing against the tide of San Francisco newspaper circulation.

The *Alameda Gazette* is published at San Leandro, by the proprietor, C. L. Goodrich; T. J. Andrus, editor. It was born in July, 1856, W. P. Rodgers being then its editor. The present proprietor bought the establishment and issued the first number of the new volume (Vol. III, No. 1) on the 20th of June, 1857. From this period to the same date next year, the *Gazette* was independent.

RED BLUFF.

The highest point of regular steamboat navigation on the Sacramento river is supplied with one paper. Tehama

---

[81]Napa City *Sun**, a semi-weekly for less than six weeks starting September 6, 1858, reported in *History of Napa and Lake Counties* (San Francisco, Slocum, Bowen & Co., 1881), p.271.

county is, strictly, an agricultural county, and its boundary forms the northern line of our agricultural newspaper region—Red Bluff being the highest point at which a journal of this class is printed.[82]

The *Red Bluff Beacon* dates from the 25th of March, 1857. It was originated in the lively interest felt by the citizens of the northern part of Tehama county in having the seat of justice removed from Tehama to Red Bluff. The press and type were procured by a well known citizen of the place, and S. D. Clark and T. R. Blanton engaged to carry on the paper, with C. W. Styles as editor. In August the names of B. and J. S. Butler appear as editors and proprietors. Next April (1858) J. S. Butler became sole proprietor and editor, and in October last C. E. Fisher purchased from him, and is, we believe, editor at the present time. The *Beacon* claimed at first to be independent, but, under Blanton and Butler, it hoisted the Democratic flag, and has been considered an Administration paper since. It is published weekly.

CACHEVILLE.

We addressed one of our press circulars to a well known resident of Cacheville, Yolo county, confident, from our knowledge of his character as a sober, industrious and moral citizen, that our questions would be correctly and even categorically answered. We were not mistaken. The following are his answers to our interrogatories:

1. Q.—How many newspapers or periodicals have been published in Cacheville?

A.—One newspaper.

2. Q.—What were their names and the names of the proprietors and editors?

A.—The *Yolo Democrat,* owned by W. L. Jernegan and edited by Samuel Ruland (myself) until the last three or four expiring numbers, when J. T. Daly attended the departing institution.

---

[82]Forthcoming Red Bluff *Northern Register** announced by San Francisco *Alta California,* March 4, 1857, to be edited by W. N. Walton.

3. Q.—When was such commenced, and how often and how long published?

A.—It was commenced in June, 1857, was published weekly, and found peace in the month of December of the same year.

4. Q.—What was the nationality and denomination of each, if political or religious?

A.—The nationality was "Pike," and the political and religious tendencies ultra Democratic.

5. Q.—What peculiar circumstances attended the origin or lives of either?

A.—If your inquiry refers to the paper the only "peculiar circumstance" of which I am aware may be stated like this: Jernegan, the proprietor, got James A. Hutton to buy the press and materials for him; got several printers to do the work on credit; got me to edit the concern and lend him cash (think of that, will you, an editor loaning cash!); and finally got away from this part of the country in debt to all of us. We trusted him under the very mistaken supposition that he hadn't got sense enough to cheat anybody!

I am too happy to have answered the foregoing inquiries propounded, and have to felicitate myself that they were so fortunately directed to me, as I am the only man in this part of the country who would or could tell you the truth on the subject. Any other "cuss" to whom you could have directed your inquiries would have told you that the *Yolo Democrat* was a mere one horse concern, owned by a mean little rascal, and edited by an ass of the first water—meaning me!

The "enlightened public" of this agricultural county behaved very magnanimously in the premises; they evinced unmistakably their generous willingness that, if the paper could support itself for a year or two, they would generously patronize it. A publisher with sufficient capital, together with unlimited stock of patient and subservient watchfulness, might, in the course of about twenty years, catch the said generous public in one of its extravagant moods, and then and there secure to himself money enough to pay his way out of the county.

You may rely on the foregoing facts.

[It is unnecessary to add that the above information is perfectly satisfactory.—Eds. Union.]

The Cacheville Spectator.—Not daunted by the fate of the first newspaper in Yolo county, a second has recently been started under the above name. The first number appeared about Nov. 20th. M. P. Ferguson editor and publisher. It is independent in politics.

TEHAMA.

The second paper started in Tehama county was published at the county seat of the same name, a few leagues below Red Bluff, on the banks of the Sacramento.

The *Colusa and Tehama Advocate* was commenced about six months after the *Red Bluff Beacon,* in August, 1857. A friend supplies us with the following sketch of its history, which will illustrate the aims and vicissitudes of country newspaper life: L. H. Sanborn, having failed to obtain such an interest in the *Beacon* as would control its columns in favor of J. E. N. Lewis for District Judge, went to Oroville and arranged for the press and material upon which had been published, or was about to be published, a paper in that place—removed it to Tehama and issued his paper. The means were subscribed by citizens. Support failing, it ceased to appear after election. Afterwards, in October, the printers of the establishment formed an "arrangement" to reinstate it, with Sanborn as editor. Made quite a respectable appearance this time; bid for county printing; didn't get it; appeared to breast adversity manfully; finally, during the Winter, the Sheriff took possession upon writs; leading citizens came to the rescue; Toomes, Thoms, Crosby and others reinstated Styles (formerly associate) as editor and proprietor. It came out regularly for several weeks; would then skip a week; then two weeks; and finally disappeared altogether. I hear that it is contemplated to again start it within two weeks.

Tehama Gazette.—The revival of the press alluded to above would appear to have taken place under a new name. We recently noticed the appearance of a journal of the above name, the first number of which was issued about the first of November; John Charlton, editor. It is weekly, like its predecessors, and has not much to say about parties. We observe that the people of Tehama keep the Sabbath, and would infer that they are competent to keep a good newspaper. J. Charlton and H. E. Salisbury are proprietors of the *Gazette*.[83]

SANTA ROSA.

There are now two presses at this place, one religious and one secular.

The *Sonoma Democrat* is published weekly at Santa Rosa, the county seat of Sonoma. It was originated by A. W. Russell, and, we are told, promised large pecuniary aid by a number of Democratic office-seekers in Sonoma county; but it afterwards was discovered that Russell did not favor their political doctrines—was, in fact, a Republican—whereupon the backers backed out, and Russell sold in August last to E. R. Budd, and S. H. Fisher, the present owners. The paper had then been published nearly eight months, having been commenced October 22d, 1857. The *Democrat* is an Administration paper, or, as the editor, E. R. Budd, assures us, "National Democratic from first to last, not cramped by any one idea."

Western Evangelist is the title of a new periodical of thirty-two 8vo. pages, published on the first Monday of each month at Santa Rosa, by Budd & Pinkham, of the *Sonoma Democrat* office, and edited by W. W. Stevenson, assisted by G. O. Burnett and J. N. Pendegast. The first number appeared in November. Its salutatory states that it is the first and only periodical in California that is devoted wholly to the teachings of the Bible just as it has been handed down to us from the holy Apostles.

SANTA CLARA.

We hear of no publication having been carried on at Santa Clara, with the exception of the monthly magazine

[83]Tehama *Valley Yeoman,** a weekly from April probably to September, 1858, listed by Kennedy.

noticed below. Both San José and Santa Clara are situated within the daily circulation of the San Francisco press, and thus the field in either place is rendered almost untenable by a local newspaper.

The Knight's Review.—We find notices in the journals of 1857 of a periodical with this title, the publisher of which was said to be S. E. V. Coon. We do not hear of more than three numbers having appeared, the last of them in the month of December. The printing was done in San Francisco. An advertisement of a forthcoming publication, to be styled the *Knight's Magazine*, is contained in the last number. It was probably never started. A friend adds the following history of the *Review:* "S. E. V. Coon established a secret society in California called the Ancient Order of Knighthood, representing it to be of more ancient origin than the Masons, Odd Fellows, etc., and published this magazine as its organ. The members soon began to demand evidence of the antiquity of the Order, but Brother Coon could furnish nothing save the statement that he had been told so by others. Discord followed; some members left the association, and the others changed the name to the Independent Order of Knighthood."

SAN RAFAEL.

The *Marin County Democrat* was the name of the first and only paper dating from the above place, and this was not printed in the county. It was only published about one month, commencing in April and stopping in May, 1858. Whitacre was editor and publisher. It was weekly and Democratic, being printed at the *Globe* office, San Francisco.

SUISUN.

The *Solano County Herald* is now published at this place. We have noticed the paper among the Benicia journals. It has lately been removed to Suisun.

MARTINEZ.

But one paper, we believe, has ever been published at the beautiful little village of Martinez, Contra Costa county, and this has been started quite recently, and is the only publication in the county.

The *Contra Costa Gazette* was first issued on the 18th of September. It is published weekly, by Bonnard & Co., and is neutral in politics.

EUREKA.

The *Humboldt Times* is now published at this place.

Our list now embraces the names of eighteen different localities in which newspapers have been printed in our Northern Agricultural Districts and along the Northern Coast. The whole number of papers printed in these places has been thirty-three, of which one has been daily, two semi-weekly, twenty-seven weekly, one monthly, and two irregular. Nine were started as Democratic sheets, three as Whig, fifteen independent, one is religious, one was literary, and one belonged to a secret society. There are three concerning whose politics we are in doubt. The following is a list of the living journals: San José *Telegraph* (Rep.); San José *Tribune* (Dem.); Suisun *Solano County Herald* (Dem.); Eureka *Humboldt Times* (Dem.); Union *Northern Californian* (Dem.); Crescent City *Herald* (Ind.); Petaluma *Sonoma County Journal* (Ind.); Napa, *Napa County Reporter* (Ind.); Napa *Herald* (Dem.); San Leandro *Alameda Gazette* (Ind.); Red Bluff *Beacon* (Dem.); Cacheville *Spectator* (Ind.); Tehama *Gazette* (Ind.); Santa Rosa *Sonoma Democrat* (Dem.); Santa Rosa *Western Evangelist* (Campbellite); *Contra Costa Gazette*, Martinez—also called Benicia *Sentinel* (Ind.) Of the above papers eight are independent, seven Democratic, and one is religious.

Southern Agricultural and Coast Counties

Efforts were made to start a newspaper in Southern California as early as the Spring of 1850. Long before there could possibly have existed any call for one, there appeared in the San Francisco papers notices of the design of certain parties to "commence, shortly, the publication of a journal in Los Angeles." This place was one of the old Mexican capitals of the country, and when Fremont was appointed Governor by Stockton, he selected Los Angeles for his seat of government. It has always been a place of note, and the favorite resort of the native Californians of the South for leagues around. Its population and characteristics are, and have long been, unlike those of other cities and towns in the country, more nearly resembling, perhaps, society in the provincial cities of Mexico. For a few years past, and until within a recent period, Los Angeles has not enjoyed an enviable reputation, on account of the habitual resort of gamblers and desperate characters thither from Mexico and Texas, and the frequent disorders growing out of their presence. Nevertheless, there were those willing to hazard the fortunes of a newspaper there in the year above mentioned. They had gone so far as to select a name for the new apostle of enlightenment. After many encouraging references to the progress which the enterprise was making, the *Alta California*, of the Spring of 1851, gravely announced that all the arrangements for the publication of the Los Angeles paper are completed, but the proprietors have not been able to obtain a press and material! This somewhat discouraging want appears to have been left unsupplied, for we do not hear of the paper being started.

The Los Angeles *Star* was the first journal to enter the new field. It had thrown its cap into the ring in the shape of a prospectus published in the San Francisco papers, some months previous to its appearance. The persons who were announced as the founders of the enterprise were J. A. Lewis and E. G. Buffum. They proposed to call their paper the *Star and Southern Pioneer*. Buffum did not finally join in the undertaking. The *Star* was established on the 17th May, 1851, by J. A. Lewis and J. McElroy, and published by them some months, when Mr. Rand became interested, and the firm was changed to Lewis, McElroy & Rand. After some months, McElroy retired, and the original publishers carried on the paper until 1853, when one or both of them withdrew. In April of the next year, J. S. Waite took the *Star*, and continued it two years. The connection of the present proprietor commenced in April, 1856. When the publication of the paper was begun, its opinions on political subjects were independent, and of marked firmness and ability. Lewis and Rand were from Massachusetts; McElroy we believe, from New York. As the population of Los Angeles increased, and the attractions of the gaming table drew thither from New Mexico and our Southern and Western border towns the turbulent classes who so long disturbed the peace of society in that section, the *Star* shone out, a solitary ray, over a waste of dark waters. Its opposition to John Bigler, in the fall of 1852, was so distasteful to a large portion of the Los Angeles community that there were mutterings and threats of violence against the paper. A. C. Russell, for having furnished the columns of the *Star* with a scrap of editorial reflecting on the conduct of one of Bigler's agents, was assaulted and badly wounded by Cornwall, a conspiracy having been laid against the former's life. Under Waite, the *Star* became a Democratic paper, and has continued in that faith to this day. It has always, so far as we can learn, been published weekly. In its early days, it contained a department in Spanish, under the direction of F. P. Ramirez, present editor of *El Clamor Publico.* The *Star* is now published and edited by H. Hamilton, formerly connected with the *Calaveras Chronicle* and one or two other mining papers. Our informant jocosely writes: "The *Star* is sound on Kansas and the Administration, (has the land sale advertisement;) thinks Weller a great man, (gets the advertisements of rewards, when a sheriff is killed, or the like;) asks no favors, and pays expenses easily." Not many of our Northern papers are so comfortable in their worldly circumstances.

Southern Californian—an independent paper, commenced in Los Angeles in July, 1854. The name of this paper is the same as that selected for a Los Angeles journal in '55, never started. It was published by C. E. Richards & Co. In November, 1854, Butts & Wheeler became proprietors, and their connection lasted until November of the following year, when A. Pico became the owner, and J. P. Brodie, editor. It died on their hands in January, 1856. During the political contest of that Fall, the *Southern Californian* became American, or Know Nothing. We are informed the connection of Pico with the paper cost that gentleman about $10,000. A lawsuit is still pending on the subject. The *Southern Californian* was the organ for a division of the State. It was published weekly.

El Clamor Publico is the title of a weekly paper, conducted in the Spanish language, with much ability, by F. P. Ramirez, formerly the Spanish writer for the *Star,* and a young man of high promise. It was started on the 8th of

June, 1855, and is the organ of the best class of native Californians in the South—the *hijos del pais*, as the American journals, with rare unction, pronounce them. *El Clamor* warmly advocated the election of Fremont to the Presidency, and carried a large number of votes in his favor. It is still Republican in sentiment, though it opposed the Republican nominee for Governor, in 1856, on account of his trimming course in favor of the "settlers," the *Clamor*'s direst foe. Next to the "squats," the fillibusters are the chiefest objects of the *Clamor*'s aversion. The paper holds a good position among the intelligent of all classes in the South.

The *Southern Vineyard* is the last of the four newspapers commenced at Los Angeles. It was begun March 27, 1858, on the material of the *Southern Californian*, by J. J. Warner, who we believe, held some interest in that paper. It is Democratic in politics, though it opposed the party at the last election, and is considered "quiet" on the subject of Kansas. Like the others, it is published weekly.

SAN DIEGO.

Three days after the *Star* appeared in Los Angeles a newspaper was established at San Diego, third seaport town on the coast of California to which the press was extended, and the southernmost newspaper station on the North Pacific. A number of young but well defined interests called for the publication of an organ in this end of the western American seaboard, though San Diego at that early day, no less than in later times, offered very little encouragement of the quality of local support to a newspaper. Any person who was willing to accept the chances of an easy living, and endure the dull routine of a little out of the way place, holding on for the advantages that must certainly come by and by, might publish a newspaper in San Diego successfully; and such a person seems to have been found in the conductor of the organ at that place.

To him belongs the merit of establishing the press on that lonely shore, although in the design and manuscript execution of a newspaper he was anticipated by some United States officers stationed near the Mission San Luis Rey. A little sheet, neatly written, and filled with really useful information concerning that section of the country, was issued from that port in September, 1850. Its aim was comicality, its name being the San Luis *Coyote*, "edited by C. Senor." We believe but one number was issued. This contained a map of that part of San Diego county.

The San Diego *Herald* took its place among the newspapers of the land on the 20th of May, 1851. The proprietor and editor of the *Herald* was, and still is J. J. Ames. The *Herald* was commenced an independent sheet, but shortly after espoused the cause of Bigler and the Democracy. The only notable circumstance recollected in its history was the advantage taken of the editor's absence by the madcap author of *Phoenixiana*,[84] to change the politics of that paper. Being left in charge of its columns during the State contest of 1853 between Bigler and Waldo, he coolly removed the name of the former, and hoisted the Whig ticket in its place at the head of the paper. As the *Herald* derives most of its support from the official advertising of the State and Federal Governments, the consternation of its editor, who it is said had gone to San Francisco on business connected with the patronage of the Administration, may be imagined. Before he could get back to his post the *Herald* had performed one or two additional somersets and a variety of other ludicrous antics, appearing once as a pictorial sheet, filled with small advertising cuts, very humorously introduced and described. The *Herald* has always been a weekly sheet, and is still published by its original proprietor.[85]

---

[84]George H. Derby.

[85]San Diego *Southern Democrat,** announced in San Francisco *Alta*

SANTA BARBARA.

Santa Barbara has been for a number of years past the seat of one of those feuds between races which are inseparable from the introduction of opposite customs, languages and religion in an old and settled community. Between the native classes and the American residents in Santa Barbara an intense ill will has prevailed, and with good reason, no doubt, on both sides. On the side of the Americans it can hardly have happened that provocation has not been given by some of those who settled in that section in 1849-'50, as not a few were expelled from other parts of the State. On the other hand, the ignorance and prejudices of the native lower classes must form a serious obstacle to an accommodation of ideas and interests on almost any subject. This war of races has spoiled the field for newspaper enterprise in Santa Barbara. But one has even been attempted there; and this, we should judge, has but a losing office in its intermediate relations to the contending factions.

The Santa Barbara *Gazette* was begun on the 24th of May, 1855. Its proprietors were R. Hubbard and W. B. Keep; the editor, T. Dunlap, Jr. It was neutral in politics and religion. One-half of the paper was printed in Spanish. But the enterprise, from the beginning, received but little encouragement from the native Californians, who constitute nineteen-twentieths of the population of the city and county of Santa Barbara. Our informant states that though many subscribed, they were generally delinquent in paying their subscriptions; and, at last, a few of the influential ones, taking offense at the publication of certain official matters reflecting upon them, succeeded in withdrawing the little support which the native citizens gave to the paper. The passage of a law by the Legisla-

---

California of October 7, 1852 as planned by A. J. Price and W. N. Walton, to be a Democratic semi-weekly.

ture was obtained making the publication of legal and official notices unnecessary in the county of Santa Barbara. Under these circumstances the proprietors of the *Gazette* found but little inducement to continue their labors, and in August, 1857, sold their office, for considerable less than it cost them, in San Francisco, to Torras & Fossas, who now issue the paper weekly in the Spanish language, with a page in English.

From Santa Barbara our course lies northward up the coast, to the locality where the last newspaper in the final division of our subject guides our way, like a beacon on a lonely shore. We pass by in our journey the extensive coast and agricultural districts embraced in the area of San Luis Obispo, Buena Vista, Tulare, Fresno, Merced and Monterey counties, all of which—an immense region, hundreds of miles in extent—are unillumined by the ray of a solitary local newspaper. The first newspaper town we meet with in the interior, north of Los Angeles, is Mariposa; the first on the coast, after leaving Santa Barbara, is

SANTA CRUZ.

At this point we finish the round of our inquisitorial labors in the connection we have undertaken. The lines of our survey end within a few metres of the spot from which they were run out, commencing with 1846, and our chain of narrative, from that date to the present, is as nearly complete as it is possible to make it. We commenced the history of the press at Monterey; we write its closing page at Santa Cruz, the rival port and nearest commercial center of that region. And the newspaper with whose brief history we conclude is the last which was published at the former place, whose fortunes we have noticed under its Monterey title.

The *Pacific Sentinel* is the new name of the paper to which we refer, one adapted to a change of residence from the old Capital to Santa Cruz. This change was effected in June, 1856; the *Sentinel* being the first to go on guard at the busy little port of Santa Cruz. It appeared on the 13th of the above month under the supervision of J. McElroy, its former editor and publisher at Monterey. Its publication is continued to the present day, "devoted to the development of the resources of Monterey and Santa Cruz counties." It is the only paper published in that region, and the only one in the country south of San Francisco as far down as Santa Barbara.

❂ ❂ ❂

Our notes of the Press in Southern counties show the number of newspaper localities to be four, and the whole number of newspapers which have been started since 1851 to be seven, of which number, singular to say, but one has departed. All were weekly, and but one was started as a Democratic sheet, the remainder being independent at their commencement, although the Spanish paper in Los Angeles, very soon after its birth, espoused the cause of the Republican party, in 1856. The present politics of the Southern journals is as follows: Los Angeles *Star*, Democrat; Los Angeles *El Clamor Publico*, independent, Republican; Los Angeles *Southern Vineyard*, Democrat; San Diego *Herald*, Democrat; Santa Barbara *Gazette*, neutral; Santa Cruz *Pacific Sentinel*, independent.

Conclusion

The very great length to which this recital of the fortunes of California newspapers has carried us will be sufficient excuse for the brief and summary manner of our conclusion. It has occupied a greater amount of space than we had assigned for it in the commencement, but as such a work will hardly ever be repeated, and as it is destined to stand in future times as an index that may be instructive to many and curious to all, we have thought it best to make it complete, even at the risk of being prolix and tedious. We are not aware of more than two previous attempts having been made in this State to compile such a narrative as this. The *Alta California*, of March 9th, 1850, published a list of all the newspapers whose names could be recollected, which had been published up to that time on the Eastern shores of the Pacific. This catalogue embraced the names of eleven Sandwich Islands publications, dating from 1836, one at the Navigator's Islands, from 1845; three in Oregon, from February, 1846; two in Valparaiso, from 1847; two in Panama, from 1849, and five in California. In the Summer of 1854, a sketch of the Press of California, detailing its rise and progress, appeared in the *Pioneer Magazine*, published in San Francisco, and edited by F. C. Ewer. The most laborious collection of newspaper statistics in past times was made in January, 1855, by A. S. Taylor, of Monterey. The fruit of his labors is preserved in the San Francisco Mercantile Library, and consists of a volume of specimens of California, Oregon, Washington and Utah newspapers then existing, seventy-three in all, and copies of thirty defunct California journals. The volume was accompanied by a printed "Bibliographical Sketch," containing notices of each of the specimens, and some historical reminiscences of the first California papers, with appropriate comparisons of our own with the press of other lands. According to this collation, the proportion of newspapers to white inhabitants was two to one greater in California than in most all the other States.

In 1850, when the census was taken, there were seven newspapers printed in California, to a population estimated at about 92,597. By the 6th of June, 1851, the number of papers in the State had increased to seventeen, and by August of the same year to twenty-one. In the same month, three years later (1854), we find fifty-four papers published in various parts of the State. In 1855, according to Taylor's collection, there were eighty-two papers, at which time the population of the State was estimated at 300,000. The next year the *State Register* gave the names of ninety-one California journals then flourishing, and placed the white population of the State at 399,000. The returns given in connection with the present history show the number of places where newspapers are published to be forty-four, the whole number of existing newspapers and periodicals eighty-nine; of which nineteen are published daily, thirty-four weekly, one semi-monthly, one monthly, and one annually. In politics, thirty-one are Democratic, two Republican, and thirty-five independent and neutral. There are six religious papers in the State, as follows: Catholic, one; Campbellite, one; Congregationalist, one; Baptist, one; Hebrew, one; Methodist, one. There are six literary papers, all published in San Francisco. There are forty-eight localities in the State at which papers have been published. The aggregate number of newspapers and periodicals which have been published in California to date, commencing with 1846, according to the returns which we have given, is 324. We shall not attempt their classification, but refer the reader to the footings of the chapters. The changes in locality, names, and, most of all, in politics, almost defy the power of analysis; it would be next to impossible to divide them accurately into intelligible parts and specify these parts.

We regret that it has not been practicable to furnish some data of the aggregate circulation of our newspapers. As nothing approaching to certainty could be gathered on this subject, it was thought best to leave it unattempted. In comparing the ratio of newspaper representation in this, with other States in the Union, the number of newspapers and their increase from year to year, proportioned to the population, will form as safe guides as the number of printed sheets issued from the press. In 1850 the estimated number of newspapers and periodicals in the United States was a little over 2,700; the white population was then about 25,000,000.

Before dismissing these pages, we must return our best thanks to those kind friends of the UNION in the different newspaper localities, north and south, who have aided us in the labor of their compilation. To their industry and the general faithfulness of their statistics does the work owe its chief value. Its preparation has occupied three or four months, and it is at last got ready just when holiday gifts are passing from hand to hand. May our Christmas offering prove an acceptable one to the readers of the DAILY UNION, and to our cotemporaries of the newspaper press of California.

Index to Newspapers

Newspapers are listed under each contemporary place of publication, with references to changes in location or name. "To date" is to the date of Kemble's compilation, December 25, 1858. Men prominent in the history of the newspapers are listed in the Biographical Index. An asterisk marks those papers which are not listed in Gregory's *Union List of Newspapers.*

ARCATA, see UNION

AUBURN

Placer County Press, see AUBURN *Placer Press*

**Placer Democrat* 202

w Ap 19-0 11 1854.

Democratic

see also: Hall, Lovick Pierce; Lynch, Philip; Shannon, John; Sherman, Edwin A.

Placer Herald 201-202, 215

w S 11 1852 to date.

neutral; Administration Democrat

see also: Anderson, James; McElroy, John; Mitchell, Charles H.; Mitchell, Tabb; Rust, Richard

Placer Press 202, 215

w Je 2 1855 to date

American, through changes, to Douglas Democrat

also as *Placer County Press;* follows Auburn *Whig*

see also: Hawkins, Hiram R.; Scobey, Joseph Woodbury; Smith, A. S.; Winkley, Charles

Whig 202
w O 21 1854-My 26 1855.
Whig
followed by Auburn *Placer Press*
see also: Hawkins, Hiram R.; Mills, M. E.; Stinson, A. L.; Winkley, Charles

BENICIA
California Gazette 221
w Mr 22 1851-F 21? 1852; prospectus F 21 1851.
see also: Denison, Charles W.; Denison, Mrs. Charles W.; Pinkham, Benjamin F.; St. Clair,

**Courier* 221n
S? 1850.

Sentinel 221, 231
w S 18 1858 to date.
independent
published by Martinez *Contra Costa Gazette* for distribution in Benicia
see also: Bonnard, Francis A.

Solano County Herald 221, 230
w N 5 1855 to 1857?
Democratic
continued by Suisun *Solano County Herald*
see also: Cellers. ; McGeorge,

Vedette 157, 221
w S 18 1853 to F or Mr 1854.
Democratic
continued by Sacramento *Democrat*
see also: Matthewson, R. C.

BIDWELL
Butte Record 206, 209
w N 12 1853-Je 28 1856.
Democratic
continued by Oroville *Butte Record*
see also: De Courcey, Henry A.; DeMott, John; Hall, Lovick Pierce; Styles, Charles W.

BIG TREE GROVE
Big Tree Bulletin, see Murphy's *Big Tree Bulletin and Murphy's Advertiser*

CACHEVILLE (Woodland)
**Bay Town Lookout.*
ir 1851-1852.
ms. circulated by S. U. Chase
reported by *The Illustrated Atlas and History of Yolo County . . .* 1879, p.78

**Spectator* 227-228, 231
ca. N 20 1858 to date.
independent
succeeded Cacheville *Yolo Democrat*
see also: Ferguson, M. P.

**Yolo Democrat* 226-227
w Je-D 1857.
Democratic
succeeded by Cacheville *Spectator*
see also: Daly, J. T.; Hutton, James A.; Jernegan, W. L; Ruland, Samuel

CALAVERAS BIG TREE GROVE
Big Tree Bulletin, see Murphy's *Big Tree Bulletin and Murphy's Advertiser*

CHICO
Record, see Bidwell *Butte Record* and Oroville *Butte Record*

CLINTON (Oakland)
**News*
w Mr 25-My 1854.
Clinton (later Brooklyn Township) was absorbed by Oakland.

COLOMA
**El Dorado News* 197, 199
w Jl 19-D 6 1851.
Whig
continued by Placerville *El Dorado News, El Dorado Republican*
see also: Harmon, F. H.; Springer, Thomas A.

Empire County Argus 155, 198, 199-200
w N 19 1853-N 8 1856; D 20 1856-Jl 23 1857.
Democratic; American; Democratic
followed by Placerville *Empire County Argus* w, *Argus* tw, *Index* tw, *Register* tw, sw

July 10.
Democratic
superceded by, and followed, Columbia *Gazette & Southern Mines Advertiser* sw; succeeded by Columbia *News* w
see also: Carder, ; Cazneau, Thomas Nugent; Duchow, John Charles; Falconer, Thomas A.; Oliver, J. Wing; Parburt, George R.; Steele, Robert J.; Yancey, Tryon C.

Gazette & Southern Mines Advertiser 185n
sw N 10 1855-Ap 5? 1856.
Democratic
superceded, and followed by, Columbia *Gazette* w; succeeded by Columbia *News* w
see also: Cazneau, Thomas Nugent; Duchow, John Charles; Steele, Robert J.

**News* 186, 192
w Ag 26 1858 to date.
independent; Democratic
succeeded Columbia *Gazette*
see also: Yocham, Dan

**Star* 182-184
w O 25, N 1, 8? 1851.
press burned N 12 1851
see also: Coffroth, James Wood; Gore, G. W.; Gunn, Lewis Carstairs

Tuolumne Courier 186, 192n
w Je 19 1857 to date.
independent, pro-Administration
followed Columbia *Clipper, Columbian;* removed to Sonora after F 4 1865
see also: Boden, Edward; Duchow, John Charles; Duchow, William A; Urmy, John B.

CRESCENT CITY
Herald 224, 231
w Je 10 1854 to date
independent
see also: Fechtig, B. Y.; Freaner, U. B.; Grubler, G. H.; Pomeroy, T. S.

DIAMOND SPRINGS
Advocate, see Diamond Springs *Miners' Advocate*

w F 11 1854 to date.
independent; Democratic
follows *Mountain Echo*
see also: Campbell, Edwin Ruthven; Helm, Alfred; Hickok, Horace D; Langton, J. C.; McDonald, Calvin B.; Wright, Washington

Sierra Democrat 197, 213
w Je 28 1857 to date.
Democratic, pro-Douglas
continued Georgetown *News,* Forest City *Sierra Democrat*
see also: Forbes, William J.; Platt, John, Jr.

EMPIRE COUNTY
Argus, see Coloma and Placerville *Empire County Argus*

EMPIRE DITCH COMPANY
Prospector, see Quincy *Prospector*

EUREKA
Humboldt Times 224, 231
w Ag 28 1858 to date.
Democratic
followed Union *Humboldt Times*
see also: Wiley, A.

FAIRFIELD
Solano Republican, see Benicia *Solano County Herald,* Suisun *Solano County Herald*

FOLSOM
**Dispatch* 213, 216
w Ap 4 1857-D 1858.
Democratic
followed Coloma *Miners' Advocate* w, Diamond Springs *Miners' Advocate* w, d, w, Diamond Springs *El Dorado County Journal* w, Folsom *Granite Journal* w; followed by Folsom *Mooney's Folsom and Placerville Express* w, later Folsom *Telegraph*
see also: Carpenter, ; Ewing, William; Penry, William M.; Wellington, G. E.

Granite Hill Miners' Exposé, see Granite Hill *Miners' Exposé*

Granite Journal 213
w Mr 8-D 25 1856.

Telegraph 205, 206
w S 22 1853- fall 1856; D? 1856-Jl 21 1858.
neutral
superceded by Grass Valley *Intelligencer;* succeeded by Grass Valley *Nevada National;* mining articles reprinted in Grass Valley *Mining Journal*
see also: Boardman, J. H.; Ewer, Warren B.; Moore, ; Oliver, J. Wing; Shipley, Henry J.

HAY FORK
**Noilpum*
1857?
ms., listed by Kennedy

HORNITOS
Mariposa Democrat 191, 192
w Je 11 1858 to date.
Democratic
continued Mariposa *Mariposa Democrat*
see also: Baer, Warren; Godfrey, William; Milne, D. B.

IOWA HILL
**Miners Gazette*
announced in Sacramento *Bee* Mr 25 1857

News 210-211, 214
w S 15 1855-N 1857.
independent; Democratic
continued by North San Juan *Star, Hydraulic Press*
see also: Miller, ; Olmstead, J. P.

JACKSON
Amador Dispatch, see Lancha Plana *Amador Dispatch*

Amador Ledger 187-188, 189, 192
w Ap 1857 to date.
Democratic
continues Volcano *Ledger*
see also: Daingerfield, E. B.; Springer, Thomas A.

Amador Sentinel 187, 192
w Ja 1 1854 to date.
Democratic
see also: Avaline, Oliver D.; Boynton, Charles

neutral; American; neutral
continued Gibsonville *Trumpet* (or *Herald*) sm, *Mountain Messenger* w; later Downieville *Mountain Messenger*
see also: Byrne, W. S.; Charlton, John; Howe, Henry J.; Myers, W. F.; Parvin, W. L.; Seabury, S. F.

LOS ANGELES

El Clamor Público 234-235, 239
w Je 19 1855 to date.
Spanish language, occasionally French or English
Republican
follows *La Estrella de Los Angeles* (Spanish section of Los Angeles *Star*)
see also: Ramirez, Francisco P

La Estrella de Los Angeles, see Los Angeles *Star*

News
listed in Gregory as a tri-weekly beginning in 1858, Dawson gives Ja 19 1860 as starting date

Southern Californian 234
w Jl 20 or 27 1854-Ja ? 1856.
independent, later American; supported division of state
see also: Brodie, John P.; Butts, William; Dimick, Kimball H.; Pico, Andrés; Richards, Charles E.; Warner, John J.; Wheeler, John O.

**Southern Vineyard* 235, 239
w Mr 24-N? 1858, sw D 1858 to date.
Democratic
see also: Warner, John J.

Star 233-234, 235, 239
w My 17 1851 to date.
Spanish section *La Estrella de Los Angeles* 1851-1855, followed by *El Clamor Público*
independent, since April 1854 Democratic
see also: Buffum, Edward Gould; Hamilton, Henry; Lewis, John A.; McElroy, John; Ramirez, Francisco P.; Rand, ; Russell, Andrew Campbell; Waite, J. S.

Star and Southern Pioneer 233
announced name for Los Angeles *Star*, not used

Vineyard, see Los Angeles *Southern Vineyard*

MAMMOTH GROVE

Big Tree Bulletin, see Murphy's *Big Tree Bulletin and Murphy's Advertiser*

MARIPOSA

**Chronicle* 189

w Ja 20 1854-Mr 1855.
neutral
see also: Blaisdell, W. W.; Gould, A.; Hopper, John C.; Whitacre, William T.

Democrat 191

w Jl 8 1856-Je 4 1857.
Democratic
continued by Hornitos *Mariposa Democrat*
see also: Baer, Warren; Godfrey, William; Milne, David D.

Gazette 189-190, 192

w Jl 1 1855 to date.
independent; fall 1858 Democratic
see also: Holmes, L. A.

**Star* 190, 192

w Je 1858 to date.
Democratic, squatters' rights
see also: Lawrence, James H.; Ross, John W.

MARTINEZ

Contra Costa Gazette 221, 231

w S 18 1858 to date.
neutral
also published Benicia *Sentinel* for distribution in Benicia
see also: Bonnard, Francis A.

MARYSVILLE

California Express 176-177, 178

tw N 3 1851-Jl 1853, d Jl 1853-My 1854, tw My 1854-N 1855, d N 1855 to date; also w Ag 21 1852 to date; and sm (steamer) My 1854 to date.
neutral, Democratic; anti-Vigilance Committee of 1856
see also: Addington, Stephen; Bloor, George W.; Brady, Andrew; Carr, M. D.; Foster, G. L.; Gee, Lewis; Giles, W. T.; Hicks, W. F.; Laird, Jane; Laird, Luther; McElroy, John; Magruder, L.; Mitchell, Tabb; Ridge, John Rollin; Russell, Andrew Campbell; Rust, Richard

Democrat
w D 16 1852
listed by Gregory as at CSmH; no record located there for Kennedy

Herald 176
sw Ag 6 1850-F 28 1851, tw Mr 4 1851-Ag 5 1853, d Ag 8 1853-My 1854, tw My 1854-N 10 1855, d N 13 1855-Ja 3 1858; also w Ag 10 1850, Jl 9 1852-Ja 1858; and as sm (steamer) 1851-1858.
neutral, Whig, American, Republican and "Stars and Stripes"; pro-Vigilance Committee of 1856
succeeded by Marysville *News, National Democrat*
see also: Allen, James; Hale, Clarkson P.; Lull, Louis R.; Marrener, David J.; Massett, Stephen C.; Randall, A. S.; Ransom, Lyman W.; Smith, William W.; Stidger, Oliver Perry; Taylor, Robert Higgins

**Inquirer* 177
d N 1 1855-Ja 3 1858.
Democratic, neutral, American, Democratic
succeeded by Marysville *News, National Democrat*
see also: Ball, Oscar O.; Buckelew, W. C.; Coulp, ; DeMott, John; Gorham, Charles M.; Gorham, George C.; Mantz, William H.; Walton, William N.

National Democrat 178
d Ag 12 1858 to date; also w O 1858 to date.
Douglas Democrat
succeeded Marysville *Herald* and *Inquirer, News*
see also: Bloor, George W.; Boulware, Walker; Christian, Samuel B.; Heatley, John O.; Randall, A. S.; Ridge, John Rollin; Whittaker, J. F.

News 177
d and w Ja 9-Ag 9 1858.
independent
succeeded Marysville *Herald* and *Inquirer,* followed by *National Democrat*
see also: Allen, James; Boulware, Walker; Christian, Samuel B.; Heatley, John O.; Randall, A. S.; Whittaker, J. F.

**Spiritualist* 177
w F-My 1857.
pro-Harmonial Philosophy of Andrew Jackson Davis

see also: Ransom, Lyman W.

**Star of the Pacific* 162, 177
m? My-Jl 1857.
Universalist
continued by Sacramento *Star of the Pacific*
see also: Edmonds, A. C.

Trumpet, see Gibsonville *Trumpet*

MOKELUMNE HILL

Calaveras Chronicle 182, 192
w O 9 1851 to date.
Democratic
see also: Ayers, James Joseph; Bingay, J. Norman; De Courcey, Henry A.; Hamilton, Henry; O'Meara, James; Shannon, John; Shuler, George L.; Whitesides, James

**California Staats Zeitung* 182, 192
w O 1858 to date.
German language
Democratic
see also: Wagner, Adolph

**Quamkeag Coyote* 182
My 1854.
humorous
see also: Noodles, Peter; Slimface, Parthenon

MONTEREY

Californian 11, 13, 14, 15, 27, 55-65
w Ag 15 1846-My 6 1847; extras S 5, 9 1846, Ja 28 1847; prospectus Mr 1847.
continued by San Francisco *Californian;* united with San Francisco *California Star* to form *California Star and Californian;* followed by San Francisco *Alta California*
see also: Colton, Walter; Dockrill, Joseph; Semple, Robert Baylor

Sentinel 66, 238-239
w Je 2 1855-My 31 1856.
independent
continued by Santa Cruz *Pacific Sentinel*
see also: McElroy, John

MURPHY'S

Advertiser, see Murphy's *Big Tree Bulletin and Murphy's Advertiser*

Big Tree Bulletin and Murphy's Advertiser 191
sw Ap 30-Jl 3 1858.
all but last number published on a tree-stump at Calaveras Big Tree Grove as *Big Tree Bulletin*
see also: Heckendorn, John

**News* 191
sw Jl 21-Ag 11 1858.
independent
see also: Palache, J.; Youcham, Daniel

**Review*
w fall 1855; proposed?
mentioned in Coloma *Empire County Argus* S 29 1855

NAPA CITY

**Herald* 225, 231
we Je 1858 to date.
Administration Democrat
see also: Lillard, J. D.; Townes, William H.; Tucker, Thomas J.

Napa County Reporter 225, 231
w Jl 4 1856 to date.
independent
see also: Cox, Alexander Jackson; Higgins, Lank; Montgomery, R. J.

**Sun* 225n
sw S 6-O 6? 1858.
see also: Cox, Alexander Jackson; Farrell, Frank

NEVADA CITY

**Coyote* 195
S 30 1854.
humorous
issued from the office of the Nevada City *Journal*
see also: Potter, A. W.

Democrat 194-195, 215
w F 1 1854 to date.
Democratic; pro-Douglas 1858
continues Nevada City *Young America*

see also: Anderson, William F.; Church, A. P.; Pearson, William B.; Rolfe, Ianthis Jerome; Rolfe, Tallman Hathaway; Russell, George; Searls, Niles; Shipley, Henry J.

Journal 193-194, 215
sw Ap 19 1851-Ap 22 1852, w Ap 25 1852 to date; also sm (steamer)
independent; Whig; American
see also: Alban, W. B.; Brown, Nat P.; Budd, Edwin Ruthven; De Courcey, Henry A.; Ewer, Warren B.; Fuller, H. M.; Sargent, Aaron Augustus; Skelton, John P.; Waite, Edwin G.

**Miner's Spectacles* 195
ir Mr? 1855.
issued from office of Nevada City *Journal;* succeeded by Nevada City *Muggins Mirror*
see also: Brown, Nat P.; Patterson, John; Skelton, John P.

**Miner's Spy-Glass* 195
sm Mr-Ap? 1855.
religious and temperance
issued from office of Nevada City *Democrat*
see also: Foster, John S.

**Muggins Mirror* 195
ir Ap? 1855.
humorous
issued from office of Nevada City *Journal;* succeeded *Miner's Spectacles*
see also: Brown, Nat P.; Patterson, John; Skelton, John P.

Young America 194
w S 14 1853-Ja 25 1854.
continued by Nevada City *Democrat*
see also: Davidge, Robert A.; Searls, Niles

NORTH SAN JUAN

Hydraulic Press 34, 214
w Ag 21 1858 to date.
independent
continues Iowa Hill *News,* North San Juan *Star*
see also: Avery, Benjamin Parke; Waters, Thomas J.

**Pioneer* 214
ir Mr-Jl 4 1856.

ms.
see also: Avery, Benjamin Parke

Star 211n, 214
w N 18 1857-Ag 14 1858.
independent
continues Iowa Hill *News;* succeeded by North San Juan *Hydraulic Press*
see also: Olmstead, J. P.; Waters, Thomas J.

OAKLAND
Alameda County Express 222-223
w Mr 18-S 1854.
neutral
continued by Oakland *Contra Costa*
see also: Bonnard, Francis A.; Dunglison, John R.

Alameda County Gazette, see San Leandro *Alameda County Gazette*

Clinton News, see Clinton *News*

Contra Costa 223
w S 1854-S 1855.
continued Oakland *Alameda County Express;* printed in office of San Francisco *Journal*
see also: Clarke, Sarah M.; Dunglison, John R.

Herald 223
w Ja 4-Ag 1855.
neutral
see also: Davison, H.

Leader, see San Francisco *Leader*

Times, see San Leandro *Alameda County Gazette*

Transcript and Alameda County Gazette, see San Leandro *Alameda County Gazette*

OROVILLE
Advertiser 209-210
w? Ap-Je 11 1858.
neutral
follows Oroville *North Californian*
see also: Smith,

**Butte County Democrat* 210
tw Ag 11-S 3 1857.

Democratic
issued from office of Oroville *North Californian*
see also: Kretzinger, George W.

Butte Record 206, 210, 215
d Jl 14 1856-S 10 1857; w to F 2 1858; tw to S 1858; w to date.
Democratic
continued Bidwell *Butte Record*
see also: Crosette, George G.; Mighels, Henry Rust

North Californian 209-210
w N 17 1855-Ap 18 1857; d Ap 22-Ag 8 1857; tw Ag 10-O 1857; w O 1857-Ap 1858.
neutral to 1857, then Republican
followed by Oroville *Advertiser*
see also: Lincoln, Charles G.; Snyder, S. L.

PACHECO
Contra Costa Gazette, see Martinez *Contra Costa Gazette*

PETALUMA
Journal and Sonoma County Advertiser 225
w Ag 18 1855-Ag 16 1856.
independent
continued by Petaluma *Sonoma County Journal*
see also: Thompson, Thomas L.; Weston, H. L.

Sonoma County Journal 225, 231
w Ag 23 1856 to date.
independent
continued Petaluma *Journal and Sonoma County Advertiser*
see also: Weston, H. L.

PLACERVILLE
American 199
American
see also: Barstow, ; Childs, ; Cole, Richard; Dietz, ; Harvey, W. H.; Park, ; Wadsworth, Wedworth

**Appeal* 199
w Mr 31-My 12 1853.
Democratic
subsidiary of Placerville *El Dorado News*
see also: Fleming, William S.; Springer, Thomas A.

continuation of Coloma and Placerville *Empire County Argus* w, Placerville *Argus* tw; followed by Placerville *Register* tw
see also: Langari, ; Phelps,

Mountain Democrat 199, 215
w F 25 1854 to date.
Democratic
see also: Gelwicks, Daniel Webster; January, William A.

**Register* 200
tw, sw Je 8-S 1858.
Democratic
continued Coloma and Placerville *Empire County Argus* w, Placerville *Argus* tw, *Index* tw
see also: Moses, H. A.; Stewart, W. Frank

QUINCY
**Fillmore Banner* 211
w Ag-N 1856.
American
see also: Caulkins, Silas

**Old Mountaineer* 211
w O 1855-Ag 1857.
American (also Republican and Democratic)
followed by Quincy *Plumas Argus*
see also: Fredonyer, A.; Lovejoy, John K.; McElwain, Edward

**Plumas Argus* 211, 215-216
w Ag 13 1857 to date.
Douglas Democratic
follows Quincy *Old Mountaineer*
see also: Lewis, John C.; McNabb, James Henry

Plumas Democrat 211-212
w Ag 26-N 4 1856.
Democratic
see also: Hogan, E. T.; Ward, John S.

Prospector 160, 188
ir Mr 3-N 17? 1855.
humorous; announced as weekly
followed by Sacramento *Times* (no. 1)
see also: Badlam, Alexander; Clark, M. B.; Wallace, W. J.

RABBIT CREEK, see LA PORTE

RED BLUFF

Beacon 226, 231

w Mr 25 1857 to date.

independent; Ag 1857 Administration Democratic

see also: Bishop, A. W.; Blanton, T. R.; Butler, B.; Butler, John S.; Clark, S. D.; Fisher, C. E.; Styles, Charles W.

**Northern Register* 203n

Mr. 1857?

see also: Walton, William N.

Shasta Courier, see Shasta *Courier*

SACRAMENTO

Age 159-160, 164

d Ag 3 1856-Mr 27 1858.

American; independent

continued Sacramento *Spirit of the Age;* followed by Sacramento *Mercury*

see also: Appleton, J. A.; Coggins, James; Farwell, Willard Brigham; Ford, T. P.; McDonald, Calvin B.; McElwain, E. F.; Marvin, John Gage; Robb, John S.; Wright, Washington

**Anti-Office-Seeker* 162n

d Ap 3-4 1857.

Republican

**Baptist Circular* 165

m Ag 1858 to date.

Baptist

see also: Shuck, John Lewis

Bee 162

d F 3 1857 to date.

independent

follows Sacramento *State Tribune* (no. 1), *California American*

see also: Coggins, Paschal; Davis, L. P.; May, Samuel J.; McClatchy, James; Ridge, John Rollin; Thompson, F. S.; Tobey, William Henry

California American 160

d Je 2 1856-F 2 1857.

continued Sacramento *State Tribune* (no. 1); followed by Sacramento *Bee*

see also: Allen, James; Allen, O. P.; Estell, James Madison;

[SACRAMENTO — *Continued*]

Hatch, Dr. ; Knight, Edward; May, Samuel J.; Ridge, John Rollin

California Express, see Marysville *California Express*

**California Farmer and Journal of Useful Sciences* 116, 132, 156-157
w My 1855-Jl 1856
agricultural
also published in San Francisco, Ja 16 1854 to date
see also: Morse, John Frederick; Phillips, James K.; Warren, James Lloyd La Fayette

California Register, see San Francisco *California Register*

California Republican 162
w Je? 1857 to date.
Republican
see also: McClatchy, James; Taylor,

California Statesman . . . 152-154, 155-156, 160, 165
d N 13 1854-Mr 1 1855; My 1- Je 24 1858.
American; Democratic
revived to follow Sacramento *Democratic State Journal* d
see also: Dunlap, Presley; Gish, John W.; Hardenbergh, James Richmond; Meredith, Henry; Raveley, Samuel W.; Russell, Andrew Campbell; Woodward, R. H.

California Statesman
w My-Je 24 1858.
follows Sacramento *Democratic State Journal* w, *State Journal* w
see also: Sacramento *California Statesman* d

California Times, see Sacramento *Times*

Californian (no. 1) 153, 156
d N 17 1852-Jl 30 1853; w Jl 2-Ag 13 1853.
Settler Democratic
purchased Sacramento *Democratic State Journal,* retained name of latter
see also: Johnson, P. C.; McClatchy, James; May, Samuel J.; Redding, Benjamin Barnard; Thomas, Daniel J.; Williamson, E.

**Californian* (no. 2) 165
d Jl 9-16 1858.

[SACRAMENTO — *Continued*]

Baptist
succeeded by Sacramento *Pacific Recorder*
see also: Alter, T.; Wheeler, Osgood Church; Willis, Edward J.

**Pacific Recorder* 157
sm Jl 15 1854-Jl 1855, w to Mr 1856.
Baptist
succeeded Sacramento *Pacific Banner*; issued in San Francisco and Sacramento
see also: Willis, Edward J.

Phoenix 164
w Ag 30 1857-F 14 1858.
scandal sheet
followed by Sacramento *Ubiquitous*
see also: McGowan, Edward

Pictorial Union, see Sacramento *Union*

Placer Times . . 29, 134-142, 143, 144, 145, 166, 169, 183
w Ap 28 1849-Ap 20 1850, tw Ap 22-Je 5 1850, d to Je 15 1851; also sm (steamer).
neutral; pro-Democrat
subsidiary of San Francisco *Alta California;* continued by Sacramento *Placer Times and Transcript,* San Francisco *Placer Times and Transcript*
see also: Aldrich, L.; Gilbert, Edward; Giles, Jesse Howard; Kemble, Edward Cleveland; Kurtz, William W.; Lawrence, Joseph E.; Per Lee, Theron Rudd; Pickering, Loring

Placer Times and Transcript . . . 112, 144, 152, 154-155
de Je 16 1851-Je 1852.
Democratic
subsidiary of San Francisco *Alta California;* succeeded Sacramento *Placer Times* and *Transcript;* continued by San Francisco *Placer Times and Transcript*
see also: Fitch, George Kenyon; Grove, M. F.; Lawrence, Joseph E.; Pickering, Loring

Settlers and Miners Tribune 144-145
d O 30-N, w D ? 1850.
Democratic; organ of Squatter Association of Sacramento
see also: Booth, Louis M.; McClatchy, James; Robinson, Charles L.; Rowe, Cyrus

[SACRAMENTO — *Continued*]

**Sign and Grip* 163n
Ag 23? 1857-?
I.O.O.F. paper
see also: McDonald, Calvin B.; Morse, John Frederick

Spirit of the Age 159
d D 6 1855-Ag 2 1856.
independent
continued by Sacramento *Age,* followed by *Mercury, Star*
see also: Atkins, J. R.; Baker, George Holbrook; Mitchell, J. A.

Star 165
d N 2 1858 to date.
Administration Democrat
followed Sacramento *Spirit of the Age, Age, Mercury*
see also: McClure, ; Montgomery, Alexander M.

**Star of the Pacific* 162, 177
m? Ag-D 1857, My 1858 to date.
Universalist
continued Marysville *Star of the Pacific*
see also: Edmonds, A. C.

**State Almanac and Annual Register* 157-158
issued by Sacramento *Democratic State Journal* office

State Journal.
w Mr 8 1855-Ap 1858.
Democratic
follows Sacramento *Democratic State Journal* w; followed by Sacramento *California Statesman* w
see also: Sacramento *Democratic State Journal* d

State Sentinel 162-163
d Jl 27 1857-Ja 5 1858.
Republican
see also: Atkins, John R.; Hossack, C. D.; Sumner, Charles A.; Wheeler, Osgood Church

State Tribune (no. 1) 158-159, 160
d Ja 8 1855-Je 1 1856.
American
rivalled by Sacramento *State Tribune* (no. 2); continued by Sacramento *California American, Bee*

[SACRAMENTO — *Continued*]

see also: Allen, James; Estell, James Madison; French, Parker H.; Gift, ; Lockwood, ; May, Samuel J.; Prindle,

State Tribune (& Citizen) (no. 2) 120, 158
d O 16-30 1855.
American
continued San Francisco *Citizen*; rivalled Sacramento *State Tribune* (no. 1)
see also: Farwell, Willard Brigham; French, Parker H.; Monson, ; Valentine,

**Students Repository*
Ag 1858.

**Temperance Mirror* 161
w Ja 1857.
in favor of Temperance and Good Morals
continued by San Francisco *Temperance Mirror* after first number
see also: Taylor, W. B.; Turrell, Oliver B.

**Temperance Register* 163-164
m, sm, m S-D 12 1857.
"Literature and Temperance"
see also: Davison, H.

Times (1851), see Sacramento *Placer Times*

Times (no. 1) 160
d D 24 1855-Mr 1856.
advertising sheet
followed Quincy *Prospector*
see also: Badlam, Alexander

Times (no. 2) 161
d Ag 15 1856-Ja 24 1857; w Ag 23 1856-1857?
Republican, pro-Frémont
see also: Coggins, Paschal; Cole, Cornelius; Crocker, Charles; Crocker, E. B.; Dalliba, H. S.; Hopkins, Mark; Huntington, Collis P.; McClatchy, James; Turrell, Oliver B.

Times and Transcript, see Sacramento *Placer Times and Transcript*

Transcript 142, 143-144, 146, 147, 166
tw Ap 1-My?, d Je 2 1850-Je 15 1851; also sm (steamer) Ap 26 1850-Je 15 1851.

[SACRAMENTO — *Continued*]

independent; in D 1850 became Democratic

united with Sacramento *Placer Times* to become Sacramento *Placer Times and Transcript,* continued by San Francisco *Placer Times and Transcript*

see also: Court, Job; Ewer, Ferdinand Cartwright; Fitch, George Kenyon; Grove, ; Hansicker, Charles L.; Julian, Jacob M.; Keating, W. J.; Russell, Theodore; Warren, Henry S.; Weld, Gilbert Cumming

Ubiquitous 164
w F 21-Je 20 1858.
scandal sheet
follows Sacramento *Phoenix*
see also: McGowan, Edward

Union . . . 9, 10, 16, 22, 33, 34, 37, 38, 39, 48, 146-151, 167
d Mr 19 1851 to date; w Ja 10 1852 to date; sm (steamer) Mr 29 1851-1858?; Ja,Ap,Jl *Pictorial Union* Ap 1852-Ja 1856?
Whig; independent; pro-Vigilance Committee of 1856
see also: Anthony, James; Clark, Alexander; Collins, John A.; Cook, Alexander C.; Court, Job; Davison, William K.; Dosh, Samuel H.; Gray, J.; Hansicker, Charles L.; Harmon, F. H.; Jefferis, E. G.; Keating, William J.; Kurtz, William W.; Larkin, H. W.; Livingston, H. B.; Morrill, Paul; Morse, Dr. John F.; Russell, Andrew Campbell; Simonton J. W.; Upson, L.

**Visitor* 164
? Mr 26-Je? 1858.
see also: Brown, ; Coggins, Paschal; Ingham, C. T.

**Watch Dog* 164
sm Ja 4?-F 1858.
scurrilous
see also: Smith, Mortimer J.

Water Fount and Home Journal 159
w D 15 1855-S 1856.
organ of the Grand Division of the Sons of Temperance
followed San Francisco *Water Fount and Home Journal*
see also: Montgomery, Alexander M.

SAN ANDREAS
**Calaveras Union* 191
w O 11-N 8 1856.

American
see also: Lewis, A. C.

Independent 190-191, 192
w S 24 1856 to date.
independent
see also: Armor, George; Clayes, ; Kooser, Benjamin Parke; Seabough, Samuel

**Times* 190n
D ? 1855.

SAN DIEGO
**Coyote* 235-236
S 1850.
humorous, manuscript
see also: Señor, C. (pseud.)

Herald 236, 239
w My 29 1851 to date.
independent; Democratic
see also: Ames, John Judson; Derby, George Horatio; Noyes, William H.; Robinson, James W.; Walton, William N.

**Southern Democrat* 236n
sw O ? 1852.
see also: Price, A. J.; Walton, William N.

SAN FRANCISCO
Abend Zeitung 118
d S 25-D? 1854.
German language
see also: Behrens, J.; Lafontaine, A. J.

Alta California . . . 21, 24, 29-37, 88-98, 101, 103, 112, 114-115, 130, 131, 132, 134, 135, 136, 138, 168, 175, 232
w Ja 4-Mr 22, Ap 9-D 2? 1849; tw D 10 1849-Ja 20? 1850; d and w Ja 22 1850 to date. sm (steamer), ir Ap 9 1849 to date.
independent (Democratic); pro-Vigilance Committees of 1851, 1856
established Sacramento *Placer Times,* continued by Sacramento, later San Francisco, *Placer Times and Transcript,* absorbed by San Francisco *Alta California*
see also: Buffum, Edward Gould; Chamberlain, Charles Henry; Conner, Edward; Durivage, John E.; Farwell, Willard Brigham; Fitch, George Kenyon; Gunn, Lewis Carstairs; Gilbert,

[SAN FRANCISCO — *Continued*]

[SAN FRANCISCO — *Continued*]

L'Echo du Pacifique 111-112, 131, 132
tw Je 1 1852-D 31 1855; d Ja - 1856 to date; also weekly
French language; independent
follows French section of San Francisco *Picayune;* p.4 as *El Eco
del Pacífico,* Spanish, 1852-1855, followed by San Francisco
El Eco del Pacífico; weekly edition as *Courrier de San Fran-
cisco,* 1856 to date.
see also: Derbec, Etienne; Reintrie, Henrique de la

El Eco del Pacífico 111, 124, 131
d Ja 22 1856 to date.
Spanish language
as p.4 of *L'Echo du Pacifique* tw, Je 1 1852-D 31 1855
see also: Blanch, ; Derbec, Etienne; Herrera,

El Dorado Republican, see Placerville *El Dorado Republican*

**Examiner and Inquirer* 128
Ja 9 1858.
see also: Brittingham, Edward L.

**Fillmore Ranger* 125
O 1856.
organ of the American party

**Fireman's Journal* 120, 132
w Ap 7 1855 to date.
devoted to interests of Fire Department; sporting, literary, news
see also: Boruck, Marcus D.; Chase, Charles Metaphor

**Le Français* 119
tw 1 month ca. 1854-1855.
French language
see also: Thiele, Theo.

**Freie Presse* 112
w fall 1853-Ja 7 1854.
German language; independent
continued San Francisco *California Staats-Zeitung*
see also: Haehnlen, Jacob; Krug, Karl

**La Gazette Républicaine* 108, 119
tw S 12-? 1850.
French language
see also: Anselm, J.; Hoogs, Octavian

[SAN FRANCISCO — *Continued*]

Home Journal, see San Francisco *California Home Journal*

**Hutchings' Illustrated California Magazine* . . 125, 132
 m Jl 1856 to date.
 see also: Hutchings, James Mason; Rosenfield, Anthony

Illustrated California News
 sm S 1-D 1 1850.

**Illustrated Guide* 109
 D 1850?
 see also: Berford,

**Illustrated Pacific News* 129, 132
 w D 1858 to date.
 see also: Davison, H.

Journal 111
 d, w, and sm (steamer) My 25 1852-Mr 27? 1856.
 Whig, Anti-Slavery; Republican
 see also: Bartlett, Washington; Bickham, W. D.; Browne, R. K.;
 Clarke, Henry K. W.; Clarke, Mrs. Sarah M.; Gee, Lewis;
 Kingsbury, Joseph; Macy, Andrew M.; Pinkham, Benjamin
 Franklin; Seymour, Paul; Washburn, Charles Ames

Journal 120
 d F 20 1855-O? 1857.
 German language
 see also: Froebel, Julius; Korn, Julius; Ruehl,

Journal of Commerce 92, 100-101
 d and sm (steamer) Ja 23 1850-F 1 1851.
 suspended Je 15-Jl 24 1850
 see also: Bartlett, Washington; Robb, John S.

** Journal of Commerce* 117
 d Ag-fall 1854.
 Whig campaign paper
 see also: Bosworth, Theodore M.; Kewen, Edward J. C.

**Law Review* 123
 w spring 1855 (no.1-3).
 see also: Pollard, Edward A.; Upton, Mattias Gilbert; Walton,
 William N.

[SAN FRANCISCO — *Continued*]

**Mirror of the Fair*
steamer S 21 1857.
for California Industrial Exhibition
copy in California State Library

Mirror of the Times 127
w S 13 1856-1858?
Negro
reprinted articles from San Francisco *Pacific* and *Post*
see also: Moore, J. J.; Newly, W. H.; Townsend, Jonas H.

Monitor 128, 131
w Mr 6-Jl 3, O 16 1858 to date.
organ of the Catholic Church
suspended for Fraser River exodus
see also: Hammill, William; Marks, James; Thomas, Patrick

**National*
O 25-? 1856.
see also: Russell, Andrew Campbell
reported by San Francisco *Alta California* O 25 1856

National 125, 131
d Ag 16 1858 to date; w S 2 1858 to date.
followed San Francisco *Globe*
see also: Guthrie, George Whitney; Johnston, George Pen; Washington, George

News 114, 116
d N 1 1853-Ja 20 1854; also sm (steamer)
united with San Francisco *Picayune* to form *News and Picayune*
see also: Bartlett, Columbus; Bartlett, Julian; Bartlett, Washington; Pinkham, F. W.

News and Picayune 114, 116
d Ja 21 1854-My 20 1856; also sm (steamer)
formed by union of San Francisco *Picayune* and *News*
see also: Bartlett, Columbus; Bartlett, Julian; Bartlett, Washington; Pinkham, F. W.; Russell, Andrew Campbell

**News-Letter*
sm Jl 14-O 14? 1851.
see also: Duncan, Joseph C.
reported by San Francisco *Alta California* Jl 5, 1851

[SAN FRANCISCO — *Continued*]

see also: Bartlett, Columbus; Bartlett, Julian; Bartlett, Washington; Conner, Edward; Paul, Almarin B.; Rhodes, William Henry

True Standard 108-109
d Mr 3-My 3 1851; sm (steamer) edition as *Pacific Standard*
rivalled by San Francisco *California Public Balance* (no. 2);
 superseded San Francisco *Balance* preceded by San Francisco
 Public Balance (no. 1)
see also: Callender, Mills L.; Casserly, Eugene; Foster, Benjamin
F.; Toomy, Henry V.

**Uncle Sam* 119
w 1852?
illustrated
"published weekly by C. P. Kimball, at the Noisy Carrier's Publishing Hall," - San Francisco Directory 1852
"purporting to be published in San Francisco and printed in Boston" in 1854, according to Kemble

Varieties, see San Francisco *Sunday Varieties*

**Voice of Israel* 126
w O 9 1856-Mr? 1857.
Jewish
Rebekka, page in German for women
see also: Bien, H.; Labatt, Henry J.

**Watchman* 107
m Ap 1-? 1850.
organ of Presbyterian Church
see also: Williams, Albert

**Water Fount* 119
1854?
advocate of hydropathy
"published in New York, though purporting to be issued in San
Francisco"
possibly the same as San Francisco *Water Fount and Home
Journal?*

**Water Fount and Home Journal* 159
w My 15-Ag 1855.
organ of Grand Division of the Sons of Temperance

[SAN FRANCISCO — *Continued*]

continued by Sacramento *Water Fount and Home Journal,* announced for joint publication
see also: Montgomery, Alexander M.

Western American 110
d Ja 15-Mr 1 1852.
pro-squatter
see also: Burnside, E; Mack, John R.; Myers, E. L.; Pickett, Charles Edward; Vignes, J. G.; Young, James W.

Western Standard 123
w F 23 1856-N 6 1857.
advocate of Mormonism
see also: Cannon, George Q.

Whig 111, 119
d My 31 1852-F 1853; also w and steamer.
French department
continued by San Francisco *Whig and Commercial Advertiser, Commercial Advertiser*
see also: Farwell, Willard Brigham; Hull, Patrick P.; Lull, Louis R.; Mathewson, R. C.; Pixley, Frank Morrison; Wells, William Vincent; Whelpley, J. D.

Whig and Commercial Advertiser 111, 119
d Mr-S 1853; also w and steamer.
French department
continued San Francisco *Whig;* continued by *Commercial Advertiser*
see also: Farwell, Willard Brigham; Hull, Patrick P.; Lull, Louis R.; Matthewson, R. C.; Pixley, Frank Morrison; Wells, William Vincent

Wide West 117
w and sm (steamer) Mr 17 1854-Jl 4 1858; *Pictorial Wide West* for the holidays.
literary
see also: Bonestell, ; Jefferis, Edward G.; Kurtz, William W.; Lawrence, Joseph E.; Williston, Henry C.

**Young America* 125
w N ? 1856.
juvenile

[SAN FRANCISCO — *Continued*]

Young America on the Pacific 117
 Ap 1854-?
 humorous, illustrated; short-lived
 see also: Doyle, Robert Emmett

SAN JOSE
 Argus 219
 d Ja 6-F 14 1851; F 21-Je ? 1851.
 Democratic
 followed by San Jose *Visitor, Santa Clara Register, Telegraph
 and Santa Clara Register, Telegraph and Mercury*
 see also: Blake, Charles Morris

 California State Journal 218-219
 sw D 14 1850-Ja 1851; d Ja 1851; sw Ja?-Mr 26? 1851.
 see also: Devoe, James B.

 Mercury, see San Jose *Telegraph and Mercury*

 Santa Clara Argus, see San Jose *Argus*

 Santa Clara Register 219
 w Ag 19 1852-O 20 1853.
 followed San Jose *Argus, Visitor;* followed by San Jose *Telegraph
 and Santa Clara Register, Telegraph and Mercury*
 see also: Emerson, ; Jones, ; Parks,

 Statesman 218
 announced in fall of 1849; equipment arrived from East F 5 1850,
 but paper never started
 see also: Marcy, William George; Robb, John S.; Robinson,
 Henry Harrison

 Telegraph, see San Jose *Telegraph and Santa Clara Register, Tele-
 graph and Mercury*

 Telegraph and Mercury 220
 w Ag 14 1855 to date.
 Republican
 followed San Jose *Argus, Visitor, Santa Clara Register, Telegraph
 and Santa Clara Register*
 see also: Murdoch, Francis Butler

 Telegraph and Santa Clara Register 219-220
 w N 3 1853-Ag 7 1855.
 Republican

pro-Vigilance Committee of 1856; independent
see also: Godfrey, Grove K.

SHAW'S FLAT (Tuolumne County)
Pick and Shovel
w announced in San Francisco *Alta California* Ja 7 1857, to be edited by Charles Tupper

SONOMA
Blunderbuss 222
? Ag 1-? 1855.

Bulletin 222
w? Je 12 1852-Je? 1855.
neutral
continued by Vallejo *Bulletin*
see also: Cox, Alexander Jackson

SONORA
Herald 179-181, 183-184, 192
w Jl 4-O 12?, N 5? 1850-Je 1856; d Je-? 1856; w Ag? 1856 to date. also steamer edition, Je 1 1853.
v. 1 no. 1 printed in Stockton *Times* office
independent; Democratic; American; independent
see also: Atkins, DeWitt Clinton; Christman, Enos Lewis; Coffroth, James Wood; Gunn, Lewis Carstairs; Haley, Dr. ; Kearney, Matthew; Marvin, John Gage; Murray, Alexander; Murray, Walter; O'Sullivan, James; Radcliffe, H. H.; Reynolds, J. R.; Rockwell, Elijah Alvord; Washburn, Charles Ames; White, John

Mountain Whig 181
w Jl-Ag 1852.
Whig
see also: Dunn, John H.

Tuolumne Courier, see Columbia *Tuolumne Courier*

Union Democrat 181, 192
w Jl 1 1854 to date.
Administration Democratic
see also: Donavan, C; Francisco, Albert N.; Greenwood, Otis; Turner, N. P.

STOCKTON
Argus 172-173
d Je 7-Jl 16 1854; tw Jl 18-D 23 1854, alternating with Stockton

*Valley Yeoman 229n
w Ap-S? 1858.
follows Tehama *Colusa and Tehama Advocate*

UNION

Humboldt Times 224
w S 2 1854-Ag 21 1858.
neutral
succeeded by Eureka *Humboldt Times*
see also: Coleman, E. D.; Vandyke, ; Wiley, A.

Northern Californian 224, 231
w D 15 1858 to date.
Democratic
see also: Whipple, Stephen Girard

VALLEJO

**Bulletin* 222n
w? N-D 1855.
continued Sonoma *Bulletin*
see also: Cox, Alexander Jackson; Eaton,

VOLCANO

Amador Ledger, see Volcano *Ledger*

Ledger 187, 189
w O 27 1855-Ap 11 1857.
neutral, Democratic
continued by Jackson *Amador Ledger*
see also: Daingerfield, E. B.; Springer, Thomas A.

Observer 189n
w O 1855?
see Volcano *Ledger?*

WEAVERVILLE

**Democrat* 208-209
w Ag 1855-Ja 19 1856.
Democratic
followed by Weaverville *Trinity Journal*
see also: Crawford, M. T.; Howe, Henry J.

Trinity Journal 209
w Ja 26 1856 to date.
independent
followed Weaverville *Democrat*
see also: Gordon, David Everett; McDonald, Calvin B.; Seaman,

Title Index to Newspapers

This is a finding list referring the reader from newspaper title to place of publication. The informal literature of the time frequently fails to give the full name of newspapers referred to, and often omits place of publication. Therefore I am including here numerous cross-references, with entries under secondary titles or subsidiary words. Thus, *Sloat's San Francisco Prices Current and Shipping List* will appear also under *Prices Current and Shipping List, Sloat's San Francisco,* and under *Shipping List, Sloat's San Francisco Prices Current and.* The frequency of the paper is omitted, except in foreign languages, as are the article "The" and the city of publication when they begin the title, but in some cases these and certain other data, not used in the main entry, are listed parenthetically in the cross-references. In such a case, the entry *(Evening) Star, Pacific* would refer to the main entry, *Pacific Star.*

[TITLE INDEX]

[TITLE INDEX]

[TITLE INDEX]

[TITLE INDEX]

[TITLE INDEX]

[TITLE INDEX]

[TITLE INDEX]

[TITLE INDEX]

[TITLE INDEX]

[TITLE INDEX]

[TITLE INDEX]

[TITLE INDEX]

County Index to Newspapers

Index to Newspapermen

An index to the publishers and editors listed by Kemble, this is not a complete who's who of newspapermen active in California from 1846 to 1858. The temptation was there to add and expand, but time and space and printer's schedules eventually brought the realization that details in such quantity would have to be left to others. After drastic cutting from extensive notes, a few annotations remain. In some cases, where the information might serve as guide to further search, it has been included. In many cases, only the date of an obituary is given. In other cases, where biographical material is readily available, a double asterisk has been used.

Particularly regretted was the necessity, in all but a few instances, of omitting dates of service on the various papers. Desirable as their inclusion might be to specialists, complete accuracy would require a corps of researchers and the availability of files of newspapers, very few of which exist except in scattered numbers. If it could be done, it would result in an encyclopedia, rather than an index to Kemble's ***History***.

I wish to thank Mrs. Joan Weinstein, to whose good judgment in deciphering edited and re-edited notes and to whose accurate typing I owe the greater part of the final manuscript. I am also grateful to our friend Emil T. H. Bunje, Ph. D., who, under the pressure of a close deadline, undertook the difficult task of proofreading. Errors which remain are my own.

Addington, Stephen

a proprietor Marysville *California Express,* 176

born N 23 1828, learned printing trade on father's paper, Fishkill (New York) *Standard,* came to Calif in 1854 or 1855, among proprietors of Marysville *California Express* for 14 years, interlude on SF *Bulletin* joined his brother John C. Addington and William Semple Green on Colusa *Sun* 1870-1886, retired to SF, died May 4 1902

Alban, W B

among proprietors Nevada City *Journal,* 193

Albin, L

proprietor SF *Messager,* 114; editor and proprietor SF *Bibliothèque Populaire,* 128n

printer of *Le Patriote de San Francisco,* died F 6 1868; Léonce Albin probably his son, listed as printer in SF in 1860's

Aldrich, L

among proprietors Sacto *Placer Times,* 142

probably Judge Lewis Aldrich, an early resident of Sacto who removed to SF in 1854 and practiced law there and in Nev until his death on My 19 1885

Allen, James

a prop Sacto *State Tribune* (no. 1), 159; ed Sacto *California American,* 160; ed and prop Marysville *Herald,* 176; ed, a prop, Marysville *News,* 177; prop Marysville *National Democrat,* 178

born Pennsylvania; ed Ohio; Mexican War; Calif 1852; Mayor of Marysville; State Printer; ed North San Juan *Hydraulic Press* 1860; ed Virginia City, Nevada *Washoe Times* at his death O 31 1863

Allen O P

son of James Allen, in firm of James Allen & Son, props of Sacto *State Tribune* (No. 1) from N 1855, continued by *California American;* resident of Marysville in 1863

Allen, Robert N

agent for interest of his brother, R. T. P. Allen, in SF *Pacific News,* Ja and My 1850; listed as joint prop, M. Winchester & R. N. Allen, My 23-O 1 1850

Allen, R T P

California agent for Postmaster General; prop as Faulkner & Allen of SF *Pacific News* in Ja 1850; returned East, his share sold by his brother R. N. Allen; while East he bought Faulkner's interest; returned to SF in My 1850, found Winchester had controlling share, instructed his brother to sell out. (See "The Pacific News; a For-

gotten Episode in California Journalism," by George L. Harding, printed for *The Colophon,* F 1931)

Alter, T

pub Sacto *Pacific Banner,* 156

Ames, John Judson

prop and ed San Diego *Herald,* 236

born Maine 1821; to San Francisco in 1849 via Panama; left San Diego *Herald* in charge of George H. Derby in 1853 with humorous results; moved to San Francisco where started *Herald* Je 1860, forced out by creditors Ja 1861; died Jl 27 1861

Anderson, James

ed and part-prop Auburn Placer *Herald* Ja 1856-Ap 1857

Anderson, William F

ed Nevada City *Nevada Democrat,* 194

born Washington D.C. 1827?; Calif 1855; District Attorney Nevada County 1856-1860; in Nevada Territory; to SF 1875, State Assemblyman 1878; died Jl 6 1883

Andrus, T J

ed San Leandro *Alameda County Gazette,* 225

Superintendent of Amador Canal and Mining Co.; died D 15 1873

A'Neal, J W

A'Neal & Co. pubs Yreka *Union,* disagreed over politics and sued partners, 203; among pubs of Yreka *Siskiyou Chronicle,* 204

Anselm, J

ed, Hoogs & Anselm pubs, SF *Le Californien,* 108

Anthony, James

business manager and a prop Sacto *Union,* 150, 151

born Ja 6 1824 in Pennsylvania, lived in Baltimore and St. Louis; served in Mexican War; was clerk and reporter on St. Louis *Republican;* arrived in Calif Ag 30 1849, in Placer Co. in 1850; moved to Sacto in 1851, joined *Union as* bookkeeper; in 1853 purchased *Union* as James Anthony & Co. with Paul Morrill and H. W. Larkin; remained the paper's most active manager and guide until its sale to the Sacto *Record* in F 1875, when he retired to SF, where he died Ja 3 1876**

Appleton, H A

H. A. Appleton & Co. pubs Sacto *Age,* 159

Armor or Armour, George

Armor Clayes & Kooser props San Andreas *Independent,* 190

Armor and Clayes (brothers-in-law) moved paper to Stockton; about end of Civil War, Armor sold to Clayes and moved East;

reported in Chicago in 1892
Armstrong, Thomas
Thomas Armstrong & Co. pubs SF *California Illustrated Times;* an Englishman, 107
Ash, G O
G. O. Ash and N. C. Briggs pubs Jackson *Students' Banner* Mr 30 1858, 188
possibly George O. Ash, Methodist pastor later active in California and Oregon
Atkins, John R
local department Sacto *Spirit of the Age,* 159; general editor and J. R. Atkins & Co. pubs Sacto *State Sentinel,* 162-163
Avaline, Oliver D
ed and pub Jackson *Sentinel* from summer 1855, 187
born 1831, Fort Wayne, Indiana; purchased Mokelumne Hill *Calaveras Chronicle* in D 1859; joined the Union army but returned in weakened health; edited the Folsom *Telegraph* until his death on D 26 1863; his widow continued as ed until Je 1865
Avery, Benjamin Parke
ed and pub North San Juan *Hydraulic Press,* 214
born N 11 1828 in New York; arrived in Calif Jl 8 1849, mined worked as druggist and storekeeper; probably was responsible for North San Juan *Pioneer* (MS.) Mr-Jl 4 1856; pub with T. J. Waters, was ed of North San Juan *Hydraulic Press* Ag 21 1858 to Je 1860; was ed and, with Company, pub of Marysville *Appeal* Je 5 1860-1862; elected State Printer in S 1861; an ed on SF *Bulletin* 1863-1874; ed of *Overland Monthly* to Ag 1874 when sailed for Peking as Minister to China, where he died N 8 1875**
Ayers, James Joseph
prop Mokelumne Hill *Calaveras Chronicle,* 182
born Glasgow, Scotland, Ag 27 1830, to U.S. in 1831, raised in New York and St. Louis; arrived Calif O 5 1849, worked as printer; in 1856 was a founder of SF *Call,* remained as ed and senior partner to My 23 1866; in Honolulu published *Hawaiian Herald;* 1872 settled in Los Angeles, managing ed *Express* from Jl 1873; delegate to California Constitutional Convention of 1878; died N 12 1897

Babb, Charles
C. Babb & W. H. Harvey pubs Sacto *City Item,* 161
listed as printer in Sacto 1859
Bacon, Jacob
Towne & Bacon props SF *Times,* 118; Towne & Bacon props SF

California Culturist, 129
Badlam, Alexander
A. Badlam & Co. pub, ed, printer, etc Sacto *Times* (no. 1), 160; M. B. Clark, A. Badlam and W. J. Wallace props, printers and editorial staff Quincy *Prospector,* 188
probably Alexander Badlam, Jr., born 1835 in Cleveland; crossed plains with father 1850; a founder of Alta Express Company; in Calif Legislature 1863; SF Board of Supervisors 1869; SF Assessor 1875
Baer, Warren
original prop with D. D. Milne, Mariposa *Democrat,* followed by Hornitos *Mariposa Democrat,* 191
Baine, A C
an ed of Stockton *San Joaquin Republican,* 172
died on Reese River, Nevada, D 21 1863
Baker, George Holbrook
ed and with J. A. Mitchell pub Sacto *Spirit of the Age,* 159; ed Folsom *Granite Journal,* 213
born Mr. 9 1827 East Medway, Mass., art training in New York; arrived California via Mexico in My 1849, various enterprises; possibly the Mr. Baker reported as editor of Granite Hill *Miners Exposé* in F 1856; active as a lithographer, 1854-1857 Barber & Baker, then independently in Sacto, from 1862 in SF; died Ja 1906
Ball, Oscar O
prop Marysville *Inquirer* Mr 1856-D 1857-177; ed and prop Downieville *Mountain Echo,* later *Sierra Citizen,* 195
from Alabama
Barstow,
Barstow & Parks props Placerville *American* N-D 1857, 199
Bartlett, Columbus
pub with F. W. Pinkham of SF *News and Picayune,* 114; a prop of SF *True Californian,* 124
brother of Washington Bartlett
Bartlett, Julian
ed SF *News and Picayune,* 114; associate ed SF *Bulletin,* 122-123
born Milledgeville, Ga., brother of Washington Bartlett; died of consumption in San Bernardino age 33 (SF *Alta* N 26 1861 2/2)
Bartlett, Washington
pub SF *Journal of Commerce,* 100-101; ed SF *Journal,* 111;ed SF *News* and *News and Picayune,* 114; a prop of SF *True Californian,* 124; Bartlett & Robb, pubs Stockton *Journal,* 170
born 1824 in Augusta, Georgia; arrived Calif via Horn N 13

1849; mayor of SF; died 1887 while governor of Calif**

Bartlett, Washington Allon

claims ed connection with SF *California Star,* 20-21; denied by Sam Brannan, 21-22; captured by Californians, 22; alcalde's forms printed by *California Star,* 68; oppressive alcalde of SF, 71; at public meeting, Yerba Buena, 75

lieut on the US *Portsmouth* 1845-1848; alcalde of SF 1846-1847; later commanded a vessel in the coast survey service in the Pacific**

Batturs, Edward T

bought SF *Sun* F 2 1855; bookkeeper in SF 1862

Bausman, William

a prop SF *Sun,* 113

born My 12 1820 in Pennsylvania; to Calif in 1855; ed of North San Juan *Hydraulic Press* 1860-1863; private secretary to Governor J. Neely Johnson; died S 20 1893

Bee, Frederick A

F. A. Bee and W. Wadsworth prop Placerville *Herald,* 199

Behrens, J

ed and pub SF *Abend Zeitung,* 118

Bell, Alexander

pub SF *American,* 123

filibuster; "He will become a regular correspondent of the Alta at Tehuantepec, which place he intends making his permanent residence." (SF *Alta* S 6 1858 2/1)**

Bell, Edwin

prop SF *Times and Transcript,* 112

Berford,

Berford & Co. pubs SF *Illustrated Guide,* 109

Bickham, W D

ed SF *Journal* 1852

Biden, Charles S

ed SF *Picayune,* 107

Bien, H

ed SF *Voice of Israel* 1856; rabbi of Emanu-El

Bigley, Daniel

among eds and props of SF *Star* N 19 1856

Bingay, J Norman

ed Mokelumne Hill *Calaveras Chronicle,* 182

wrote series of "Suburban Sketches" for Sacto *Union* in 1872

Bishop, A W

owner with John S. Butler of Red Bluff *Beacon*

Biven, Rasey
joint ed Stockton *Post,* K 172; ed Stockton *Democrat,* 173
filibuster with Crabb in Sonora**
Biven, William
bought Stockton *Journal,* employed material in *Argus,* with Henry Crabb, 171; prop Stockton *San Joaquin Republican,* 171; prop and joint ed Stockton *Post,* 172; pub Stockton *Argus,* ed and sole prop Stockton *Democrat,* 173
assaults O'Neil (SF *Alta* F 16 1875 1/1); death (Sacto *Union* My 10 1875 2/1); "William Biven, managing editor of the Stockton *Herald,* was killed yesterday morning by being thrown from a horse in that city. He was an old Californian, was connected with the *Evening Spectator* in 1864-65, and also with other papers in the state."
Blaisdell, W W
with John C. Hopper, pubs Mariposa *Chronicle* 1855
Blake, Charles Morris
C. M. Blake & Co pubs and eds San Jose *Argus* 1851, 219
born D 24 1819 in Maine, grad Bowdoin College 1842; to Calif via Mexico 1849, left ship at Cape San Lucas, 84 days overland to San Diego; mining and teaching; assoc ed with cousin Jonas Winchester on SF *Pacific News;* M.D. and minister
Blakeslee, S V
associate ed, SF *Pacific,* 109-110
Blanch,
Herrera & Blanch, eds SF *Eco Del Pacifico,* 124
Blanton, T R
S. D. Clark and T. R. Blanton pubs Red Bluff *Beacon,* 226
Bloomer,
Savage, Bloomer & Co. pubs SF *Eagle of Freedom,* 125
Bloor, George W
prop Marysville *California Express,* 177; prop Marysville *National Democrat,* 178
from Wisconsin
Boardman, J H
W. B. Ewer & Boardman props Grass Valley *Telegraph,* 205
S 10 1859 to N 19 1859 ed Grass Valley *Nevada National*
Boden, Edward
Duchow & Brother, and E. Boden, present props Columbia *Tuolumne Courier,* 186
F 19 1859 Boden withdrew from firm; returned east because of father's illness

Bonestell, C K
Bonestell & Williston pubs SF *Wide West* 1854, 117

Bonnard, Francis A
pub SF *Sun* 1853, 113; Bonnard & Co. pubs Benicia *Sentinel* and Martinez *Contra Costa Gazette,* both in Martinez, 221; Bonnard & Co. pubs Oakland *Alameda County Express,* 222; Bonnard & Co., pubs Martinez *Contra Costa Gazette* 1858, 231

Bonnard, Ewer & Co pub SF *Sunday Dispatch* (SF *Alta* Jl 15 1851 2/3); prop Dispatch Job Printing Office and Prices Current & Shipping List, SF 1852

Booth, L M
assoc ed Sacto *Settlers' and Miners' Tribune,* 144

Boring, Rev. Dr. J
ed SF *Christian Observer,* 110

Boruck, Marcus D
ed SF *Fireman's Journal,* 120

death (SF Call Je 26 95 7/4), came to Cal in 1850, and 1855 became prop with Charles Chase of *Fireman's Journal.* With it until it merged with *Spirit of the Times,* "leading turf paper of state" with which he remained until he died.

Bosworth, Theodore M
pub SF *Journal of Commerce,* 117; owner and ed SF *Mercantile Gazette and Shipping Register,* 125

Boulware, Walker
prop Marysville *News,* 177; prop Marysville *National Democrat,* 178

from Kentucky

Boust, Ellsworth Burr
pub and ed Yankee Jim's *Placer Courier,* 215

death Sacto *Union* Ag 4 1893 1/4: "He conducted papers in Dutch Flat, Santa Barbara and Sacto in the early days."

Boynton, Charles
ed and pub Jackson *Owl,* humorous, 186-187; ed and pub Jackson *Amador Sentinel,* sold to O. D. Avaline and went to the Atlantic States, 187

Bradford, A C
ed Stockton *San Joaquin Republican,* 172

arrived Calif 1849 on *Niantic;* lawyer, Judge of the 13th Judicial District; died (Union F 16 1890 4/1)

Bradley, L
pub and ed Folsom *Granite Journal,* 213

pub and ed Diamond Springs *El Dorado County Journal* Ja 1-F

17, 1856
Brady, A
prop Marysville *California Express,* 117
Brannan, Samuel
Mormon expedition to Calif, 10; "powerful exhorter," 16; pub Yerba Buena (SF) *California Star,* 20; denies W. A. Bartlett's connection with SF *California Star,* 21-22; leaves *Star* office in charge of Kemble and Eagar, 23; names Kemble ed of *Star,* 24; sells *Star* to Kemble, 28; printer and pub of Mormon journal in New York, had idea of starting *California Star* in D 1845, 68; pub of *California Star,* 69, 70; Californian quoted, 73; sold material of SF *Star* to Kemble for $800, 85; discouraged founding of SF *Alta* as impractical *Alta* succeeded, so press at Sutter's Fort might be supported, 135; Sacto *Placer Times* (second location) on lot leased by Brannan, 39**
Brauer,
Brauer & Co. ed and prop SF *California Chronicle,* 114n
Brayton, Isaac H
ed SF *Pacific,* 109
d Nevada (*Alta* Ap 14 1869 1/2) grad. Hamilton College, settled at San Jose 1850, moved to Marysville 1852, ed of *Pacific* 1856
Briggs, Nash Corwith
G. O. Ash and N. C. Briggs pubs Jackson *Students' Banner,* March 30 1858, 188
Brinsmade, P A
ed SF *Picayune,* 107; started SF *Post,* 107; ed and pub SF *Post,* 109; SF directory 1854 p. 30 "Brinsmade, P. A. agent for claims against U.S. Government, and conveyancer."
Brittingham, Edward L
pub SF *Examiner and Inquirer,* 128
Brodie, John P
ed LA *Southern Californian,* 234
Brooks, W H
W. H. Brooks & Company pub SF *Pioneer* 1854-1855
Brown,
Tyson & Brown present publishers Yreka *Union,* 203-4
Brown,
Brown, Ingham & Co., pubs Sacto *Visitor,* 164
Brown,
John Patterson, Brown and Skelton pubs Nevada City *Miners' Spectacles,* 195
Brown, J B
J. B. Brown and F. F. Fargo props SF *California Evening Path-*

finder, later SF *Post and Pathfinder,* 125

Brown, Jonas W

among pubs Yreka *Siskiyou Chronicle,* 204

Brown, Nat. P

a prop Nevada City *Journal,* 193; N. P. Brown and J. K. Dallison pubs *Directory of Nevada, Grass Valley and Rough and Ready,* 195

Browne, R K

ed SF *Journal,* 111

Buckelew, Benjamin Rush

arrived in SF 1846, watchmaker, 81; ed SF *Californian,* withdrew in favor of real estate, 81-82; on weighing gold, 83; props of SF *Californian* in debt to him for material, 85; offended by *Alta,* decided to establish SF *Public Balance* as rival, quarrelled with his editors, 108; sent H. T. O'Connor to New York to purchase material for paper, quarrelled and took Casserly as partner, quarrelled with him and ran paper alone, said to have lost over $30,000 in venture, 108-109

Buckelew, W C

ed Marysville *Inquirer,* 177

Budd, Edwin Ruthven

Sargent & Budd props, Sargent ed; Budd & Skelton props, Budd ed, Nevada City *Journal,* 193; ed and prop Grass Valley *Intelligencer,* 205; ed and joint owner Santa Rosa *Sonoma Democrat,* 229; Budd & Pinkham pubs Santa Rosa *Western Evangelist,* 229

native of Ohio; judge; died in Ukiah Je 2 1875

Buffum, Edward Gould

ed Alta during part of Kemble's absence, 96; chief ed SF *Alta,* 97; went to Europe, 97; Farwell and Buffum, eds SF *Citizen,* 120; announced as founder of LA *Star,* did not participate, 233

author *Six Months in the Gold Mines***

Bugbee, W H

in Matthewson, Russell & Co., SF *California Public Balance* (no. 2) Mr 31-My 7 1851

Burnett, Glenn O

assistant ed Santa Rosa *Western Evangelist,* 299

Burnside, E

one of practical printers pub SF *Western American* Ja 15-Mr 1 1852

Butler, B

B. & J. S. Butler eds and props Red Bluff *Beacon,* 226

Butler, John S

B. & J. S. Butler eds and props Red Bluff *Beacon,* 226

Butler, Warren C
ed SF *California Mail*
Butts, William
Butts & Wheeler props LA *Southern Californian*, 234
Byrne, W S ("Will Winter")
ed La Porte *Mountain Messenger*, 212
with John P. Skelton purchased interest in Grass Valley *Telegraph* Ap 24 1862, Byrne & Co., Byrne as editor of tri-weekly; added new equipment, burned out Je 11 1862, no insurance (Nevada *National* since Ag 1858); towns-people lent $900, new outfit bought, paper reappeared as tw Jl 19 1862; edited paper with J. R. Ridge from Je 17 1864, sold out to C. S. Wells on Ap 8 1865 (Nevada City directory 1865 p. 113)

Callender, Mills L
Casserly, Callender & Co. props SF *True Standard* Mr 3-My 3 1851
Campbell, Edwin Ruthven
ed Stockton *San Joaquin Republican*, 172; ed Downieville *Sierra Citizen*, 196
Campbell, W
ed Forest City *Sierra Democrat*, 197
Cannon, George Q
pub and ed SF *Western Standard*, moved to Salt Lake City 1857, 123
prominent Mormon**
Carder,
Duchow & Carder leased Columbia *Gazette* Ag 16 1856-F 1867
Carlton,
writer on SF *California Illustrated Times*, 107
Carpenter,
Carpenter & Wellington props Folsom *Dispatch*, 213
Carr, M D
prop Marysville *California Express*, 177
Carter, W H
duel with H. A. De Courcey of Mokelumne Hill *Calaveras Chronicle*, 182
Casey, James P
ex-convict from State Prison of New York and professional ballot-box stuffer, attacked in SF *Bulletin* by James King of William, 122; prop and "editor" SF *Sunday Times;* killed James King of William, hanged by Vigilance Committee of 1856, 123-124
Casserly, Eugene
ed and pub SF *Public Balance* (no. 1), later *Balance*, later *True*

Standard, 108-109

lawyer, born 1822 in Ireland, to US in 1824, ed and contributor to Eastern papers, Calif via Panama Ag 1850; partner and then rival of Buckelew in battle of the *Balances;* elected State Printer My 1 1851, sued Fitch to get office; US Senator 1869-1872, resigned to continue law practice in SF; died Je 14 1883**

Caulkins, Silas

ed Quincy *Fillmore Banner,* 211

Cazneau, Thomas Nugent

ed and prop Columbia *Gazette,* 185

born in Boston; in SF in 1851; pub Columbia *Gazette & Southern Mines Advertiser;* general; appointed Adj.-Gen. of Calif by Gov Haight**

Cellers,

McGeorge & Cellers pub Benicia *Solano County Herald,* 221

Chamberlain, Charles Henry ("Mountaineer" *pseud.*)

Columbia correspondent of SF *Alta* (SF *Alta* Ag 28 1853 2/4)

Charlton, John

among editors of La Porte *Mountain Messenger,* 212; ed, joint prop Tehama *Gazette,* 228-229

resigns as ed *Mountain Messenger* N 1 1858 (Hesperian I:201); death SF *Call* Mr 6 1898 4/2

Chase, Charles Metaphor

C. M. Chase & Co. props SF *Fireman's Journal,* 120

Chase, S U

ed Cacheville *Bay Town Lookout,* MS., 1851-1852 (*Illustrated Atlas and History of Yolo County, Cal . . .* 1879, p. 78)

Chemin, Léon

ed SF *Passe-Partout,* 119

ed SF *Le Phare* 1858, *L'Union Franco Américaine* 1860

Childs,

Wadsworth & Childs, later Harvy & Childs, ed and pub Placerville *American,* 199

Christian, Samuel B

a prop Marysville *News,* 177; a prop Marysville *National Democrat,* 178

printer, from Michigan

Christman, Enos Lewis

ed and prop Sonora *Herald,* 180-181

from West Chester, Pa.; arrived Calif F 8 1850; left Sonora for West Chester Je 21 1852

Church, A P
a prop Nevada City *Nevada Democrat,* 194
Clark, Albert H
ed with Edward Pollock of SF *American* (*Alta* O 28-N 21 1855)
Clark, Alexander
founder of Sacto *Union,* printer, 147; only Jeffries, Keating and Clark remained of original props of Sacto *Union,* 149; Keating sold interest in Sacto *Union* to Morrill, Larkin, Anthony and Clark, 150; lost at sea; his interest in *Union* sold, 150-152
Clark, M B
M. B. Clark, A. Badlam and W. J. Wallace, props, printers and editorial staff Quincy *Prospector,* 188
Clark, S D
S. D. Clark and T. R. Blanton pubs Red Bluff *Beacon,* 226
Clarke, Henry K W
prop SF *Journal,* 111
attorney; death (SF *Alta* My 21 1878 1/1)
Clarke, Sarah Moore (Mrs. H. K. W.)
ed Oakland *Contra Costa,* 223
ed SF *Journal;* death (*Alta,* Ap 17 1880 1/2); native of Maine, aged 60, relative of Grace Greenwood, "and had written with considerable poetical talent."
Clayes, Orlando M
Armor Clayes & Kooser props San Andreas *Independent,* 190
native of Joliet, Ill, came to Calif in 1855; brother-in-law of George Armor; moved to Stockton with the *Independent;* elected State Printer in 1864; died Je 24 1892, age 55
Coffroth, James Wood
born 1828, arrived Calif 1850; worked on Sonora *Herald* in 1851; orator and politician, State Senator; died O 9 1872**
Coggins, James
local reporter on Sacramento *Age* (SF *Alta* O 3 1857)
Coggins, Paschal
ed Sacramento *City Item,* 161; ed Sacramento *Visitor,* 164
death (Sacto *Union* N 19 1883) "In 1856, Paschal Coggins, associated with O. Terrill, James McClatchy, H. S. Dalliba, and ex-Senator Cornelius Cole, started for the Fremont campaign the Daily Times of Sacramento, the first Republican daily of the state. The capital for the venture was furnished by Ex-Governor Stanford, Charles Crocker, E. B. Crocker, C. P. Huntington, and Mark Hopkins. The Daily Times of Sacramento was published from August

1856 to January 24, 1857."

Cole, Cornelius

C. Cole & Co. pubs, C. Cole ed, Sacramento *Times,* 161

lawyer, born in New York State 1822; overland to California, arriving in July 1849; later Congressman and Senator from California**

Cole, Richard

ed Coloma *True Republican,* 198; T. A. Springer and R. Cole, ed and pub Placerville *El Dorado Republican,* 199; Cole and Dietz eds Placerville *American,* 199

purchased Harmon's interest in Placerville *El Dorado News* and changed name to *El Dorado Republican;* ed and, with Springer, pub Je 11-S 1853

Coleman, E D

prop and ed Union Humboldt *Times,* 224

left Calif in 1855

Collins, John A

substituted as ed of Sacto *Union,* 150

death SF *Call* Ap 5 1890 8/5

Colton, D D

among pubs Yreka *Union,* 203

Colton, Walter

offers editorial talents, 13; statement in Monterey *Californian,* 15; chaplain of the frigate Congress, started newspaper in Monterey, 55; first American civil magistrate in Calif, 56; "Three Years in California" quoted on type and press, 57; Colton & Semple, pubs of *Californian,* 57; dropped from firm, 63; "now dead", 64; California *Star* quoted, 73-74**

Colville, Samuel

assistant ed, Sacto *Illustrated Historical Sketches of California, With a Minute History of Sacramento Valley,* 157

arrived California Ap 21 1849

Conley, J M

prop Stockton *San Joaquin Republican,* 171

Comny, J

ed Weaverville *Trinity Times,* 208

Conklin, S B

in Matthewson, Russell & Co., SF *California Public Balance* (no. 2) Mr 31-My 7 1851; Conklin & Haskins, pubs SF *Town Talk, Times and Town Talk, Times,* My 10 1857-1858

Conner, Edward

former mail clerk in New York *Herald* office, agent for Hoe's machine

press, 92; sells steam press to *Alta,* 92-93; in East in Je 1851, 94; began SF *True Californian,* 97; spring 1857 established printing office and newspaper in Valparaiso, 97; prop of SF *True Californian,* 124; went to Chile in summer 1858, 131

returned to SF *Alta* Ag 13 1859 2/3; death *Alta* Ag 15 1867 2/1

Conness, John

Gelwicks, Garfield[e] & Conness, eds and pubs Coloma *Miners' Advocate,* 198

born in Ireland; with Coloma *Empire County Argus;* in State Legislature; defeated for Governor by Stanford; US Senator 1863-1869**

Cook, Alexander D

a founder of Sacto *Union,* printer, 147; sold interest in Sacto *Union* to H. W. Larkin, 149

Coon, S E V

pub Santa Clara *Knight's Review* 1857, 230

Cornwall, W A

assaulted and badly wounded A. D. Russell for editorial in LA *Star* reflecting on agent of Bigler, 233-234

Coulp,

ed Marysville *Inquirer,* 177

Court, Job

C. L. Hansicker, J. Court and W. J. Keating started Sacto *Union,* 146; a founder of Sacto *Union,* printer, 147; withdrew from Sacto *Union* at end of Jan 1852, selling to W. W. Kurtz, 149

burned to death in Sacto hotel, *Alta,* Ja 10 1875 1/4

Cox, Alexander Jackson

pub Sonoma *Bulletin,* 222

from So Carolina; to Calif in Co. C, NY Volunteers; pub Vallejo *Bulletin;* later connected with Napa papers

Crabb, Henry A

prop Stockton *Journal,* 171; pub with Wm. Biven, first ed of Stockton *Argus,* 172

Sonora filibuster**

SF *Register* (My 20-22 1857) appears to have existed to report Crabb massacre

Crane, James M

Simonton denies he was partner with Crane & Rice in SF *Courier,* 37; James M. Crane & F. W. Rice, pubs of SF *California Courier,* 104; letter writer in Washington before 1849, 105-106; revived SF *California Courier,* 106; in Washington seeking recognition as delegate from Carson Valley Territory, 106

ed and prop SF *Pacific Courier,* announced in Extra [finally appears Je 1 1850 as SF *California Courier*] SF *Alta* D 22 1849 2/2; death Sacto *Union* S 28 1859, delegate to Congress from Territory of Nevada; d. at Gold Hill, Carson Valley, native of Virginia, connected with press of that state

Crawford, M T

H. J. Howe and M. T. Crawford, props Weaverville *Democrat,* 208

Cremony, John Clare

real ed of James P. Casey's SF *Sunday Times,* 124; ed SF *Sun,* 113

native of Maine, b. 1815, death SF *Alta* Ag 25 1879 1/7

Crocker, Charles

capital for Sacto *Times* furnished by Stanford, Charles Crocker, E. B. Crocker, C. P. Huntington, and Mark Hopkins - pubs. C. Cole & Co., pro-Fremont (Sacto *Union* N 19 1883, P. Coggins obit.)**

Crocker, E B

among those furnishing capital for Sacto *Times***

Crosby,

among citizens supporting Tehama *Colusa and Tehama Advocate,* 228

Crosette, George H

G. H. Crosette and H. R. Mighels eds Oroville *Butte Record,* 210

author "The press of Butte county" (In the *History of Butte county, California* . . . 1882, p. 195-197); sold Butte *Record,* publ at Chico, to Rev. Jesse Wood. *Record* started at Bidwell Bar "more than 33 years ago." Crosette traded hotel for printing equipment. When gold gave out moved paper to Oroville, after some years to Chico (SF *Call,* S 20 1887 6/1)

Crowninshield, J C

ed Weaverville *Trinity Times,* 208

Cummings, Dr.

purchased "for other parties," Yreka *Mountain Herald;* "The former Editor retires not in the best of humor, being, as he seems to think, driven out by fear of competition." (SF *Alta* Je 14 1855 2/2)

Cutter,

E. A. Rowe and Cutter, props Weaverville *Trinity Times,* 208

Daggett, Rollin Mallory

ed and co-prop SF *Golden Era* 1852, 112

an editor of Virginia City *Territorial Enterprise;* active in Nevada politics; US Minister to Hawaii; died in 1901 at age 71**

Daingerfield, E B

T. A. Springer and E. B. Daingerfield props Volcano *Ledger* and

Jackson *Amador Ledger,* 187
Dalliba, H S
on Sacto *Times* (no. 2)
Dallison, J K
N. P. Brown and J. K. Dallison, pubs *Directory of Nevada, Grass Valley and Rough and Ready,* Ja 1856, 195
Daly, J T
ed last 3 or 4 numbers of Cacheville *Yolo Democrat,* 226
Damon, John F
ed Stockton *Gazette,* 172; Damon, Emerson & Jones pubs San Jose *Visitor,* 219
Danglison, *see* Dunglison, John R
Davidge, Robert A
ed Nevada City *Young America* later *Nevada Democrat,* 194
ostensibly pub and ed of Nevada *Young America* S 14 1853 to D 7 same year; said by rival papers to front for other persons; died Nashville F 27 1864; comments on career, Sacto *Union* Je 9 1864 2/1
Davis, L P
among props Sacto *Bee,* 162
Davison, H
pub SF *Leader* 1854, 118; pub SF *Phoenix* 1856 [i.e., 1857], 124; pub SF *Times,* unsuccessful experiment in November 1856, 126; ed, prop, printer of SF *Illustrated Pacific News,* 1858, 129; Lynch, Davison & Rolfe pubs Sacto *Index* 1851, 145; among pubs Sacto *Union* 1851, 147; Ap 3 1852 sold interest in Sacto *Union,* 149; H. Davison & Co., pubs Sacto *Temperance Register* 1857, 163; pub and ed Oakland *Herald* 1855, 223
to pub Daily Evening *Telegraph,* SF O 15 1858 (SF *Alta* S 27 1858)
Davison, William K
a founder of Sacto *Union,* 147
Day, Mrs. F H
Mrs. A. M. Shultz and F. M. Day eds SF *Hesperian* My 1858; "Mrs. Day now sole ed," 129
De Courcey, Henry A
prop and ed Mokelumne Hill *Calaveras Chronicle,* duel with Carter, 182; Alban & De Courcey props, De Courcey ed Nevada City *Journal,* 193; among props Bidwell *Butte Record,* 206; fought with L. P. Hall, went to jail, 206
pub with Matthewson, Russell & Co. SF *Public Balance* Mr 31-My 7 1851; died of apoplexy S 11 1854

DeMott, John (Jack)
J. DeMott & Co., props Marysville *Inquirer,* 177; prop Bidwell (later Oroville) *Butte Record,* 206
death Sacto *Union* Ja 27 1860
Denison, Mr. and Mrs. Charles W
ed and literary ed, Benicia *California Gazette* prospectus F 21 1851
Dennis, J H
ed and pub Jackson *Independent,* 188
Denslow, Mellville
listed as pub SF *Journal* S 1852
De Prefontaine, A J
ed Stockton *San Joaquin Republican,* 172
Derbec, Étienne
established SF *Echo Du Pacifique,* 107; ed and prop SF *Echo Du Pacifique* and SF *Eco del Pacifico,* 111; edited several columns in French in SF *Picayune,* 107; ed, SF *Eco del Pacifico,* 124**
Derby, George Horatio
author of *Phoenixiana;* changed politics of San Diego *Herald* from Democratic, pro-Bigler, to Whig, pro-Waldo, during pre-election absence of friend J. J. Ames; put out pictorial issue with small advertising cuts - fall 1853; 236**
Devoe, James B
pub San Jose *California State Journal,* 218
"J. Winchester, Esq., formerly publisher of the New York *World,* and James B. Devoe, Esq., late editor of *Daily American Patriot,* passed through town last week bound for the mines." (Sacto *Placer Times* Ag 1 1849 2/1); "formerly attached to the *Pacific News*" to start San Jose *California State Journal* (SF *Alta* N 21 1850); pub SF *Placer Times and Transcript* S 1852
Dietz,
Cole and Dietz eds Placerville *American,* 199
Dimick, Kimball H
among pubs of Los Angeles *Southern Californian* Ag to N 2 1854
Dockrill, Joseph
crewman on Congress, discharged to be first printer on *Californian,* 55; mechanical overseer, SF *Californian,* 82
from Canada; worked in SF newspaper offices until 1852; went to mines and died in 1856
Dodson, William Burr Harrison
physician in Sacto 1851-1854; ass't ed Sacto *Democratic State Journal* 1854; solicitor *State Journal* 1855; ed Red Bluff *Sentinel;*

death SF *Call* S 19 1893 3/6
Doherty, George O
part owner of SF *Picayune* when it expired in March 1852, 107; prop SF *Times,* Ap 18-My 5 1852, 110
Donavan, C
ed Sonora *Union Democrat,* 181
Dosh, Samuel H
a founder of Sacto *Union,* 147; sold out to partners for $600 when Sacto *Union* turned Whig, 149; S. H. Dosh, J. C. Hinckley, A. Skillman props Shasta *Courier* 1852, now Skillman & Dosh, 200
born 1826 in Virginia; Calif in 1849; sole ed of Shasta *Courier* from 1853 to his death in 1861
Douglass, Rev. J W
ed of SF *Pacific,* 1851, 109
returned East after six years in Calif (SF *Alta* My 9 1855 2/2
Doyle,
Johnson & Doyle, props SF *Pacific Whalemen's List*
Doyle, R E
ed SF *Young America on the Pacific,* 117
Dryer, T J
city ed and reporter, SF *California Courier,* Sept. 1850
Duchow, John Charles
ed and prop Columbia *Gazette,* 185; Duchow & Urmy props Columbia *Tuolumne Courier,* Urmy for few months only; Duchow & Brother, and E. Boden, "present props," Duchow ed, 186
born O 14 1830, Salem, Mass; arrived SF by Clipper Ag 13 1852; ed and prop Sonora *Tuolumne Independent;* died Ja 21 1901
Duchow, William A
joint prop Duchow & Brother, and E. Boden Columbia *Tuolumne Courier,* 186
joined firm Je 11 1857, withdrew and left Columbia Mr 1 1860
Duncan, Joseph C
ed SF *Globe,* 124-125; pub SF *California Home Journal,* 129
printer in SF 1850; pub SF *News-letter* 1851; press destroyed by fire in 1851, became auctioneer; from 1856-1861 prop daily *Globe* and *California Home Journal* of SF; organized Pioneer Bank of Savings and Deposit, also Safe Deposit Company of SF, which failed in 1877; several trials ended in dismissal
Dunglison, John R
ed Oakland Alameda *County Express,* 222
clerk US Surveyor's Office, SF 1852; perhaps pub Oakland *Contra Costa* 1855, Mrs. S. M. Clarke ed

Dunlap, Presley
sued by Hardenbergh, to recover possession of Sacto *California Statesman,* 156
born Ja 10 1817 Pennsylvania; arrived Calif Ag 17 1849; lawyer, expert on land titles; member constitutional convention of 1878; died S 23 1883

Dunlap, T Jr.
ed Santa Barbara *Gazette,* 237

Dunn, John H
pub SF *Police Gazette,* murdered after a few weeks by printer, 117; assassinated, 130; prop Sonora *Mountain Whig* 1852, Canadian by birth, 181
Foley, drunk, stabbed Dunn with sword cane; arrested; Dunn aged about 30 (SF *Alta* My 12 1854 2/1)

Dunn, William
built first press manufactured in California, for SF *Pacific News,* March 1850 (SF *Pacific News* quotes in NY *Tribune* My 11 1850)

Durivage, John
assistant ed *Alta,* 91; purchased interest in *Alta,* 92; retired from *Alta,* 94; went East in 1851, ed and actor by turns, 1858 on stage, 97; "has taken to the stage," 131

Eagan, Charles P
among eds and props of SF *Star*

Eagar, John
printer on California *Star,* left in charge of censorship with Kemble by Brannan, afterwards joined Salt Lake Mormons, 76

Eaton,
Cox & Eaton pub Vallejo *Bulletin,* 222n

Eckman, Rev. Julius
ed Jewish SF *Gleaner,* SF *California Family Visitor,* 126

Edmonds, A C
Universalist Clergyman, ed Sacto *Star of the Pacific,* 162; ed Sacto *Covenant and Odd Fellow's Magazine,* 163; ed and prop Marysville *Star of the Pacific,* Universalist 177
publishing Marysville *Star of the Pacific* at Petaluma in July 1859 (North San Juan *Hydraulic Press* Jl 9 1859)

Edson,
with Woodworth, pubs of Sacto *Eye Glass,* "an independent weekly observer . . . Israel M. Pecksniff is the Pickwickian editor." (SF *Alta* Ag 25 1857)

Edwards, Dr. James
bus. mgr. SF *Star of Empire* O 1 1856

Elespura,
Lafonte, Leguizamont & Elespura, pubs SF *Sud Americano,* 120
Elwell, W. B. (*see* Ewer, Warren B.)
Emerson,
Damon, Emerson & Jones pubs San Jose *Visitor,* 219; Emerson, Jones & Parks pubs San Jose *Santa Clara Register,* 219
Estell, James Madison
ed Sacto *State Tribune,* 158
promoted filibustering expedition to Sandwich Islands (SF *Picayune* O 31 1851 2/5); "General James M. Estell, having given up the management of the State Prison . . ." on lease. (SF *Alta* Jl 19 1855); connected with Sacto *California American,* winter 1856-1857
Evans, Morris
on pub com of SF *Christian Observer* 1851-2, Pacific American Conference of the M E Church, South
Evert,
Evert & Co. pub SF *Sun* (1852), 111n
Ewer, Ferdinand Cartwright
ed SF *Pacific News* 1850, Episcopal clergyman in SF 1858, 100; ed SF *Pioneer,* 116; "has taken to the pulpit," 131; a prop Sacto *Transcript,* literary ed, 143; minister in SF, 167; ed *Pioneer Magazine,* 240
Bonnard, Ewer & Co. pubs SF *Sunday Dispatch* (SF *Alta* Jl 15 1851)**
Ewer, Warren B
ed Nevada City *Journal,* 193; W. B. Ewer & Boardman props Grass Valley *Telegraph,* Ewer ed, 205; ed Grass Valley *Mining Journal* and *Telegraph* reprinted in *Mining Journal,* 205-206
his *Calif Mining Journal,* pub in Grass Valley, was the first paper in the state devoted entirely to mining and the forerunner of his *Mining and Scientific Press***
Ewing, William
present ed Folsom *Dispatch,* 213

Fair, S P
among pubs Yreka *Siskiyou Chronicle,* 204
Falconer, Thomas A
ed and prop Columbia *Gazette,* 185
Fargo, Francis Frederick
J. B. Brown and F. F. Fargo props SF *California Evening Pathfinder,* later SF *Post and Pathfinder,* 125
born Warsaw, NY Ap 1824; "in 1851 he took his third wife and

went to California . . . worked on the *Alta* and *Bulletin* and established the *Pathfinder*," member of Assembly and Clerk of Supreme Court; returned east in 1861; married widow W. G. Fargo 1883; died of nervous prostration Ja 12 1891 in Buffalo, NY (Sacto *Record-Union* Ja 14 1891 1/1)

Farrell, Frank

with A. J. Cox, started Napa *Sun*

Farwell, Willard Brigham

senior ed SF *Alta* 1858, 97; editorial department SF *Commercial Advertiser*, 111; Farwell and Buffum, eds SF *Citizen*, 120; Farwell, Monson & Valentine, printers of SF, purchased interest of Parker French in Sacto *State Tribune* (no. 1), attached paper, printed SF *Citizen*, continued by Sacto *State Tribune* (& *Citizen* no. 2), 158

death (SF *Call* F 11 1903 5/3)

Faulkner, Francis William

(son of William Faulkner) printer on SF *Pacific News* 1849

Faulkner, George L

(son of William Faulkner) printer on SF *Pacific News* 1849

Faulkner, William

previously published a Democratic paper in Norwich, Conn., moved office to California in gold rush, pub SF *Pacific News*, 99

"Among the adventurers who are to set sail from Mystic, Ct., on the 15th inst., we notice the name of Mr. Faulkner of the *Norwich News*. He takes out with him a printing press, types, and paper, a two-story house, and provisions for himself and a party for a year and a half . . ." (NY *Herald* Ja 12 1849 3/1, from Springfield *Republican;* died Oakland (Sacto *Union* Mr 29 1878 3/4), came to Calif 1850 with two sons, started *Pacific News* in connection with Warren Leland

Fechtig, B Y

Fechtig and U. B. Freaner pubs Crescent City *Herald*, 224

B. Y. Fechtig and U. B. Freaner, eds and props of Crescent City *Herald* June 10 1854, Fechtig withdrew in Sept. 1854 (Hist. of Humboldt county, 1881 p. 218)

Ferguson, M P

ed and pub Cacheville *Spectator*, 228

Ferris, Hiram Gano

among pubs of Yreka *Union*, 203; among purchasers of *Mountain Herald* (Yreka), 203

Fisher, C E

ed and prop Red Bluff *Beacon*, 226

Fisher, Rev. O

ed Stockton *Pacific Methodist,* 173

Fisher, S H

joint owner Santa Rosa *Sonoma Democrat,* 229

Fitch, George Kenyon

Pickering, Fitch & Co., props of SF *Alta,* 96; Fitch and Pickering props, SF *Times and Transcript,* 112; pub SF *Shipping List and Prices Current,* 110; owned half of State printing and of Sacto *Times and Transcript,* 134-135; prop Sacto *Transcript,* Fitch, Upham & Co., Fitch and Ewer eds; brought material to California; concerned? in the printing of the Panama *Star,* 143; sold interest in Sacto *Transcript* to Mr. Grove, 143; got State Printing for Sacto *Transcript,* claiming to be Democrats, 144; of Sacto *Transcript,* in SF, 166-167**

Fitzgerald, Rev. Oscar Penn (Rt. Rev. ad d.)

ed SF *Pacific Methodist,* 123; editorial manager of SF *Pacific Methodist,* removed from Stockton, 173

died (SF *Exam* Ag 6 1911 1/4)

Fleming, William S

Wm. S. Fleming & Co., pubs Placerville *Appeal,* 199; Fleming and C. B. Lawton pubs Diamond Springs *Miners' Advocate,* 207;

employee of Placerville *News,* was ed of Placerville *Appeal* published in *News* office, Mr 31 to early My, 1853, in attempt to discourage Placerville *Herald*

Foard, John Macdonough

ed and prop SF *Golden Era,* 112; sub. SF *California Mail,* adv't. (lit.) O 30 1854-S 1855, 118

age 21 in 1852, founded SF *Golden Era* with Rollin M. Daggett, age 19; died (SF *Call* Ja 16 1892 8/6), came to SF in 1849; estab *Golden Era* in 1852 with Rollin M. Dagget; after 1860 assoc with G. B. Densmore in pub *Golden City;* assoc with many SF papers; wrote for *Call* and Sacto *Transcript***

Foley, T

pub SF *Herald* (SF dir 1858 p. 286)

Folsom,

contributed to Nugent for SF *Herald,* 101

Forbes, William J.

Platt and Forbes pubs Downieville *Sierra Democrat,* Forbes ed, 197; ed Coloma *Empire County Argus,* 198

died (SF *Alta* O 31 1875) as ed Battle Mountain, Nev., *Measure for Measure*

Ford, T P

prop, with J. A. Appleton, of Sacramento *Age* (SF *Alta* O 3 1857)

Forrester, P A
among eds and props of SF *Star* N 19 1856
Fossas, P
Torras & Fossas, props Santa Barbara *Gazette,* 238
Foster, Benjamin F
printer and pub of SF *Californian,* 84; acquired interest of Sheldon & Weaver in SF *Californian,* left it to Kemble and sailed for Sandwich Is., 86
with Casserly, Callender & Co., SF *True Standard;* also *Pacific Standard*
Foster, George I
prop Marysville *California Express,* 176-177
in Mattherson, Russell & Co., SF *Calif Public Balance*
Foster, John S
pub Nevada City *Miners' Spy-Glass,* 195
Foushee, H S
pub Sacto *Mercury,* 164
Foy, John E
Foy, Nugent & Co., pubs of SF *Herald,* 101; sold out share of SF *Herald* to Nugent, 101
France, Jules de
ed SF *Tam-Tam,* 119
pub SF *Le Californien* w Ja 17-F ? 1850, lithographed (Campbell & Hoogs' SF & Sacto City Dir Mr 1850); pub SF *Revue Californienne* w Je 2-16 1851, litho. (*Alta* Je 10 1851 2/1)
Francisco, Albert N
prop Sonora *Union Democrat,* 181
printer, from Ohio
Freaner, U B
a pub Crescent City *Herald* with others, 224
B. Y. Fechtig and U. B. Freaner, eds and props Crescent City *Herald* Je 10 1854; Sep 1854 Fechtig withdrew, S. H. Grubler assumed his place; June 4 1856 last issue by Grubler and Freaner; T. S. Pomeroy joined Freaner; Aug 19 1859 Freaner withdrew (*Hist. of Humboldt Co,* 1881, p. 218)
Fredonyer, A
edited 3 cols of Quincy *Old Mountaineer,* pro-Republican, during political campaign of 1856, (Giffen p. 59)
French, Parker H
ed and pub SF *California Register,* 126; Parker H. French and S. J. May eds Sacto *State Tribune* (no. 1); sold to May and left to join Walker in Nicaragua, 158; returned from Nicaragua, purchased

back interest in *State Tribune* (no. 1), did not pay, went to SF, sold interest to Farwell, Monson & Valentine, printers in SF, who attached paper, 158**

Froebel, Julius
ed SF *Journal* (German), 120; went to Germany, 131

Fuller, H M
E. G. Waite, N. P. Brown, H. M. Fuller and Jno. P. Skelton Nevada City *Journal* props, 193; retired from Nevada City *Journal* after fire, 193

Fuller, N W
editor Coloma *Empire County Argus,* 198
may have been editor of Coloma *Empire County Argus;* not connected with Diamond Springs *Miners' Advocate,* but with Coloma *Empire County Argus* 1853

Gandonnière, A
ed SF *La Presse,* 119
ed *Le Phare* 1856

Garfielde, S
Gelwicks, Garfield & Conness, eds and pubs Coloma *Miners' Advocate,* 198
with Snyder, ed of Coloma and Diamond Springs *Miners' Advocate,* 1852-3

Gee, Lewis
Pinkham, Gee & Co., pubs SF *Journal,* 110-111; prop Marysville *California Express,* 176
Gee, Giles and Company pubs Marysville *California Express,* notice of first issue in *Nevada Journal* of Nov 6 1851 - probably correct; pub SF *Evening Journal* S 1852

Geiger, Vincent E
V. E. Geiger & Co. pubs Sacto *Democratic State Journal,* 152; wrote editorials on Sacto *Democratic State Journal,* 152; Indian Agent at the Nome Lackee Reservation, 152; Indian Agent, 167
censured for indenture of Indians (Sacto *Union* F 4 1861); died (*Union* D 18 1869) Valparaiso, Chile; came to Calif overland from Charleston, Va.; State Printer; "killed a man at Red Bluff, and has since been a fugitive from justice"

Gelbrecht,
Wagner & Gelbrecht, pubs SF *Deutscher Democrat,* 121

Gelwicks, Daniel Webster
Gelwicks, Garfield & Conness, eds and pubs *Coloma Miners' Advocate,* 198; Gelwicks & Co. pubs Coloma *Empire County Argus;* dis-

agreed politically with publishers, withdrew from firm, 198; D. W. Gelwicks & Co. established Placerville *Mountain Democrat* "ed to date," 199

and Co., pubs Coloma *Empire County Argus,* first issue Nov 19 1853, Gelwicks ed Mar. 10 1855, in *Mountain Democrat,* Gelwicks said that A. A. Van Guelder was founder of *Argus.* Gelwick soon withdrew, no ed listed in Jan 1854

George, Givens

prop San Jose *Tribune* at founding, afterwards bought out W. S. Letcher, was ed & prop, 220

Gerberding, C O

C. O. Gerberding & Co., props SF *Bulletin,* 121

German, had been in bus dept NY *Courier* and *Enquirer;* with James King of William and Abel Whitton, founder of SF *Bulletin;* bought Thomas King's interest Ja 17 1858, later sole owner; King's interest purchased by James W. Simonton, Mr 31 1858; C. O. Gerberding & Co. dissolved Ja 1861; retired ill-health; died D 24 1863 (SF *Bulletin* Ja 3 1893 13/14)

Gift,

Gift, Prindle, and Lockwood withdrew from pubs of Sacramento *State Tribune* (no. 1), replaced by O. P. Allen, firm became James Allen & Son (SF *Alta* Ja 21 1856)

Gihon, Dr. John Hancock

prop SF *Picayune,* 107

died (Sacto *Union* F 12 1875 1/4) at Shreveport, La., where practicing medicine; private secretary to Gov. Geary; with Nisbet and Soulé, author *Annals of San Francisco***

Gilbert, Edward

lieut in Stevenson's regiment, takes census SF 1847, 24; joins Kemble to found SF *Alta California,* 28-29; career, 29; returns from Washington, 30; duel with James W. Denver, 30-31; death, 31; effect of death on Kemble 31-32; E Gilbert & Co, dealings with William L. Newell, 35-37; joined SF *Star and Californian,* 87; founder of SF *Alta California,* 88-89; officer in Stevenson's New York regiment, practical printer and accomplished writer, 88; senior ed, proposed name of SF *Alta California* 89; delegate to Constitutional Convention from District of San Francisco, reporter at Monterey for *Alta,* 91; elected to Lower House of Congress, 1849, 91; returned from East in May, 1851, 93; resumed place as senior ed of *Alta* summer, 94; victim of duel with J. W. Denver, 94-95; fate already mentioned, 130**

Giles, Jesse Howard
former printer in NY *Tribune* office, 138; agent of E. Gilbert & Co., ed and pub Sacto *Placer Times,* 138-139; of Sacto *Placer Times,* married and settled in Mass., 166
Giles, W T
prop Marysville *California Express,* 176; ed and prop Downieville *Mountain Echo* (see Downieville *Sierra Citizen*), 195; brought press into (Downieville) valley, superintending descent down hill on "skids," publishing Douglas paper in Illinois, 196
Gish, John W
business manager Sacto *Democratic State Journal,* 152; retired from Sacto *Democratic State Journal,* 152; J. W. Gish & Co. pubs Sacto *California Statesman,* 155; Gish and Woodward filed suit for $20,000 claiming money and government printing promised as reward for political support; suit dismissed, 155-156
Gist, W H
Heckendorn, Gist & Wilson, props *Columbia Clipper,* 185
pub with John Heckendorn *Columbia Clipper* My 13 1854 - soon replaced by Wm. A. Wilson
Glascock, J A
Thornbury & Glascock pubs Yreka *Siskiyou Chronicle,* 204
Gloor, G W
assoc ed Marysville *California Express* (Marysville dir 1856 p. 108) *see* Bloor, Q W
Gober, W R
on pub com of SF *Christian Observer* 1851-2, Pacific American Conference of the M E Church, South
Godfrey, Grove K
pub Shasta *Vigilante,* 201
Godfrey, William
"present prop Hornitos *Mariposa Democrat,*" 191
Goodrich, C L
prop San Leandro *Alameda Gazette,* 225
Gordon, David Everett
Seaman & Gordon props Weaverville *Trinity Journal* 1856, Gordon sole prop 1858, 209
Gordon, Robert
ed of *Californian,* 81
Gore, G W
prop Columbia *Star;* Ramage press destroyed, 183
Gorham, Charles M
ed Marysville *Inquirer* Ja 1856; died Ja 1882

Gorham, George C
ed Marysville *Inquirer,* 177
prop Marysville *Inquirer* Jan. 1856; Clerk of City (Marysville)
Gould, A L
W. T. Whitacre and A. L. Gould props Mariposa *Chronicle,* 189
Gould, A S
prop SF *Sun,* 113
Gray, J
on SF *Alta California,* did not plan to start rival paper, 36-37; bought P. Morrill's third interest in Sacto *Union,* 151
Greeley, Robert F
chief ed SF *Golden Era,* 112; ed SF *California Mail,* 118
Greenwood, Otis
ed Sonora *Union Democrat,* 181
Griffiths, Thomas J
in Matthewson, Russell & Co, SF *California Public Balance* (no. 2) Mr 31-My 7 1851
Grove,
bought Fitch's interest in Sacto *Transcript,* 143
Groves,
Parker and Groves, pubs Yankee Jim's *Mountain Courier,* 214-215
Grubler, G H
pub Crescent City *Herald* when he died, 224
born Zurich, Switzerland, to Texas 1830, Calif 1850, first merchant Crescent City, died at 42, "Herald now edited by J. W. McComb" (Sacto *Union* Je 16 1856 3/1)
Gubler, G H
see Grubler, G H
Gunn, Dr. Lewis Carstairs
ed and prop Sonora *Herald,* 180; native of U.S., Sonora *Herald,* 181; assaulted by ex-Nicaragua filibuster, 181; sold Ramage Press to G. W. Gore, 183-184;
author (with wife) *Records of a California Family* . . . San Diego 1928**
Guthrie, George Whitney
prop SF *National* (formerly *Globe*), 125
deputy surveyor of port of SF, 1854-61, and owner and pub of the *National Herald, Mirror* and the Daily *Republic*

Haehnlen, Jacob
prop SF *Freie Press,* 112
pub SF Calif *Staats Zeitung* Jl 1852 - fall 1853

Hale, Clarkson P
prop and pub *Herald* (Marysville dir 1853 p. 50)
Haley, Dr.
ed and prop Sonora *Herald,* 180
Hall, Lovick Pierce
among props Bidwell *Butte Record,* ed, known as "Long Primer Hall," 206; fought with De Courcy, who went to jail, 206
ed of Auburn *Placer Democrat* for six weeks in Jl-Ag 1854, discharged by Shannon, who later wrote, "every person that knows him knows that he is not responsible for anything — being a coward by nature and a drunkard and liar from force of habit" (Auburn *Placer Democrat* S 27 1854); arrested for treason (SF *Alta* My 9 1865); as ed Yolo *County Democrat* (from My 1 1869) occasioned libel suit by Yolo *Mail,* which caused his retirement
Hammill, William
pub SF *Catholic Standard,* 113
ed SF *Monitor* Mr 6 1858 -
Ham,
King, Ham and Wright pubs Downieville *Mountain Echo,* 196
Hamilton,
assoc ed succeeding William Walker, SF *Herald,* 101-102; died in spring of 1853, 102
Hamilton, Henry
prop and ed Mokelumne Hill *Calaveras Chronicle,* 182; pub and ed of *LA Star,* 234; formerly connected with *Calaveras Chronicle* and one or two other mining papers, 234
in Matthewson, Russell & Co., SF *California Public Balance* (no. 2) Mr 31 - My 7 1851; b Londonderry, to US 1848, Calif 1849; long and successful career in S. Calif and Hawaiian publishing**
Hamilton, W G
pub San Leandro *Alameda County Gazette,* Ag 30 1856
Hansicker, Charles L
C. L. Hansicker, J. Court and W. J. Keating started Sacto *Union,* 146; a founder of Sacto *Union,* printer, 147; Hansicker & Co. (C.L.) see Sacto *Union* for members of Co, 147; sold out of Sacto *Union,* 149
death (*Union* D 2 1859) at Covington, Ind.
Harcombe, A W
ed SF *Legal Intelligencer,* 124
Hardenbergh, James Richmond
Mar 1 1856 commenced suit against Presley Dunlap, to recover possession of Sacto *California Statesman,* 156

founded Sacto *Democratic Standard* F 26 1859, Charles T Botts, ed; long public career**

Harmon, F H

founder of Sacto *Union,* printer, 147; sold out after Sacto *Union* turned Whig, 149; Springer & Harmon props Coloma *El Dorado News,* 197; F. H. Harmon and T. A. Springer, ed and pub, Placerville *El Dorado News,* 198-199

sold his interest in Placerville *El Dorado News* to Richard Cole, June 1853, who changed name to *El Dorado Republican* June 11

Harvey, W H

C. Babb & W. H. Harvey pubs Sacto *City Item,* 160-161

Harvy,

Harvy & Childs ed and pub Placerville *American,* 199

Haskin,

Conklin & Haskin, pub & prop SF *Town Talk.* later SF *Times & Town Talk,* later SF *Times* My 10 1857-1858

Hatch, Dr.

one of eds of Sacramento *California American,* (Sacto dir 1856 p. 122)

Hatch, H S

sold interest in Mokelumne Hill *Calaveras Chronicle* (Sacto *Union* Jan 2 1860 4/4)

Hatch, T

among eds and props of SF *Star* N 19 1856

Hawkins, Hiram R

ed Auburn *Whig,* followed by *Placer Press,* Ja 20 1855 - O 1857; born 1826, New York State, arrived in Calif via Horn Je 11 1849; died as US Consul in Tumbez, Peru N 20 1866

Hayes, Thomas

duel with John Nugent over *Herald's* attitude on city lands, 102

Head, W S

among props and eds of La Porte *Mountain Messenger,* 212

Heatley, John O

prop Marysville *News,* 177; prop Marysville *National Democrat,* 178

Heckendorn, John

Heckendorn, Gist & Wilson, props Columbia *Clipper,* Heckendorn, ed, 185; ed and prop Murphy's *Big Tree Bulletin,* 191

Je 1856 sold interest in Columbia *Clipper* to J. Wing Oliver.

Heitzeberg, P

ed and prop, with Rapp and Hinton, of SF *Le Phare,* 123

Helm, Alfred

A. Helm and H. Hickok props Downieville *Sierra Citizen,* 196; prop

La Porte *Mountain Messenger*, 212

founded Gibsonville *Herald* or *Trumpet* N 19 1853 (SF *Alta* N 23 1853); sold "his interest in Gibsonville *Messenger* to John M. Lovejoy, Esq., who will also mount the editorial chair" (ibid., Ja 25 1855 2/1)

see Gibsonville *Trumpet*

Hempstead, Charles H

superintendent of the Mint, 113, 130; ed SF *Sun* 1856, 113

Secretary of State (SF *Alta* O 8 1855 2/1); death, Salt Lake (*Alta* O 1 1879 4/1), came to Pac Coast from Penna and was Gov. Bigler's private sec., during CW on staff of Gen. Connor, Second Calif Volunteers

Hensley, Sam'l J

Hensley, Reading & Co., Sutter's Fort; Hensley, Merrill & King, bankers, Sacto; James King of William in firm, 121

Herrera,

Herrera & Blanch, eds SF *Eco del Pacifico,* 124

Herrick, William Francis

prop of SF *Alta,* 96

Heslep, August M

pub SF *Plaindealer,* 127

Hess, Fr

& Co., pub SF *California Democrat* (SF dir 1858, 1860); bought paper age of 16 (SF *Alta* S 16 1881)

Hickock, H

A. Helm and H. Hickok props Downieville *Sierra Citizen,* 196

Hicks, W F

prop Marysville *California Express,* 176-177

printer, *California Express* office, Ark (Marysville dir 1858 p. 59) present props W. F. Hicks & Co (p.88)

Higgins, Lank

apprenticeship under Montgomery & Cox of *Napa County Reporter,* April 1857; 1870 was ed

Highton, H E

ed SF *Spirit of the Times,* 127

becomes chief writer of above (SF *Alta* O 25 1858)

Hinckley, J C

S. H. Dosh, J. C. Hinckley, and A. Skillman props Shasta *Courier* 1852; Hinckley sold out, 200; and H. C. Moffitt pubs and eds Shasta *Republican,* 201

sold out early in 1853

Hinton, W M
ed and prop with Heitzeberg and Rapp of SF *Le Phare,* 123; W. H. Hinton & Co. pubs SF *Telegram,* 129
Hittell, John Shertzer
ed of *Alta* during part of Kemble's absence, 96; still in SF *Alta,* 98; assoc ed SF *California Chronicle,* 155**
Hittell, Theodore H
assoc ed SF *Bulletin,* 122-123**
Hoffman, H F W
Wheelock and Hoffman pubs SF *Republican,* 129
business manager of SF *Calif Chronicle,* causes its suspension by $1000 judgment, My 12 1858 - Sacto *Union* My 17 1858 3/2
Hogan, E T
E. T. Hogan and J. S. Ward, eds Quincy *Plumas Democrat,* 211
Holmes, L A
original pub and "present" ed and prop Mariposa *Gazette,* 189-190
died Stockton S 8 1862, native of Connecticut, aged 35
Holt, J T
pub of Placerville *Herald* Apr 30 to Nov 5, 1853, with owner and ed W. Wadsworth, and with F. A. Bee to June; sold equipment to Coloma *Empire County Argus*
Hoogs, Octavian
Hoogs & Anselm, pubs SF LA *Gazette Republicaine,* 108
Hooton,
Hooten & Co. pubs Suisun *Solano County Herald,* 221
Hopkins, Mark
capital for Sacto *Times* furnished by Stanford, Charles Crocker, E. B. Crocker, C. P. Huntington, and Mark Hopkins—pubs C. Cole & Co., pro-Frémont (Sacto *Union* N 19 1883, P. Coggins obit.)
Hoppe, J D
ed of *Californian,* 87; retired from *Californian,* 84
Hopper, John D /or O? /
ed Mariposa *Chronicle,* 189
Hossack, C D
C. D. Hossack & Co. pubs Sacto *State Sentinel,* 163
Howard,
Howard & Hudson pubs SF *Golden Hill News,* 117
Howard, J G
ed Weaverville *Trinity Times,* 208
possibly Howard, Jerome B., *Herald* office, (Marysville dir 1853 p. 32)

Howard, William Davis Merry
contributed to Nugent for SF *Herald,* 101
Howe, C H
C. H. Howe & Co., pubs of Stockton *Item,* 172
Howe, Henry J
A. J. Howe and M. T. Crawford, props Weaverville *Democrat,* Howe ed, 208-209; among eds of La Porte *Mountain Messenger,* 212
Hubbard, G C
printer, founder of SF *Alta California,* 88-89; sold interest in *Alta* T. R. Per Lee, 90; returns to the East, 90; froze to death on journey, 97
Hubbard, R
R. Hubbard and W. B. Keep props Santa Barbara *Gazette,* 237
Hudson,
Howard & Hudson pubs SF *Golden Hill News,* 117
Hull, Patrick P
prop with L. R. Lull of SF *California Courier,* few days before demise of paper, 106; Hull, Matthewson & Co. publishers SF *Whig and Commercial Advertiser,* 111; married Lola Montez, 131; prop SF *Times* (ex *Town Talk*), 118
Hull, P. P. & Co., props *Daily Whig,* S 1852
Hung Tai
see Too Yune, Ze, 161
Huntington, Collis P
capital for Sacto *Times* furnished by Stanford, Charles Crocker, E. B. Crocker, C. P. Huntington, and Mark Hopkins—pubs C. Cole & Co., pro-Frémont (Sacto *Union* N 19 1883, P. Coggins obit.)**
Hutchings, James Mason
ed and prop SF *Hutchings' Illustrated California Magazine,* 125
reported as "California Holiday Pictorial"—Hutchings & Rosenfield, pubs (SF *Alta* N 20 1857 2/1)
Hutchinson, C A
prop Stockton *San Joaquin Republican,* 171
Hutton, James A
bought press for Jernegan, Cacheville *Yolo Democrat,* 227

Ingham, Charles T
Brown, Ingham & Co., pubs Sacto *Visitor,* 164
Ingham C. T., printer, Standard office (Sacto dir 1859 p.64) death (*Call* Ap 20 1890 2/7) veteran printer, came to Calif 1850

Jackson, Orin F
John Tabor and Orin F. Jackson bought Stockton *Journal;* Jackson

withdrew, 170

January, William A

pub Placerville *Mountain Democrat,* 199

Jefferis, Edward G

pub SF *Wide West,* 117; a founder of Sacto *Union,* printer, 147; E. G. Jefferis & Co. pubs Sacto *Union,* 149; only Jefferis, Keating and Clark remained of original props of *Union* in 1852, 149; Jefferis and Kurtz sold their interests in *Union* to Larkin, Morrill, Keating and J. Anthony, 150

death *Alta* Mr 29 1880 1/6 "foreman of the State Printing Office, well-known printer . . ." nearly 52 years old

Jernegan, W L

prop Cacheville *Yolo Democrat,* left owing money to all, questionnaire answered by his editor Ruland, 226-227

Joffre, J

pub SF *La Cronica,* 118

Johnson,

Johnson & Doyle props SF *Pacific Whalemen's List.* sm O 24?-D 19 1855?

Johnson, P C

Redding, Johnson & Co. props Sacto *Democrat State Journal;* Ap 1854 Johnson sold his interest to Snowden, 153; C. B. Lawton and P. C. Johnson, pubs Diamond Springs *Miners' Advocate,* 207

Johnson, S O

pub of SF *Shipping List and Prices Current,* 110

pub *Prices Current & Shipping List* (Sept 1852)

Johnson, George Pen

ed SF *National* (see *Globe*); fought duel with W. I. Ferguson, State Senator from Sacto, retired on opponent's death, 124-125

Johnston,

Clerk of the US Circuit Court, SF, 130

Jones,

Damon, Emerson & Jones pubs San Jose *Visitor,* 219; Emerson, Jones & Parks pubs San Jose *Santa Clara Register,* 219

Jones, Elbert P

ed SF *California Star,* 20; signed first editorial in *Star,* 21; evicted, 22-23; makes fortune in real estate, 23; ed of *California Star,* 70-71; salutation to the public, 70; practiced law in Tennessee, 71; opinion of *Californian* and its staff, 73-74; report on public meeting on beach lots, 74-75; retired from editorship, *California Star,* 76; resigns or is fired from *California Star,* goes into real estate, makes money, retires to his home in Southern States, dies, 76-77

owner Portsmouth House SF, advt Ag 14 1847; death 1852, Charleston, S.C.
Julian, Jacob M
Fitch, Upham & Co., props Sacto *Transcript,* 143
death (SF *Chron.* Ja 15 1905 37/7)
Julian, P
pub SF *Patriote de San Francisco;* d My 5-Jl? 1856

Kan, Lee
assoc ed SF *Oriental,* 119, 120
Kearney, Matthew
pub Sonora *Herald,* Irishman, 180
Keating, William J
C. L. Hansicker, J. Court and W. J. Keating started Sacto *Union,* sent to NY to purchase press and types, 146; a founder of Sacto *Union,* printer, 147; only Jefferis, Keating and Clark remained of original props of *Union* in 1852, 149; bought more shares My 16 1853, 150; sold out Je 5 1853, 150
listed as printer, Sacto *Union* office, from Missouri, 1859
Keep, W B
R. Hubbard and W. B. Keep, props Santa Barbara *Gazette,* 237
Kemble, Edward Cleveland
biography, 9-39; printer with Brannan on the *Brooklyn,* becomes ed SF *California Star,* 46; served with Frémont during winter, returned in early Ap, 76; eviction of Elbert P. Jones, 76-77; returned from mines S 1848, 85; bought *Star,* 85; acquired SF *Californian* mid-N 1848, 86; founder of SF *Alta California,* 88-90; went East in O 1850 with Gilbert, 93; returned in My 1851, 93; went to Europe, fall 1852 [*i.e.* 1853], 96; returned fall 1853 [*i.e.* N 2 1854], found *Alta* insolvent, 96; 1855 began pub of SF *Californian,* abandoned, 97; connected with Sacto press, 1858, 97; wrote leading articles for SF *California Chronicle* S-D 1857, 116; Brannan discouraged his founding *Alta* as impractical, but it succeeded, so a press also might at Sutter's Fort, 135; brought Ramage press to Sacramento, 136; difficulties of printing Sacto *Placer Times,* 137-138; ed and pub Sacto *Placer Times,* 138
born N 11 1828 in Troy, NY; arrived Calif Jl 31 1846; author of *History of California Newspapers;* married Cecilia Amanda Windsor, son Edward Windsor Kemble; Lt.-Col. in Civil War; Inspector of Indian Affairs under Pres Grant; asst manager Associated Press office in NY; died F 10 1886 at Mott Haven NY**
Kelly, J W
on pub com of SF *Christian Observer,* Pacific American Confer-

ence of the M E Church, South, SF 1852
Kenaday, Alexander M
prop SF *Satan's Bassoon,* 112
from Virginia; printer Sacto *Standard* 1859, SF *Bulletin* 1861-1863
Kennedy, J B
prop Stockton *San Joaquin Republican,* 171
Kerr, George
bought Stockton *Times* Ap 27, burnt out My 6, 1851, 169; prop *San Joaquin Republican*
newspaper training in Pennsylvania and New Orleans: Capt in Mexican War; State Printer; a pub SF *Placer Times and Transcript;* died Mr 5 1854 age 27
Kewen, Edward J C ("Harry Quillem")
pub SF *Journal of Commerce,* 117
filibuster with Walker; later lawyer and dist atty in LA, member of State Legislature, Atty Gen**
Kies, George O
Wheelock & Kies props Coloma *True Republican,* 198
ed and pub Coloma *Times* 1859-1861, then moved it to Placerville; death SF *Call* N 18 1889
Kimball, Charles Proctor ("Noisy Carrier")
pub SF *Uncle Sam* (SF directory 1852)
King,
King, Ham and Wright pubs Downieville *Mountain Echo,* 196
King, Homer
ed and pub Jackson *Democratic Standard,* 187
death Sacto *Union* F 29 1876 3/1
King, S T
S. T. King Co pubs SF *Spirit of the Times* 1858
King, Thomas Sim
ed SF *Bulletin,* 122
brother of James King of William; retired from paper Ja 17 1859; death Buffalo, NY Ap 11 1911
King of William, James
murdered, 103; effect of murder on city papers, 103-104; effect on SF *California Chronicle,* 115-116; ed SF *Bulletin,* 121; biography, 121-122; assassinated, 130**
Kingsbury, Joseph
ed SF *Journal,* assaulted (SF *Alta* Mr 27 1856); ed SF *California Chronicle* during its Republican period, 1856 to election of Buchanan

Knight, Edward
local reporter, Sacto *California American*
Knight, Samuel
among pubs Stockton *Journal* 1851, 170; Samuel Knight and B. W. Owens pubs *Journal* 1854, 171
Kooser, Benjamin Parke
Armor Clayes & Kooser props San Andreas *Independent,* ed to S 18 1858, 190
Korn, Julius
ed SF *Journal* (German), 120; Warden of the Port of SF, 130-131
Kretzinger, George W
ed Oroville *Butte County Democrat,* 210
Krug, Karl
ed SF *Freie Presse,* 112
ed SF *California Staats Zeitung*
Kuhl, F
printed SF *Golden Hills' News* Ap 28-? 1854, lithographed, in Chinese
Kurtz, William W
W. W. Kurtz & Co. pubs SF *Wide West,* 117; bought Court's interest in Sacto *Union* Ja 1852, 149; Jefferis and Kurtz sold interests in Sacto *Union* My 16 1853, 150
death SF *Alta* Ja 22 1863, age about 36

Labatt, Henry J
pub SF *District Court Reports,* 126
co-editor with Bien of SF *The Voice of Israel,* 1856
Labatt, Theo.
2nd assoc ed SF *Star* 1856 (SF *Bulletin* S 3 1856)
LaChapelle, A de
ed of French section SF *The Present and the Future, Le Present et l'Avenir,* 114; ed SF *Messager,* 114, 119; went to France, 131
Lafontaine, A J
pub SF *Abend Zeitung,* 118
death (SF *Alta* Mr 2 1872 1/2) ". . . kept the Mountaineer Job Office . . ."
Lafuente, J T
pub SF *La Cronica,* 118; Lafuente, Laguizamonte & Elespura, pubs SF *Sud Americano,* 120; in penitentiary from SF for homicide, 130
Laird, Jane
prop Marysville *California Express,* 177

took over deceased husband's share in 1857, till Je 1860; one of two women actively in papers

Laird, Luther

& Co. purchased Marysville *California Express,* Je 1854; death (SF *Alta* Je 24 1857), formerly a resident of Tennessee, age 33

Lancey, T M

see Yancey, Tryon M

Langari,

Langari & Phelps pubs Placerville *Index,* 200

Langhorne, Maurice M

pub Columbia *Columbian*

Langton, J C

prop Downieville *Sierra Citizen,* ed and pub, 196

Larkin, Henry W

bought interest in Sacto *Union,* 149; Larkin, Morrill, Keating and J. Anthony bought Jefferis' and Kurtz' interests in *Union,* 150; Keating sold interest in *Union* to Larkin, Morrill, Anthony and Clark, 150; J. Gray, H. W. Larkin and J. Anthony props *Union,* 151

born 1819, Norwalk, Conn., printer NY *Tribune, Herald,* others, to Calif in 1850; though in NY for several years after 1862, continued part of firm J. Anthony & Co. until *Union* merged with Sacto *Record* F 1875; real estate and mining stocks, made and lost fortune, died N 10 1878**

Larrabee,

purchased job office of SF *Sun* at $2900 (SF *Alta* Ja 28 1855)

Lawrence, James W

J. W. Ross and James Lawrence eds and pubs Mariposa *Star,* 190

Lawrence, Joseph E

owner SF *Sun,* 113; ed and part owner SF *Wide West,* 117; ed Sacto *Placer Times,* 139; L. Pickering, J. E. Lawrence and L. Aldrich bought *Placer Times;* soon after, Pickering and Lawrence bought out Aldrich, 142; Pickering & Lawrence half owners of State printing and Sacto *Placer Times and Transcript,* Pickering, Fitch & Lawrence eds; moved to SF, 134-135; Customs receiver SF, 166

came to Calif in 1849; after *Times and Transcript* moved SF, continued with it until 1854; after that one of props of the *Golden Era;* died Flushing, L.I., 1878**

Lawton, C B

Wm S. Fleming and C. B. Lawton pubs Diamond Springs *Miners' Advocate* O 1855 to winter, then Lawton and P. C. Johnson, then removed to Folsom, 207

Lecount,
Lecount & Strong pubs SF *Pioneer,* 116
Leguizamont,
Lafuente, Leguizamont & Elespura, pubs SF *Sud Americano,* 120
Leland,
brother of Warren Leland, succeeded him in SF *Pacific News,* 99
Leland, Warren
pub SF *Pacific News,* sold out, returned East, 99; from Norwich, Conn., a proprietor of Metropolitan Hotel, New York, 99; sketch in NY Sunday paper described him as " founder of the first newspaper in San Francisco," 99-100
Leonori, Rufus U
in Matthewson, Russell & Co, SF *California Public Balance* (no. 2) Mr 31-My 7 1851
Letcher, W S
founded San Jose *Tribune,* afterwards sold out to Givens George, 220
Lewis, A C
ed San Andreas *Calaveras Union,* 191
Lewis, John A
one of founders of LA *Star,* from Massachusetts, 233
Boston reporter, followed William H. Rand, a relative, to Sonora mines in S 1849, later joined him in SF; founded LA *Star* with McElroy, later joined by Rand; sold paper in Ag 1853; in 1854 assoc with SF *Chronicle*
Lewis, John C
J. H. McNabb and J. C. Lewis pubs Quincy *Plumas Argus,* 211
L'hériter,
ed SF *Revue Californienne,* 119
Lillard, J D
ed and prop Napa City *Herald,* 225
Lilley,
Lilley and Oliver pubs Grass Valley *Telegraph,* S 22 1853
Lincoln, Charles G
ed and pub, Oroville *North Californian,* 209
died (Sacto *Union* D 19 1884 2/4)**
Little, Milton
stock of goods from Islands advertised in Monterey *Californian,* 64
born New York State 1820, settled in Monterey 1843, storekeeper and real estate, married Mary Eagar of NY (sister of the printer) in service by Rev. W. Colton

Livingston, H Beeckman
J. W. Winans and H. B. Livingston eds Sacto *Index,* 145; assoc ed Sacto *Union,* after being connected with paper for several months, 149-150

Lockwood,
Gift, Prindle, and Lockwood withdrew from pubs of Sacto *State Tribune* (no. 1), replaced by O. P. Allen, firm becoming James Allen & Son (SF *Alta* Ja 21 1856)

Loehr, Dr. Ferdinand von
ed SF *California Demokrat,* 114; wounded in duel for article written, 130
died 1876

Logan, William
ed Jackson *Owl,* Ag 25 1854

Long, W S
ed Sacto *Mercury,* 164

Lovejoy, John K
founder Quincy *Old Mountaineer,* 211; among props of La Porte *Mountain Messenger,* 212
born ca. 1810 in Illinois, Abolitionist family, printer; to Calif in 1849 or 1850, mined; Ja 1855 bought Gibsonville *Mountain Messenger* from A. Helm (SF *Alta* Ja 25 1855), strong defender of miners who presented him with enough gold for cane-head; with the *Mountain Messenger* till S 1855; O 1855 with Edward McElwain started the Quincy *Old Mountaineer* and continued till sold Ag 1857 to become *Plumas Argus;* editor in Nevada; died Ja 25, 1877

Lull, Louis R
prop with P. P. Hull of SF *California Courier,* 106; ed SF *Commercial Advertiser,* 111; ed and prop Marysville *Herald,* 176
ed SF *Whig,* S 1852; married at Marysville: "editor of the Marysville *Herald*" to Miss Josephine, daughter of L. W. Ransom, pub and prop of that paper (SF *Bulletin* My 31 1856 3/1); Marysville direc 1856 lists him as ed and prop (p.61)

Lynch, Philip
Lynch, Davison & Rolfe pubs Sacto *Index,* 145; Lynch & Sherman, eds and props Auburn *Placer Democrat,* 202

Mack, John R
practical printers pub SF *Western American* Ja 15-Mr 1 1852

McCallum, J G
ed and co-prop Georgetown *News,* 208

McClatchy, James
assoc ed Sacto *Settlers' and Miners' Tribune,* 144; Redding, Johnson & Co. (incl McClatchy) props Sacto *Democratic State Journal,* editorials written by Redding, McClatchy and May, 153; sold interest in *Democratic State Journal* to D. J. Thomas; ed for month after William Walker left, 153-154; McClatchy and Thomas, eds Sacto *Californian,* 156; replaced J. R. Ridge as ed Sacto *Bee,* with S. J. May, 162
born Ireland, banking in NY, then on NY *Tribune;* to Calif via Panama in 1849 as *Tribune* correspondent, left ship in Baja Calif and walked to San Diego; mined a little, worked on Sacto papers with Cornelius Cole, founded *Bee* in 1857**
McClure,
McClure & Co., pubs Sacto *Morning Star,* 165
McCreary, H L
ed with William S. Wood, of Sacto *Hesperian,* Franklin High School, Ag 1858
McCrellish, Frederick
prop of SF *Alta,* 97
born Phila O 2 1828, came to Calif in 1852; identified with SF *Ledger* and in 1853 with *Herald;* joined *Alta* later part of 1854 and in 1856 became part prop, in this capacity till death (SF *Call* N 1 1882 1/8, N 2 1882 2/1)
McDermott, D A
business man of SF *Alta California,* 36
McDermott, Hugh F
pub SF *Cosmopolitan* My 5-? 1855 (SF Ap 27 1855 2/1)
McDonald, Calvin B
literary ed first number Sacto *Herald of the Morning,* 164; ed Downieville *Sierra Citizen,* 196; George E. Tallmadge and C. B. McDonald pubs and eds Downieville *Old Oaken Bucket,* 196; ed Weaverville *Trinity Journal,* 209
ed Sacto *Age,* with Washington Wright (SF *Alta* Ag 16, 1851); contributor to Sacto *Sign and Grip,* Ag 25 1857; an inmate of the Sierra County Alms House (SF *Alta* Mr 11 1877 1/2)
McDonald, J
J. McDonald & Co. props Sacto *Herald of the Morning,* 164
McDonald, J C
printer, Standard Office, Sacto 1859, from Pa.
McElroy, John
ed and pub Monterey *Sentinel,* 66; prop Marysville *California Express,* 176-177; of LA Star, from New York, 233; one of early

publishers of LA *Star,* 233; ed and pub Santa Cruz *Pacific Sentinel,* formerly prop Monterey *Pacific Sentinel,* 239
replaced E. Gould Buffum, with *Star to* N 4 1851; left LA to become assoc with northern journal; ret to *Star* O 1854, left same year; 1855-6 pub Monterey *Sentinel*
McElwain, Edward F
prop with Lovejoy, Quincy *Old Mountaineer,* 211
prop Sacto *Age* (SF *Alta* Ag 1857 2/4)
McGeorge,
McGeorge & Cellers, pubs Benicia *Solano County Herald,* 221
McGowan, Edward ("Ned")
prop Sacto *Phoenix,* followed by *Ubiquitous,* 164
reported shot at; arrested for libel, assault; headed conspiracy of rebel officers, part in murder of James King of William; wrote reminiscences, died SF D 8 1893, aged 90 years
McLean,
Masters, McLean and Savage, pubs 3rd issue SF *Eagle of Freedom* sm? juvenile, Republican (SF *Alta* O 12 1856)
McNabb, James Henry
J. H. McNabb and J. C. Lewis, pubs Quincy *Plumas Argus,* 211
to Calif in 1849, candidate for State Senate, Sonoma City (*Alta* Je 17 1862 2/2); died (San Jose *Pioneer* Ja 15 1900 p.13) "For nearly forty years . . . one of the editors of the Petaluma *Argus.*"
Macy, Andrew M
ed *Prices Current and Shipping List,* SF, S 1852; came to Calif in 1851 and in autumn became connected with SF *Picayune* as commercial ed; with George O. Doherty, he purchased the *Picayune* (SF *Alta* Mr 13 1852); physical infirmities from birth made health poor; died (*Alta* O 7 1853 2/1)
Magruder, Lloyd
prop Marysville *California Express,* 177
murdered (Sacto *Union* N3 1863) in Idaho Territory with Charles Allen formerly of Sacto; Magruder was running for Congress in Ter. and may have met the men at a political meeting; large sum of money stolen
Mansfield, Joseph
of Stockton *Republican,* killed by Tabor of *Journal,* 170; prop Stockton *San Joaquin Republican* when killed over editorial in *Journal,* 171
Mantz, William H
pub SF *Town Talk* (later *Times*), 118; W. H. Mantz & Co., estab SF *Telegram,* 129; editor Marysville *Inquirer,* 177

Marcy, William George
Marcy, Robb & Robinson to be pubs San Jose *Statesman,* announced but not pub, 218
Marks, James
Marks, Thomas & Co., pubs SF *Monitor,* Catholic, 128
Marrener, David J
prop Marysville *Herald,* 176
death (SF *Call* Ap 1 1890) for two years ed Marysville *Herald,* ret to NY and engaged in glass business; died in NY; prop of paper 1851-1852
Marriott, Edward [i.e. Frederick]
pub SF *News-Letter,* 127
Marvin, John Gage
formerly of Sonora *Herald,* succeeded J. R. Atkins in local dept of Sacto *Sacramento Age,* 159; Marvin & White bought Ramage Press from Radcliffe of Stockton *Times* for Sonora *Herald,* 179; ed and prop Sonora *Herald,* 179-180; native of US, 181
grad of Harvard Law School 1844, served there as law librarian, published 800 pp. legal bibliography Phila 1847; to Calif in 1849, settled in Empire City, Tuolumne County, edited 15th-17th numbers Sonora *Herald;* served as QM of Mariposa Btn and first Supt of Public Instruction (letter My 4 1852 from Howard Jay Graham to Calif State Library): died in Honolulu D 1857
Massett, Stephen C
part prop Marysville *Herald,* 176; lecturing in East, 178
an ed and pub Marysville *Herald* Ja 28 1851 - N 29 1851; afterwards connected with other Calif pubs, including *Pioneer,* first literary mag, but does not seem to have been ed of any but *Herald;* writer, musician and composer, concerts SF 1849
Matthewson, R C
Hull, Matthewson & Co, pubs *SF Whig and Commercial Advertiser,* 111; ed Sacto *Democrat,* formerly of Benicia *Vedette,* 157; ed and pub Benicia *Vedette,* formerly connected with SF *Balance* (no. 2) afterwards with Sacto *Democrat,* 221
bought *Balance* (no. 2) from Buckelew, Mr 31 - Je 7 1851
May, Samuel J
Redding, Johnson & Co (incl May) props Sacto *Democrat State Journal,* Je 1854 May sold to Redding & Snowden, editorials written by Redding, McClatchy and May, 153; Parker H. French and S. J. May eds Sacto *State Tribune* (no. 1) to S 1855 when French sold to May, 158; May & Co, late props Sacto *State Tribune* (no. 1), started no. 2 in Sacto rivalling no. 1 continued in SF, 159; Jas. Allen

J. R. Ridge and S. J. May props Sacto *California American,* 160; J. R. Ridge and S. J. May eds Sacto *Bee,* 162

death (*Union* Jy 13 1872 4/7) age 32; born in Boston; Calif in 1849; ran drugstore, obit says "Dr.", city ed *Bee* at death

Mayfield, W I

Mayfield & Co, pubs Yreka *Siskiyou Chronicle,* 204

Mendenhall,

"starting new paper at Yreka (with Thornbury) to be called the *Northern Herald*", 203n

Meredith, Henry

principal ed Sacto *California Statesman,* 155

born Hanover Cty, Va, Ag 14 1826; grad College of Columbia, Mo; ret Va, studied law; crossed plains to Calif in 1850, mined; practiced law last 6-7 years Nevada [City]; killed by Indians, Utah Territory, as captain Nevada Rifles (SF *Alta,* My 30 1860 2/4)

Merman, I A

pub San Leandro *Alameda County Gazette,* Ja 10 1857

Merriam, William P

among eds and props of SF *Star* N 19 1856

Merrill, Annis

prop *Alta California* Printing and Publishing Co, 96

Merrill,

Hensley, Merrill & King, bankers Sacto (James King of William in firm), 121

Merritt, P Gordon

ed with Frank F. Fargo of SF *Pathfinder and Post* (SF *Alta* N12 1856)

Mighels, Henry Rust

G. H. Crosette and H. R. Mighels eds Oroville *Butte Record,* 210

first ed Marysville *Appeal,* Ja 23 1860, till B. P. Avery & Co bought *Appeal,* Avery becoming ed, Je 5 1860

Miller, J H

Miller & Olmstead, pubs Iowa Hill *News,* 210

"J. H. Miller & Co. are to be the publishers of the Iowa Hill newspaper" (Sacto *Union* Ag 9 1855 p.2)

Miller, William

ed SF *Medical Journal,* 120

Mills, M E

ed Auburn *Whig,* 202

Milne, David D

D. D. Milne and W. Baer orig props Mariposa *Mariposa Democrat,* 191

Miro, F
ed SF *Star of Empire* O 1 1856
Mitchell, Charles H
ed and prop Auburn *Placer Herald,* 201
Mitchell, J A
G. H. Baker and J. A. Mitchell pubs Sacto *Spirit of the Age,* 159
Mitchell, Tabb
prop Marysville *California Express,* 176-177; R. Rust and T. Mitchell props Auburn *Placer Herald,* 201
ed and pub *Placer Herald* D 2 1854
Moffitt, H C
J. C. Hinckley and H. C. Moffitt pubs and eds Shasta *Republican,* 201
Monson, B H
Farwell, Monson & Valentine, SF printers, purchased Parker H. French's interest in Sacto *State Tribune* (no. 1), attached paper, 158
in Matthewson, Russell & Co, SF *Calif Public Balance* (no.2) Mr 31-My 7 1851; Monson & Valentine, printers SF *Pioneer* 1854-1855; Monson, Haswell & Co, Commercial Printing and Job Office, SF S 1852
Montgomery, Alexander M
Alex. Montgomery & Co., ed and pub Sacto *Water Fount and Home Journal,* 159; assoc ed Sacto *Mercury,* 165; ed Sacto *Morning Star,* 165
born Missouri 1824; died Yreka Jl 1902, ed Yreka *Union*
Montgomery, Robert T
ed and part pub *Napa County Reporter,* 225
born 1821 Richmond, Va; came to Calif in 1853, taught school till 1856, joined press; married sister of his partner, A. J. Cox (*Reporter* issue of Je 13, 1857 printed in red ink to celebrate); with *Reporter* to O 1863, then ed of *Napa Valley Register* on death of founder J. I. Horrell, then a partner to Ja 1 1866; returned My 1867 continuing to O 23 1869, except for six months ending Jl 1 1868 when with SF *Times;* his editorial work "never excelled and seldom equalled"; drank himself to death, in county hospital, D 4 1878
Moody,
Moody & Co, pubs SF *Globe,* 124
Moore,
Oliver & Moore, founded Grass Valley *Telegraph* w in 1853; sold in N 1854 to W. B. Ewer

Moore, J J
among pubs SF *Mirror of the Times* (Negro) 1857-8 (SF *Alta* S 9 1856

Moore, R Cutler
partner in *Alta,* 91; printer from NY *Sun* office, arrived on Apollo with J. B. Ormiston, 91; Moore and Ormiston sold interest in *Alta* to Durivage, 92; returned to NY, 92; purchased SF *Alta;* formerly partner in E. Gilbert & Co, 96; supported Vigilance Committee of 1856, 97; went to Mexico, 131

Morrill, Paul
bought Davison's interest in Sacto *Union,* 149; Jefferis and Kurtz sold their interests in Sacto *Union* to Larkin, Morrill, Keating and J. Anthony, 150; Keating sold interest in *Union* to Morrill, Larkin, Anthony and Clark, 150; sold his one-third share of *Union* to J. Gray, 151

death (SF *Alta* My 28 1880 1/3) 68 years old, born Hillsboro, N.H. 1812, employed composing room NY *Sun* of which he was part prop 4 years; he and W. H. Dinsmore were sole owners until 1848, when they sold to Democrats; compositor on NY *Tribune* until 1850 when came to Calif via Isthmus; very welcome on *Alta;* when foreman of composing room went East selected to fill place; lacking capital to buy share prosperous SF journals, went to Sacto 1851, soon became a prop of *Union,* held post 20 yrs; *Union* "edited with spirit and judgment," most profitable newspaper in US for time; Props sold out in 1875, when he moved to SF; accepted post 1877 as Surveyor of the Port, Dinsmore his Deputy**

Morse, Amos C
ed and/or pub Sacto *News Letter,* 155n

Morse, "Dr." J F
pub SF *Bon Ton Critic,* sentenced to San Quentin for grand larceny, 116-117

imposter? *see* next entry

Morse, Dr. John Frederick
ed Sacto *Union,* 37-38; ed *Union* 1851, printer, founder; letters to New Orleans *Delta* attracted attention, 147; retired from editorship of *Union,* 150; ed SF and Sacto *California Farmer and Journal of Useful Sciences,* 156-157; ed Sacto *Illustrated Historical Sketches of California, With a Minute History of Sacramento Valley,* 157

arrived Calif 1849; had hospital with Stillman in Sacto; contributor to columns of Sacto *Sign and Grip,* IOOF paper, Ag 23? 1857-? (SF *Alta* Ag 25 1857)**

Moses, H A
ed and pub Placerville *Register,* 200
printer, State Printing office; s.; Ill.; Sacto 1859
Moulder, Andrew Jackson
on staff of SF *Herald,* became assoc ed, 102; elected Comptroller of SF, 103; State Supt of Public Instruction, 130
Regent, Univ of Calif, etc.**
"Mountaineer" (*pseud.*)
see Chamberlain, Charles Henry
Mulligan, William
started SF *Sunday Varieties,* 124
Murdoch, Francis Butter
pub and ed San Jose *Telegraph,* 220
Murray, Alexander
prop Sonora *Herald,* bro of Walter Murray, formerly on *Herald,* Englishman, 180
Murray, Walter
prop and ed Sonora *Herald,* bro of Alexander Murray, Englishman, 180
Myers, E L
practical printers pub SF *Western American* Ja 15-Mr 1 1852
"My Self" (*pseud.*)
"A new paper, called 'My Paper,' has been started in Sacramento; the editor and proprietor of which is 'My Self' " (SF *Alta* Ja 14 1857 2/1)
Myers, W F
among props La Porte *Mountain Messenger,* 212
pub with A. Helm of Gibsonville *Trumpet* (forerunner of above) N 19 1853; perhaps continuous through change to Gibsonville *Mountain Messenger* (N ? 1854) to removal to La Porte (S 1855)

Newell, William L
letter clarifying his dealings with E. Gilbert & Co, 35-37; foreman of *Alta* office, agent for Boston firm of type makers, kept type ordered for *Alta* and started *California Chronicle,* 115; owner SF *California Chronicle,* 116; sold SF *California Chronicle,* 116; ed SF *Call,* 126
Newly, W H
among pubs of SF *Mirror of the Times* (Negro) (SF *Alta* S 9 1856)
"Nimrod of the Mountains"
see Holmes, L. A., Mariposa *Gazette,* 189-190

Nisbet, James
assoc ed SF *California Chronicle,* 115; assoc ed of SF *Bulletin* with James King of William, ed for week after King's death, 122
with Gihon and Soulé wrote *Annals of San Francisco;* died in the wreck of the *Brother Jonathan* Jl 30 1865**
"Noodles, Peter" (*pseud.*)
ed Mokelumne Hill *Quamkeag Coyote,* 182
Noyes, William H
ed San Diego *Herald* Ap 21 1855-My 1 1856 (Dawson p.61)
Nueval, A
pub SF *Le Spectateur*
Nugent, John
pub and ed SF *Herald,* 101; bought Foy's interest in SF *Herald,* supposedly staked by Folsom, Howard, and others, 101; remained ed of SF *Herald* 102; duel with Alderman Cotter, received compound fracture of thigh bone but recovered, 102; duel with Thomas Hayes, Nugent recovered from compound fracture of arm, 102-103; withdrew all but his name from SF *Herald,* 103; turned against Vigilance Committees and popular movements, brought *Herald* to Democratic party, 104; ceased to write regularly for *Herald* after Vigilance excitement subsided; his name still listed, though he holds a Federal appointment on Puget Sound, 104; wounded in duel, for articles written, 130; US Commissioner to Fraser River, 130
came overland to San Diego with Col. Hays; "Senior editor" of *Alta* (Gilbert) apologizes to ed of *Herald* (Nugent) (SF *Alta* Mr 13 1852); Nugent and SF *Herald* locked out by Sam Brannan (Sacto *Union* O 17 1856)**

O'Connor, M T
sent to New York as agent for Buckelew to purchase material for a paper, then to establish and edit it in SF; Buckelew quarrelled with him before paper was started (*Public Balance*), 108
O'Doherty, George
see Doherty, George O
Oliver, J Wing
ed Columbia *Gazette,* first weekly to support S. A. Douglas, 185; prop and ed Columbia *Columbian,* 186; ed Yreka *Siskiyou Chronicle,* 204; ed Grass Valley *Telegraph,* 205; prop and ed Georgetown *News,* 208
Olmstead, J P
Miller & Olmstead, pubs Iowa Hill *News* 1855, Olmstead & Co pubs 1856-1857, 210-211; J. P. Olmstead and T. J. Waters pubs North San Juan *Star,* ed, 214

moved press and materials of Iowa Hill *News* to North San Juan, continued with first no of North San Juan *Star* N 18 1857, to last issue Ag 14 1858, sold to become *Hydraulic Press*

O'Meara, John

ed Mokelumne Hill *Calaveras Chronicle,* 182

State Printer, from NY

Ormiston, John B

printer from NY *Sun* office, arrived on *Apollo* with R. C. Moore and newspaper and job material, 91; partner in *Alta* 91; Moore & Ormiston sold interest in *Alta* to Durivage, Ormiston ret to NY summer of 1850, 92; in NY 1858, 97

Osborn, Timothy Coffin

ed Stockton *Journal* until sold to Crabb and Biven after death of Mansfield, 171

death (SF *Alta* Ap 20 1864 1/5) age 35, came to Calif '49 in ship *Splendid,* "local editor of the Stockton *Independent*"

O'Sullivan, James

ed and prop Sonora *Herald,* Irishman, 180

Owens, B W

Samuel Knight and B. W. Owens pubs Stockton *Journal,* from death of Mansfield until sold to Crabb and Biven, 171

Palache, J

D. Youcham and J. Palache eds and pubs Murphy's *Semi Weekly News,* 191

Parburt, George R

ed Columbia *Gazette,* 185

ed Columbia *Gazette* around end of 1857, retired Ja 19 1858 till spring, Mr 18 purchased *Gazette,* paper expired with issue of Jl 29

Park,

Barstow & Park props Placerville *American,* 199

Parker,

Parker and Groves, pubs Yankee Jim's *Mountain Courier,* 214-215

Parks,

Emerson, Jones & Parks pubs San Jose *Santa Clara Register,* 219

Parvin, W L

among eds of La Porte *Mountain Messenger,* 212

Patrick, H C

prop Stockton *San Joaquin Republican,* 171

death (SF *Chronicle* My 26 1902 3/4)

Patterson, John

John Patterson, Brown and Skelton pubs Nevada City *Miners'*

Spectacles, 195

Paty, John B

reception for Stockton, 69**

Paul, Almarin B

born S 13 1823, Bridgetown NJ; to Calif in 1849; Almarin B. Paul & Co. with William H. Rhodes ("Caxton") and W. Bartlett & Bros props SF *True Californian;* mining in Nevada City and Washoe

Pearson, William B

prop I. J. Rolfe & Co., Nevada City *Nevada Democrat,* 194n

killed in Nevada City fire, Jl 19 1856

"Pecksniff, Israel M"

"Pickwickian editor" of *Sacto Eye Glass,* Edson and Woodworth pubs 1st no. reported (SF *Alta* Ag 25 1857)

Pendegast, J N

assistant ed Santa Rosa *Western Evangelist,* 229

Penry, William M

W. M. Penry & Co. present pubs Folsom *Dispatch,* 213

Per Lee, Theron Rudd

former officer in Stevenson's New York Regiment, bought Hubbard's interest in *Alta,* sold interest in *Alta* to partners, 90; civil magistrate in Santa Cruz, 97; wholly unacquainted with the business of a newspaper office, 138; T. R. Per Lee & Co. pubs of Sacto *Placer Times,* partners the owners and eds of SF *Alta,* after two weeks left to sell out his interest to his remaining partners, 138

Phelps,

Langari & Phelps pubs Placerville *Index,* 200

Phillips, James K

Warren & Son and J. K. Phillips & Co pubs Sacto and SF *California Farmer and Journal of Useful Sciences,* 157

Phoenixiana, author of

see Derby, George Horatio, 236

Pickering, Loring

Pickering, Fitch & Co., props of SF *Alta,* 96; of Sacto, in Europe, 166; Fitch and Pickering props, Pickering ed SF *Placer Times and Transcript,* 112; Pickering & Lawrence half owners of State printing and Sacto *Placer Times and Transcript,* Pickering, Fitch & Lawrence eds, 134; L. Pickering, J. E. Lawrence, and L. Aldrich bought Sacto *Placer Times,* soon after Pickering and Lawrence bought out Aldrich, 142

born Richmond, N. H. 1812; crossed plains in 1849; at death D 28 1892 was senior prop of SF *Call* and *Bulletin***

Pickett, Charles Edward ["Philosopher Pickett"]
ed SF *Western American,* 110
ed *The Flumgudgeon Gazette and Bumblebee Report* in Ore during summer 1845, about dozen issues; came to Calif 1846; acquitted in first criminal trial at Sutter's Fort (SF California *Star* D 23 1848 2/2); " Newspaper *Ishmaelite* planned for Pickett and James McClatchy" (Sacto *Democratic State Journal* N 19 1855 2/4); reported trying to start new paper (Sacto *Union* N 24 1856 3/1)**
Pico, Andrés
A. Pico owner LA *Southern Californian;* lost $10,000, lawsuit pending 234**
Pierson, William
see Pearson, William B
Pillet, Charles Edmund
has taken to the stage, 131
first appearance (SF *Alta* Ag 3 1853 2/4)
Pinkham, Benjamin Franklin
Pinkham, Gee & Co. pubs SF *Journal,* 110; pub SF *News and Picayune,* 114; St. Clair, Pinkham & Co. pubs Benicia *California Gazette,* 221; Budd & Pinkham pubs Santa Rosa *Western Evangelist,* 229
death (SF *Call* Ag 12 1895 1/5, Ag 13 1895 8/3)
Pixley, Frank Morrison
ed SF *Whig and Commercial Advertiser,* 111
death (SF *Call* Ag 12 1895 1/5); career (*ibid.* Ag 13 1895 8/3)
Pollard, Edward A
with M. G. Upton and W. N. Walton, prop of weekly law journal in SF, 123
"I have discovered [Edward A.] Pollard was associated with William Walker, the filibuster, on the *Democratic State Journal* around 1853-55." Letter from J. P. Melvin, II, Baltimore, My 16 1947 (California State Library); published 3 nos. SF *Law Review;* not in Sacto directories
Pollock, Edward
ed SF *American* 123; ed and prop SF *Ledger,* 127; ed Weaverville *Trinity Times,* 208
death 1858, poet, author
Pomeroy, Theodore Sedgwick
ed, part pub, Crescent City *Herald,* 224
in 1861 James O'Meara and T. S. Pomeroy started *Southern Oregon Gazette,* so pro-southern that it was banned from mails in a few months (Ore H soc Q 33:316 D 1932)

Porter,
Porter & Co pubs SF *Ledger,* 127
Potter, Col. A
pub Nevada City *Coyote,* humorous, 195
ed? Nevada *Coyote,* humorous paper S 30 1854. "It may be had at Potter's." (Potter's was the bookstore)
Price, A J
A NEW PAPER—"The steamer Ohio, that leaves tomorrow, takes down the materials necessary for issuing a paper in San Diego. Messrs. A. J. Price and W. N. Walton, both practical printers and experienced workman, are the originators of this enterprise. The paper will be issued semi-weekly, and bear the title of the *Southern Democrat.* The name indicates the politics of the paper." (SF *Alta* O 7 1852 1/5)
Prindle,
Gift, Prindle, and Lockwood withdrew from pubs of Sacramento *State Tribune* (no. 1), replaced by O. P. Allen, firm became James Allen & Son (SF *Alta* Ja 21 1856)
Purdy, J H
pub SF *Pacific Statesman,* 117; SF *California Chronicle,* 116

Rabe, Dr. William
began SF *Hombre* in Ap 1851, weekly satirical paper, 109
death (SF *Bulletin* Je 24 1864) aged 45
Radcliffe, H H
pub with John White of Stockton *Times,* Englishman, borrowed Ramage press from SF *Alta;* sold to George Kerr, 168-169; sold Ramage press to Marvin & White for Sonora *Herald,* keeping some interest, 179
Ramirez, Francisco P
ed Spanish dept LA *Star,* ed LA *El Clamor Publico,* 234; a young man of high promise, 234
born 1838 in LA; in Ures, Sonora 1859-1862 as ed *La Estrella de Occidente* and dir of public printing; 1862 ed SF *El Voz del Nuevo Mundo;* Calif state translator 1865; LA *La Crónica* in 1870's
Rand, William H
among pubs LA *Star,* from Mass, 233
to Calif from Boston in 1849; mining, then publishing with relative John A. Lewis and John McElroy; later a co-founder of Rand McNally and Company
Randall, A S
prop Marysville *News,* 177; prop Marysville *National Democrat,*

178
Randall, C H
added as ed to Santa Barbara *Gazette* when enlarged Ja 15 1857
Randolph, Edmund
ed SF *Herald,* 101
born Va 1818, to Calif 1849; lawyer; died S 8 1861**
Ransom, Lyman W
prop Marysville *Herald,* 176; pub and ed Marysville *Spiritualist,* 177
Jl 1851 in Taylor, Massett & Co., sold his share in O 1851; bought again F 16 1854, sole prop; *Call* Ja 16 '94 10/2 death
Rapp, A H
ed and prop, with Heitzeberg and Hinton, of SF *Le Phare,* 123; wounded in duel for article written, 130
duel with Thiele of *Le Spectateur* (SF *Alta* Ja 28 1858 2/4)
Raveley, Samuel W
pub Sacto *Democratic State Journal,* 154; pub Sacto *California Statesman* (no. 2), 165
ed and prop Knight's Landing *News,* Mr 19 1864; death (SF *Call* Ap 9 1892); died age 64, a printer for 30 years in SF
Rayle, Philip W
purchased interests of most of the hands of Sacto *Democratic State Journal,* 154
Alta O 8 '68 1-5 death at Napa of smallpox, prominent lawyer
Reading, Major Pierson Barton
Hensley, Reading & Co., Sutter's Fort, 1849; James King of William in firm, 121
1816-1868; crossed plains 1843 with Sam'l J. Hensley and some 25 others, worked for Sutter 1845, hunted & trapped over N. Calif, W. Nev, S. Ore. Enlisted under Frémont for Mexican War. 1848 - one of first to visit site of Marshall's disc'y. Explored gold regions.
Redding, Benjamin Barnard
became one of managers of Sacto *Democratic State Journal* after Washington's departure, 153; Redding, Johnson & Co. props *Democratic State Journal;* June 1854 May sold to Redding & Snowden; editorials written by Redding, McClatchy and May, 153; Redding & Thomas bought Snowden's interest in *Democratic State Journal,* June 1857 paper sold under attachment to printers, 154
Mayor of Sacto, State Printer, Cal. Sec. of State**
Reed, T M
owner with John Conness of Coloma *Empire County Argus* 1853-1855; *Alta* O 29 1857 2-1, The *Sacto Journal* says that T. M. Reed,

late Treasurer of El Dorado county, is a defaulter to the amount of $18,000

Reichert, J A

pub SF *California Democrat,* 114

Reintrie, Henrique de la

edits Spanish page (*El Eco del Pacifico*) of SF *Echo du Pacifique* Je 1 1852 (SF *Alta* Je 2 1852)

Reynolds, Judge J R

prop Sonora *Herald,* ex-Judge of the First Instance, 180; native of U.S., 181

Rhodes, William Henry ("Caxton")

ed and one of props of SF *True Californian,* 124

author, poet

Rice, Francis W

James M. Crane & F. W. Rice, pubs SF *California Courier,* 104; went to Panama, 131

letter from, carried by Mr. M. D. Boruch, tells how while US consul at Acapulco he protested seizure and sale of American steamer; reports himself jailed without charge or warrant; asks national vessel be sent (SF *Alta* Je 26 1852 1/4); Com. Sloat regrets no force available (*ibid.,* Je 28 1852 2/1)

Richards, Charles E

C. E. Richards & Co. pubs LA *Southern Californian,* 234

Ridge, John Rollin

chief ed succeeding Jas Allen, to end of Sacto *California American,* 160; Jas Allen, J. R. Ridge and S. J. May props Sacto *California American,* 160; J. R. Ridge and S. J. May eds Sacto *Bee,* retired summer 1857, 162; ed Marysville *California Express,* 177; ed Marysville *National Democrat,* 178

born Georgia, Mr 19 1827, his father Cherokee chief, educ in mission school, who had married " refined New England woman . . ." 1888, his father and grandfather killed in tribal quarrel; after educ in New England, came to Calif in 1850; edited various papers and contributed to *Hesperian* mag; died Grass Valley O 5 1867**

Robb, John S ("Solitaire")

ed Sacto *Age* (formerly *Spirit of the Age,* 159; Bartlett & Robb pubs *Stockton Journal,* Robb ed; firm became John S. Robb & Co., still ed; sold to John Tabor and Orin F. Jackson, 170; went east to get printing office for projected San Jose *Statesman,* returned with two presses and material, 218; Marcy, Robb & Robinson to be pubs of San Jose *Statesman,* announced but not published, 218

pub, with Washington Bartlett, of SF *Journal of Commerce,* Ja 23

(I:1) to Jl 24 1850

Roberts, George D

ed Grass Valley *Nevada National,* 205

ed Grass Valley *Nevada National* during campaigns of 1858 and 1859; with Rufus Shoemaker purchased half the Grass Valley *Telegraph* in Jl 1858; succeeded him as ed

Robinson, Dr. Charles L

principal ed Sacto *Settlers' and Miners' Tribune;* remembered for part in Squatter riots, 144; of Sacto *Settler's Tribune,* famous free State Governor of Kansas, in troubles of 1855 and '56, 167

(1818-1895) leader of conservative free soilers**

Robinson, Henry Harrison ("Otello")

Marcy, Robb & Robinson to be pubs of San Jose *Statesman,* announced but not published; Robinson elected first State Printer, 218

Robinson, James W

left in charge of San Diego *Herald* by Ames in August 1852, ousted by William N. Walton on Dec. 4, until Ames' return in March 1853; died in San Diego (SF*Alta* N 20 1857 2/9)

Rockwell, Elijah Alvord

ed SF *Call,* 126; ed and prop Sonora *Herald,* native of US, 180

replaces E. C. Kemble as ed of SF California *Chronicle,* (Sacto *Union* Ja 4 1858 2/1); *Alta* N 17 1877 1/5 death

Rodgers, W P

ed San Leandro *Alameda Gazette,* 225

Rojo, Manuel Clemente

conductor of Spanish section of LA *Star, La Estrella;* lawyer, in 1851 partner of Isaac S. K. Ogier; editor, translator, and contributor

Rolfe,

Lynch, Davison & Rolfe pubs Sacto *Index,* 145

Rolfe, Ianthis Jerome

I. J. Rolfe & Co. props Nevada City *Democrat,* 194

I. J. Rolfe and Co. pubs Nevada *Democrat* June 1854 until it failed in 1863, several changes in the partnership during the life of the paper

Rolfe, Tallman Hathaway

printer on California *Star,* left for mines; one of conductors of Nevada *Democrat,* 79; printer on one of the Oregon papers in 1847, and year following in mechanical dept of *California Star,* 194; ed since summer 1857 Nevada City *Democrat,* 194

ed Nevada *Democrat* June 1854 to June 1855, returned Jan. ? 1857 to 1863 at failure of paper

Rockwell, Elijah Alvord
native of US, Sonora *Herald,* 181
Rosenfield, Anthony
Hutchings & Rosenfield, props SF *Hutchings' Illustrated California Magazine,* 125
Ross, John W
ed and pub, with James Lawrence, of Mariposa *Star,* 190
Rowe, Cyrus
brought types from Maine for Sacto *Settlers' and Miners' Tribune,* 144
Rowe, E A
E. A. Rowe and Cutter, props Weaverville Trinity *Times,* 208; ed Weaverville *Trinity Times,* 208
Ruehl, Charles
Ruehl & Co. pubs SF *Journal* (German), 120
left for East, ten years assoc with SF German press, with Froebel on *Journal,* also ed *Democratic Press,* also at one time in one of scientific depts of US branch mint (SF *Alta* O 30 1865 1/2)
Ruland, Samuel
ed Cacheville *Yolo Democrat;* answered Kemble's questionnaire; lent money Jernegan, prop, who absconded, 226-227
death (SF *Call* My 31 1890 8/4)
Russell, Alpheus W
ed Santa Rosa *Sonoma Democrat,* lost backers because he was Republican, sold out, 229
Russell, Andrew Campbell
ed *Alta* during part of Kemble's absence, 96; in Marysville *Express,* 98; ed SF *Picayune,* 107; ed SF *Bugle,* 112; pub SF *Picayune,* 116; dangerously wounded with knife for article written, 130; ed Sacto *Union,* 150; ed Sacto *California Statesman* (no. 2), 165; ed Stockton *San Joaquin Republican,* 172; ed Stockton *Argus,* 172; ed Marysville *California Express,* 177; assaulted and badly wounded by Cornwall, for editorial in LA *Star* reflecting on one of Bigler's agents, 233-234
in Matthewson, Russell & Co on SF *California Public Balance* (no. 2) Mr 31-My 7 1858; duel with Captain Joseph Folsom (SF *Alta* S 11 1851 2/4); "now editor of Memphis *Bulletin*" (*Union* Ja 7 1856 3/2; ed SF *National,* first issue "this afternoon" (SF *Alta* O 25 1856); ed Marysville *California Express* Ag 4 1858 to Mr 26 1859; came to LA Ja 1864, opened office as notary public; S 3 1864 new ed LA *Star,* to last issue O 1 1864 when bought by Phineas Banning**

Russell, George
prop, I. J. Rolfe & Co., Nevada City *Democrat,* 194
Russell, Theodore
Fitch, Upham & Co., props Sacto *Transcript,* 143
Russell, William Henry
perhaps to have been ed of SF *California Star,* 20; Orator of the Day, reception for Stockton, 68; "employed as permanent editor" of the *California Star,* 71
of Missouri, "lately arrived overland," "the type of the coming man that is to shape the destiny of California for a time . . ." (Kemble in "Yerba Buena - 1846" Sacto *Union* O 21 1871 8/1)
Rust, Richard
Sutherland, Rust & White, pubs of SF *Pacific Evening Star,* 109; ed Sacto *Democratic State Journal,* 154; R. Rust & Co estab Marysville *California Express,* ed and prop, 176-177; in State Department, 1858, 178; R. Rust and T. Mitchell props Auburn *Placer Herald,* 201
to Calif in 1849 as sec of Boundary Commission; alcalde and County Clerk in San Diego; a partner and ed Marysville *California Express* to Jl 26 1857; serio-comic duel with O. P. Stidger of Marysville *Herald* in Je 1853; partner in Jackson *Amador Sentinel;* ed Mokelumne Hill *Calaveras Chronicle;* died Ag 15 1872
Ryan, R F
pub SF *Cosmopolitan,* 121

St. Clair,
St. Clair, Pinkham & Co pubs Benicia *California Gazette,* 221
Salisbury, H E
J. Charlton and H. E. Salisbury props Tehama *Gazette,* 229
Sanborn, L H
prop Tehama *Colusa* and *Tehama Advocate,* 228
Sargent, Aaron Augustus
ed and part-prop Nevada City *Journal,* retired Jl 13 1855, 193; N. P. Brown and J. K. Dallison, *Directory of Nevada, Grass Valley and Rough and Ready,* Ja 1 1856, historical sketch of Nevada county by A. A. Sargent, 195
probably responsible, at least in part, for the humorous papers that appeared in Nevada City; later US Senator and Minister to Germany**
Sargent, F L
ed Stockton San Joaquin *Republican,* 172
Savage,
Savage, Bloomer & Co pubs SF *Eagle of Freedom* no. 1; no. 3

McLean and Savage (SF *Alta* S 14, O 12 1856)
Saxton, J B
ed SF *Christian Recorder* O 10 1855
Schoyer, Raphael
pub SF *Argus,* 127
Scobey, Joseph Woodbury
ed Auburn *Placer Press,* 202,
became ed Ag 14 1858; death (SF *Alta* S 26 1866) aged about 43, at Gila City, Arizona, on way with other officers to offer services to Republican Govt of Mexico
Scott, William Anderson
says SF *Pacific* is not organ of the Presbyterian Church, 35**
Seabough, Samuel
ed San Andreas *Independent,* 191; asst pub and ed Folsom *Granite Journal,* 213
born in Pa, to Calif 1850; Calaveras Co miner, Justice of Peace; ed Stockton *Independent;* with Sacto *Union* 1867-1875; SF *Chronicle,* leading editorial writer to his death (SF *Call* N 1 1884 1/3)
Seabury, S F
among eds La Porte *Mountain Messenger,* 212
Seaman,
Seaman & Gordon props Weaverville *Trinity Journal,* 209
Searls, Niles
ed Nevada City Nevada *Democrat,* 194
born D 22 1825 in New York State; to Calif in 1849; ed Nevada City *Young America* followed by *Democrat* D 7 1853 - Je 1854; lawyer, Chief Justice of Calif Supreme Court**
Semple, Robert Baylor
ed Monterey *Californian,* letter concerning Ramage press and founding of paper, 13-14; opinion of type, 15; California in 1846, probably from Illinois, Democrat, 56; laying out the new town of Benicia, 60; move to small quarters, 62; pub (sole) of *Californian,* Ap 24 1847, 63; moves *Californian to* Yerba Buena after My 6 1847, 64; California *Star* quoted, 73-74; moves *Californian* to Yerba Buena to be nearer to Benicia, My 1847, then sells out Jl [10] to be nearer, 80-81; ed Monterey *California,* promoted Benicia, moved to SF to be nearer, finally gave up SF for Benicia, 220
to Calif from Kentucky in Hastings party, 1845; Bear Flag Revolt; Constitutional Convention; farmer in Colusa Co 1853, where he died in 1854 at age 48**
Señor, C (*pseud.*)
ed San Diego *Coyote* (ms.) Sept 1850, issued by some U.S.

officers stationed near the Mission San Luis Rey, 236

Seymour, Paul

pub SF *Journal* 1852

Shannon, John

prop and ed Mokelumne Hill *Calaveras Chronicle,* 182

born in Ohio ca. 1817, to Calif in 1849; John Shannon & Co pubs Auburn *Placer Democrat,* Shannon ed last two months; sold *Calaveras Chronicle* 1859; bought *Tulare County Record,* renamed it Visalia *Delta;* killed in fight with William Gouverneur Morris, ed Visalia *Sun,* N 15 1860

Shaw,

ed and co-prop Georgetown *News,* 208

Sheldon, Henry L

printer, editorial supervisor of SF *Californian,* My 10 1848, 82; printer and pub, also ed, of SF *Californian* O 7 1848, 84; released interest in SF *Californian* to Foster, sailed for Sandwich Islands in mid-November, 1848, 86

Shepard, J M

J. M. Shepard & Co. pubs Sacto *Democrat* 1854, 157

Shepard, W W

assoc ed SF *Picayune,* Ag 3 1850, 107; started SF *Post* My 24 1851; 107; ed and pub SF *Post,* 109

lawyer from NY to Calif in 1849; member of Assembly in 1856

Sherman,

Lynch & Sherman, eds and props Auburn *Placer Democrat,* 202

Shipley, Henry J

Henry Shipley & Co pubs Sacto *Democratic State Journal;* ed followed by R. Rust, 154; ed Nevada City *Nevada Democrat,* 194

ed Grass Valley *Telegraph* Ap 27 1854 to May 29 1855; ed *Nevada Democrat* Je 6 1855 to Ja 2 1856; born Peperill, Mass, 1829; grad Amherst 1850; druggist; to Calif in 1853 or 1854; Southern Dem on staff of Marysville *Herald,* then to Grass Valley, then Nevada City; Lola Montez claimed editorial insult, tried to horsewhip and tongue-lash Shipley, scarcely noticed and not responsible for his subsequent suicide as alleged; death N 17 1859, Sacto

Shoaff, Peter L

a prop Stockton *San Joaquin Republican,* 171

death (SF *Call* Ag 15 1893 8/2) "ex-State Printer"

Shoemaker, Rufus

ed Grass Valley *Nevada National,* 205

long an important figure in Nevada Co journalistic circles; ed Grass Valley *Nevada National* Sept. 4, 1858 to May 7, 1859; between

election campaigns, when George D. Roberts was ed; death (SF *Call* Mr 10 1893 1/8) ed Grass Valley *Telegraph;* born Miss., to Calif in 1852; at one time Secretary of State Bank Com

Shuck, Rev. John Lewis

pub Sacto *Baptist Circular,* 165

death (Sacto *Union* N 23 1863 4/6) Barnwell Court House, S. Carolina, 51 yrs old; born Va, Southern sympathies, served Confed as chaplain and reportedly Colonel; "Once noted in this city as a Baptist preacher, a Chinese interpreter, and a Celestial agent generally, for a consideration." Many years missionary in China, six yrs in Sacto, left state in 1861

Shuler, George L

ed Mokelumne Hill *Calaveras Chronicle,* 182

has retired from the conductorship of the *Calaveras Chronicle.* In his valedictory he expresses his grateful acknowledgments to providence for opening him an avenue in the troubles of San Francisco, whereby he may escape to private life and obscurity. The meaning of this is the people of his neighborhood withdrew from him their patronage as soon as he heard of what he terms the "great mob" of this city. He hopes none will weep over his downfall. (SF *Alta* July 26 1858 1/7) death (SF *Alta* My 18 1862 1/5) at San Andreas; Rep of Calaveras Co in State Legis 1857

Shultz, Mrs. A M

Mrs. A. M. Shultz and F. M. Day eds SF *Hesperian;* Mrs. Day then sole ed, 129

retires as ed (*Hesperian* 1:40)

Silversmith,

Silversmith & Taffia pubs SF *Criticus,* 120

Simonds, Rev. Samuel D[raper?]

prop *Alta California* Printing and Publishing Company, 96; assoc ed with Washburn on *Alta,* 96; minister of Methodist Episcopal Church, 96; ed SF *California Christian Advocate,* 113

Chron O 13 '03 16/5 death, sketch

Simonton, James W

letter correcting statement that he was a partner in SF *California Courier,* 37-38; partner and assoc ed SF *California Courier,* 106; formerly Utah special corres NY *Times,* arrived Sacto beginning of 1851 with printing office, intended to establish Whig paper

ed and pub, Simonton & Co SF *Globe,* SF 1858; death (SF *Call* N 3 1882 2/1) an owner of SF *Call* and *Bulletin;* born NY 1822; in Wash as Congr corres for NY *Courier* and *Enquirer;* arrived Calif to start *California Courier* 1850, but found Whig papers; ret

NY 1851 and was one of founders NY *Times;* 1859 ret Calif, bought interest *Bulletin,* assumed ed control; when other interests bought in, ret NY but retained interest; ret Calif, 1881, lived Napa City till death

Skelton, John P

among props Nevada City *Journal,* 193; Skelton retired after fire of 1856, 193; John Patterson, Brown and Skelton pubs of Nevada City *Miners' Spectacles,* 195

printer, *Union* office, from Pa, Sacto 1859; with W. S. Byrne purchased interest in Grass Valley *National* Apr 24, 1862; burned out June 11, 1862, no insurance, townspeople lent $900 to re-supply, started again July 19, 1862; still owns quarter, is business manager with J. R. Ridge ed (1865)

Skillman, Archibald

Winchester, Skillman & Co. pubs SF *Pacific News,* 100; S. H. Dosh, J. C. Hinckley, and A. Skillman props Shasta *Courier* 1852, Skillman & Dosh 1858, 200

death (San Jose *Pioneer* Ag 1900 p. 127)

Slade, W D

among pubs Yreka *Mountain Herald,* 203

"Slimface, Parthenon," *pseud.*

ed Mokelumne Hill *Quamkeag Coyote,* 182

Sloat, L W

pub SF *Sloat's San Francisco Prices Current and Shipping List,* 110

sec. Chamber of Commerce; ed Sloat's SF *Prices Current and Shipping List* Ap 21 1852 v. 1 no. 6 pub by Bonnard & Co

Smart, W S

ed Weaverville *Trinity Times,* 208

Smith,

Smith & Co., pubs Oroville *Morning Advertiser,* 209, 210

Smith, A L

among props and eds La Porte *Mountain Messenger,* 212

perhaps when it was Gibsonville *Mountain Messenger* May 10 1854-S 1855?

S 1855?

Smith, A S

Smith & Co. props Auburn *Placer Press,* 202

ed Auburn *Placer Press* Oct. 1857 to Ag 14, 1858

Smith, F N

ed SF *Telegraph Hill,* 130

Smith, H F

ed an pub, Placerville *Empire County Argus,* 199-200

revived Coloma *Empire County Argus,* next summer moved it to Placerville, where it reappeared Aug. 13, 1857, after a three-week suspension

Smith, Mortimer J

owner and ed SF *Clarion,* 110; ed Sacto *Watch Dog,* scurrilous paper, 164

ed SF *Spirit of the Times,* Jl 1857 to O 1858 (SF *Alta* Jl 14 1857, O 25 1858); death at Sacto (SF *Alta* F 21 1864 1/5), born NY abt 40 yrs old, left wife and children indigent but friends and legislators " had collected several hundred dollars . . ."

Smith, William W

prop Marysville *Herald,* 176

May 1852 had bought share of Marysville *Herald,* sold in Dec. 1852; with Seymour Pixley, architect, built first theatre in Marysville, opened in D 1852, season of more than two months; bldg burned 1854 (Marysville dir 1856 p. 8)

Snowden,

1856 Snowden sold interest in Sacto *Democratic State Journal* to Redding & Thomas, 154

Snyder, Fred A

pub Diamond Springs *Miners' Advocate,* 207

and Co, pubs Coloma *Miners' Advocate,* Snyder and Garfielde eds; with Garfielde, ed of Coloma and Diamond Springs *Miners' Advocate*

Snyder, S L

C. G. Lincoln and S. L. Snyder pubs Oroville *North Californian,* 209

Snyder S. L., printer, from Pa. Sacto 1859; death (Grass Valley *Union* O 12 1890) printer

Soulé, Frank

Frank Soulé & Co bought newspaper office from Wm. Newell, 36; ed of *Alta* while Kemble was East, 93; ed term expired, 94; went to Australia, 97, 131; pub SF *California Chronicle,* 114; pub SF *California Chronicle,* attacked by *Bulletin;* opposed Vigilance Committee then reversed policy too late; withdrew from editorship when paper became Republican, 115-116

returned from Australia (SF *Alta* Ja 15 1859 2/1); author, with Gihon and Nisbet, of *Annals of San Francisco***

Spear, William S

ed Downieville *Bugle,* 196

with Major Ormsby at Pyramid Lake, My 1860

Speer, Rev. William
ed and pub SF *Oriental,* 119
Springer, Thomas A
T. A. Springer and E. B. Daingerfield props, the sole ed and prop Jackson *Amador Ledger,* 187; Springer & Harmon props Coloma *El Dorado News,* 197; F. H. Harmon and T. A. Springer, ed and pub Placerville *El Dorado News,* 198-199; T. A. Springer and R. Cole, ed and pub Placerville *El Dorado Republican,* 199
pub with Richard Cole of Placerville *El Dorado Republican* Je 11 to late S 1853, then alone to end, F 25 1854; sold plant to *Mountain Democrat;* violently opposed to establishment of second paper in town Placerville *Mountain Democrat* Je 10 1854; death (SF *Alta* F 27 1874 1/2) born Richmond, Md, 53 years old. "State Printer and an old resident of the State"
Stakes, A G
ed Stockton *Argus,* 172
Steele, Robert J
ed Yankee Jim's *Placer Courier,* 215
co-pubs Columbia *Gazette* Ag 19 1854 to O 15 1855?; Duchow & Steele & Co. pubs Columbia *Gazette* Ap 5 1856 to Ag 16, leased by Duchow & Carder for 6 months F 14 1857; Duchow withdrew, Steele assumed control to end of year?
Sterritt,
with A. C. Russell will revive SF *Picayune* (SF *Alta* D 9 1853)
Stevenson, W W
ed Santa Rosa *Western Evangelist,* 229
Stewart, Capt. W Frank
ed Placerville *Register* (SF *Alta* Je 9 1858)
Stickney, Augustus Allen
printer, *Union* office, from Miss. Sacto 1859; in Sacto *Union* Ja 29 1853 ("Voice of the Valley") review article by his son, E. A. Stickney refers to him as "part owner of 'The Californian' "; death (*Union* Mr 31 1880 3/2) recently empl in State Printing office and for several yrs prop of Alaska *Herald*
Stidger, Oliver Perry
prop Marysville *Herald,* 176
duel with Richard Rust (SF *Alta* Je 20 1853 2/3); co-owner of Marysville *Herald* as James Allen & Co. Ag 8 1853 to F 13 1854; Attorney at Law, Marysville 1855; death (Sacto *Union* Jl 3 1888 1/4; to Calif from Ohio 1849; died at North San Juan, ed San Juan *Times,* judge, "a prominent man here and a staunch

Republican"
Stinson, A L
[C. Winkley] and A. L. Stinson props Auburn *Whig,* 202
Strong,
Lecount & Strong pubs SF *Pioneer,* 116
Styles, Charles W
among props Bidwell *Butte Record,* 206; ed Red Bluff *Beacon,* 226; ed and prop Tehama *Colusa and Tehama Advocate* 1858, 228
Sullivan,
on staff of Sonora *Herald* N 10 1851
Sumner, Charles A
ed Sacto *State Journal,* 163; ed and pub Sacto *Eye Glass,* 163
Civil War; Congressman, died F 1 1903 in SF
Sutherland,
Sutherland, Rust & White, pubs SF *Pacific Star,* 109

Tabor, John
pub Stockton *Journal,* killed Joseph Mansfield of the Stockton *Republican* over article in *Journal;* sentenced to be hanged; pardoned by Gov. Bigler; to Nicaragua with Walker; proposes taking press with him on next invasion, 170-171; native of Texas, 171
birthplace, Georgia; res Louisiana; occupation printer (*DAR* Calif census of 1852, v.8, p. 161)
Taffia,
Silversmith & Taffia pubs, SF *Criticus,* 120
Tai, Hung
see Ze too Yune
Tallmadge, George E
George E. Tallmadge and C. B. McDonald, pubs and eds Downieville *Old Oaken Bucket,* 196
no contemporary accounts in other newspapers mention Tallmadge in connection with the *Old Oaken Bucket*
Tallmadge, D P
ed of Coloma *Empire County Argus* after Gelwicks, according to Sioli until Woods bought the paper; may have been longer
Taylor,
McClatchy & Taylor, props Sacto *California Republican* (SF *Alta* My 24 1857)
Taylor, M A M
pub SF *Bon Ton Critic,* 117
Taylor, Robert Higgins
founder of Marysville *Herald,* joined by Stephen C. Massett, 176;

lawyer practicing in Downieville, 178
"first ed of first newspaper in Northern Mines" prop and ed Marysville *Herald;* introduced outstanding workers, Stephen C. Massett as co-editor ("Jeems Pipes of Pipesville"), John R. Ridge ("Yellow Bird"), Louise Amelia Knapp Clappe ("Dame Shirley"), Maria Buchanan ("Maria"), etc.; born NYC Ag 17 1822, died SF 1905 or 1906

Taylor, W B
ed Sacto *Temperance Mirror,* 161

Theller, Dr. Edward A
ed and prop SF *The Present and the Future, Le Présent et L'Avenir,* 114; ed SF *Argus,* 127
death SF *Alta* F 8 1859 2(3) at Hornitos; came from Panama 1853; ed and prop first of SF *Public Ledger,* afterwards *Argus;* at one time SF Supt of Schools; at time of death prac medicine

Thiele, Theo
ed SF *Le Francais;* ed SF *Mineur;* ed SF *Spectateur*, 119
prop of SF *Le Phare* and *Cronica Italiana* Ja 23 1863

Thomas, Daniel J
bought McClatchy's interest in Sacto *Democratic State Journal.* Redding & Thomas bought Snowden's interest in Sacto *Democratic State Journal,* 153-154; McClatchy & Thomas, eds Sacto *Californian,* S. J. May bought Thomas' interest 156; ed Sacto *Californian* (2), 165
ed Sacto *Democratic State Journal* 1856; death (Sacto *Union* Mr 26 1881 8/6)

Thomas, Rev. Eleazer
ed SF California *Christian Advocate,* 113-114
born Chatham's Corners NY, Ja 16 1814; appointed to Peace Commission to Modoc Indians, slain by them in lava beds, Ap 11 1873

Thomas, Patrick
Marks, Thomas & Co., pubs SF *Monitor,* Catholic, 128

Thompson, F S
among props of Sacto *Bee* at present, 162
from NY

Thompson, T L
prop and ed Petaluma *Journal and Sonoma County Advertiser,* succeeded by Petaluma *Sonoma County Journal,* 225

Thoms, *i.e.* Thomes
among citizens supporting Tehama *Colusa and Tehama Advocate,* 228

Thomson, F S
see Thompson, F S
Thornbury, Caleb
among pubs Yreka *Mountain Herald*, ed 203; Thornbury & Glascock pubs Yreka *Siskiyou Chronicle*, 204
Thornbury and Mendenhall starting new paper down towards Oregon, to be called *Northern Herald*. (SF *Alta* S 27, 1852 2/2); Yreka *Mountain Herald*
Tilson, J D
pub Sacto *Covenant and Odd Fellow's Magazine*, 163
Tobey, William Henry
W. H. Tobey & Co. props Sacto *Bee*, 162
death (SF *Chronicle* O 16 1906 15/7); 1828-1906
Too Yune, Ze
see Ze Too Yune
Toomes, Albert C
among citizens supporting Tehama *Colusa and Tehama Advocate*, 228
death (SF *Alta* O 5 1873 4/1) at Tehama
Toomy, Henry V
in Casserly, Callender & Co., SF *True Standard* Mr 3-My 3 1851; on SF *Pacific Standard*
Torras, V
Torras & Fossas, props Santa Barbara *Gazette*, 238
Toubin,
ed SF *Colibri;* ed SF *Patriote*, 119
ed SF *Semaine Literaire*, v. 1 no. 1 Ap 28 1856, ref to as "Dr." (SF *Alta* Ap 29 1856)
Towne, James W
Towne & Bacon props SF *Times* 1858, 118; Whitton, Towne & Co. pubs SF *Legal Intelligencer*, 124; Towne & Bacon owners SF *California Culturist*, 129
Townes, William H
second ed of Napa City *Herald*, fall 1858
Townsend, Jonas H
ed SF *Mirror of the Times* (Negro), 127
among pubs of SF *Mirror of the Times* (Negro) 1857-8 (SF *Alta* S 9 1856)
Townsend, L R
among eds and props SF *Star* N 19 1856
Trask, E
ed Weaverville *Trinity Times*, 208

Trask, Dr. John B
Drs. J. B. Trask and David Wooster, pubs SF *Pacific Medical Journal,* 128
death (SF *Alta* Jl 5 1879 1/1) born Roxbury, Mass, abt 1824, on coast since early days, first state geologist (for some years), later similar post in Nevada, physician of many years prac, Army of Virginia in CW
Tucker, Thomas J
ed Napa City *Herald,* 225
death (SF *Call* Ja 15 1896 4/2)
Tupper, Charles
SF *Alta* Ja 7 1857 announces forthcoming weekly, to be edited by Charles Tupper: Shaw's Flat (Tuolumne County) *Pick and Shovel*
Turner, N P
ed Sonora *Union Democrat,* 181
Turrell, Oliver B
Wadsworth and Turrell estab SF *California Culturist,* 129; printer and pub Sacto *Temperance Mirror,* 161
ed staff Sacto *Times* (no. 2) (Sacto *Union* N19 1883, P. Coggins obit.)
Tyson, Joseph
among pubs Yreka *Union,* later Tyson & Brown, 203
among purchasers of Yreka *Mountain Herald,* 1855

Udell, J H
J. H. Udell & Co, props SF *Post* 1856, 125
Upham, Samuel C
Fitch, Upham & Co, 1st props Sacto *Transcript;* Upham soon sold his fifth interest to G. C. Weld, 143
"Reminiscences of pioneer journalism in California," San Jose *Pioneer,* Ap 7 1877, p.1, by Upham: "local reporter, printer's devil, business manager, 'deadhead,' etc."
Upson, Lauren
ed Sacto *Union,* 150
twelve years ed-in-chief (*Union* Ja 10 1891 1/3); Surveyor General (*Alta* My 31 1867 1/1); from Alabama
Upton, Mattias Gilbert
ed SF *Herald* post-Vigilance Committee of 1856, 104; with E. A. Pollard and W. N. Walton prop of weekly law journal in SF, 123
death (SF *Call* F 6 1897 14/4) born Ireland, journalist in NY, city ed NY *Herald;* moved to Calif about 1852; SF *Law Review;* with SF *Herald;* then principal writer and ed of *Alta;* 1872 or '73

invited to be ed writer on SF *Bulletin;* remained with latter paper and had close assoc with George K. Fitch, one time journalist and prop

Urmy, John B

Duchow & Urmy, props Columbia *Tuolumne Courier,* 186

ed Columbia *Columbian* My 9-J 11 1857, then bought paper with Duchow and started *Courier;* death (*Alta* Ap 19 1867 1/1) Major John B. Urmy, born NY where married, age 43; Civil War with General Connor's Third Regt of Calif Volunteers, then to Ariz with Seventh ditto; suicide over divorce proceedings

Valentine,

Farwell, Monson & Valentine, SF printers, bought Parker H. French's interest in Sacto *State Tribune* (no. 1), attached paper, 158

Monson & Valentine, printers, SF *Pioneer* 1854-1855

Van Choate, H S

among pubs Yreka *Mountain Herald,* 203

Vandyke,

Vandyke and Wiley props Union *Humboldt Times,* 224

Van Guelder, A A

real owner Coloma *Empire County Argus,* N 19 1853 to purchase by Woods

Vesian,

ed SF *Courrier de la Californie,* 119

Vignes, J G

practical printers pub SF *Western American* Ja 15-Mr 1 1852

Vincent, George

& Co, pubs Coloma *Empire County Argus* Ja 1854

Wadsworth, Wedworth

Wadsworth & Turrell pubs SF *California Culturist,* Wadsworth ed, 129; ed and pub Placerville *American,* 199; F. A. Bee and W. Wadsworth props Placerville *Herald,* 199; prop Placerville *El Dorado Republican,* 199-200

sold equipment to Coloma *Empire County Argus;* death (Sacto *Union* N 2 1874 3/2) "at one time connected with the *Rural Press,* of San Francisco, and subsequently with other papers," prominent in organizing Capital Beet-sugar Co of Sacto

Wagner,

Wagner & Gelbrecht, pubs SF *Deutscher Democrat,* 121

Wagner, Adolph

pub and ed Mokelumne Hill *California Staats Zeitung,* 182

estab above (no. 1 reported by SF *Alta* O 25 1858 1/6)

Waite, Edwin G

E. G. Waite, N. P. Brown, H. M. Fuller and Jno P Skelton, Waite ed, Nevada City *Journal,* 193; Brown & Waite, props above, 193

ed Nevada *Journal* Jl 13 1855 almost continuously to 1861 when paper suspended; ed *Transcript* (Sacto?) to close of CW 1865; chief political writer SF *Times* in Grant campaign 1868; Sacto *Union* during Booth campaign for governor & second Grant campaign; born NY (SF *Call* O 31 1894 12/3) came to SF 1849; State Assembly 1856; became writer and later Sec of State

Waite, James S

pub LA *Star,* 233

his first issue Ap 22 1854; added McElroy O 1854, still Demo; became postmaster D 1855; his last issue Ap 12 1856; sold out; 1859 elected JP in San Bernardino Co; succeeded J. J. Ames in San Bernardino *Herald* Ja 1861 to middle of Ap when sold to Edwin A. Sherman for new San Bernardino *Patriot;* farmer at Santa Cruz 1876

Waldron, H G

becomes one of props SF *Spirit of the Times* (SF *Alta* O 25 1858)

Walkely, C *see* Winkley, Charles

Walker, William

assoc ed SF *Herald,* imprisoned for remarks about Judge Levi Parsons, 101; succeeded by Hamilton as assoc ed *Herald,* 101-102; ed SF *Commercial Advertiser,* 111; filibuster in Lower California and Nicaragua, 131; wrote editorials for Sacto *Democratic State Journal,* left to raise first Nicaragua expedition, 153; joined in Nicaragua by Parker H. French of Sacto *State Tribune* (no. 1), 158; has taken and lost Nicaragua, and is preparing to take it again, 167**

Walkley, C (*see* Winkley, Charles)

Wallace, W J

M. B. Clark, A. Badlam and W. J. Wallace props, printers and ed staff Quincy *Prospector,* 188

not mentioned in other accts of *Prospector,* not on masthead v.1 no.10 or reported from Huntington file

Walsh, James W

ed and prop SF *Sunday Varieties,* 124

Walton, Jesse

1st assoc ed SF *Star,* a night school paper (SF *Bulletin* S 3 1856)

Walton, William N

with M. G. Upton and E. A. Pollard, prop of weekly law journal [*Law Review*] in SF, 123; in penitentiary from SF for larceny, 130; ed Marysville *Inquirer,* 177

steamer Ohio to take materials down for paper in San Diego, to be called the *Southern Democrat,* A. J. Price and W. N. Walton originators of enterprise (SF *Alta* O 7 1852 1/5); to edit Red Bluff *Northern Register,* "late legislative reporter for several of the San Francisco papers" (*Alta* Mr 4 1857 2/3; walked in and took over San Diego *Herald* from J. W. Robinson, claiming authority from Ames, prop, name on masthead from D 4 1852 until Ames returned in Mr, shortly before which Walton disappeared, leaving the *Herald* office in bad shape

Walz, Benjamin
pub SF *California Staats Zeitung*

Ward, Frank
Chief Marshal, reception for Com. Stockton, 68

Ward, J S
E. T. Hogan and J. S. Ward, eds Quincy *Plumas Democrat,* 211

Warner, John J
prop LA *Southern Vineyard;* may have held some interest in LA *Southern Californian,* 235

Southern Vineyard "to provide a healing agent for the bitter feelings against Americans and Spanish Californians; Jonathan Trumbull Warner, known in Calif as Juan José or John J; born Conn, went to St Louis and N Mex in 1830; clerk for Jedediah Smith at time of latter's death; settled in LA 1834; went East in 1839 and lectured in Rochester on far west, with special ref to Pacific RR; ret 1841; in 1844, naturalized, he was grantee of Auga Caliente rancho nr San Diego, where he lived to 1857; trouble with Indians at another grant, Camajal y el Palomar; to a certain extent Warner was Larkin's confidential agent for US; after 1857 resided LA; Assemblyman 1859; federal assessor and notary public; considerable historical writing; died 1895**

Warren, Henry S
Fitch, Upham & Co, props Sacto *Transcript,* 143

death (SF *Alta* N 29 1879) at Colusa; a foreman, practical printer; *Gold Hill News* quoted as saying "a bigger hearted man never lived," had sister in Maine and apparently from there (*Alta* D 4 1879 1/2)

Warren, James Lloyd LaFayette
pub SF *California Farmer,* 116; Warren & Son and J. K. Phillips & Co, pubs Sacto and SF *California Farmer and Journal of Useful Sciences,* 156-157

death (SF *Call* Ap 24 1896 7/3); born Ag 12, 1805, Brighton, Mass; came to Calif in 1849**

Washburn, Charles Ames
ed of *Alta* during part of Kemble's absence, 96; turned *Alta* to support Broderick, 96; duel with Washington, ed of *Times and Transcript,* over *Alta's* support of Broderick, 96; publishing paper in Chicago, Ill, 97-98; ed SF *Journal,* 111; wounded in duel for article he had written, 130
1852 on Sonora *Herald* staff; went to Benicia then to SF; communications ed SF *Star of Empire* 1856; born South Livermore, Maine, 2 brothers in Congress, both became Ministers to foreign countries; himself Min to Paraguay; death (SF *Call* Ja 30 1889 4/3)

Washington, Benjamin Franklin
ed Sacto *Placer Times and Transcript,* 96; ed SF *Placer Times and Transcript,* 112; Collector of the Port of SF, 130, 152, 167; left Sacto *Democratic State Journal* to become ed-in-chief *Placer Times and Transcript,* 152-153

Washington, George
ed SF *National* (see *Globe*), 125

Waters, Thomas J
J. P. Olmstead and T. J. Waters pubs North San Juan *Star,* 214; Avery & Waters pubs North San Juan *Hydraulic Press,* 214
with B. P. Avery pubs *Hydraulic Press* Ag 21 1858 to suspension in 1863?; printer, perhaps & Co with Olmstead on North San Juan *Star* N 18 1857 to Ag 14 1858

Weaver, W E
printer and pub SF *Californian,* 84; released interest in *Californian* to Foster, sailed for Sandwich Islands, 86

Weed, Joseph
& Co, pubs SF *California Free Press* (SF *Alta* Je 28 1857 2/2); pub SF *Pacific* 1858

Weekes, Mrs. Cora Anna
ed and pub SF *Athenaeum,* three numbers only; from New Orleans, soon left for Australia; sold subscriptions in Stockton, Sacto, SF before flight, 128

Weeks, James Edward Pickering
assoc ed Sacto *Union* 1859; death (SF *Alta* Ag 29 1877 1/8) "for nearly twenty years news-editor of Sacto *Union* and *Record-Union*"

Weld, Gilbert Cumming
bought fifth interest in Sacto *Transcript* for $10,000 soon after founding in April 1850, died by August 10, when paper appeared in mourning for him, 143

Wellington, G E
Carpenter & Wellington original props Folsom *Dispatch,* then Well-

ington alone, sold to William Ewing Je 14 1858, 213

Wells, William Vincent

ed dept SF *Whig and Commercial Advertiser,* 111; ed SF *Times,* 1858, 118

came to Calif as mate of ship *Edward Everett;* wrote biog (2 vols) of his great-grandfather, Samuel Adams; author of *General Walker in Nicaragua;* death SF *Alta* Je 3 1876 2/1

Weston, H L

prop Petaluma *Sonoma County Journal,* 225

Wheeler, John O

Butts & Wheeler props LA *Southern Californian,* 234

former merchant and LA Ranger; lost two judgments to Benjamin D. Wilson in N 1855, mortgage foreclosed by Andrés Pico in D 1855; S - N 1856 had charge of English page in *El Clamor Público*

Wheeler, Osgood Church

O. C. Wheeler and E. J. Willis eds Sacto *Pacific Banner,* 156

ed Sacto *State Sentinel* at beginning, Jl 27-S 20 1857; death (SF *Call* Ap 18 1891 3/6)

Wheelock,

Wheelock and Hoffman pubs SF *Republican,* Wheelock ed, 20, 129; Wheelock & Kies props Coloma *True Republican,* 198

Kennedy lists A. A. Wheelock and H. Wheelock as eds of the latter paper

Whelpley, J D

ed dept of SF *Whig and Commercial Advertiser,* 111

Whipple, Stephen Girard

ed and prop Union *Northern Californian,* 224

Whitacre, William T

W. T. Whitacre and A. L. Gould props Mariposa *Chronicle,* 189; ed and pub San Rafael *Marin County Democrat,* 230

White, John

Sutherland, Rust & White, pubs SF *Pacific Star,* 109; chief ed Sacto *Democratic State Journal,* 153-154; H. H. Radcliffe and John White pubs Stockton *Times,* 169; ed Stockton *San Joaquin Republican,* 172; Marvin & White bought Ramage press, 179; ed and prop Sonora *Herald,* Englishman, 179-180

Whitesides, James

with John Shannon purchased the Mokelumne Hill *Calaveras Chronicle,* (SF *Alta* Oct. 27, 1857 1/1)

Whittaker, J F

prop Marysville *News,* spring, 1858, 177; prop Marysville *National*

Democrat fall 1858, 178
from Illinois; printer on Marysville *Express* 1853
Whitton, Abel
Whitton, Towne & Co. pubs SF *Legal Intelligencer,* May 1856, 124
to Calif from Maine in 1850; on SF *Bulletin* with James King of William; pub SF *Christian Recorder;* death at age 82 (SF *Call* D 4 1902 15/4)
Wiley, Austin
Vandyke and Wiley props Union *Humboldt Times,* Wiley prop in Eureka 1858, 224
Williams, Rev. Albert
ed of SF *Watchman,* 107
Williams, C E
ed Weaverville *Trinity Times,* 208
Williamson, E
E. Williamson & Co props Sacto *Californian,* 156
Willis, Edward J
O. C. Wheeler and E. J. Willis eds Sacto *Pacific Banner,* 156; ed *Pacific Recorder,* 157
county judge 1850-1853; later admitted to ministry
Williston, Henry C
ed and co-pub SF *Wide West,* 117; went to Victoria in summer of 1858, 131
died in Brooklyn (SF *Alta* Jl 1868 2/3)
Wilson, Robert
ed Stockton *Journal,* 170; Heckendorn, Gist & Wilson props Columbia *Clipper* 185; Oliver & Wilson, props Columbia *Columbian,* 185-186
sold *Clipper* Ja 1 1856; dissolved partnership in *Columbian* Ja 3 1857
Winans, Joseph Webb ("Glycus")
J. W. Winans and H. B. Livingston eds Sacto *Index,* 145
born in 1820; to Calif in 1849 via Horn; lawyer
Winchester, Jonas
purchased SF Pacific *News,* 100
pub in NY; arrived in Calif Jl 6 1849; chief ed SF Pacific *News;* State Printer 1850; article on early journalism (Sacto *Union* Ja 16 1868 3/3); death (SF *Call* F 26 1887)
Winkley, Charles
prop with A. S. Stinson, Auburn *Whig,* 202
H. R. Hawkins and C. Winkley pubs Auburn *Placer County Press,* 1856

Winter, Will, *pseud., see* Byrne, W S

Wood, William S

ed with H. L. McCreary Sacto *Hesperian,* Franklin High School, Ag 1858

Woods, C

ed Coloma *Empire County Argus,* 198; managing partner of bankrupt house of Adams & Co, attacked by James King of William, 121

Woods, Isaiah Churchill

part owner of SF *Picayune,* 107; filed suit with J. W. Gish on Mr 1 1855, Sacto *California Statesman,* 155

from Pennsylvania, printer on Sacto *Union* 1859; death (SF *Alta* My 23 1866 1/4) "at one time proprietor of the *California Express.*"

Woodworth,

with Edson, pubs of Sacto *Eye Glass,* "an independent weekly observer . . . Israel M. Pecksniff is the Pickwickian editor" (SF*Alta* Ag 25 1857)

Wooster, Dr. David

Drs. J. B. Trask and David Wooster, pubs SF *Pacific Medical Journal,* 128

death (SF *Call* S 21 1894 9/1)

Wright, Washington

ed Sacto *Age,* 159; King, Ham and Wright pubs Downieville *Mountain Echo,* 196; asst ed and pub Downieville *Sierra Citizen,* 196

Yancey, Tryon M

prop with Duchow of Columbia *Gazette,* 185

printer from Mississippi; death (SF *Call* Ja 13 1898 3/4)

Yates, J D

printer on Calif *Star,* left for mines, 79

Youcham, Daniel

ed and prop Columbia *News,* 186; D. Youcham and J. Palache eds and pubs Murphy's *News,* 191

printer from Kansas; pub Columbia *Columbian* D 27 1855 - Je 11 1857; in Sacto 1859

Young, James W

practical printers pub SF *Western American* Ja 15 - Mr 1 1852

Ze Too Yune, *alias* Hung Tai

pub Sacto. *Chinese News,* 161

Zechtig, F B Y, *see* Fechtig, B Y

General Index

This book has been designed and printed
at The Talisman Press, Los Gatos, California
in an edition limited to 750 copies.
August, 1962

CALIFORNIA DAILY COURIER.

RICE, Editors and Proprietors. SAN FRANCISCO, WEDNESDAY, DECEMBER 25, 1850. VOLUME I.—NUMB

FRANCISCO PRICES CURRENT. SHI

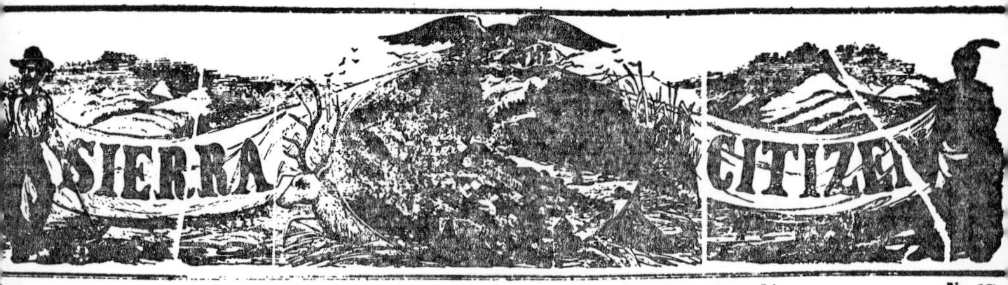

. 1. Downieville, Sierra County, California, Saturday, June 3, 1854. No. 17.

SIERRA CITIZEN

San Joaquin Republican.

VOL. I. STOCKTON, WEDNESDAY MORNING, SEPTEMBER 17, 1851. NO. 37.

PRICES CURRENT AND SHIPPING LIST.

. 2. SAN FRANCISCO, OCTOBER 5, 1853. NO. 38

SANTA CLARA REGISTER.

PUBLISHED WEEKLY IN THE APPLETON BUILDING, MARKET STREET—TERMS, $6 00 PER ANNUM, IN ADVANCE.

Stockton Journal.

OLUME IV. STOCKTON, FRIDAY, DECEMBER 17, 1852. NUMBER 2.

CALIFORNIA GAZETTE.

ST. CLAIR, PINKHAM & CO., (Terms: $10 per Annum, In Advance.) PUBLISHERS AND PROPRIETORS.

VOLUME I. BENICIA, SATURDAY, JULY 12, 1851. NUMBER 17.

HE CALIFORNIA STATE GAZETTE.

The Evening Picayune.

Vol. I.—No. 106. SAN FRANCISCO, MONDAY, DECEMBER 8, 1850. Price Six Cents.

Daily Alta California.

VOL. III. SAN FRANCISCO, TUESDAY MORNING, JANUARY 13, 1852. NO. 12.

ROBERT B. PARKER'S

BROKEN TRUST

THE SPENSER NOVELS

Robert B. Parker's Broken Trust
(by Mike Lupica)

Robert B. Parker's Bye Bye Baby
(by Ace Atkins)

Robert B. Parker's Someone to Watch Over Me
(by Ace Atkins)

Robert B. Parker's Angel Eyes
(by Ace Atkins)

Robert B. Parker's Old Black Magic
(by Ace Atkins)

Robert B. Parker's Little White Lies
(by Ace Atkins)

Robert B. Parker's Slow Burn
(by Ace Atkins)

Robert B. Parker's Kickback
(by Ace Atkins)

Robert B. Parker's Cheap Shot
(by Ace Atkins)

Silent Night
(with Helen Brann)

Robert B. Parker's Wonderland
(by Ace Atkins)

Robert B. Parker's Lullaby
(by Ace Atkins)

Sixkill
Painted Ladies
The Professional
Rough Weather
Now & Then
Hundred-Dollar Baby
School Days
Cold Service
Bad Business
Back Story
Widow's Walk
Potshot
Hugger Mugger
Hush Money
Sudden Mischief
Small Vices
Chance
Thin Air
Walking Shadow
Paper Doll
Double Deuce
Pastime
Stardust
Playmates
Crimson Joy
Pale Kings and Princes
Taming a Sea-Horse
A Catskill Eagle
Valediction
The Widening Gyre
Ceremony
A Savage Place
Early Autumn
Looking for Rachel Wallace
The Judas Goat
Promised Land
Mortal Stakes
God Save the Child
The Godwulf Manuscript

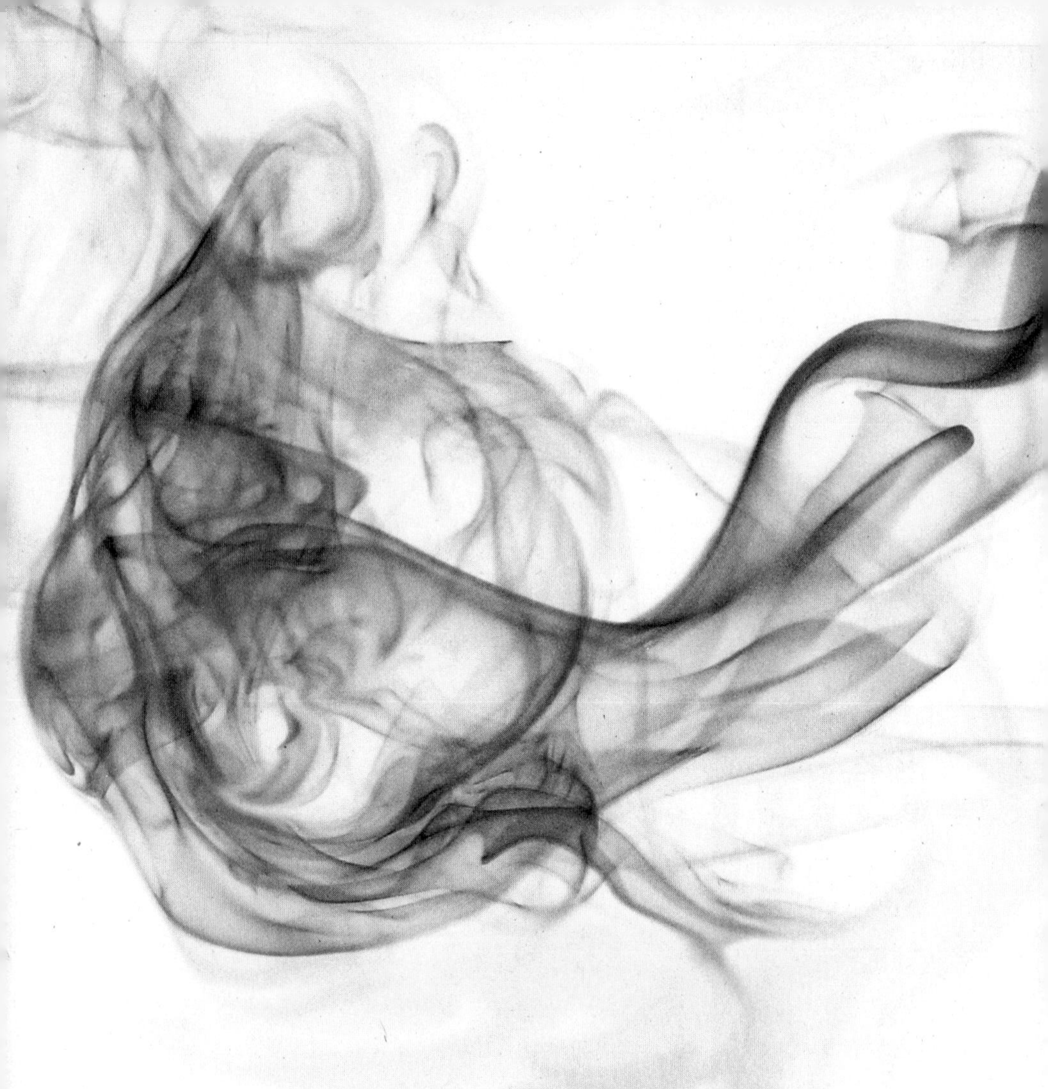

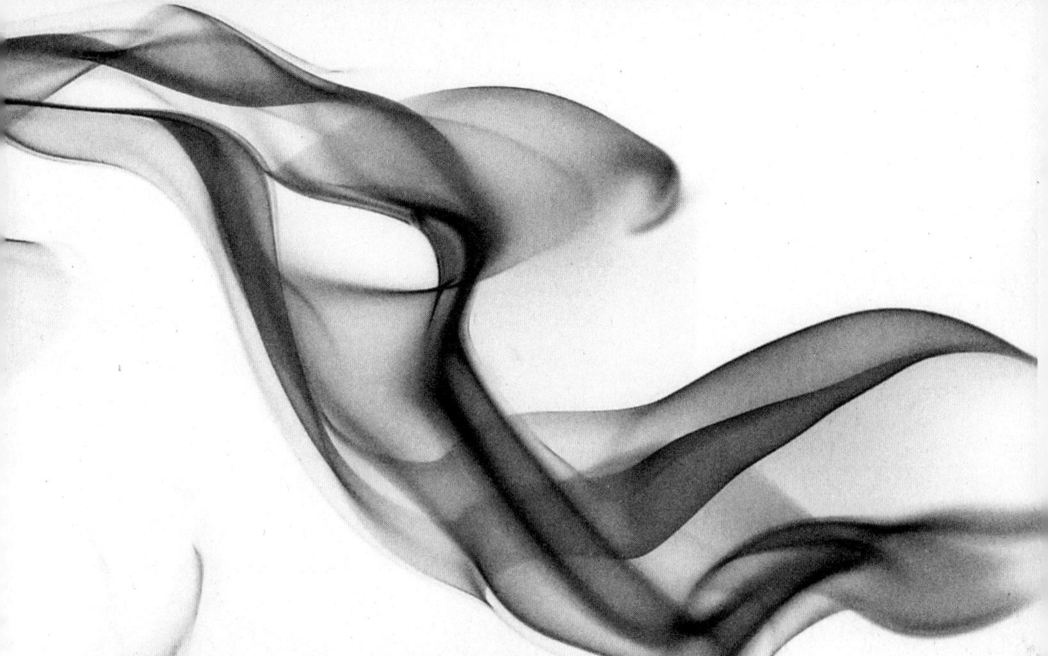

ROBERT B. PARKER'S

BROKEN TRUST

MIKE LUPICA

G. P. PUTNAM'S SONS • NEW YORK

PUTNAM
— EST. 1838 —

G. P. PUTNAM'S SONS
Publishers Since 1838
An imprint of Penguin Random House LLC
penguinrandomhouse.com

Library of Congress Cataloging-in-Publication Data has been applied for.

Hardcover ISBN 9780593540244
Ebook ISBN 9780593540251
LCCN 2023944419

Printed in the United States of America
1st Printing

Book design by Elke Sigal

This is a work of fiction. Names, characters, places, and incidents either are the product of the author's imagination or are used fictitiously, and any resemblance to actual persons, living or dead, businesses, companies, events, or locales is entirely coincidental.

This book is for my friend James Patterson.

Spenser's
BOSTON
to Susan's home and office,
Linnaean Street, Cambridge
Charles River Dam Bridge
CHARLES STREET
Massachusetts
General Hospital
Charles River
ESPLANADE
Longfellow Bridge
CAMBRIDGE STREET
ESPLANADE
State House
STORROW DRIVE
BEACON HILL
The Paramount
to State Police,
Boston Post Road
Hatch Shell
BEACON STREET
to Fenway Park
Boston Common
CHARLES STREET
The Taj Boston
(formerly the Ritz-Carlton)
Public Garden
MARLBOROUGH STREET
BERKELEY STREET
ARLINGTON STREET
Swan Boats
Four Seasons Hotel
and Bristol Lounge
COMMONWEALTH AVENUE
BOYLSTON STREET
Spenser's office
Jacob Wirth
Davio's
Boston
Public Library
Copley
Square
Old Boston Police
Headquarters
STUART STREET
Grill 23
TREMONT STREET
to Boston Police Headquarters,
Roxbury

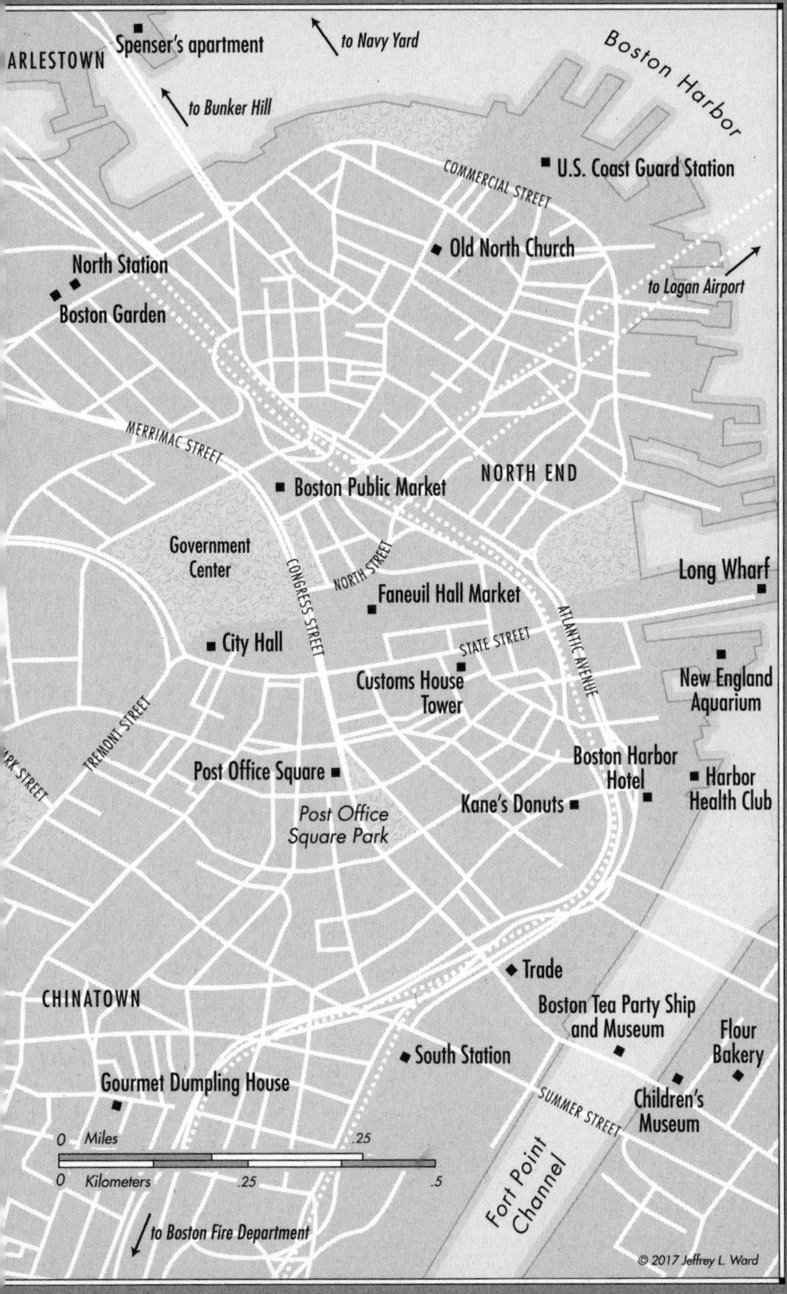

ARLESTOWN
Spenser's apartment
to Navy Yard
Boston Harbor
to Bunker Hill
U.S. Coast Guard Station
COMMERCIAL STREET
Old North Church
North Station
Boston Garden
to Logan Airport
MERRIMAC STREET
Boston Public Market
NORTH END
Government Center
CONGRESS STREET
NORTH STREET
Faneuil Hall Market
Long Wharf
ATLANTIC AVENUE
City Hall
STATE STREET
Customs House Tower
New England Aquarium
TREMONT STREET
RK STREET
Post Office Square
Boston Harbor Hotel
Harbor Health Club
Kane's Donuts
Post Office Square Park
Trade
CHINATOWN
Boston Tea Party Ship and Museum
Flour Bakery
South Station
Gourmet Dumpling House
Children's Museum
SUMMER STREET
0 Miles .25
0 Kilometers .25 .5
Fort Point Channel
to Boston Fire Department
© 2017 Jeffrey L. Ward

ROBERT B. PARKER'S

BROKEN TRUST

ONE

I was sitting at my desk drinking my third cup of coffee of the morning. I was doing this guilt-free, having read that two to five cups a day not only prevented a long list of diseases, but also helped you live a longer, if more caffeinated, life. But then you can always find somewhere on the Internet that tells you what you want to hear, about almost anything.

I was certain that if I looked long enough, I could find a site promising a reasonably priced way for me to look like Bradley Cooper.

By now I had already made short work of the second Boston Kreme I'd picked up at the Dunkin' just down Boylston from my office, the one near the Public Library. Two blocks down, two blocks back. But I had walked briskly, telling myself it was exercise, even if the prize had been the donuts, which didn't extend your life, just made it more worth living.

Dunkin' Donuts had long since rebranded and was just calling itself Dunkin' now. I had considered doing something similar, but knew it was too late for that. And when it came to branding yourself with just one name, I had frankly been way ahead of the game.

Carol Sloane's voice was coming out of the tiny speaker near the Keurig machine and I was methodically making my way through the print edition of *The Globe*, as I still did every morning, front to back, section by section, saving sports for last. The man who owned *The Globe* also owned the Red Sox. The paper was having a far better September than his baseball team was.

But then just about everybody was. It had reached the point where I was no longer certain that the two guys who were supposed to be our top starting pitchers were actually still right-handed.

"Maybe you should think about finding a new hobby," Hawk had said the other day after listening to me bitching again about the local nine.

"I've got too much time invested in them," I said. "It's the same reason I'm still with you."

"You're with me," Hawk said, "because I don't have no bad years."

We had just finished moving the last of my furniture that we could carry ourselves into my new apartment, which just happened to be a few doors down from the one I'd been burned out of a few years ago. It was the event that had prompted my move away from Marlborough Street and all the way to the Charleston Navy Yard.

At the time Susan Silverman, trying to mitigate my loss, had said that while it had been the equivalent of a forced eviction, it might have been time for a change, even though she knew better than anyone that I liked change about as much as I liked TikTok.

"Most people do move sooner or later," Susan said.

"The Red Sox haven't," I said.

She had promised that I would embrace the new place once I was in it, and proceeded to move in and decorate it like an invading ground force. And eventually I had grown both fond and familiar with my new surroundings, the neighborhood, the proximity to the Navy Yard, even the younger vibe over there, as if I were the one who was young and had moved to Boston all over again.

But recently I'd done some work for a man named Kevin Boles, who owned great big chunks of property in Back Bay, getting Boles's son out of a jam with Tony Marcus that involved substantial gambling losses that Tony had decided required more than just money in payment. Tony wanted real estate favors from Kevin Boles, specifically involving a particular building he hoped to use for a new escort service on Charles Street now that COVID was over and the sex trade was booming again.

Boles had come to me and I had gone to Tony, reminding him that he owed me a favor. Tony told me that he didn't owe me shit and get the fuck out of his office. But being as transactional as he'd always been, an accommodation had been reached and he got the building he wanted. Kevin Boles considered it a small price to pay to get his son clear of Tony, and even after he'd generously settled up with me, he said that he was the one who now owed me a favor.

About a week later he'd called and told me that an apartment on Marlborough near the corner of Arlington had opened up, having remembered me mentioning that I'd lived on the same part of that street before what I called the Great Boston Fire. Boles said that the apartment hadn't yet gone on the market, and asked if I might be interested in moving back to the old neighborhood. I surprised myself at how quickly I said that I was. He said he could give me a break on the rent. I told him that wasn't necessary. He insisted. A month away from the end of my lease in Charlestown, I signed the lease that day, put down a deposit, and just like that Daddy was home.

"Do you know how much I've missed walking to work?" I said to Susan the first time we stepped into the empty apartment.

"At this point, people in outer space know that."

She asked me just how much Kevin Boles had paid for my services, and how much of a break he was giving me on the rent. I told her. At which point she had smiled, wickedly. Susan has a lot of smiles, most of which make me feel light-headed and oxygen-deprived when directed at me.

This one, I knew from experience, was going to cost me money.

"I know that look," I said.

"What look is that?" she asked innocently.

"The one where you can't wait for the stores to open."

She'd kissed me then and said, "Don't you worry your pretty little head about it."

The new apartment, about the same size as the old one, didn't actually feel like home yet. But I was getting there. Pearl the Wonder Dog had already settled in quite nicely when she and Susan would be there for sleepovers. Pearl hadn't come right out and said how much she liked it that she could walk to work with me, too, when Susan would leave her with me. It was more something I had intuited.

Now I just needed work, as there hadn't been any since I'd saved Kevin Boles's son.

"If you can walk to work but there ain't no work," Hawk had said, "answer me something: What's the fucking point?"

I was pondering that, and whether I should walk back down to Dunkin' for more donuts before I got too close to lunch, when there was a knock on my door and the wife of the sixth-richest man in America came walking in.

TWO

Laura Crain was a friend of Susan's from a couple charity boards they both served on in Boston, one of which—the Jimmy Fund—was as famous a charity as there was in the city, aligned with the Dana-Farber Cancer Institute, and deeply connected to the Red Sox all the way back to when Ted Williams had first gotten involved.

Susan and Laura Crain shared a Pure Barre class a couple times a week and would meet occasionally for lunch. I knew that Susan liked her very much, as rich and famous as Laura and her husband were, and not just in Boston.

Laura had met Andrew Crain when they were both students at Harvard. Laura was an English major. He was a full-fledged, card-carrying Division of Science nerd, along with his best friend, Ethan Lowe. I knew the general outline of their shared biography, because by now most people in America knew it. Five years after Lowe and Andrew

Crain graduated, working out of a small rented lab in Dorchester, they had invented a synthetic form of lithium that had reimagined the world of batteries forever.

Susan had mentioned in passing a few weeks earlier that I might be hearing from her friend Laura about a problem she was having, one she'd shared in confidence with Susan.

"Are you treating her now?"

"Not professionally. Just hearing her out as a friend and offering advice when she's asked for it."

"And she has a problem that you can't solve?" I said. "What is it, the melting of the ice caps?"

"She'll tell you when the two of you meet," Susan said, "if she doesn't lose her nerve."

"Couldn't she buy some nerve?" I'd asked. "I assume she can afford it."

"Let's just wait and see," Susan said. "She should be the one to tell you what's happening in her life. But I told *her* that if anybody could help her, it's my cutie."

Now Laura Crain sat across my desk from me. Tall. Honey-colored hair hanging to her shoulders. Blazer, white jeans that fit her the way God intended jeans to fit women with legs as long as hers, ankle boots. Whatever her actual age was, I had already decided she looked younger. She reminded me of a slightly younger version of Julia Roberts, not that I would ever say that to Julia.

A knockout by any measure. It was something I knew I couldn't verbalize without sounding as if I were objectifying her, and being on my way to Weinstein Island.

But Andrew Crain, I could see, hadn't just gotten stupidly rich. He had even gotten the girl.

"So you're Spenser," she said, crossing one long leg over the other.

"I am he," I said.

I had come around the desk to greet her when she'd arrived. In the post-pandemic world I'd first asked if she wanted to shake hands before extending mine. She'd said she'd risk it if I would.

"People often say 'I am him,'" I said. "But that's ignoring the fact that 'he' is actually supposed to be a predicate nominative renaming the subject."

She smiled. It was, by any measure, a high-wattage dazzler, if not of Susan quality, at least in the conversation. Susan had prepared me for how lovely Laura Crain was. I was certain I would be cross-questioned later about just *how* lovely *I* thought she was.

"Susan told me about you," she said.

I ducked my head in false modesty.

"The rugged good looks?" I said. "Or devilish charm?"

She shook her head slowly from side to side, as if in the presence of a precocious child.

Which, all things considered, she was.

"She actually told me how hard you'd try, almost immediately, to show me what a literate detective you are," she said. "And that if I didn't acknowledge that fact you might get the bends."

"I can also diagram some sentences if you want," I said.

"Maybe when we know each other better."

Now I smiled at her.

"Want to can the small talk?"

"I'd be willing to pay you," she said.

I asked if she wanted coffee. She said thank you, but she'd pass, she was trying to quit caffeine. I told her I didn't want to live in that world. She managed to contain her laughter, but I sensed it was difficult for her.

"Might I offer just one last tiny bit of small talk?" she said.

"Okay, but *just* one."

"You really are as big as Susan said you were."

"Well, sure, but I come by it naturally."

We sat there in silence for a few moments, as if each of us were waiting for the other to make the next move. It often went this way with potential clients, like an awkward first date, and just how much they wanted to drop their guard.

"So how can I help you, Mrs. Crain?"

"Please. *Laura*."

"So how can I help you, Laura."

Her blue eyes were so pale as to be as clear as glass.

"That's the thing," she said. "You probably can't."

THREE

It was always best to let them tell it their own way, at their own pace, editing their own narrative as they went along. Editing just how much of their own truth they wanted to share with a complete stranger.

There was another long silence now as she stared down at hands as lovely as the rest of her, as if suddenly remembering they were there. The nails were clear, no color to them. A single gold wedding band, no other jewelry of any kind. She clasped her hands tightly now in her lap.

When she looked up again she said, "Susan said I could trust you, even if you choose not to take me on as a client."

I smiled at her now. Not my big one. She was clearly having a hard time with all of this, and hitting her with my big smile, what I thought of as the Whopper, might cause her to lose control. Or, at the very least, her train of thought.

"I have to be honest, Laura," I said. "The only thing that might dissuade me from taking you on as a client is if you put a cigarette out in one of my eyes."

Now she laughed, even if the sound seemed to die somewhere between us and land on the paper plate where the donuts had been.

I wanted to get up and make myself another cup of coffee, but we finally seemed to be getting somewhere. In moments like these I tried to pretend I was Susan, who had once told me that people in her line of work who talked too much with patients or interrupted too frequently should perhaps think about finding another profession.

"It's my husband," she said.

I waited for her to elaborate. She did not, at least not right away. Maybe she thought telling me would be as easy as it had been for her to tell Susan, whatever she had told Susan.

Either way, she'd get to wherever we were going when she did and I had no desire to speed up the process.

"We love each other very much," she said finally.

"I think I've seen you referred to as the planet's power couple," I said, "now that Bill and Melinda . . ." I shrugged helplessly, with palms up, a gesture that seemed to take in their breakup and divorce, and the whole damn thing.

"So sad about them," she said. "I thought they'd be together forever." She shrugged. "But I guess that's what people always say when it ends for people like them."

"Not just people like them."

"But they're both still friends of ours. Melinda and I are making another Africa trip next spring, as a matter of fact."

She made it sound as simple as a donut run.

I wanted to ask her if the alimony that Bill Gates had to pay in his divorce might have enabled her own husband to move up on the money list, but knew better. It was only the two of us in my office. Hardly a challenge for me to read the room. I could already see how hard this was for her.

And Susan had made me promise, if Laura Crain did indeed end up here, that I would do my best to behave.

"When you say your husband, are you referring to your marriage?" I said. "Are the two of you having problems?"

"Oh, no," she said. "That most certainly *isn't* the problem that brought me here, Mr. Spenser. Oh, God, no. No two people could love each other more than we do."

I knew two others. But telling her that wasn't going to do either one of us any good.

All I had so far was her husband. I remembered a story now about a well-known novelist spitballing possible movie ideas with a producer. Finally the producer, excited, said, "I've got it. World War Two!"

"What about World War Two?" the novelist had asked.

And the producer said, "Hey, you're the writer."

Her husband was the problem.

I was the detective.

"He's in some kind of trouble," she said, "and it's making the most kind and gentle man I've ever known suddenly behave erratically, almost like he's having some kind of breakdown. He routinely flies off the handle into these fits of rage over nothing at all, or what seems like nothing at all to me, even though that's never been his nature, all the way back to when I first met him in college." She sighed. "And there are these awful nightmares, sometimes waking him up screaming."

"You're his wife, you must have some idea about what's bothering him. Some sort of indication. Or have at least asked."

She shook her head.

"I did ask, repeatedly, until I finally gave up," she said. "He just said he's going through some things, but will work them out himself. At one point I even suggested that he see Susan. That only made him erupt again. He screamed at me that he didn't need a shrink, and stormed out of the room."

"Has he thought about seeing someone besides a friend of yours?"

"He won't even consider it. It's why I'm the one seeing you."

I waited now, the way I knew Susan would have. It had occurred to both of us, on multiple occasions, that our chosen professions possessed remarkable similarities, especially in the sometimes-artful way we had to draw out our clients. Susan's work just didn't involve her having to shoot people from time to time, or punch their lights out.

I waited as long as I could before finally saying, "You sound as if you're in pain yourself."

"It's why I'm here," she said. "I want you to see if you can find out what kind of trouble my husband might be in, whether it's personal or professional, before he loses his fucking mind."

Her language was like a glass shattering.

She paused then.

"And maybe loses his company."

FOUR

Susan and I were having dinner at Bistro du Midi on Boylston Street, at an upstairs table with a panoramic view of the Public Garden, a view of which I never grew tired, from any possible angle. Boston's version of Central Park, just in miniature.

"I take it you're taking the case," she said.

"Not until I can figure out a way in."

She reaches under the table and gives my thigh a squeeze. "And here I thought you'd finally gotten the hang of that."

"Do they teach you to talk like that at Harvard?"

"No, big boy. That's all you."

She'd let me choose the restaurant tonight, as she and Pearl were having a sleepover. Susan had patiently explained to Pearl before we left the apartment that we would walk her in the park when we returned.

"What if all that walking after dinner tires me out to the extent that it dims my ardor for you when we're finally in bed?" I'd asked her.

"It is my belief that not even a missile attack while the two of us are looking at the swan boats could do that."

"Want to know why I picked this place?"

"Because we could walk to it?" She gave my thigh another squeeze. "I sleep with a detective, remember?"

"You lucky duck."

Susan smiled, this one full of mischief and promise. "You did say *duck*, right?"

I liked to dress up when we went out to dinner, though not as much as she did. Tonight I was wearing my new Brooks Brothers blazer, purchased about fifty yards from my office at the mother ship. Gray slacks, tattersall shirt open at the collar, perfect maroon pocket square, tasseled Ralph Lauren loafers, no socks. It was as much sartorial game as I could muster short of a tuxedo, or my one good suit.

I still looked like a bouncer sitting across from Susan Silverman.

She had taken even longer than usual getting herself ready tonight, to the point where we were nearly late for our reservation, which wouldn't have been the first time. It was all because of what she called "The Process": Lengthy shower after a day of seeing patients, then blowing out the hair just right, something that could occasionally take longer than the opera. At that point she was really just warming up. Then came makeup, and reviewing the jewelry options she'd given herself in her overnight bag. Eventually the only jewelry tonight turned out to be a necklace of cultured pearls I'd purchased for her at Tiffany, spending some of Kevin Boles's money. She was wearing the necklace with a simple and elegant navy blue dress, just short enough to show off her sensational legs as we made our way across the park to the restaurant. There was just the faintest scent of what I was pretty sure was a new perfume.

The other Spenser, Edmund the poet, had once written of sovereign beauty.

That was Susan Silverman, in total.

Once our drinks had been delivered, a Kir Royale of just the perfect shade for her and a Tito's martini with a twist for me, she raised her glass and I raised mine, as we toasted each other.

She saw me staring at her, and smiling myself, before I reached for my glass.

"Something you'd like to share?"

"Nothing you haven't heard before."

"Love talk, I hope."

"Yup," I said.

"Give it to me," she said. "I can handle it."

"Not only can't I believe you love me," I said. "I still can't believe you talked to me."

"Back at you."

Now we both drank, in no rush to even look at the menu.

"I know you've been waiting to talk about Laura Crain," she said.

"You probably know most of it."

"First I want to hear what she told you, and what you think," Susan said.

She took a sip of Kir. Though "sip" might have been a rather generous assessment. Generally when Susan was working on an adult beverage she reminded me of a hummingbird pecking at sugar water.

I, however, took a much healthier swallow of my martini. It was icy cold and merely wonderful. But then it had always been my experience that even a bad martini was better than none.

"I'll take all the help I can get with this," I said.

She sighed.

"I'm sure she's already conveyed to you what she thinks about her husband's recent behavior, and how alarmed she is by it, Suze."

"That he's acting like a total wingnut? She has."

"Ah, yes, Dr. Silverman," I said, stroking an imaginary beard and affecting a bad German accent. "Would wingnut be from the structionalist school, or functionalist?"

"Swampscott High School."

She took another small sip. I sometimes wondered what the point of ordering the drink even was. It was like watching her attack a salad, half a lettuce leaf at a time.

"She told me he's starting to act even more secretive and paranoid lately," I said.

"On a good day, from what I gather."

"But she says when he's out in public, or making an appearance somewhere, he still comes across like a lovable sitcom dad. It's one of the reasons he's as popular around the world as his friend Bill Gates. You know he's just as generous. If a good cause anywhere needs money, he's the first to raise a hand. The past decade or so, he's focused most of his money and energy on supporting women's rights, especially in countries known for oppressing women. Iran. The United Arab Emirates. Mostly Saudi Arabia, my God, the most gender-segregated country on the planet. He *hates* them."

"He sure doesn't need oil from the bastards," I said.

"No," Susan said. "He does not."

"Now his wife really is convinced the guy's on the verge of some kind of breakdown, at what would be a very bad time."

"Is there ever really a good time for a nervous breakdown?" Susan asked.

I'd finished my martini. I caught our waiter's eye and discreetly pointed at my glass.

"I'm talking about a bad time professionally, at least according to Laura," Susan said. "Because of the merger. Even you've heard about the merger, right, even though it hasn't been covered in the Sports section of *The Globe*?"

Crain's company was on the verge of merging with an electric-car company from Canada called Prise, a French word that basically meant plug-in. Prise had quickly and quietly moved up into second in the market behind Tesla and ahead of the Germans, and was looking to expand in both the U.S. and Europe.

"Hawk told me," I told Susan. "He gives me information like that on a need-to-know basis."

Susan smiled. "I think that's wise."

"But in the grand scheme of things, what does it matter if that merger doesn't happen somehow?" I said. "They're already rich as shit."

"But just remember," Susan said. "If money could buy happiness, I'd be out of business."

"I've heard that it can't," I said, "but consider it to be irresponsible gossip."

"On top of everything else," Susan said, "as I'm sure Laura told you, Andrew is giving even more money away than usual, in an almost manic way."

"Even in his world, I don't see how that could be considered a bad thing."

"In mine," she said, "we contextualize things whenever possible. And in this context, his wife does think it's a bad thing, no matter who it benefits. He's acting out and she doesn't know why."

"Is she worried that he's going to give it all away before he's through?" I asked. "Didn't the guy who owned The North Face give it all away to fight climate change?"

"Patagonia," Susan said.

I grinned. "He wanted to fight Patagonia?"

She took a real sip now.

"You're an idiot sometimes."

"But I'm your idiot."

I ordered the sweet corn soup and then duck breast with baby kale and figs as my main course. Susan ordered the arugula and endive salad and king salmon. Salmon was often her go-to entrée, no matter where we were dining. Tonight she had studied the menu the way she would have studied for a final in Counseling Psychology once, finally putting it down and saying, "I've made my decision."

"Salmon?" I'd said.

"Aren't you funny."

"Kind of," I said.

I politely asked then if she thought we should order

pommes frites on the side, this being a French restaurant and all.

"Rhetorical question?" she said.

"Oui."

We passed on dessert and then walked back home to walk Pearl. When she had finished her nighty ablutions and we were all on our way back to Marlborough Street, Susan and I had returned to talking about Andrew Crain, whom his wife wanted me to investigate without him knowing he was being investigated.

"I have a bad feeling about this, Suze," I said. "It's why I haven't officially said yes to her yet."

"Which parts? Or all of it?"

"All of it," I said. "She wants me to find out what's tormenting the sixth-richest man in America without him knowing that she's hired me to do just that."

"When you put it that way," she said, "it does sound like a hairball. But aren't those your specialty?"

"Only one of them," I said, and when we were back upstairs I showed her a few more. With undimmed ardor.

When she had shown me a few specialties of her own, she fell back on her pillow, flushed and sated and out of breath and somehow glowing at the same time while I tried to get my own breathing under control.

"Ooo la la," Susan said.

FIVE

Because of my move, Hawk and I had taken to running along the Charles again, usually at least three times a week, alternating with track work at Harvard.

My knees felt better than they had in years, even though I had relented to getting an occasional cortisone shot. I knew I was keeping up with Hawk only because he was letting me—something which he took endless pleasure in reminding me—but I felt that I was more than holding my own lately, even when we dialed it up to five miles the way we had today.

We had crossed over the Fiedler Footbridge, run down to the Mass Ave Bridge and then over to the Cambridge side, heading along Memorial Drive before finally turning back, the view even better from the Cambridge side, taking in all of Back Bay.

Hawk wore a BLACK MAMBA T-shirt, black Lululemon

running tights that looked as if they had been applied to his legs with a lacquer brush, and Adidas running shoes that I was certain had cost him more than my first car. I had dressed down because I didn't know any other way when working out, decked out in a Harvard sweatshirt with the sleeves cut to my shoulders and baggy gray sweatpants and old New Balance gray shoes that I was sure were going to once again catch the fashion curve any day.

When we were finished we sat on a bench before heading back over the footbridge, drinking from the water bottles we'd both Velcroed to our upper arms. My breath had slowly returned to normal. It was different with Hawk. It always was. He was neither sweating nor breathing hard, giving no sign that we'd just run as far and as hard as we had, especially at the finish, when he'd delighted in running away from me the way Michael Johnson had famously run away from everybody in the 200 in the Olympics once.

Hawk, in fact, did not look as if he'd just done anything more strenuous than retie his laces.

We had not yet decided whether we wanted to have breakfast at Mike's on Washington Street or Victoria's on Mass Ave after showering at the apartment. While we waited to make the call, Hawk was explaining to me exactly how Andrew Crain and Ethan Lowe had won the lottery with their invention after they'd left Harvard.

"Think of it this way," Hawk said. "Crain be Gates. Lowe be Paul Allen, he should rest in peace."

He proceeded to give me a brief but detailed tutorial on lithium and its uses and most of all its value, especially in the age of the electric car, all of it delivered as only Hawk could, in his spectacular street patois, as if he were the second lead in *The Wire* telling you how to split the atom.

"So am I your Gates?" I said.

"First among equals? Fuck no. I got no equals."

He leaned back and let the sun hit his face, smiling as he did, looking neither young nor old, looking serene and completely comfortable in his own skin and his own impressive self, looking the same as he always had to me, which meant looking like Hawk.

"Okay, you can be Gates and I'll be Allen."

"You gonna keep interrupting, or you want me to explain this shit to you in a way even you can understand?"

"I promise to shut up now."

He snorted. "When pigs fly."

He turned and leaned an arm over the back of the bench. "You understand why the world needs lithium, right?"

"Batteries?"

He nodded. "Lithium-ion currently be going at a compound rate 'bout thirty percent. And that don't even figure in what the number might go to over the next ten years on account of all the cheap Teslas gonna be on the road 'fore long. I was reading something the other day, *The Times,* all about how lithium *is* gonna make electric cars more affordable, and how this one lithium mine, up to Quebec, basically feels like it walked into a way to just start printing money."

I watched and listened, fascinated, not surprised by the intelligence and curiosity, they'd always been there, even in his leg-breaking days. I was just knocked back all over again at how well versed he was about so many different things.

"Them lithium-ion batteries, just them, they charge faster, last longer, and have a higher power density for a longer life."

"I could use something like that," I said.

Hawk grinned. "Be called Viagra, leastways for old white men like you."

I grinned. "But you digress."

"Yowza," Hawk said. "So all of a sudden these two nerds come up with a way to make they own. Nobody knows how they do it, but they do it. And now this country don't have to go beggin' to Chile or Argentina or Australia or Quee-bec for lithium. Or fucking Bolivia."

"And Crain and Lowe are the ones printing money and saying they're going to use a boatload of it to save the planet."

"Or at least give the planet one of them extreme makeovers."

"And while all that is going on they're supposed to live happily ever after, Crain especially," I said, "because he out-kicked his coverage with his significant other."

"Look who's talkin'."

"Only now his wife is worried that he's having a nervous breakdown, even if only she knows it yet."

"And she don't know why."

"And wants us to find out why, lippity lop, if I decide to take the case."

"*If* you decide?" Hawk said. "You know you gonna take it."

He theatrically raised his eyebrows then. "And did I hear you say *us*?" he said, now sounding as if he belonged in *The Crown*, making the transition as effortlessly as he always did.

"Indeed you did, old boy."

"Yo, Jeeves?" Hawk said. "Who you callin' 'boy'?"

SIX

I had called Laura Crain first thing the next morning and told her I was taking her case. I asked if her husband's business partner shared her concerns. She said that he did. I asked if he would be willing to meet with me. She said she could check, and called back later and said that Ethan Lowe would be more than willing to meet with me, as early as today.

The old John Hancock Tower was now officially 200 Clarendon Street. So it had been rebranded, too. But if you lived in Boston you still thought of it as the Hancock. It was still the tallest building in the city, and in New England, whatever people wanted to call it.

Lith, Inc. was located on the forty-ninth and fiftieth floors. These were where their business offices were headquartered. The factories where their product was produced were scattered around the country. The site closest to Boston was right off 495 in Lowell. I had seen photographs of it. The buildings looked quite modern, and not at all as if they were helping to change the world, with LITH in huge block letters on the side of the largest one.

Ethan Lowe didn't want to meet at the office. When I called he asked if I knew where the Friendly Toast breakfast place was on Stanhope, saying it was just a short walk from the Hancock. I told him I knew exactly where it was.

"I can walk there from my office, too," I said, making no attempt to hide the pride in my voice.

I was waiting for him when he walked in. I had gone to the Internet to remind myself what he looked like. He turned out to be taller than I expected him to be, even realizing that guessing someone's height by merely looking at a head shot was like trying to guess their weight at the same time.

He wore a black crewneck sweater and khaki pants and white Federer sneakers I recognized because Susan had a pair just like them. He was mostly bald in that way that had become fashionable, just a fringe of blond-gray hair. He wore wire-rimmed glasses, was quite tan and whippet-thin, yet somehow his sweater looked one size too small.

I got up when he got to the table I had managed to score for us. He grinned as we shook hands. "Laura told me to just find someone who looked like he could lick any sonofabitch in the house."

"John L. Sullivan said that," I said.

"I happen to know he was born in the same section of Roxbury I was," Lowe said.

"Ward Bond played him in *Gentleman Jim*," I said. "In glorious black-and-white."

"I've always thought the world looked better in black-and-white," Lowe said.

"You seem to have done just fine in this one."

"I have these bursts of nostalgia," he said. "But I'm not crazy."

He ordered a cold brew.

"Thank you for meeting with me," I said. "I'm sure this must be awkward for you."

"It is," he said. "But since we're both here, you already know how difficult it is to say no to Laura Crain."

"I held out a whole day."

"Wow," Lowe said. "Now I'm sure you *can* lick any sonofabitch in the house."

His cold brew was delivered. The waiter topped off my hot coffee. I didn't like iced coffee. Susan said it was a generational thing and I just told her to go ahead and add it to the list. She said the list would eventually be longer than the phone book used to be.

When the waiter was gone Lowe said, "It goes without saying that this meeting never took place."

"What meeting?" I said.

"But as I'm sure Laura told you, I'm as concerned about Andrew as she is. As is Claire."

"Claire?"

"Laura didn't mention her? She's the woman we call the other Mrs. Andrew Crain. Claire Megill. His executive assistant. He met her in California when he hired her to work for us, and she eventually fast-tracked her way here, and to the office outside his. Andrew and I joke all the time that if the company plane ever went down with us on it, Claire could take over without missing a beat. She's truly like Andrew's other brain."

"Maybe I should talk to her, too."

"She may share our concerns, but I'm not sure how forthcoming she'd be with a stranger," Lowe said. "I myself don't see meeting with you as a breach of loyalty, but rather an act of loyalty toward my partner. She would. She just wants to write this all off to stress."

"Involving the sale?"

"Just the accumulated stress of having been Andrew Crain, all the way back to when we hit it as big as we did. She thinks it's just finally caught up with him. That he's going through a phase." He put air quotes around the last word. "Claire sees what she wants to see. And what she's always seen with Andrew is an honest-to-Christ American hero."

"See no evil, even now?"

"And hear no evil, even when he's acting out the way he has been lately."

"Is she married?"

You poke at things when the opportunity presents itself, nibbling at the edges. We seemed to have gotten off-point with Claire Megill, but perhaps not.

"Claire was married briefly, a long time ago. She never talks about it, other than to say that the only good that came out of it was her son. Cameron. He's a junior at Cal Poly. Andrew is quite fond of him. I have no doubt that Andrew will find a place for him at Lith when he graduates. He's already worked summers for us as an intern."

"I need to ask this," I said. "But is there a chance that

his relationship with Ms. Megill might be more than professional. It wouldn't be the first time something like that has happened in an executive suite."

"I'd be shocked," Lowe said. "As loyal as he is to Claire and she to him, Andrew is even more connected, more reliant, on his wife. I tell him all the time that he's the most married man in America."

I saw the waiter go by with a blueberry muffin the size of a football, and wanted to tackle him from behind, if I thought I could catch the muffin before it hit the floor.

"I've done some reading on both you and Andrew," I said. "It appears that he's the first among equals."

"Sixty-forty," he said. "It was that way from the start, because he did most of the science. My role was more entrepreneurial."

He took off his glasses, pulled a small cloth out of his pocket, cleaned them carefully, put them back on. Everything about him was meticulous, with even the smallest movements.

"What if he woke up one day and decided he didn't just want to spin off the software company, but cash out of Lith, too?"

"At that point," Lowe said, "there wouldn't be a goddamn thing I could do to stop him. Somebody else would own his share, and I'd probably be thinking about selling mine, maybe to the same person, though the list of people who would have the kind of money it would take would be a short one." He shrugged. "Ownership of our company would make the fucking earth move, I know that."

"What would you do if that happened?"

He took his phone out of his pocket, looked at it,

frowned, put it away. I liked him better for not keeping it on the table in front of him while we'd been talking.

"Him selling, or both of us selling?"

"Either way."

He looked at me and grinned. "How did we get here from talking about Andrew's behavior?"

I shrugged then. "I have a short attention span."

"Somehow, Mr. Spenser, I doubt that. We've only known each other a few minutes, but I have a good sense of people. You need one from what I guess you could call my perch. And my sense already is that people who underestimate you probably end up getting carried off the field on a stretcher."

I drank more coffee. It was very good coffee.

"So what do you really think is going on with your partner? You're the one who's known him even longer than his wife has, from what I've read."

"I guess that's true," Lowe said. "He spent his first couple years at Harvard just worshipping Laura from afar. So technically I have known him longer."

"So the two of you have been in each other's lives, passionately joined, for more than two decades."

"Just not continuously," he said.

"I'm not sure what that means."

"It means," Lowe said, "that I lost track of him for a couple years after college. But then pretty much everybody did."

SEVEN

I knew how much easier research was now because of technology, and had been since the first www.com. But there was a part of me that still missed going to the Boston Public Library when I needed to look things up regarding a case or a client.

Additionally I missed calling a friend like Wayne Cosgrove, the columnist who had become editor of *The Globe*, and asking him to go into the magical place I thought of as "the clips" when I needed information.

I'd mentioned this to Susan on the phone this morning.

"Please tell me this isn't going to be another occasion when you wax poetic about microfilm," she said.

"Those were the days."

"If you miss them that much, you can always Google them," she said.

Instead I spent the morning and then into the afternoon

intensely Googling Andrew Crain, even though when I thought of it that way I always imagined inappropriate touching.

A lot of it I already knew, not just about his invention and the formation of his company, but about his passion for saving the oceans and supporting the right political candidates and nearly buying one of the big pharmaceutical companies during COVID, because he believed he and Ethan Lowe could somehow speed up the vaccine process.

He and Lowe had started charter schools from Africa to Serbia. There was no telling how much of his own personal wealth Crain had directed to Ukraine by now, in support of its president and its army.

All in all it was a modern American success story, another one out of the tech world, this one originating in Boston the way Mark Zuckerberg's had with Facebook.

Just like that, another nerd ruled.

When it happened, I always pictured another angel getting its wings.

Two nerds in this instance, Crain and his partner.

Looks-wise, Andrew Crain reminded me of a grown-up version of Harry Potter, just with red hair and not black. Tall, skinny, round and oversized Harry glasses. Even now, more than twenty years after Harvard, he still looked as if he were late for class.

There was just one gap in his history, the one Ethan Lowe had mentioned over coffee, the two years after graduation and before Crain and Lowe went into business together, when Andrew was completely off the grid.

His story, one that had never changed, a story he repeated almost word for word every time he told it, was that he had strapped on a backpack and gone off to find himself. His parents, both dead by then, had left him enough money, or so he said, to finance a search for meaning in his life from Boston to the Himalayas and back.

He sounded like Larry Darrell in *The Razor's Edge*. Maugham's character had been traumatized by World War I. I wondered what might possibly have traumatized Andrew Crain, who'd found not only meaning in his life when he had come back to civilization, but the pot of gold at the end of the rainbow along with it.

"I got my head out of books," he told Diane Sawyer in an old interview I'd watched, "and tried to understand the world as a way of trying to understand myself."

Laura Crain had sat with him for that interview. She'd smiled and said to Sawyer, "He didn't call, he didn't write."

"All part of my master plan to win your heart," he said, "just praying that my absence would make it grow fonder."

"Well," his wife said, "mission accomplished."

"She was out of my league then," Crain said, "and still is now."

Somehow the two of them were genuine enough and clearly loved each other enough that watching a sit-down like this didn't cause a sugar high, even seeing it all this time later.

At breakfast I'd asked Lowe if he'd ever pressed Crain on at least some of the places he'd gone and things he'd done.

"He has always been light on specifics," Lowe said.

"In the end he just makes the whole thing actually sound like a religious experience. When it was over he said he knew the person he wanted to be. And, better yet, knew the one he didn't want to be."

When he did come back he and Lowe did a modern-day version of Thomas Edison telling Watson to get his ass into his office, just with secondary cell construction, and the rest was history.

Both of them had apparently lived quite happily ever after until Andrew Crain had started to act as if he had a screw loose.

I was finally getting ready to leave the office when Susan called and said that we were having dinner tomorrow night with Andrew and Laura Crain.

"You're welcome," she said.

EIGHT

I had a long-standing date to meet Martin Quirk at the Street Bar at The Newbury, which was previously The Taj, and before that had been the Ritz since around the time the *Mayflower* landed. If you had been around long enough, and Quirk and I both had, the place would always be the Old Ritz. The bar inside, right off the Arlington Street entrance, was still the best in the city and one of the best anywhere.

"I can walk here from my new apartment," I told Quirk when I arrived.

"So I heard."

"Who told you?"

"Everybody," he said.

He was now assistant superintendent of the Boston Police Department. He'd been captain before that and homicide detective before that. Cop-wise, at least in this city, he was the equivalent of Tom Brady. When I'd told him that one time he said, "I never left to wear a fucking pirate helmet in Florida."

Quirk never aged, the way Hawk never seemed to. More gray to the hair these days, more lines around the eyes, well earned, he liked to point out. He wore a tweed jacket despite unseasonably warm weather this week, blue button-down shirt with the Brooks Brothers roll to the collar, navy knit tie. Big hands, thick fingers. Having known him as long as I had, I was aware that he knew how to use them when a situation presented itself.

He rarely changed expression. And was not someone you ever wanted to needlessly antagonize. I'd once seen him put a small-town southern cop who'd falsely arrested me against a wall and say, "You want to fuck with me, dick breath?" After that you could have cleaned away the officer in question with a mop.

All in all, Quirk was Quirk the way Hawk was Hawk.

We both ordered martinis. I had my usual lemon peel with mine. Quirk told the waiter he could skip the fruit in his. We had the table situated squarely in front of the picture window, looking across at the Public Garden.

"This going to be social," he said, "or do you want something from me?"

"Fellowship?"

"Join a book club."

It had been months since we'd seen each other. I asked him how Frank Belson was, once Quirk's top sergeant, now a lieutenant, working for a homicide captain, Glass, whom Belson privately called Nurse Ratched.

"He asked me to thank you for not making any work for him lately," Quirk said.

"Ah, but the night is young."

I told him about Andrew Crain and his wife and everything else I'd learned about him over the past couple days. When I finished I said, "Any advice?"

"Yeah," Quirk said. "Run."

"I was hoping for somewhat more positive reinforcement than that."

He might have smiled just slightly. Or, and more likely, there had just been an involuntary twitch to his lips. But there was no real change of expression, his cop eyes never leaving me.

"Oh, shit," he said finally. "You were serious with that part about the positive reinforcement."

We both watched a young woman in tight faded jeans walk past the window, in the direction of Newbury Street. She was young and pretty and had buds in her ears and I wasn't sure, watching her until she disappeared across the street, how she'd managed to get into the jeans. And didn't care.

When I turned back toward Quirk he said, "Doesn't make either one of us a bad person."

We both drank. I told him that the only way I could approach this case was as a cold case, and asked how he handled things when he'd open a file on an open unsolved.

"You look at what you already know," Quirk said, "but that doesn't get you anywhere, you'd know that if you ever opened up the file before. If it did get you anywhere, the goddamn case wouldn't be unsolved."

"What I mostly know about this guy is what everybody seems to know, that he's a prince among men."

I told him that it was Susan's professional opinion that Crain was exhibiting signs of buried guilt.

"How's Susan doing, by the way?" Quirk said. "Obviously she's still with you."

"If a thing loves, it is infinite," I said.

"Should I write that down?" Quirk said.

The crowd in the bar began to increase, as did the noise level. A lot had changed at this hotel over time. Just not the dimensions of this room, and the general look of it. The furniture was obviously new. Green chairs at the bar. Blue chairs once you stepped down into the area where we were. A green wraparound soft in the middle of everything. And the vast and unchanging view of the park across the street.

"Maybe this guy is just having a midlife crisis," Quirk said. "Apropos of no bad shit in his past. He wouldn't be the first, no matter how much money he's got in the bank."

"But maybe something from his past has reached out and grabbed him by the balls."

"Is that a line of poetry from Blake, too?"

"You knew that was Blake before?"

"There's a lot of layers to me," Quirk said. "I thought you, being an ace detective, would have picked up on that by now."

I waved for another martini. Quirk put his hand over his own glass. "I'm driving," he said. "I know, I know, you can walk."

"All I've really got is those two years when he went to find himself and it sounds like nobody could find *him*," I said.

"Can you ask him where he went and what he did at dinner?" Quirk said.

"If I do, I need to be artful about it, so as not to make him think it's some kind of cross-examination."

Quirk took another sip, put his glass down, and then shook his head.

"Artful?" he said. "Shit, I was afraid of that."

NINE

Susan had a meeting for the Margaret Fuller Neighborhood House, located over on Cherry Street in Cambridge. After that she and a few of her fellow board members were having dinner at Harvest.

So I was cooking for one. I had spent a lot of my adult life cooking for one, even after Susan and I were together. I liked cooking, the passion for it being something I had inherited from my father and from my uncles. Tonight I was keeping things relatively simple, a lemon-pepper chicken dish that had become one of my favorites, pasta primavera on the side, featuring the vegetables I'd picked up the day before at the Copley Street Market.

I'd prepared the same dish for Susan a couple weeks earlier. When she'd tasted it she demanded to know what exotic marinade I'd used.

"Newman's Own," I'd said.

I was listening to Diana Krall and having a civilized glass of chardonnay and thinking about chopping up the vegetables when Mattie Sullivan called from Los Angeles.

She had been there since the start of the summer, working with Zebulon Sixkill, who now had his own detective agency Out There. Mattie had postponed taking the police exam, at least for now, after visiting Z. I suspected she was a goner from the first time she'd walked up and down Abbot Kinney in Venice. Now she was living in Z's spare room and helping him out at work, effectively having turned in a cop badge she hadn't yet earned, at least for now.

She was even dating a young actor from some Netflix series that she had tried in vain to describe to me, about an alien and his human sidekick and time travel, until I begged her to stop. She said he played the sidekick, for what it was worth.

Having her with Z was like having two grown-up children living together.

"You can't believe what I did today," she said.

"Found USC without using Waze?"

"Went to Bunda for the first time."

"Bunda?"

"It's in West Hollywood. The best full-body workout in L.A. Hottest exercise place in town. Z knows somebody there."

"Come home now."

She laughed. "Keanu Reeves was there."

"OMG!" I said.

She asked what I was working on. I told her.

"Susan and I are having dinner with him and his wife

tomorrow night," I said, "at which point I will artfully try to gather information."

"You?" Mattie said. "Artful? You're so fucked."

"Quirk basically said the same thing," I said. "See that, if you'd stayed and taken the exam you'd be on your way to making detective."

"Can't lie," she said. "I really like it here, Spenser."

"Almost everybody does until their show gets canceled."

"I've been to a bunch of Dodger games to watch Mookie Betts. It's practically like I was the player to be named later after the Sox traded him here."

She pronounced it "Sawx," as always. You can take the girl out of Boston.

"Okay, that's it, I'm hanging up on you," I said. "You know Mookie is the name that must not be spoken."

"You need help on the case I can always fly back," she said. "It actually sounds like fun."

"Trust me, kid, it's not."

"Let me ask you something," Mattie said. "What if you find out that your very own Bill Gates has some deep, dark secret that could wreck his life, and stop him from fixing all the things in the world he's trying to fix?"

"The best way to explain it is in a way you will completely understand," I told her. "I have no fucking idea."

She told me how much she missed me then, and Susan and Boston and Pearl and Hawk, just a little less than she expected when it was seventy-five and sunny every freaking day. I told her weather wasn't everything.

"Yeah?" Mattie said. "Ask Mookie."

I did not watch the Sox game while I ate dinner tonight.

The Mookie-less Sox. I switched the music over to Sarah Vaughan and Clifford Brown. I had read somewhere that it was her favorite album. I also knew it had been released the year before Clifford Brown had died in an automobile accident on his way to a gig in Chicago.

My mind was so often filled with random information like this. I knew that Mookie Betts's real name was Markus Lynn Betts, because his parents wanted him to have the initials "MLB." I knew that Elvis and Babe Ruth had died on the same date, August 16. I knew that a man named Percy Spencer—Spencer with a *c*—had invented the microwave when he was working at Raytheon, in Burlington, Mass.

I had switched from wine to Bushmills by now, sitting at my kitchen table and studying some of the notes I'd taken. I knew more today about Andrew Crain than I'd known the day before. So that was progress. Wasn't that progress?

I finished my first Bushmills and poured myself another as Sarah and Clifford Brown eased their way into "You're Not the Kind."

After a while I put the notes away and went to stand at my picture window, the draperies Susan had ordered still not having been delivered, late the way things still so often were in the post-COVID world. The view from my living room was different than it had been at the old place. But then so was I. When I'd first lived a couple buildings over, I didn't have Z in my life. Or Mattie. Now I had both of them, even if they were three thousand miles away. Mattie said she'd be back. Maybe for a visit, I thought. But my instinct was that she wanted to live there now.

Bunda, I thought.

Tip of the iceberg.

So often in the past, or so it seemed to me, I had taken on new clients who had come to me because they found themselves at risk. Or in danger. Or some loved one was. Just not always. Once Paul Giacomin, who I'd treated like a son the way I now treated Z like a son, had shown up at my office with a young woman who wanted me to find out how her mother had died back in the seventies, a bank robbery gone wrong. I had eventually discovered that the woman wasn't her mother at all, and that she was in fact the granddaughter of a mobster. None of which I had shared with her in the end, because I didn't think the knowing would improve a single day of the rest of her life.

How much did Andrew Crain's wife need to know about him, if I uncovered something bad he had buried in his past?

How much did *I* want to know?

Gabriel García Márquez had written about public lives, private lives, secret lives.

What would it be like if my Bill Gates, as Mattie had called him, had some kind of a secret life once?

I was nursing the second Bushmills and considering a third. This was a good time of the night for whiskey, alone in the new apartment except for Sarah and Clifford Brown's trumpet.

Sometimes I wondered about the value of the kind of work I did, and had done for a long time, and done well, in a modern world where everybody seemed to know everything, *about* everybody.

Now there were things that Laura Crain did not know about her husband, things I was intuiting, with little to go on, at least so far, that she might not want to know. But in her mind, it was her husband who was now at risk, which is how she had ended up at my office.

Sarah had circled back now to "September Song," the song with which she and Cliff Brown had started the album and was now ending it.

"I played me a waiting game . . ."

I finished the last of my Irish whiskey then and rinsed my glass and took one last look at the Public Garden, at least for tonight. It was still here and so was I.

It was just Mookie who wasn't coming back.

TEN

We ate at Davio's on Arlington Street. Susan had picked it, but not until she had made me promise that we would eventually venture out of the neighborhood again when dining out.

"Come and get me, copper," I growled.

"Bogie?"

"Cagney. *White Heat.* You can't tell the difference?"

"God, no."

Laura Crain said that Davio's was actually on the short list of Boston restaurants her husband liked, and that they had a car bringing them from Brookline so as not to have to worry about driving home after a few drinks.

"I just like being able to walk here again from my apartment," I said when we were all seated.

"Sigh," Susan said.

"She thinks I've become too territorial," I said to the Crains.

"Somewhat like a wolf," Susan said.

Andrew Crain looked less geeky than he did in photographs and on television. Gone at last were the long bangs hanging down to his eyes. His hair was much neater tonight. And as skinny as he still was, I could see from the way his long-sleeved polo shirt fit him that he was in good shape, as if he'd gotten with a personal trainer and stayed with one.

He didn't take off his Red Sox cap until he was seated.

"Don't take it off on my account," I said.

He grinned. "It's more a way to avoid too much eye contact on my way into a room like this than a pledge of allegiance."

When our first round of drinks had been delivered—Crain had surprised me by ordering a jalapeño tequila—his wife raised her glass in a toast.

"To Susan," she said.

"Any particular reason," I said, "other than her extreme wonderfulness?"

"For finally making this night happen," she said.

I had told Susan that Armando, the maître d', would almost certainly give us one of their small, private dining rooms if I asked him. But Laura said the main room would be just fine, that even as recognizable as her husband was, he generally didn't cause a stir when they did dine out.

Andrew Crain hung back on the conversation at the table, but did not appear bored by it. It was almost as if he were eavesdropping on the rest of us from the next table.

And he did pose questions about Susan's work, finally asking her if she'd ever envisioned herself in a committed relationship with someone in my line of work.

Susan smiled at him now. "I'd actually hoped to run away with someone like you, Andrew."

"Hey, wait a second," I said.

Crain laughed along with the rest of us.

"I was just joking, honey buns," Susan said to me.

As our entrées were being delivered, he asked where I had grown up.

"Wyoming," I said. "Laramie. I was raised by my father and uncles after my mother died."

"I spent some time in Laramie after college, working on a road crew one summer," he said.

He had opened the door, if only a crack.

"Hopefully not a crew from the Albany County Jail," I said.

Crain laughed again. "No, nothing as colorful as that. They were just doing some work on Interstate 80 when I was passing through, and I managed to sign on."

"Eighty was the road I took out of town when the time came," I said.

"I took the same road," Crain said. "But I was hitchhiking."

"Part of that period when you talked about going off to find yourself," I said.

"I see you've done your homework," Crain said.

"He's always liked being the smartest boy in class," Susan said.

"Got me out of Wyoming," I said.

I saw a sudden shift in Andrew Crain's attention then,

to a young couple a few tables away, on the Arlington Street side of the restaurant, against the wall. There is rarely a slow night at Davio's, here or at their sister place at the Seaport. But not all of the tables in the main room were full tonight, and neither was the bar, so it wasn't as loud as it could sometimes be at high tide.

I followed Crain's eyes to the young couple. The guy was leaning forward, hand on his date's arm, face red. His face, not hers.

He was making no attempt to keep his voice down.

"You don't get to decide when we leave," he said, leaning closer to her. "*I* decide."

I heard Laura Crain ask her husband how he liked his halibut. But he appeared not to hear. He was focused on these two strangers having a very bad moment, one becoming an increasingly public event. The woman was quite pretty, but you could see the tension on her face from where we all sat, how pale she looked.

"Please lower your voice," she said.

"Why? Am I embarrassing you again?"

"I want to leave," she said now.

"We leave when I say we leave."

"Andrew, what's the matter?" Laura said at our table, seeing the tension on her husband's face, all of us feeling it.

"He's a bully," Crain said, not looking at his wife, still looking at the couple. "You know I hate bullies."

I looked at Susan, saw the concern in her eyes.

The young woman got up, shaking her arm loose. "You're hurting me," I heard her say, making no attempt to lower her voice now. The guy reached for her again, but she had already grabbed her purse and was walking as fast as she could toward the front door, her high heels sounding as loud as tap shoes.

Her date, red-faced, oblivious to the scene he had made and was still making, tossed a fistful of cash on the table and followed her.

"Enough," Andrew Crain said as we all watched him go. *"Enough."*

He took his napkin from his lap and spiked it like he was Gronk, the old Patriot, spiking a football after catching another touchdown pass from Tom Brady. Then Andrew Crain was pushing his chair back. It was like watching a kettle that had now come to full boil.

Crain reached for the Red Sox cap and pulled it down over his eyes, as if that was going to do anything to hide his identity at this point.

"Andrew, no," his wife said in a small voice.

"Let them go," she said.

She was the one reaching for his arm. But it was too late for that.

"Spenser," Susan said.

"Andrew," I said quietly, "you're the last guy in this restaurant who wants to be anywhere near this. Let me go deal with that guy."

Andrew Crain wheeled around.

"I'll take care of this," he snapped, as if speaking to all of us at once.

"Enough," he said again.

A man used to being in charge, and having people do what he told them to do.

He followed the couple out of Davio's.

No one spoke at our table as we watched him go. The main dining room had gotten much quieter. I had seen some cell phones go up as Crain made his way across the room. I wanted to check mine, just to have something to do with my hands.

When I couldn't wait any longer, I got up from our table and headed for the door myself.

"See if he needs help," I heard Laura Crain said.

But when I got out onto Arlington Street her husband was gone.

The only one standing there was the jerk Andrew Crain had followed out of the restaurant. He was staring up Arlington in the direction of the park.

I spun him around.

"Hey," he said. "Take your hands off me."

"Where is he?" I said.

"Was that who I think it was?"

He started to back away from me. I reached down and grabbed his left hand. If I put any more pressure on it than I already was, I would start to feel bones crack. In the moment it was not an unappealing thought.

"Where is he?" I said.

"It was crazy," he said. "I'm trying to figure out which way my date went, yelling her name. I don't even hear him come up behind me. Then I feel this tap on my shoulder and when I turn around I see that he's already got his fist back, like he's ready to throw a punch. So I start to back away. But then he stops himself at the last second." The guy shrugged. "Like he'd left himself hanging."

The guy looked down at his hand. "You're going to break my fucking hand," he said.

"Not until I want to," I said. "Tell me what happened next."

"What happened next is that rich guy ran like he owed me money."

ELEVEN

Laura Crain called the next morning to tell me that her husband hadn't returned to their home in Brookline, and hadn't spent the night at their brownstone on Chestnut Street on Beacon Hill, as she would have gotten an alert on her phone if someone had disabled the alarm system there before entering.

"Don't you have the app where you can track his location with his phone?" I said.

She said that normally she would have been able to do that, except that he'd asked her to keep it in her purse during dinner so he wouldn't be tempted to check it every five minutes during dinner like a high school sophomore.

"He keeps saying he's trying to quit acting as if it might explode like a pipe bomb if he misses a text or a call," she said.

"Has his partner heard from him?" I said.

"I called Ethan first thing. He said that the last time they'd spoken had been at the office late yesterday afternoon. He told me he'd actually been surprised, Andrew had acted more like himself than he had in weeks."

"What about his assistant?"

"I called Claire right before I called Ethan," she said. "The last time she'd seen him was at the office when he'd left for dinner."

"Why doesn't someone as rich as your husband have a bodyguard?" I said.

"He has several at his disposal. He just doesn't like to use them as often as he once did."

"Any particular reason?"

"Andrew said that having someone around all the time was another way of making him feel like a prisoner."

"Of what?"

"Being Andrew Crain."

I was at my desk. *The Globe* was unopened in front of me. I was working on my second cup of coffee, having had one at the apartment before I'd walked over. I took comfort in the fact that only I was counting.

"Has he done anything similar to this since his behavior began to spin out?"

"There have been occasions when he stormed out, either here or when we were at the brownstone," she said. "But he's always come back eventually, usually after taking an epically long walk. Andrew has always thought that long walks can cure everything except beach erosion."

I drank some coffee, then leaned back and put my sneakers up on the desk, noticing that they were starting to look older than the Paul Revere House. Maybe a visit to Marathon Sports was in order this morning, right past Dunkin', as luck would have it.

"You have his phone," I said. "Has anybody tried to reach out to *him* this morning?"

"No." There was a long pause at her end. "How long before you start to think about filing a missing-person report?"

"We're nowhere near that, Laura," I said. "Once you call the cops and tell them that Andrew Crain is missing, he'll be trending on social media in about five minutes, and then the whole thing blows up."

"You have to find him," she said.

"I will," I said.

I tried to sound far more confident than I felt at the moment. I asked if they had any other homes. She said there was a cabin in the Berkshires, and their place on Martha's Vineyard, but all of them were linked by the same computer security system, and he hadn't been to either one of those, she'd checked to make sure.

I asked if he might have just checked into a hotel, but she said they shared credit cards, and none had been used since he'd paid for dinner at Davio's in advance of sitting down.

Her voice rose suddenly, as if she'd hit the volume button on her phone.

"I have no idea what's going on in his brain right now," she said. "I don't even know where to tell you to begin to look for him."

"How about I begin by talking to his other brain?" I said, and asked for Claire Megill's number.

TWELVE

I had my picture taken at the Lith reception desk in the lobby after Claire Megill had left my name down there. They gave me a badge to wear up to the fiftieth floor.

The assistant to Andrew Crain's assistant, a young guy whom I would have thought looked like the kid who'd played Theo on the old *Cosby Show*, if you were even allowed to still reference anything Cosby in polite society without getting canceled.

His name plate read MR. BAKER.

"Do I look fat in this picture?" I said to him, showing him my badge. "They wouldn't let me retake my driver's license picture, either, and now I'm stuck with it."

He gave me the kind of bored look that I was sure guys his age had to practice until they had it down.

"That's probably the saddest story I'm going to hear all day." He checked his list. Looked back up at me. "Mr. Spenser?"

"There is but one," I said. "Like May in the year."

"It's September."

"I was making a larger and poetic point."

"She's waiting for you inside," Baker said.

I started to walk away.

"Be nice to her," he said, barely loud enough for me to hear.

I turned.

"Odd thing to say."

"Not everybody around here is," he said. Then he added, "Kind."

Claire Megill's office was next door to Andrew Crain's and with the same view, which I thought might extend all the way to the White Mountains. For some reason, I had expected someone older, a head mistress type. But even though her short black hair was flecked subtly with gray, she was not that. Susan had made a continuing and concerted effort to get me to stop objectifying women, at least not in the first thirty seconds of being in their presence, by their physical beauty, or lack thereof. But I continued to fall short of her expectations for me in that regard. Claire Megill was quite attractive, managing to show off a terrific figure in a slim navy skirt suit.

We shook hands.

"Ms. Megill."

"Claire," she said.

"Your assistant is funny," I said.

"And a bit of a genius," she said. "Mostly with numbers. Which Andrew and I aren't."

I smiled, but in moderation, not wanting her to overheat, we'd just met. "You and Andrew seem to be doing just fine."

"Do you have a first name, Mr. Spenser?"

"I do," I said. "But I try not to make a big thing out of it."

I looked around the room, wondering how much bigger and better-appointed her boss's could possibly be next door. It featured an antique desk, the top of which was covered with spreadsheets of some kind, and three TVs bracketing into the wall to my left showing stock-markety things. To my right was a small sitting area with a couch and two chairs and coffee table, giving the office the feeling of being a small suite. Claire Megill gestured for me to take the couch. She took one of the chairs across from it. I sat. She sat. She crossed her legs.

And I heard a melody.

"Laura said I could trust you," she said.

"Even with classified documents," I said. "Including the kind you're not supposed to keep."

She smiled. Maybe she did think I was funny.

She said, "Laura told me what you do for a living, but added that you were a friend of a friend who happens to be a Harvard-trained psychologist."

I shrugged. "I'm frankly as surprised by that as anyone," I said. "But I think it was one of those ancient Greeks who said that fortune favors the foolish."

I heard her phone buzzing from where she'd left it on

her desk. If Claire Megill heard, she didn't acknowledge that she had.

I nodded when the buzzing stopped. "Aren't you worried that it might have been the boss calling from an undisclosed location?"

"Not on that phone," she said. She reached into the side pocket of her jacket and pulled out another one. "He calls on the red phone," she said. "Literally, as you can see."

"I'll ask you what I asked Laura a few minutes ago," I said. "Has he done anything like this before?"

"Anything like disappearing into the night after nearly getting into a fight on the street with a stranger?" Just a hint of sarcasm, but I managed to roll with it. "No, he hasn't done anything quite like that."

She recrossed her legs. If she did it a few more times, I'd be used to it. "But has he gone off and not wanted any of us to reach him? He has."

"In what circumstances?"

"Laura told me I could be open with you, Mr. Spenser. But I'm not sure how open."

She stood now, stiffly, wincing slightly, arching her back the way cats do.

"Sorry," she said. "My back doesn't allow me to sit for long periods anymore. From a lifetime of doing too much sitting. The most essential hour of my day is my noon yoga at the Equinox over on Dartmouth. It's like I have a lunch date every day with my back."

"A friend of mine once said that a bad back is like having a second job," I said.

"Sounds like a wise man."

"Woman, actually."

"I'm not surprised."

"So has your boss gone off like this before?"

"We call them walkabouts," she said. "But they never last long."

"Overnight?"

She hesitated slightly. "Yes," she said finally.

"Has he ever shown up at your place?"

"Yes," she said. "But not last night."

There was a lengthy silence between us then. It did not appear to make her uncomfortable. Nor me. Claire Megill didn't know me well enough to know that I could wait for her to resume speaking until we had both calcified.

"Can I share something with you off the record?" she said.

"I'm not here working on a profile for *The Globe*."

"What I'm asking is if you're going to share everything I tell you with Laura, even if it's not germane to this particular event."

"Only after I decide if it's germane or not," I said.

She took in a lot of air and let it out.

"Andrew and Laura have been spending quite a lot of time apart lately," she said. "More than usual, even given their busy lives. And more than she's let on, I gather."

"Has it been business that's been keeping them separate from each other?" I said. "Or something else."

She seemed to be studying me now, like an item in a store she was considering purchasing.

"I'm not much of an expert on marriage, Mr. Spenser. I had a bad one. Or maybe the worst one. But Andrew and Laura had a good one, for a very long time."

"But not so much now?"

"You're a detective and will likely find this out eventually," she said. "But there have been some very preliminary conversations about separation, put it that way."

Oh, ho, I thought.

"Whose idea?" I said.

"Hers, I believe," Claire Megill said.

THIRTEEN

We both let that settle. I had worked enough divorce cases to know that Massachusetts wasn't a 50/50 state when it came to assets. According to the law, those assets would eventually be divided "fairly," but not necessarily equally, by the court. If it came to that in the case of the Crains, whether the split was equal or not, Laura Crain would likely walk away with the kind of heart-stopping money that her friend Melinda Gates had.

The phone on Claire Megill's desk buzzed behind her. She ignored it once again. Probably some B-lister. Probably the number I'd been given.

"I'm curious," I said. "Why are you telling me this?"

"What do they say in court?" she said. "I believe it speaks to his state of mind."

"But the Crains aren't formally separated, right?"

"When you have as many residences as they do, and you're just operating off the short list, you can be as separate as you want to be," Claire Megill said. "Their night out together with you was quite rare these days."

"You're obviously of the opinion that his marriage is a contributing factor here," I said. "But what do you feel is the primary factor for his disappearance."

"He's come to hate his life, and it's tearing him up inside," she said, without hesitation. "Just my opinion. It's as if he's tired of being Andrew Crain, billionaire businessman and philanthropist." She made air quotes around the two descriptions of her boss. "A good man who still wants to change the world seems to be constantly carrying the weight of it on his shoulders, if that makes any sense. It's not just one thing. It's everything, in my opinion. His marriage. The merger. Getting older. All of it."

I was about to ask about the merger when her door opened. No knock. A man stepped into her office.

"Claire, we need to talk."

She didn't move from where she was leaning against the desk. But she somehow seemed to back up in that moment, or shrink from her visitor, as if whoever the man was, he had done more than simply interrupt us.

"As you can see, Clay, I'm with someone," she said, her voice tight.

"It can wait," he said. "I can't."

"This is Clay Whitson, Mr. Spenser," she said. "Our top attorney." She tried to smile, but didn't do very much with it. "Just ask him."

"Is that supposed to be some kind of joke, Claire?" he said.

"Evidently not," I said now.

He turned to me, as if suddenly remembering I was there. He was about my size. Curly black hair not flecked with gray. Smallish dark eyes. Five-o'clock shadow even in midmorning. Despite his size and barrel chest he was wearing one of those tight suits with tight pants that made him look to me like a bull in tights.

"Who the hell are you?" he said.

"I'm with the band," I said.

"Mr. Spenser is a friend of Laura's," Claire said quickly.

"What are you doing here?" he said to me.

"We were having a conversation, one that has just ended rather abruptly."

"A conversation about what?" Whitson said.

I wasn't sure why I felt a sudden urge to annoy him. But I did. I slowly got to my feet now, just to give him a better sense that he wasn't the biggest guy in the room.

"I'll be in touch," I said to Claire Megill, and walked between them toward the door, coming as close as I possibly could to brushing up against Clay Whitson.

"I asked you a question," Whitson said.

"Two," I said.

"What?"

"First you asked me what I was doing here, and then you asked what my conversation with Ms. Megill was about. That's two questions."

"What are you, some kind of tough guy?" Whitson said.

He seemed a bit flushed. But perhaps went through life that way.

"I am actually a very tough guy," I said. "But now I'm leaving, just so Ms. Megill doesn't start to get the impression that *I'm* the asshole here."

And I left.

Not even noon yet, and I'd already made a new friend.

FOURTEEN

Laura Crain couldn't come into the city to meet me at their brownstone, but sent someone she actually described as their houseman instead. Carlos was his name. He said he would wait and lock the place back up and reset the alarm when I was finished looking around inside.

I didn't think I'd find any kind of clue as to Andrew Crain's whereabouts. But I needed to start looking somewhere, and this was closest.

"Just keep telling yourself that he hasn't yet been missing for twenty-four hours," I told Laura Crain on the phone.

"Keep reminding me of that," she said.

I had decided I would ask her about possible trouble in her marriage in person.

The inside of the place on Chestnut was both tasteful and spectacular at the same time, with enough paintings hanging on the walls, just on the first floor, to make it look like an annex to the Museum of Fine Arts. I poked around down there for a few minutes, then made my way to the second floor, where Laura Crain said her husband's "ego room" was located. Up there I found some of the framed certificates for humanitarian awards he'd received from countries all over the globe, and photographs of him posing with everyone from Nelson Mandela to Barack Obama to George Clooney, even one with Mookie Betts. He and Mookie were in front of the Green Monster at Fenway and looked happy. So was I when Mookie was still at Fenway.

There was also a picture on the fireplace mantel of him with Queen Elizabeth, which made me smile, not at the sight of the late monarch, but at something Hawk had said when she passed.

"Still watching *The Crown*," Hawk had said. "Thanks for the damn spoiler alert."

I went through Crain's desk and found nothing interesting. There was an oversized Mac on the desk, but I did not have the password and had not asked for one. I continued to make my way from room to room. The whole house was spotless, but then Laura Crain had told me the housekeeper had been in the day before. On the third floor was a small theater, with recliner seats and a large screen and even a popcorn machine.

The master bedroom was on the second floor. I stopped back in there, went through his closet and hers, which was about five times the size of his. I went through the drawers of the two bedside tables, hoping I wouldn't find things that would make me feel like a voyeur. Fortunately I did not, just a small bottle of cannabis oil, probably a sleep aid. Her side of the bed.

There was no sign that Andrew Crain had been here recently. Or that she had. Or that anybody except the housekeeper had. I went back down to the ego room again, then down to the first floor to admire the art, both paintings and sculptures. Despite the personal touches, there was no sense that this was someone's home. Instead it felt like a lavishly furnished and designed spec house for the rich and famous, as if the Crains might be ready to turn it around and sell it to some other rich guy.

As I stepped outside, I was thinking about the lawyer again, and how quickly he *had* annoyed me to the extent that he had.

I had mentioned him to Laura Crain.

"Have you ever seen *A Few Good Men*?" she asked.

I told her that by now I was pretty certain I nearly had the movie memorized.

"Clay is the company's version of Colonel Jessup," she said. "He was Ethan's hire. My husband's partner has convinced himself and keeps trying to convince Andrew that they need Clay on that wall."

She hesitated and then said, "I just think he's mean."

I told her what I'd said to Whitson on my way out of Claire Megill's office.

"I'm sorry I missed that," she said.

"Not a fan?"

"My husband occasionally fantasizes about shooting

him out of a cannon. But Ethan won't allow it, not this close to the big merger."

Carlos was waiting in his car out in front of the house. He got out when I was back on the street. He went inside. I was picking up a sandwich at DeLuca's once I got to Charles Street when I picked up the tail.

FIFTEEN

I didn't want to stop and stare, which would let him know I'd spotted him. But I had gotten a good enough look to see that I was being casually followed by a slightly larger version of Hawk. Like the next size up.

If I wasn't working as diligently as I was at non-objectification, my first reaction would have been that he looked as if he should have been playing power forward for the Celtics.

He was bald and wore a soft-looking gray hoodie and jeans and white high-top sneakers. Even from a distance I could see the midday sun gleaming off the top of his head, and giving the illusion—literally—of a headlight.

He was hanging back about a block, sometimes switching sides of the street as a way of not making himself obvious. But he was clearly following me, finally making the turn on Charles that I'd just made. When I crossed over and acted as if I were taking a picture of the Charles Street Meeting House with my phone, he stopped, too.

I headed for the park then. When I slowed before getting to the corner of Charles and Beacon, I allowed myself a brief look over my shoulder and saw that he had stopped in front of DeLuca's, as if studying their assortment of cheeses with great interest, nose practically pressed to the glass.

I crossed Beacon and walked into the park and made my way diagonally toward the statue of George Washington. I meandered my way toward Boylston and Berkeley, where my office had been since the British were coming. If he knew where my office was, which he might if he knew who I was, the route made sense.

I crossed Arlington against the light, jogging to dodge traffic as a way of putting some distance between the two of us, heading toward The Newbury. He was still about a hundred yards behind me, talking on his phone or at least wanting it to look as if he were.

I did not feel threatened. But I did not believe in coincidence. I had been to the office of Andrew Crain's executive assistant that morning, had met with her and then gone out of my way to insult their lawyer. Maybe after I had left she had told the lawyer that I was looking into Andrew Crain's disappearance. And I had just come from the Crain residence on Chestnut Street.

Now I was being followed.

Before I got to The Newbury I took a hard right, ducking into the Public Alley and sprinting for the first cover I could see, a blue dumpster. I crouched behind it, having decided in that moment not to let the game come to me, and still angry at myself for letting Andrew Crain get away from me at Davio's the way he had.

I looked down the alley from where I waited and saw that there were no other people between here and Berkeley.

I heard him before I saw him. But when I did see him walking tentatively past the dumpster, I was up and out of my crouch and bum-rushing him across the alley and toward another dumpster across the way, getting hold of his right arm as I did and twisting it behind him, in the general direction of his shoulder.

Then I shoved him harder into the dumpster and said, "Got an existential question, I guess you could call it."

If I was hurting him, he wasn't showing it. Or making any move to get his arm loose, perhaps afraid I might snap it like a twig.

"What's the question?"

British accent. He sounded a bit like Hawk doing Jeeves.

"Why are we here?" I said.

He still made no attempt to separate himself from my grasp. "I was following you. But you obviously know that, don't you, mate?"

"I don't like being followed," I said.

I twisted his arm more, bringing it up. He turned his head just slightly. And I could see him smiling.

"Now please let me go," he said, "before I'm the one who has to hurt you."

"How do I know you won't try to do that if I do let you go?"

He was still smiling.

"Because we're both gentlemen," he said, "and know that fighting rarely solves anything."

I told him to speak for himself.

SIXTEEN

In the spirit of hands-across-the-globe internationalism, we were in my office a few minutes later, neither one of us having tried to prove who was the better fighter.

He somehow appeared even bigger sitting down than he did standing up, making the client chair in which he sat look as if I'd borrowed it from a kindergarten class.

He said his name was Reggie Smythe. He spelled the last name out for me and said it rhymed with "blithe." I told them there had been a Reggie Smith, which rhymed with Smith, who'd played with the Red Sox on their Impossible Dream team in 1967.

He greeted the news with far less interest than if I'd just told him his fly was open.

"I'm a football man myself," he said.

"Yours or ours?"

"There is only ours," he said.

"Don't tell Belichick that," I said.

I asked if he wanted coffee. He said he'd prefer something stronger. I told him it was a little early for that.

"Maybe in your country," he said. "Not ours."

I got the bottle of Jameson out of the bottom drawer of my desk and one of the glasses I kept in there with it and poured him some and he drank.

"Why are you following me?" I said.

"As head of security at Lith," he said, "my responsibilities are both plentiful and diverse."

"Happy for you."

"And being quite good at my job, I thought there might be a chance that you could save me some trouble and perhaps even lead me to Mr. Crain."

"How did you know that I'd be at his brownstone?"

He smiled again. His teeth were almost as white as his sneakers. "None of your bloody business," he said.

"So you don't know where he is, either," I said.

He shook his head. "It's not yet reached the point where it's a problem at the company," he said. "But we'd very much like it to not become one, especially not at the present time."

"Because of the merger, you mean."

"Imagine, if you will, if Tim Cook the Apple man suddenly disappeared right as he was about to buy another company, something he does almost on a monthly basis, were you aware of that?"

"I wasn't," I said. "But I do know the date when Benny Goodman and his orchestra recorded 'Sing Sing Sing.' Want to know what year?"

"Do I have a choice?"

"Nineteen thirty-seven," I said. "Sixth of June. In Hollywood."

"Brilliant," he said.

He drank. He seemed quite comfortable sitting across the desk from me. He probably didn't know that I had my .38 in the slightly open top drawer next to my right hand.

"This isn't the first time Crain has disappeared," I said.

"Has he disappeared," Smythe said, "or have we simply not found him yet?"

"A distinction," I said, "not a difference."

There was still a lot of whiskey in the glass. I could practically taste it, no matter what the hour, knowing what the first sip would feel like, the way it would feel making its way through me like warm, running water. But even the thought of drinking hard liquor this early in the day made me start to feel sleepy. And would do nothing at all to get me to where I wanted to go with Reggie Smythe.

"Did you follow me from the Hancock and I just didn't make you sooner? If so, it could only be Claire Megill or the lawyer who put you on me before I'd left the building."

He ignored the question, finished his drink in a healthy swallow, and stood.

"Since you're of no use to me," Smythe said, "it would be best if you leave the search for Mr. Crain's whereabouts to us."

"I have a client who might feel differently about that," I said.

"I don't care," he said.

"You must know who my client is."

"Same answer."

"And if I choose not to back off?"

"Then the next time we meet you won't see me coming," he said.

He finally nodded in the direction of my top right-hand drawer. "Gun?" he said.

I nodded.

"So we're clear," I said, "I'll be out of it when my client tells me I'm out of it."

"You've now been told," he said. "What you do from here is entirely up to you."

"You think it's harder to sound tough with a British accent?" I said.

I stood now, looking up at him, but not enough to make me feel less like a tough guy myself.

"Are we done here?"

"For now," he said.

"Brilliant," I said, affecting an accent of my own.

He walked out and left my door open. I could hear him whistling "God Save the King" until he was all the way down the hallway and gone. If I had intimidated him, he'd kept a stiff upper lip about it, I had to give the Limey bastard that.

SEVENTEEN

Later in the afternoon I met Hawk in what had long ago become our own private boxing gym at the Harbor Health Club. The only reason the gym was still part of Henry Cimoli's club was because Hawk and I were both ex-boxers and so was Henry, who had once been the most accomplished of the three of us.

The gym had gotten smaller recently after Henry had knocked down a wall to build another yoga studio.

"You really need more damn yoga here, you old dog?" Hawk said.

"That's downward dog to you," Henry said.

Before I had left the office I had bagged the glass that Reggie Smythe had used, planning to drop it off with Lee Farrell at police headquarters tomorrow, just in case the gentleman bruiser might have something on his résumé other than the ability to talk pretty.

Hawk was showing off on the speed bag when I arrived, having already finished the rest of his workout. I was about to start my own progressions on the contour bag Henry had purchased for us, one that was shaped slightly more like a human body and which gave you more realistic targets for your punches than the normal heavy bag next to it.

"Who had faster hands when you were a kid," I asked Hawk when he finished. "You or Ali?"

"Me."

"Then explain to me how come he's the one who became the greatest."

"He didn't have to augment his income as a thug," Hawk said.

He was wearing white Adidas boxing shoes and long black satin shorts and another of his endless supply of "Black Mamba" T-shirts, this one with Kobe Bryant's likeness on it. In comparison, I was the one who looked like the thug, in a Red Sox T-shirt cut to the shoulders and baggy gray sweatpants and sneakers to match.

"Good news for you," Hawk said, watching me move from side to side in front of the bag, "is that your workout clothes won't never go out of fashion, on account of never having been in no fashion in the first place."

"You planning to review my workout along with my functional attire?" I said.

"Don't require much planning. You been letting your elbow fly out from underneath your shoulder lately when you throw your hook."

"You're just pointing that out now?"

"Been workin' up to it, I know how sensitive you are 'bout what's left of your form."

I quickly sped up my progressions, Hawk having made it clear that he was ready for a beer as soon as he showered. But it didn't take long for me to feel as if I had found a perfect rhythm, what Hawk liked to call synchronice-ness, with my movement and with my punches and my breathing. Jab, cross. Slide step to my left and do it again. Then to my right. Same combination. Then jab, cross, hook. The contour bag helped you get a sense of where punches would be landing on an actual opponent. The other benefit of the new bag, because of the material with which it was made and a softer core, is that your hands bounced off it more easily, almost like a spring effect.

"Cross is still too damn long," Hawk said. "Like you sending an email it's on its way."

I grunted in response.

"What's that you say, my good man?" he said.

"I hate it when you're right."

"Shit, you ought to be used to that by now."

I concentrated even harder on both form and footwork now. Jab, jab, cross. Putting a little more snap into every punch, knowing I could do it because my core was as strong as it was. Jab, cross, jab, cross, hook. The hook was a beauty.

"Good," Hawk said.

"You like me," I said. "You really like me."

"Still gonna make you buy the drinks for keeping me waiting."

I told him I had my reasons for getting here late, but would wait to tell him when we got to the bar, which today was the Rowes Wharf Bar at the Boston Harbor Hotel, one of our favorites.

Rowes was starting to fill up by the time we got there about forty-five minutes later with the after-work crowd, mostly young. But despite that demographic, it was everything a good bar should be. Not exactly The Street Bar at the Old Ritz, but not all that far away, either, the atmosphere and feel of the place and the looks of it. Mahogany walls, wine-red carpet, old-school light fixtures hanging from a coffered ceiling that looked as if they came out of another time, which seemed to be the point.

We were both drinking Lord Hobo Boomsauce out of cans, an IPA that had become one of my favorites and was now one of Hawk's when he was in a rare mood for beer.

"So why you think somebody at the home office would send some hard case after you?" Hawk said.

"You don't think he was telling me the truth about hoping I might lead him to Crain?"

"Fuck no," Hawk said.

He was smiling now, but not at me. And perhaps getting ready to write songs of love, also not for me. I followed his eyes and saw a striking young woman sitting at the far end of the bar, shyly looking at Hawk over her phone. She had flawless skin the color of coffee, short-cropped black hair that served only to accentuate features that seemed pretty flawless to me as well, from a distance and in this light. Even only seeing the top half of her, the body was clearly by God.

"I thought you were in a committed relationship with the Bank of America lady," I said.

"Changed banks," Hawk said, "like people do."

He turned back to me. "So Idris Elba threatened your ass?"

"Right before he left my office," I said. "But I managed to remain steadfast."

"Maybe they just all more worried about the big boss being cuckoo for Cocoa Puffs than they letting on," Hawk said. "But what I can't figure is why they seeing you as the threat when the threat seems to be the guy nobody can find, leastways not yet."

"This seems to be a major concern to all concerned," I said. "It sounds like they're trying to mitigate any possible risk until they close the deal, and before the SEC signs off."

"Look at you," Hawk said, "going all *Squawk Box* on me."

"You watch *Squawk Box*?"

"Don't everybody?"

By now the young woman had been joined by a date. But when the bartender placed new beers in front of us, he also slid a piece of paper to Hawk.

"Uh-huh," Hawk said.

"You starting to think that maybe it ain't all one big happy family over there on the fiftieth floor?" Hawk said.

"Did I mention that Crain's assistant said there might be problems in the Crains' marriage?" I said to Hawk. "Just to add a little special sauce to the whole thing?"

Hawk drank down about half of his new beer and smacked his lips after he did. "You a big-picture guy," he said to me now. "What happens when you step back and just look at what you got so far?"

"A bad feeling, that's what I've got," I said.

"Wouldn't be the first time," Hawk said. "Look at it that way."

EIGHTEEN

Laura Crain said that instead of meeting for coffee the next morning I should join her for her morning walk near her home in Brookline.

"I've talked myself into believing that today's the day I hear from him," she said. "Or that he's just going to come walking through the door as if he's just taken a longer walk than usual."

"Put me down for either one," I said.

At a little after eight o'clock I met her at the Edith Baker School in Brookline, next to the Blakely Hoar Sanctuary, between Leatherbee Woods and Hancock Woods. Laura said that she varied her morning walks, but the sanctuary was close to her house, and the hiking place she considered most beautiful, even if the trail was shorter than others in the area to which she had easy access. I told her I'd actually walked it myself a few times with Susan Silverman when she was having Walden Pond urges and didn't want to drive to Concord.

"There's nothing wrong with being at one with nature closer to Linnaean Street," she'd explained at the time, and I told her I could respect that, but wasn't entirely certain how Henry David would have reacted to selfish thinking like that.

Even though there were those longer trails in Brookline, Laura Crain explained, none of them filled her with the sense of peace that Blakely Hoar did. And said she was looking for some peace this morning, the more the better.

She had received no phone calls from her husband last evening, or this morning, had seen nothing on social media that even hinted that anyone had heard from Andrew Crain for the past few days, which meant that everybody at Lith was keeping the company's circle tight.

And she still wasn't ready to contact the police.

"He's been acting out lately, no one is more aware of that fact than I," she said. "Perhaps what's going on right now is just extreme acting out. There's so much going on at the company. But I think it's something more than that, I just don't know what."

"But it's still his company, in terms of control," I said.

"Are you sure about the control part?" she said.

"You aren't?"

She started to say something, then shook her head and said, "It's something we can talk about another time. Perhaps sooner rather than later."

We were just beginning our walk, passing the tennis courts at the Blake School and making our way toward a path that had made me feel, on my previous visits here with Susan, like a trip back in time, the trail occasionally guarded by low stone walls that I knew had been here for hundreds of years.

"I have to ask you something," I said. "Actually, there is more than one thing about which I want to ask you this morning. But I need to know if you think your husband is capable of harming himself."

She had taken a slight lead as the path briefly narrowed, and had to look back over her shoulder now to answer me.

"I'm not seeing depression from him, Mr. Spenser, if that's what you're asking. I'm just not, and believe me I've looked. What I see is high anxiety. And occasionally manic behavior, without question. But not classic or clinical depression. I understand that Susan is only going off what I've told her, but she agrees with me."

"Something triggered that reaction at the restaurant."

"I agree. But you have to agree with something: When my husband did get outside with that awful man, and with whatever rage he was feeling in the moment, he did pull himself back."

"Before running as if being chased," I said. "I almost would rather he'd stayed and started a fight that I could have broken up."

As we went deeper on the trail, she pointed out pools and ponds and various wildlife, getting as excited as a bird watcher when she spotted a goldfinch. I didn't feel as if she were trying to change the subject as much as trying to distract herself, if only momentarily, from the reality of why we were here.

"That's a bat house on that tree," she said at one point.

"Thanks for the heads-up," I said. "And I mean that sincerely. I like bats as much as I like snakes."

I told her then about having been followed by Reggie Smythe, and my conversation with him at my office.

"Andrew has no use for Reggie, just so you know," she said. "It's probably the biggest reason he doesn't like using him as a bodyguard. He was Ethan's hire all the way and Andrew just went along, the way he often does when Ethan gets stuck on something, and the way he goes along with Clay Whitson. Ethan had gotten stuck at the time on extra security, for the company and for himself. Ethan sees the world as an increasingly dangerous place, and has become increasingly paranoid, especially the last year or so."

"I don't think anyone thinks it's getting safer," I said.

She nodded. "Ethan even takes Reggie with him now when he travels. Andrew asked Ethan one time if it wouldn't be cheaper to have a night-light. He said Ethan didn't find that amusing."

I hoped she didn't see me take one last look back at the bat house. You couldn't trust the gnarly bastards, whether it was daytime or not. Flying snakes, that's how I looked at them.

"Who do you think sent Reggie to follow you?" she said.

"Since I'm assuming it wasn't you, only Ethan and Claire Megill know I'm looking into Andrew's disappearance. And perhaps the charming lawyer."

"I've already mentioned that Andrew has no use for Clay."

"Then why is he still around?"

"Because Ethan also managed to convince Andrew that Clay is indispensable, having done so much of the heavy lifting on the merger. A merger over which both Ethan and Clay have become increasingly paranoid, as if the whole thing is going to blow up in their faces any second. I can't prove it, but I think they're keeping things from Andrew about it."

"He could find them out, I assume."

"He has always trusted Ethan, occasionally to a fault."

"Sounds like a fun shop these days."

"Tell me about it."

"Does your husband want the merger to happen?"

She sighed. "He understands why it *should* happen," she said. "I guess that's the way to put it. It's a way for them to eventually pass Tesla and Musk and dominate the electric-car business into the future, which Clay assures everybody they will."

We were walking under what felt like a cathedral ceiling of white hemlocks and maples and oaks. The experience was as peaceful as she said it would be.

"But Andrew's position has shifted lately. He increasingly talks about enough being enough. Others disagree, as you can imagine."

"But he has sixty percent of the company."

"He does. And the right to buy out Ethan if it ever comes to that. But I don't believe he ever would, even with cause. He and Ethan have always been like brothers. Loving each other like brothers, fighting like brothers, making up afterward. And even though Andrew has the biggest stake, Ethan has always had a way of getting my husband to where he, Ethan, wants him to go. I've always thought his greatest ability as a salesman has been selling things to my husband. And managing him. More like an agent than a partner."

"You didn't mention any of this when you came to my office."

"My husband hadn't run off and hidden at that point," she said and sighed. "I've told you a lot about my husband and his current circumstances, Mr. Spenser. But not everything."

"Now his head of security has come around telling me to back off."

"How did you respond to that, by the way?"

I told her what I had told Hawk about remaining steadfast.

"I'll bet," Laura Crain said.

We had made the turn at the end of the trail and were headed back by now. She was dressed in leggings that had some sort of floral design and a black nylon vest over a long white T-shirt. Her hat said NATURE CONSERVANCY.

"If *you* had to pick one person you think might have sent Smythe to watch me, who would it be?"

"Clay Whitson. One hundred percent. Clay's really the same kind of enforcer that Reggie imagines himself to be, he just has a law degree."

"But why would he be this threatened by me?"

"Clay believes in keeping the circle tight, and doesn't trust anybody he doesn't know," she said. "He is obsessed with any hint of bad publicity that could somehow slow the merger. Andrew said to me not long ago that Clay would be willing to kill to see this thing through. I don't think he was exaggerating, frankly."

She stopped and looked at me. "He called me last night, furious that I'd brought someone from the outside into this without telling him."

"What did you say?"

"I told him to kiss my ass."

In that moment, it was Laura Crain I wanted to kiss.

We were still standing at the point where we'd begun our hike.

"You have to find Andrew," she said. "Tell me you'll find him."

"I'm very good at this kind of work," I said.

Then I told her there was one more question I needed to ask.

"Are you and your husband contemplating divorce?" I said. "Because if you are, that's something else that would have been helpful for me to know."

"Who told you that?"

There was no point in not telling her who had. She would easily be able to figure it out for herself. And she was my client.

"Claire Megill," I said.

"If wishing could only make it true for the long-suffering Claire," she said.

Then she added, "That bitch."

Then she turned around and headed back up the trail without saying goodbye.

I continued to have a very bad feeling about all of this.

About what I knew already and the new information that kept coming in, on what felt like an hourly basis.

I recalled that Thoreau had written once that an early-morning walk could be a blessing for the whole day.

If he were around right now, I would have told him he could kiss *my* ass.

NINETEEN

I had invited Susan and Pearl to a family dinner at my apartment, with the promise to Susan of a flight of heavenly transport afterward.

"So the usual?" Susan said.

I told her that was my ambition, yes.

"Then I'll have what he's having, bartender," she said.

I was making us turkey burgers and fries seasoned with salt and pepper and black truffle oil. Not everything in the modern world had made things better. But it was my opinion that truffle oil had vastly improved French fries if you knew what you were doing in the kitchen. And I did.

"I could have cooked tonight," Susan said when she and Pearl arrived. "Especially now that you've given me multiple tutorials on how to make turkey burgers."

I poured us each a glass of Riesling and put the bottle in the ice bucket on the kitchen counter.

"Why don't we hold off on having you cook us turkey burgers for a special occasion," I said.

"Such as?"

"Jesus coming back?" I suggested.

"That kind of talk isn't going to help you get me out of these clothes, mister."

"I've got a solid game plan, don't worry."

"With turkey burgers?" she said.

"The food of love."

"You think Cheetos are the food of love," Susan said.

She sat at the counter and watched me cook. While I did, I told her about my nature walk with Laura Crain, and the way she had reacted at the very end when I'd asked about divorce.

"Has she ever mentioned that they're considering divorcing each other?" I said.

"She has not. We have talked about a lot of things. Not that."

I caught her up on the rest of it, Ethan Lowe and Clay Whitson pushing harder than anyone for the merger, almost as if the lawyer had become a third partner in the firm. I told her what Laura had said about her husband being opposed to the merger. And about Reggie Smythe ending up in my office. Susan did not interrupt, letting me tell it my way, my own rhythm and pace, with as much or as little detail as I saw fit. When I told her about the goldfinches, her eyes lit up and she did interrupt long enough to say, "I love finches." I told her that's why I'd brought them up.

Otherwise her focus, as always, was almost fiercely present, part of what I knew, if only anecdotally, about her immense skill as a therapist, even if all she was doing in my kitchen was listening to me as I went through the preparations for our dinner.

When I finished, she was smiling.

"It sounds as if the security man was less than intimidated by my cutie," she said.

"He will be when he gets to know me better," I said.

"Which I'm assuming he will," she said.

"Hey, he started it," I said.

Susan was in no rush to eat and neither was I. I had already chopped the mushrooms and onions before she arrived, sautéed them until they were soft, and had them cool. Now I was ready to mix them in with the ground turkey and bread crumbs, one egg, salt, pepper, and just a splash of Worcestershire sauce before carefully making the patties. I always made extra patties. They were for me, not Susan. It was more of an understood-type thing.

The fries were already in the oven. When the skillet was ready I put the patties into it. Generally I cooked them for four minutes a side. But I wasn't a slave to the clock, I just waited until I thought I had the firmness just right.

"You're sure I can't help?" Susan said.

"Actually, I do have an important job for you." I grinned. "You can toast the English muffins."

"Now you're just being mean," she said.

She set the table while she toasted the muffins. I removed the truffle fries from the oven. She poured us more Riesling. After that it was just like all the dinners we'd ever had, at her place or mine, because it didn't matter where we were sitting, just that we were sitting across from each other, and I was again breathing the same air as she was.

"So what do you think?" I said.

"It's wonderful."

"About the Crains, I mean."

"I assume you're looking for a symptomatic psychological diagnosis?"

"No such thing as a free lunch," I said. "Even when it's dinner."

Another smile from her, which reminded me of a line from the poet who happened to be my namesake, if not a distant relation. The other Spenser, as Susan liked to call him.

Her eyes look lovely and upon them smile.

"Clinically speaking," she said, "I think job one is finding the sonofabitch. But you don't need me to tell you that."

We ate and cleaned up and drank a little more and then the transport part was as promised, and like the first time, all over again.

We were both asleep later, Pearl snoring away from her spot on my couch, when my cell phone chirped.

Belson

"Stop me if you've heard this one before, but got a body," Frank Belson said.

I waited.

They were never social calls from Belson, and never at this time of night.

"Mrs. Andrew Crain," Belson said. "Quirk says you know her."

TWENTY

Susan offered to go with me to Brookline, but I knew she didn't want to be anywhere near a crime scene, especially one involving a friend.

I told her I'd talk to her when I got back, whenever that was. She said there was no way she was going back to sleep, and said she was going to take Pearl back to Cambridge now, she had an early appointment today she couldn't move.

"This is like waking up to a nightmare," she said when I was dressed and on my way out the door, and I told her I had nothing to add to that.

By official definition, the unattended death scene really began all the way back at Independence Ave, the construction site for a new community center. That's where the television trucks were set up. The media already knew who the victim was because the media always seemed to know, at the highest speed of high-speed Internet.

I knew Belson and the Crime Scene Response Unit would be somewhere up the path I had walked with Laura Crain, wherever the body had been found. They'd be tag-teaming with a State Police unit, which probably meant Brian Lundquist, the homicide captain who'd replaced my old friend Healy, who'd finally retired from scenes like this and nights like this.

Belson had left my name with two of the uniforms at the edge of the perimeter, between the construction site and the Baker School. I saw a variety of police vehicles, some with flashing lights, between the television trucks and the uniforms. A couple Ford Explorer hybrids. Two sedans marked BROOKLINE. As I headed up the trail, I saw the first couple investigators in their white Tyvek jumpsuits, carrying evidence bags. Because this was Norfolk County, there were two guys in windbreakers about fifty yards up from the white jumpsuits who had to be assistant district attorneys. Hail, hail, the gang was all here.

Now I was, too.

There was more activity when I got to the place off the trail by a few yards, which Belson had described as a body-sized spot between the root system of the trees and one of the rock walls Laura Crain had pointed out to me the other day. The path was muddy, I could feel it more than see it, the forest floor having almost risen up with water because of a heavy rain the night before. This is where a man taking a late-night walk with his dog had discovered the body of Laura Crain.

I was confident as I approached Belson and Lundquist that there would be no jurisdictional turf war going on between the Boston Police and State Police. Belson and Lundquist had worked together before the way Belson and Martin Quirk had worked with Healy once, and somehow managed to do that without one of them threatening to steal the other's lunch money.

There was a photographer taking still pictures near where the body must have been found, yellow tape now extending from one tree to another across the trail. There was another guy, BPD on the back of his blue jacket, carrying a digital recorder. It takes a village. They had left the crime scene sprinter van at the mouth of the trail, which wasn't wide enough for it to come any farther. All in all, there were nearly enough of Belson's guys and Lundquist's guys for a pickup basketball game. I counted at least eight but may have missed the ones who had fanned out into the woods.

Laura Crain's body must already have been bagged, because behind me I could see the sprinter van slowly starting to back away from the trail.

I nearly bumped into one of Belson's guys, a sergeant named Chris Connolly, walking around with a notebook and a pen, keeping a log.

"You made good time," Belson said.

"Highly motivated," I said. I nodded at Brian Lundquist. "Hey," I said.

"Hey," he said.

Before I could ask, Belson took the unlit cigar out of his mouth and said, "Strangled, from the looks of it."

"How long was she here before the dog walker found her?"

"To be determined," Frank Belson said.

"She liked to come here in the morning," I told them. "We walked right past this spot the other day."

"She mention ever coming here at night?" Lundquist said.

I shook my head. "Hard to believe she'd come out here alone, though."

"What about with somebody?" Belson said.

I shrugged. "Something else to be determined."

Belson said, "You got any theories about who might have done something like this to the wife of the fifth-richest guy in the US of A?"

"Sixth," I said.

"Fuck off," Belson said. "She mention anything about being concerned for her safety?"

"Maybe she didn't think she needed to be worried because she had me," I said.

"How'd that work out for her?" Belson said.

Then I told him that I'd known Laura Crain for only a few days, that she'd come to me for something other than bodyguard work.

"Why had she?" Lundquist said. "Come to you."

There was no point in confidentiality at this point, she was gone.

I told them of her concerns about her husband.

"Stop me if you've heard *this* one before," Belson said, "but with an event like this, the first person we very much like to have a sit-down with is the spouse. But he's not at their house here, and he's not at their place up on

Chestnut, we already checked. You have any idea where he might be?"

I described the scene outside Davio's for them.

"I might have been the last person to see him," I said.

"And maybe her," Belson said. "What are the odds?"

TWENTY-ONE

At a little before four in the morning Belson and I were drinking coffee at an IHOP on Soldiers Field Road, north of Brookline and south of the Mass Pike. Even in the middle of the night, I found myself wanting to order everything on one side of the menu. I hadn't been inside an IHOP for a while, and found it pleasing that the menu still consisted of pictures, as if the world had forgotten what a short stack with eggs on the side looked like.

"You know you want to," Belson said when he saw me slide the menu away.

"I eat now," I said, "and it throws off my whole schedule of good intake the rest of the day."

"So you're worried about fitting the donuts in later, is what you're telling me."

"No wonder you finally made lieutenant," I said. "By the way? Where was Nurse Ratched tonight?"

"If you are referring to my immediate superior, Captain Glass, it turns out that just this week she once again tested positive for COVID," he said. "Though I'm frankly surprised that COVID didn't test positive for her."

I took him through what I knew, even if it wasn't *everything* I knew so far. I wasn't entirely sure why I held back what Claire Megill had told me about problems in the Crains' marriage. But I did.

Belson had placed his cigar on his saucer. I nodded at it now and said, "You use those things like chew toys."

"Pacifiers," he said. "And *you* suck on it."

There were a few other booths occupied. Late-shifters getting off work. Early-shifters on their way in, most likely. There were a couple college boys, at least they looked like college boys to me, trying to get a jump on what I was pretty sure were inevitable hangovers, caught somewhere between the end of the party and the point later when they would have to decide whether or not they were waking up or coming to.

"The husband could be dead, too, we just don't know it yet," Belson said.

"The thought has occurred."

"Guy's wife is dead," Belson said. "Somebody at his company is going to have a hard time getting out in front of this if he's missing when she is dead."

Belson shrugged. "If we assume he is still among the living, where the fuck is he?"

He looked tired. But that seemed to be his natural state. He was as great a cop as Quirk had been when he was the one who was the star of the Homicide Division. He would just never have Quirk's management skills. Or had ever expressed any interest in acquiring them, or any other people skills for that matter. Sitting across the booth from him, it was as if I could see the accumulated weight of a thousand nights like this one.

"What aren't you telling me?" he said.

"I gave you all I got," I said. I grinned and held up my hand. "Scout's honor."

I was holding up two fingers. Belson shook his head as if I'd just flipped him off.

"That's the Cub Scout salute, you dumb shit."

I poured us both more coffee out of the pot they'd left. "With the husband," I said, "I keep going back to the scene at the restaurant, and how the way the dumb shit was acting with his date pushed Crain's buttons. If he didn't get the head start he did, I would have gone after him."

"You said that people in his office were worried how bad publicity might affect this merger," Belson said. "Well, they're about to have a shitload of bad publicity now."

"Or maybe she did take a walk in the night by herself and it turned out to have nothing to do with who she was or who he is."

"So, scout," Belson said, "do you honestly think it was just bad luck? After she hires you and her husband does a runner and the husband's company has about a gazillion more dollars on the table?"

"I need to find him, is what I think, Frank," I said. "After that I need to find out if he's got any thoughts about who might have done this to her."

"Staying out of my way in the process."

"I thought that was an understood-type thing."

"Yeah, since when?" Belson said.

He picked up the cigar and dipped the end of it in his coffee and put it back in his mouth.

"The husband isn't my client. She was."

"You said yourself she didn't ask you to watch her. So it's not as if this happened on your watch."

"You know me better than that, Frank," I said.

"Yeah," he said. "Unfortunately, I do."

TWENTY-TWO

When I had parked my car behind the building it was still not yet five in the morning. I had no way of knowing whether or not Susan somehow had managed to get some sleep, so I didn't call.

I didn't want to talk right now. Or try to sleep, at least not at the moment. I needed to walk. So I made my way across the Public Garden and then across the Common and up to Tremont, back down Boylston to Arlington, and around again. It was dawn by now, the soft gray light changing by the moment, the morning becoming brighter, as if a retractable roof over the park was slowly being opened. I thought back to the drunk college boys at the IHOP, and felt suddenly as if I were the one walking something off.

Could Andrew Crain have done this to his wife? She had spoken of him pulling himself back from the edge with a perfectly obnoxious stranger when we'd all dined out together. What if it had been his wife who had set him off and this time he wasn't able to bring himself back from the edge?

Hawk had once described what I did for a living as opening closed doors, then finding out what was on the other side of them. But what did I know, really, about what had gone on behind closed doors with Andrew Crain and his wife?

Belson was right, I knew, the first thing any good cop needed to do was eliminate the spouse as a subject.

But first you had to find the spouse in question.

Instead of turning right on Arlington, I walked down Boylston to the Dunkin' and got a large coffee with cream and sugar. It was still only seven-thirty when I got back to the apartment, Susan and Pearl already long gone.

I remembered then that I had left my phone in my car, walked around back and got it, saw a text from Susan telling me that she and the baby had left early and that she would call me when she had some free time so I could catch her up, and how horrible it all was, and how sorry she was.

I saw she had made the bed. Of course she had. She was Susan. I lay down with my clothes still on, stopping only long enough to take off the muddy Red Wing boots I'd worn to Blakely Hoar.

Somehow I managed to fall asleep then, having no idea how long I'd been asleep when Frank Belson awakened me for the second time that morning.

"Turn on the TV," he said.

TWENTY-THREE

The press conference, about to air live, was being held at a conference room at the Lith, Inc. offices on the forty-ninth floor of the Hancock. I observed that they were correctly calling it 200 Clarendon for their viewing audience, which now included me.

It meant the stars of the show were one floor below where Andrew Crain's office was, and Ethan Lowe's, and Claire Megill's. Ethan Lowe was standing behind a lectern with what I knew was the Lith logo on the front, sparks coming out of a battery.

Andrew Crain was standing next to him.

"Shazam," I said in my living room.

Lowe thanked everyone for coming on such short notice, and then informed the media in the room that they wouldn't be taking any questions about what he described as "a tragic death in our family."

Then Lowe introduced Andrew Crain, as if he needed introducing, and stepped away from the microphone. You could see the small piece of paper in Crain's hand fluttering like a single leaf on a tree in the winter.

"There are no words" is the way he began.

He stared down at the paper, almost as if he were afraid to look out at the audience in front of him.

"I have lost the love of my life," Crain continued, "who has become one more victim of random violence in America. I will step aside now and allow the authorities to do their work finding out who committed a crime like this against such a good and gentle creature of not just our country, but the world, because my Laura was a true and valued citizen of the world. Ethan and I will spare no expense in aiding that effort. Thank you all very much for coming here today. I will have no further public comments on this tragedy, or my loss."

Then he walked away from the lectern and out of the conference room, the cameras tracking his movements until he finally disappeared down the glass-walled hallway. There were questions shouted at him as he made his way toward the door. Andrew Crain did not acknowledge them, or look back, or slow down.

I called Belson back.

"You plan to talk to him?" I said.

"Trying," Belson said. "I believe Quirk is handling the official request for an interview."

"You think he'll do it?"

"Most people think they're required to talk to the cops," he said. "You and me, we both know they aren't. But I have a feeling that a high-profiler like Crain isn't going to want it out there that he refused."

I had no way of knowing whether or not Andrew Crain had left the building once he was out of the conference room. But even though he said he didn't want to talk to anybody right now, it didn't change the fact that I wanted to talk to him. His wife had hired me to find things out about him and, up to now, what I had found out could have fit inside a shot glass.

Martin Quirk might have to go through channels. I did not. Andrew Crain wasn't my client. His wife had been, and still was, and would be until I decided she wasn't.

I was going to head over to the Hancock and wait for Andrew Crain in the hope that he was still inside and, being a trained investigator, find out how he exited the building when he did exit the building.

But when I came walking out the front door of my own building, Reggie Smythe was standing on the sidewalk, in front of a black Lincoln Navigator parked illegally on Marlborough.

"Let's take a ride," he said.

"I'm not sure I know you well enough to get into a car with you," I said.

"Just get in the fucking car," he said.

I did.

TWENTY-FOUR

The ride to Brookline took about twenty minutes. The Crains' estate was, appropriately enough, in what was known as the estate section of the town, on Cottage Street. I knew that the man who owned the Red Sox also lived somewhere in this part of Brookline. Maybe before I headed back downtown I could stop in and give him my thoughts on improving the Sox next season, and how much of his money I thought it might take to do that.

I worried sometimes that he didn't fully grasp how important his team was to me.

Smythe stopped at an elaborate wrought-iron gate and punched in a code before we made our way up a driveway that seemed as long as the Commonwealth Ave Promenade. The Navigator finally came to a stop in the circular drive near the front door of a massive colonial, mostly brick, that reminded me of an exterior for *Downton Abbey*.

There was another car, also a Navigator, already parked there, and a sleek-looking silver Mercedes. Smythe hadn't said much during the ride. Nor had I, seated next to him in the front seat.

At one point I did ask how his boss was doing, and Smythe, without taking his eyes off the road or changing his expression, said, "You're the detective. Why don't you see if you can figure it out now that we're here."

"I'm starting to sense that the two of us have gotten off on the wrong foot, Reg."

"See, there," he said, "you're detecting at a high level already. Brilliant."

Because of the other cars, I expected to find company with Andrew Crain once I was inside, perhaps Ethan Lowe, perhaps Claire Megill. But the only person occupying the living room was Crain himself, seated at the end of a long wraparound sofa. He had changed out of the blazer he'd been wearing at the press conference. Now he wore a red v-neck sweater with a plaid shirt showing underneath it and jeans and boat shoes.

He did not stand to greet me, just motioned for me to sit across from him in an antique chair that looked as if it might collapse underneath me like some kind of prop once it absorbed my full weight.

I carefully lowered myself down.

"I'm very sorry for your loss," I said, because I couldn't think of anything better to say at the moment, and also because it happened to be true. His loss, my loss, everybody's.

At first I was afraid that he hadn't heard me, or hadn't processed what I'd just told him. He seemed to stare past me, blinking rapidly, his eyes fixed on some point on a wall covered by more expensive art.

"I understand you were one of the last people to see Laura alive," he said.

The only people who knew about my walk with Laura Crain were Susan and Hawk. But obviously Crain's wife had told someone about it, unless Belson had told Quirk and Quirk had told Crain.

"I'm curious as to how you know that," I said.

He stared past me again without answering. It was as if there were some kind of technical delay at work here, the kind you got on the Zoom calls I'd been forced to use with clients during COVID, on the rare occasions when I'd actually had clients during COVID.

"She . . . Laura kept an old Filofax organizer," Crain said. "It was on the kitchen table. Your name was in it for the other morning."

"May I see it?" I said.

"No," he said, "you may not."

I let it go.

"We took a walk along the same trail where they found her body," I said.

He nodded now, like a bobblehead doll, as if this were the most fascinating piece of information he would receive all day.

"How . . . How did she seem? Was she anxious?"

"She was worried about you."

Then he was nodding again, as enthusiastically as before, eyes wide.

But said nothing in response.

"Where have you been, Mr. Crain?"

Another slight pause. "Away."

"Away where?"

Now his eyes focused on me. "Does it matter?"

"It would have mattered to your wife," I said. "And thus matters to me."

He pointed to his right now, in the direction of the front door. "We have a place out in western Mass."

"How did you get there?" I said. "And how did you get inside without Laura having gotten an alert on the alarm system?"

"It was, ah, deactivated."

"Without her knowing?"

"Is this a grand jury, Mr. Spenser?" he snapped at me then, as if I was the one who had tripped an alarm inside him.

"It's not," I said, keeping my own voice even. "I'm sorry if it sounded that way."

Susan often told me that there was no proper way, or even educated way, to quantify grief, or analyze it with any great certainty. But in this moment, in the big room in the big house, he seemed more upset about my line of questioning than he was about his wife's death.

"I'm simply honoring her wishes in wanting to know your whereabouts, just after the fact," I continued.

"This isn't the way the story was supposed to end," he said, his own voice quiet again. "Can you appreciate that, Mr. Spenser?"

"Of course."

"We were . . . supposed to be together forever." He smiled. "I always knew that, that we were meant for each other, long before she did."

He took a couple deep breaths.

"I did everything for her," he said.

He was like a drunk at the end of the bar at closing time, talking and not listening. Nobody in the place, 'cept you and me.

"There was more she needed to know from me," he said. "Things I'll never get to tell her now."

He had tucked himself into a corner of the couch, as if using the arm as a ballast.

"We were meant to be together," he said, and started nodding again, in self-affirmation.

There was no point, at least not today, in me raising the subject of divorce, or asking him about behavior that had brought his wife to me in the first place.

"I need to pay you," he said. Nodded again. "Yes, I do."

"For what?"

"I was under the impression that Laura was worried enough about me that she hired you."

It was something he could have learned only from his partner or from his assistant or cops trying to set up a formal interview and maybe giving him information as an enticement. Because why would Laura Crain have told him she hired me? Because she wanted to share that she thought he had snakes crawling around inside his head lately?

"You don't owe me anything," I said. "I did nothing for your wife. I certainly didn't help keep her alive."

"I need to pay you something for your services," Andrew Crain said, as if everything in his life were transactional, even now.

"I never expect any kind of compensation for a job I don't finish, or sometimes don't even start," I said. "Your wife died while she was a client of mine. It's why this is no longer business with me, just personal."

I stood. "I'll be in touch."

Somehow in this moment, he seemed intensely focused on me, as if I'd just now come into focus.

"No, you won't."

Now I was staring at him.

"I'm not sure I understand."

"I don't want to see or hear from you ever again, Mr. Spenser," he said. "I do not want you to contact me or anyone with whom I associate. Your business with my wife, whether you consider it personal or not, is now concluded and her death is in the hands of the police."

He was blinking again, and nodding.

"Now please leave my house," he said, and got up from the sofa and walked out of the room.

"Okay, be that way," I said when he was gone, my voice sounding quite loud in the empty room, as if I'd just shouted something at Monet.

TWENTY-FIVE

"Well," Susan said, "it's not as if you haven't been fired before. So you can take some consolation in that."

"But I've never been fired by somebody who'd never hired me," I said.

"Maybe it's a sign you're still evolving," she said.

"God, you're good."

"Why I make the big bucks."

"Good thing, now that I'm unemployed again."

"Just when job numbers in the country have been improving."

We were in her living room. She had just finished with her last client of the day, a few minutes before five. I poured her a chardonnay. I had already begun my own cocktail hour with a Boomsauce while waiting for her. She was still in her work clothes. Today that meant a sleek black dress with a scoop collar. Or what I thought should be described as a scoop collar. She had kicked off her low heels and curled up in her favorite chair, organizing her legs underneath her, somehow managing to show off just enough of them as she did, and making me want to scoop her up.

We talked some about how she was still trying to process, even though we had done that already at a point earlier in the afternoon when she'd been between clients. She told me again that there was no point in me blaming myself, there was nothing I could have done to change the outcome.

"Are you trying to shrink me?" I said now.

"I'm a full-service girl."

It got a smile out of me. "You don't have to tell me that," I said, and then proceeded to describe my odd meeting with Andrew Crain, in great detail.

She seemed to be relieved that we were talking about him for the moment and not his wife.

"This may just be a continuation of some kind of breakdown," she said, "exacerbated by grief and shock. Him telling you this isn't the way their story was supposed to end was both sad and predictable at the same time."

I drank some of my beer. "Before we continue, Doctor, I have a question. How come you always manage to look so elegant and swellegant and I look as if I just carried in some furniture and you were nice enough to offer me a beer?"

She winked. "Maybe you've touched on one of my fantasies about hunky deliverymen."

"Got another question," I said. "Do your male patients find you as distracting as I do?"

She winked again. "Why limit it to male patients?" Susan said.

It was something the two of us had done plenty of times before, in moments like this, using small talk and humor to deflect from the subject at hand, the murder of her friend, in this case. I noticed that she had finished most of her wine, which, for Susan, was the equivalent of drinking out of the bottle. But she told me it had been an emotional last hour for her with a patient outside the clinical definition of gender binary, not elaborating beyond that, just that the person was adrift in no-man's-land. Or no-woman's-land.

She held out her glass now for me to refill it, somehow managing to look elegant doing that.

"What are you going to do?" she said when I sat back down on her couch. "I know you well enough to know that you're not going to walk away from this."

"Not even at gunpoint."

"So?"

I grinned at her. "Actually I'm the one with the him/her problem."

"I see what you did there," she said.

"I was originally hired to find out what Andrew Crain's problem was. His wife seemed quite sincere about wanting to know, as she had made that clear to you as well. But now I have to find out why what happened to her happened."

"And whether it might possibly have something to do with the issues she wanted you to investigate."

"And who done it," I said, "as we crime-stoppers like to say."

"Any theories?"

"Not a one."

"No wonder you got fired," she said.

We were dining tonight at Alden & Harlow on Brattle, just a few minutes away by car. Sometimes, when feeling ambitious, we walked the mile or so to the restaurant. Not tonight. I asked Susan if she were planning to change. She looked at me as if I'd just asked if she were planning to get a neck tattoo.

"But I won't be long," she said.

I knew from experience that even though the lie was benign, it was still a lie.

"I need to know more about the life and times of Laura Crain," I said.

"Any thoughts on where you plan to start?" Susan said as she headed for the bathroom.

"I was thinking Harvard."

"You'll never get in," Susan said.

TWENTY-SIX

In my reading about Andrew Crain I had discovered that his best friend as an undergrad at Harvard had been a graduate assistant in the English Department named Paul Dockery, whose name popped up in several articles about Crain's younger years, Crain often pointing out what an unlikely friendship it had been, since Dockery barely knew one end of a double-A battery from another. But according to what I'd read they had hit it off, to the point where when Crain came back to Boston after the wanderlust years, Dockery allowed him to live rent-free in the second bedroom of his house in Watertown.

Dockery had also been friends with Laura Crain, even providing some tutoring for her during her senior year.

"What I didn't have to pay in rent I was able to put toward the small lab Ethan and I had fashioned for ourselves," Crain once told *Forbes*. "And more than anybody, with the possible exception of Ethan, it was Paul who convinced me to chase my dreams."

Susan helped me find a phone number for Dockery in the Harvard directory, as he was now a fully tenured professor in the English Department. I called the office number and left a message on his office phone, explaining who I was, and that I had questions about Andrew and Laura Crain that he might be able to answer. He called back about an hour later, telling me he was finishing up a brief writer's conference in Bretton Woods, New Hampshire, but would be happy to meet with me when he was back tomorrow.

I didn't say I was a cop. Didn't say I wasn't one, either. But he was a Harvard man. I was confident he'd figure it out.

I called Claire Megill the next morning, but was sent straight to her voicemail. I texted her that we needed to talk, and as soon as possible, without specifying about what. She didn't respond to either my message or my text. She probably would have if I'd been special enough to have the inside number for the Bat Cave.

I did not have her home address. I knew I could find it if I had to, either with trickeration or with the assistance of the Boston Police Department. But for now I decided to take the more direct route to her, remembering her telling me about her yoga class at the Equinox club, a short walk from the Hancock, every day at noon.

When in doubt, follow someone.

Or annoy someone.

On good days, I had frequently managed to do both.

I decided to walk to the club, over next to Dartmouth

Street and Back Bay Station. I stopped at the Starbucks on Dartmouth and bought a large coffee and a blueberry scone and found a bench on Dartmouth about twenty yards from the entrance to Equinox. I sat on it and watched the incoming traffic of people on their way to exercise or on their way home, or to the office. I saw more women than men. Most wore their exercise pants, all of the pants form-fitting to the extreme, on their way into the gym. Few seemed to need the work, at least to my trained eyes. I tried to remember the dark place men were in before women wore exercise pants so routinely on the street, whether they were on their way to exercise or not.

I made short work of the scone. I was more judicious with my coffee, not wanting to leave my post and head back to Starbucks to use the restroom, for fear of missing Claire Megill when she arrived. It was still only eleven-forty-five. I imagined her to be a creature of habit and organization, particularly since she worked for a man she must have occasionally tied a rock to, for fear he might float away.

I sat on the bench while I waited for her and observed the life of the city, this part of the city, anyway, in the middle of the day. I had grown up in the west. But I loved city life, its rhythms and energy and soundtrack. When I was in New York City, I found myself walking even more than I did in Boston. But now I was walking Boston again, every chance I got. Perhaps I was the creature of habit and organization.

I sat and watched people navigate their way up and down the sidewalk and into the train station, some cutting off others like cars swerving in front of others as they changed lanes. I wanted to ask some of these people where the fire was, but then wondered if anybody even said that anymore.

I finished my coffee. There was a Dunkin' close to where I sat. But I stayed where I was and waited for Claire Megill, still not certain she would show up. There were other ways for me to contact her. For now, this one made the most sense. And afforded the path of least resistance, a method of detecting I had always employed whenever possible.

Or was it the road less traveled by?

I saw her then, heading in my direction. Now she was one of the fast walkers on Dartmouth Street. Bag slung over her shoulder. Wearing sunglasses and what was obviously a work dress, just with sneakers as an accessory.

I tossed my cup into the wire bin next to the bench and was about to head her off before she entered Equinox when I saw Clay Whitson appear, almost out of nowhere, to block her way.

When she tried to get around him, he grabbed her arm and jerked her toward him.

Jerk, I thought, being the operative word.

I felt as if I were back at Davio's with Andrew Crain, close enough to hear her say, "Don't touch me!"

Then I was one of the fast walkers on Dartmouth.

TWENTY-SEVEN

It was as if they were both trying not to make a scene even as they were in the process of making one on the busy street.

Whitson held on to her arm and pulled her in the direction of a brick pillar between the Dunkin' and the entrance to the station, away from the pedestrian traffic.

"Just tell me who you told," I heard Whitson say.

His back was to me. Claire Megill was focused entirely on him, as she tried to get her arm loose. I covered the last few yards and clamped my hand on Whitson's shoulder and spun him around. Once we were facing each other and I had his full attention, I used both hands to shove him hard into the pillar.

"See, there, Clay," I said. "I was right at the office that day. One of us *is* an asshole."

He tried to come off the wall. But I was too close to

him and he was too slow getting his own hands up. I shoved him back, even harder this time. Then I had him by the lapels of the skinny suit he was wearing today, one I was wrinkling the hell out of at the moment.

"Please let go of him," Claire Megill said from behind me.

"Not just yet," I said.

"You need to mind your own goddamn business," Whitson said.

He tried to raise up both of his arms now and break my grip. But he was still too close. I jerked his jacket up a little higher. If I kept going, pretty soon it was going to be a bonnet.

"Clay," I said, "I am going to release you now. But if you annoy me further, I am going to take one of your elbows and see if it's possible to shove it down your throat."

His face was the color of an apple, and his jacket being as tight as it was around his throat was making breathing difficult. His eyes looked slightly unfocused.

He finally nodded, having decided that escalating our interaction further was not in his best interest.

"Mr. Spenser," Claire Megill said. "This is between Clay and me."

She was standing to my right.

"Well," I said. "Not at the moment."

I stepped to the side so I could see both of them. To her I said, "What's this all about?"

Before she could answer, Whitson said, "Like the lady said. It's between us."

"You should have considered that before taking the matter into the public square."

"Please go now," Claire Megill said. "Please . . . You will only make things more difficult than they already are."

I kept my eyes on Whitson.

"More difficult for whom?" I said.

"For me," she said. "Now, please. *Both* of you, leave me alone."

"Is there some sort of problem between you and Ms. Megill?" I said to him as she walked away from us and into the Equinox club.

"The one with the problem now is you," Whitson said, "if you don't stay away from her, and me, and our company."

"Or?" I said, dragging the word out.

"Or maybe next time it will be somebody coming up from behind you," Whitson said.

People kept telling me that.

Whitson moved past me then, and confidently made his way across Dartmouth, avoiding the two-way traffic as he did, as if he were back to being a tough guy and he'd just jammed me up and not the other way around.

When I had lost sight of him, seeing no reason to follow him, I called Hawk and informed him that I'd just been threatened on a street corner by a corporate lawyer.

"He threaten to scratch your eyes out?" Hawk said.

"In fairness," I said, "I did threaten him first."

"Man needs a hobby," Hawk said.

TWENTY-EIGHT

Paul Dockery's office was in the Barker Center. I had passed the building on multiple occasions while attending events on campus with Susan, who had gotten a terminal case of Harvard while getting her degree there.

I had always liked walking around the school. I knew that some of *Good Will Hunting* had been filmed there and likewise knew that Matt Damon, who wrote the movie along with Ben Affleck, had been an English major there. I was more impressed with the fact that Damon was a Red Sox fan, and wondered if he was still as upset about Mookie being traded or had finally managed to let it go.

But there had never been a time when I was on the campus or near it when I hadn't expected to be asked for some sort of ID. Or at least asked to explain my thoughts on "The Discourse on the Method."

Dockery had left my name at the front desk in the lobby.

"I'm here to see Mr. Chips," I said to the young man checking his list.

The kid looked up at me with complete indifference.

"Are you referring to the original, or the remake with Peter O'Toole?" he asked.

"Sorry," I said. "Forgot where I was for a moment."

"We hardly ever do," the kid said, and told me that Dockery's office was on the third floor.

Paul Dockery did not look anything like Peter O'Toole. He just looked like an older version of the grad student he'd been when he had first met Andrew Crain. He was tall, slightly stooped, with shaggy, silver-blond hair, wore a denim shirt with a frayed collar, jeans. His reading glasses were on top of his head. The desert boots he was wearing looked as old as the Yard.

"You're a policeman, I gather," Dockery said.

"Former."

"But on the phone you said you were investigating Laura's death."

"I am," I said, and explained my professional relationship with her, as brief as it had been.

He ran a hand through his hair, nearly knocking his glasses off before he remembered they were up there.

"I've tried to reach out," he said. "To Andrew, I mean. But he's harder to reach lately, for obvious reasons."

"But you two have stayed in touch?"

"We did until the past few months," Dockery said. "Then he stopped returning my calls."

He checked the Apple watch on his wrist. "Listen,

I've got a student coming in about fifteen minutes," he said. "Maybe you could explain exactly what you need from me."

"I'm just trying to understand them both better," I said. "I feel as if I came to them about halfway through the book, without having read the first half."

"You could be one of my students talking like that," he said.

I grinned. "Where I could dream my time away?"

He nodded approvingly. "Wordsworth," he said. "Not bad."

"Got it off a fortune cookie."

"Somehow I doubt that."

He leaned back down, put the boots up on his desk, clasped his hands behind his head. "They were always such an odd couple," he said. "Andrew and Laura. When they finally became a couple, that is."

"Just from my research," I said, "it sounds like unrequited love that finally got requited."

"Andrew was a geek," Dockery said. "Like *The Big Bang Theory* geeky. Like the Sheldon character."

I nodded as if I understood the reference. I was vaguely aware there had been a TV series with that title, but had no idea who Sheldon was.

"Hell, Andrew and I were an odd couple, when I think back on it. I'd only taken a couple science courses here because I had to. He had no interest in any book that didn't involve diagrammatic illustrations. But we met one night at Cambridge Queen's Head. It's a pub nearby."

I told him I'd been there.

"And for some reason we hit it off. Maybe because we were different. His senior year. Somehow we got to talking about girls. And I got an earful about the fair maiden who belonged to another."

"Laura was in another relationship at that time?"

He nodded. "A heavy one, according to Andrew. With someone Andrew characterized as a bad guy unworthy of her. I just thought it was because the other guy was with her and he wasn't."

"Do you remember the guy's name?"

He leaned forward now and tapped his forehead with a closed fist. "Rob. I'm pretty sure it was Rob. If I ever got his last name, I don't remember it. I think Laura broke it off with him at one point, but then right before graduation, Andrew told me that the guy was still coming around."

"What finally happened?"

"Sometime after graduation, as best I can recall, they broke up for good. Laura and the Rob dude. But Andrew and Laura didn't get together then, because he picked that moment in time to go off and find himself. Like he wasn't worthy of her yet. He told me once he wanted to come back from his travels a better man."

"But they finally got together when he came back to Boston, right?"

"And love was born of the heavenly line." He winked. "More Wordsworth," he said.

I thought about Andrew Crain saying that this wasn't the way what he obviously considered a great love story was supposed to end.

Paul Dockery checked the Apple watch again. I felt like one of Susan's patients coming to the end of a session.

"You've known Andrew Crain a long time," I said. "And the two of you are obviously friends. I still have to ask if you think he's capable of having killed his wife?"

"Not in five million years," Dockery said. "You need to understand something, Mr. Spenser. Andrew had his dreams. He's told the world how often I was in his ear telling him to chase them. But the only one dream that ever really mattered to him was having her."

"Who can you remember from those days who might know something about the old boyfriend?" I said.

"You think he might have come back after all this time?"

"If he did, I need to know about it."

"It would mean the guy might have been more obsessive about Laura than Andy was." He shrugged. "Maybe you don't need an English professor to help you out. Maybe you need a shrink."

"I'm sleeping with a Harvard-educated psychologist," I said.

I asked him if he might possibly come up with a list of Laura Crain's classmates, and roommates. He said he'd do a little digging and come up with some names.

"I wish I could be more helpful off the top of my head," he said. "But I was smoking a lot of weed in those days."

"I would have expected nothing less of an English major."

I gave him my card, one that had all of my phone numbers on it, and my email address.

"I get the impression," Dockery said, "that you can be pretty obsessive yourself on occasion."

"To the point of compulsion," I said.

"Where do you go from here?" he said.

"Not entirely sure," I said. "It's too early for the Yale game."

TWENTY-NINE

Susan had another committee meeting tonight.

She'd actually told me which committee it was, and whom it benefited, but I had forgotten. I did know that it was somewhere in Cambridge and that her attending it meant I was on my own for dinner.

Before she left the house I called and asked if she wanted me to come collect Pearl and bring her to my place, or at least take her out and allow her to pull me up and down Linnaean Street for a while.

"The baby is fine," she said. "I just took her on a long walk myself."

I told her I loved her then, and wished her good luck saving the whales.

"It's for the bike and pedestrian paths along Memorial Drive," she said.

"Hey," I said. "I was close."

Frank Belson called and told me, because he said he knew I cared, that Blakely Hoar was still being treated as an active crime scene. As hard as his ME had looked, he could find no physical evidence on Laura Crain's attacker, and any footprints that might have been useful upon what he called further review had been washed away by the heavy rain the night before.

"Am I allowed to go back and walk the trail without fear of being arrested?" I said.

"The BPD has gotten together as a group and decided it's too late to find any new evidence there, after the rain."

There was a pause at his end.

"I assume you got nothing useful for me."

"Less," I said. "But you know that if I do come up with anything . . ."

He hung up on me.

On my way to the sanctuary I stopped in Watertown at Not Your Average Joe's for the BBQ meatloaf. I ate at the bar and drank Samuel Adams draught with my meatloaf and mashed potatoes and watched the start of the Red Sox game. The empty seats at Fenway told you everything about the way their season was ending.

"Well," I said to the bartender, "wait till next year."

"Make me," he said.

It was dark by the time I drove over to Brookline. I wanted to walk the trail in the night, experience the same sights and sounds and hopefully even the solitude that Laura Crain had experienced in the last moments of her life.

Tomorrow I would try to learn more about her old boyfriend, as little as I had to go on so far. At some point

I knew I would have to come up with a creative way to ask Andrew Crain about him, since Dockery had made it clear Crain considered Rob with no last name to be a member of the bad boyfriend club.

"You got yourself fighting one of your two-front wars," Hawk had said on our morning run along the river. "You still haven't found out what she wanted you to find out about him. And now you gots to find out what happened to her."

"But I have the strength of ten," I said.

He'd snorted. "One more thing you exaggerate the size of."

"Snob," I said.

When I arrived at the sanctuary I parked my new Jeep Cherokee at the construction site. I was going to bring a flashlight with me on my walk, but there was more than enough light from the moon tonight. I did take my new Smith & Wesson .38, the 586 model I'd gifted to myself on my last birthday, out of the glove compartment and stuck it into the side pocket of my leather jacket.

Then I started up the trail I'd walked with Laura Crain that morning. The brook that stretched all the way back to the tennis courts at the Baker School was swollen from the previous night's rainfall, the sound of the water loud in the night.

Had she come out here alone? Or had the person who had killed her been someone she knew, someone she had come here to meet?

The yellow tape was still stretched across the trail. I ducked underneath it and walked over to the place where they'd found her next to the rock wall.

"It always gives me the feeling that I've taken a walk back in time," she'd said on our morning walk.

Now the moon lit the crime scene like a spotlight, and there were the night sounds all around me. I leaned down and picked up a tree branch the size of a baseball bat that must have fallen there in the storm. I started back up the trail finally, pretending the branch was a walking stick, on my way back to my Jeep.

I heard my phone then, that marimba ringtone that sounds like everybody else's and always has everybody reaching for their own phones when it goes off in a public place.

But now it was just me, and my phone.

I looked at the luminous screen.

Unknown caller

"This is Spenser," I said.

"I'm supposed to tell you this is your one and only warning," a voice said.

The Boston accent made it come out "wah-ning."

Before I could say anything I got hit with the first blow from behind.

THIRTY

It was some kind of club, a free shot behind my shoulder blades, one that staggered me and knocked me forward but didn't put me down even though it hurt like hell.

My phone came flying out of my hand.

The guy who'd hit me tried to wrap his arms around me as a second muttonhead came out of the woods to my right. There was enough light from the moon for me to see he was wearing a ski mask, and was my size, at least. And heavier.

The second guy had what looked like a tire iron in his right hand, and started to swing it at me. But I broke the grip of his partner in time to slip-step to my right and force the one with the tire iron to miss, even though I could feel the breeze from the swing close to my face.

I cleared just enough space then to turn and swing the branch in my hand at the legs of the guy behind me, hearing the crack as I connected with what I hoped was one of his knees. He went down like he was the tree falling.

If they had come here to kill me, I'd be dead already, I told myself.

They were just here to give me a beating after what hadn't been frankly much of a warning.

I could hear the guy I'd knee-capped groaning and could see him rolling around in the mud out of the corner of my eye. There was no time for me to clear the .38 from my jacket as the second guy was back on me, the tire iron connecting with my left shoulder.

But he still didn't put me down this time as I managed to set my feet like I was Mookie still swinging for the fences at Fenway. I didn't go low, and instead swung for the middle of him like a shooter aiming at center mass, and heard a crack from him now.

"I think he broke my fucking arm."

I swung at him again, but missed, and then the second guy was back up and on me, hitting me on the side of my head with his fist, connecting enough that I felt as if sirens were going off.

I went down, but with purpose.

"Kick the shit out of him, Eddie," I heard.

But as Eddie's work boot came forward I rolled toward him and grabbed it and flipped him to the ground, and then I was back up. The second guy had one arm hanging at his side, but kept coming. The branch was somewhere around me but would do me no good now, so I stepped toward him and threw a hook to his stomach and heard the air come out of him with a *whoosh* and then threw a straight right to the middle of his face.

He went down, but the guy already on the ground hit me with something across the ankle and this time I went down for real. Somehow I managed to roll away into the grass and mud and get my hand on the .38 now and fire a warning shot into the air.

They ran then, two shadows running into the woods, one of them limping badly, the broken arm of the other one flopping at his side.

I let them go and then the night was silent again, except for the screech of what sounded like a single owl.

I found my phone and started limping myself toward my Jeep and tried to take consolation in the fact that I'd just given a lot better than I'd gotten before I called Hawk and told him what had happened.

"Shit," he said. "Maybe you do have the strength of ten."

"Told you," I said.

THIRTY-ONE

Hawk said, "Whoever sent them boppers only sent two? You ought to be insulted."

"They seemed to be under the mistaken impression that bad intentions made them bad men."

"How come you didn't shoot them, you had the chance?"

"It didn't seem like an appropriate response after I determined they weren't there to kill me."

"Weren't there to kill you this time, you mean."

Hawk had a key to my apartment and was already there when I got back from Brookline. After I cleaned up and assessed the damage, he asked me where it hurt. I told him everywhere. He asked if I could be a little more specific and I told him that the hit parade started in my upper back and went all the way down to my right ankle, which miraculously hadn't been broken when Eddie or the other guy, I'd lost track at that point, was the one swinging for the fences. Hawk went and got two ice packs from the freezer and told me to place one of them behind my shoulders and then had me stretch out my right leg and placed one of them behind my knee.

I told him I'd taken a blow to my ankle, too.

"What's your point?"

"Thank you, nurse."

"Now I'm a damn caregiver," Hawk said. "Probably be like this when you're old."

"Why can't Susan be the caregiver?"

"She be long gone by then."

Then he said, "Beer or whiskey?"

I told him where to find the bottle of Bushmills. He came back with a glass for himself and handed me one. He'd asked for champagne and I told him sorry, I was fresh out.

"I don't know how I put up with somebody as common as you," he said.

"If I'd known I was going to entertain tonight," I said, "I would have run to the wine store and picked up a bottle of Dom."

"Think you meant to say Veuve Clicquot," Hawk said, "not to make too fine a point of shit."

He was dressed in a soft-looking hoodie I knew had to be expensive, jeans, boxing shoes. There was no way for me to know if I had woken him, if he'd been alone when I called or with somebody. He had moved again, this time to Mission Hill, without giving me an exact address. As always, as close as we were—and we were as close as brothers—there were parts of him that I could not reach, parts he held back because he always had. He'd come back from Paris a month ago, having gone there to determine whether a young woman there was his daughter. She was not. When I'd asked upon his return if he wanted to talk about it, Hawk had said he did not, and we did not. And I did not ask whether he was sad about that or happy or relieved because that was another part of himself he held back.

"Looks like you've done gone and poked another bear."

"Which bear is the question."

"Didn't that lawyer tell you that maybe somebody'd come up behind you one of these days?"

"So he did."

I drank some whiskey. The warm feeling as it made its way through me went nicely with the ice packs, I thought.

"So you think maybe he sent a couple proud boys after me because I made him look like something less than a manly man in front of Claire Megill?"

"Uh-huh."

"I sensed some tension between them," I said. "Whitson and Claire Megill, I mean. I thought it might be sexual."

"Best kind," Hawk said.

I moved my ankle slightly and the ice pack fell off. Hawk got up and walked over to me and put it back where he'd had it before.

"I give and I give and I give," he said.

We sat and drank. The whiskey wasn't making all of the places where I'd been hit hurt any less. But they weren't hurting any more. I knew I'd been lucky tonight, even if the guys who had come for me had been amateurs in the end, punching above their weight.

"Last warning," the guy had said on the phone, before he hit me.

My friend Wayne Cosgrove told me once that all stories came from somewhere, and that once they did, the first question you always had to ask was who benefited from them.

So who benefited by sending Eddie and his pal to give me a beatdown tonight?

"Say you're right and it is the lawyer. Why would he or anybody else at Lith be worried about me getting in the way of a merger?"

Hawk smiled. "You too banged up, I could go ask him."

"Let's hold off for the time being."

He drank. I drank. I had no idea what time it was by now. I couldn't even make an educated guess about how many late nights there had been with Hawk and me talking like this. Or not talking, when we'd worked our way around to that.

Finally Hawk said, "You give a rat's ass about a merger gonna make rich people even richer?"

I slowly shook my head no, feeling myself wince as I did.

"Knew before I asked," Hawk said. "Why we got to focus on who did that to the man's wife."

"We?"

"Hell, yeah," Hawk said. "Look what happens, I let you go off on your own. And if something happens after this and whatever you got yourself into is bigger than we think and you get yourself killed, you know Susan's gonna blame me."

"You told me one time you weren't afraid of anything or anybody," I said.

"'Cept for her," Hawk said.

"Same," I said.

THIRTY-TWO

Paul Dockery called in the morning with enough information on Laura Crain, maiden name Mason, that it was as if he were one of his own students and had just pulled an all-nighter.

I had told him I was mostly interested in her senior year, which is when she had begun dating the old boyfriend.

"I called the Alumni Office," Dockery told me over the phone. "Got a buddy there. He already knew a fair amount about her time here because he'd done some research when Andrew Crain's name went up in lights. Her mother died when she was young. Her father was a high school teacher in Perrysburg, Ohio, and *he* died when she was a sophomore here. No other living relatives he knew about."

Laura had lived in Claverly Hall, on Mount Auburn, in a three-bedroom her senior year. One roommate was named Missy Jones. The other was Angela Calabria. Both, Dockery said, were now married, according to school records. Missy Jones, a lawyer herself now, had married a Seattle lawyer and moved there. But Angie Calabria, now divorced, was an elementary school teacher in Carlisle, Mass.

Dockery had a number for her. I told him I appreciated the legwork he'd done. He said, "Nobody should die like that, whether they've got all the money in the world or not."

"I've done a lot of reading since she died on her own charity work," I said. "Her husband wasn't the only one who wanted to save the world."

I called Hawk after I got off with Dockery and asked if he wanted to take a ride to Carlisle with me.

"Carlisle where the great Jim Thorpe grew up?" he said

"That was Carlisle, Pennsylvania."

"So it finally happened," Hawk said.

"What finally happened?"

"You know something I don't know other than baseball or some song got written when FDR was president."

He asked if we were going to have breakfast first. I told him we'd be fools not to, and that's how we came to stop at Jimmy's in Burlington. I had Irish eggs Benedict and Hawk had eggs with Greek sausage and pancakes on the side. While we ate as if both of us were on our way to the chair, I called Angie Calabria and caught her between classes. I told her who I was and how I'd gotten her number and what I wanted to talk to her about. She asked if I could be there by twelve-thirty, which was when she took her lunch break.

Hawk had picked me up in his new Jaguar. How he seemed to have one expensive ride after another was just something else about him that I accepted as part of the natural and mysterious order of things.

It meant one more thing he knew and I didn't, and if he wanted me to know, he'd tell me and until then not to fucking worry about it.

"I like her already," Hawk said. "Harvard girl like herself gone off to teach kids."

"We might even run into a clue while we're with her."

"You always have been an optimistic bastard."

"It's the Irish in me."

"Hell it is."

An hour later Angie Calabria sat with us on the front steps of the Carlisle Public School complex on School Street underneath a warm midday sun. She looked younger than I knew she had to be, pretty and blond with violet eyes. She had been waiting for us when Hawk pulled up and parked the Jag as if the SCHOOL ZONE signs didn't exist.

"Is that your car?" Angie asked Hawk. "I *love* cars."

"'Course you do," Hawk said.

She wore a cotton pullover and jeans and sneakers and made it easy for me to see her as the college girl who had been Laura Mason Crain's roommate.

"Did the two of you stay in touch?" I said.

She smiled. "You mean after she became *Laura Crain*?" She practically shouted out the name. "Yeah, we did. She liked to remember where she came from, even if it was Harvard."

"When was the last time you heard from her?"

"I guess it was a couple weeks ago. She called me, which was unusual, most of the time it was the other way around. She said that Andrew's behavior was starting to freak her out and she had no idea what was causing it, because he refused to talk to her about it. I told her she needed to see somebody about it. A shrink. Somebody. I don't know if it was our conversation, but apparently that somebody turned out to be you, Mr. Spenser."

She looked intently at me, almost fiercely, the effect intensified by her eyes. I knew how rare the color was. Back when dinosaurs roamed the earth, Elizabeth Taylor had eyes like hers.

"She came to you for help and now she's dead," Angie Calabria said, in response to absolutely nothing.

"Is that an accusation?"

"More an observation," she said. "I meant no offense by it."

"None taken," I said. "Nobody feels worse about what happened than I do."

"*Were* you able to help her?"

"Still efforting that," I said. "Just after the fact."

I asked her then about Laura Crain's old boyfriend.

Her eyes widened, almost in fright.

"Oh, God," she said, as if I'd thrown a fright into her. "Is that why you're here? Did he come back into her life?"

"Wouldn't she have said something to you if he had come back into her life?"

Angie Calabria shook her head. "She didn't like to talk about him then, maybe she didn't want to talk about him now."

"Did you ever meet him?"

She shook her head again. "It was like she had a whole separate life with him. He never came around school. She always went to him, sometimes for a week at a time even while she kept going to her classes. I think he had a place in Watertown. Or maybe it was Allston. She wouldn't say where."

She looked at me again. "But when he called, she went running, almost like she was afraid not to."

"She was afraid of her own boyfriend?"

She nodded.

"Toward the end of senior year I asked why she didn't just break up with him once and for all, because she'd done it once before," Angie Calabria said. "We'd gotten into a bottle of white wine pretty good that night and it had gotten late. We were both pretty drunk. But she didn't sound drunk when she told me that if she ever did try to break it off again, she was afraid of what he might do."

She heard a bell ring from inside the building closest to us.

"That was the night she told me he hit her sometimes," Angie Calabria said.

THIRTY-THREE

Susan and I were watching Pearl the Wonder Dog chase pretty much everything moving in the Public Garden.

"I just don't understand people who don't love dogs," she said.

"How much did you love her last week when she turned those new Christian Arroyo shoes of yours into chew toys?"

"Christian Louboutin," she said. "And the Arroyo person is a baseball player, right?"

"Look at you. Next you'll be reading box scores."

"And if you're being fair, you'll recall that I didn't raise my voice about what the baby did to my shoes until she was out of the room."

"At which point a nice Jewish girl from Swampscott swore like a rapper."

"Fuckin' ay," Susan said.

As we sat on a bench and watched Pearl dash hither and yon, I caught her up on my meeting with Angie Calabria.

"She said he was abusive," I said.

"Physically?"

"Yes."

"What did he do for a living?"

"According to Angie he was a bartender. But Laura would never tell either of her roommates *where* he bartended. It was as if Laura were ashamed of him, of the relationship, his hold on her, all of it."

"Ashamed of herself," Susan said. "A classic element to the dynamic."

Pearl came back to me with a stick in her mouth, dropping it at my feet. I threw it as far as I could in the direction of Charles Street and was sorry as soon as I did, because it felt like my sore shoulder had just exploded all over again.

"And the roommate did not have this man's last name."

"She did not."

"And she really never laid eyes on him?"

I shook my head.

"And she never knew of the abuse until that night?" Susan said.

"Angie told me that Laura just suddenly pulled up her sweater and showed her some bruises. Angie said she was going to call the police. Laura begged her not to, she said that the argument had been her fault."

"Isn't it always," Susan said drily.

Pearl came back with the stick and plopped down, finally exhausted. From experience, we both knew it wouldn't be for long.

"How and when did the relationship finally end?" Susan said.

"Angie said it lasted at least into the summer after graduation," I said. "Angie went off to backpack through Europe with some other girlfriends, and when she came back, Laura told her it was finally over."

"Did she finally screw up the courage to walk away?"

"I asked Angie. She said Laura didn't want to talk about it, that it had ended horribly but that at least had ended. That his hold on her, literally, had finally ended."

"Did the guy leave town?"

"I got the impression from Angie that he had, but that Laura didn't know where at the time. And didn't seem particularly interested in finding out."

Susan knelt in the grass now and gently scratched Pearl behind the ears. But I could see her processing the information I was giving her, focusing all of her intelligence and curiosity and education—all of her immense self—on the young woman that Laura Crain had been when she was still Laura Mason.

She looked up at me. "And she never heard from him again?"

"Angie said that if Laura had, she was certain Laura would have mentioned it. But she never did."

Susan hooked up Pearl's leash to her harness and the three of us began to make our way past George Washington, toward Marlborough Street.

"*Could* he have come back?" Susan said as we were crossing Arlington.

"It would be useful for me to know," I said. "But I don't even have a full name for him."

"Which would also be useful for you to know."

"You don't miss a trick, do you?" I said, grinning at her.

She had handed the leash to me, and took my free hand then, and gave it a squeeze.

"What can I tell you," Susan said. "I have a master detective as a love slave."

I asked her if she was willing to prove that, even in the middle of the afternoon, and Susan said, as luck would have it, she was.

THIRTY-FOUR

I thought I could perhaps enlist Claire Megill in my effort to get Andrew Crain to see me, so I could ask him what he might know about his wife's old boyfriend. But Claire still wasn't returning messages or texts and it was starting to affect my self-esteem.

So I took a walk over to the Hancock in the late afternoon as people were beginning to leave work on the outside chance that even with security, Reggie Smythe or somebody else, Crain might come walking out the main entrance. By six o'clock, he had not, and I gave up.

On my way back to my own office I called Vinnie Morris and told him I needed help trying to locate a bartender who had worked around town twenty years ago, or thereabouts.

"Where'd he work?"

"I don't know."

"What's his name?"

"Rob."

"Rob what?" Vinnie said.

"All I got."

"Are you drunk?" Vinnie said, and I told him I wished, and he said he'd ask around and that I should say hello to Susan for him, he'd get back to me as soon as he could, he was in the middle of something, which he so often was, and about which I rarely asked.

When I got back to my office Hawk was back on my couch and got up only long enough to get two beers out of my small refrigerator.

"Ask you something?" he said when I'd settled in behind my desk.

He pronounced it "axe," but we both knew that was just part of the act. As always, it was difficult, even for me, to separate the mask from the man. But the quest to do that remained endlessly entertaining to me, and endlessly fascinating.

"Please don't make it a hard question," I said.

"Always try not to," Hawk said, "since I know that can make your head hurt something awful."

He sat up on the couch so he was facing me. "Where does a Boy Scout like you come down on the end justifying the means?" he said.

"So it's a philosophical question you ask," I said.

"Uh-huh."

I had my feet up on my desk. The refrigerator kept beer very cold. If it didn't, what was the point of even having it?

"You're asking me how far I'm willing to go to set things right in this crazy world?" I said.

"Like you did that time in San Francisco," Hawk said.

It was a long time ago and we were fugitives, out there to rescue Susan from a rich control freak named Russell Costigan, with whom she'd had an affair but then had been held against her will. Hawk and I were on the run because I had broken him out of jail in a town called Mill Valley, one owned by Costigan's father, and we had finally holed up in the apartment of two prostitutes.

I had eventually killed their pimp because if I hadn't I was certain he would have killed the two women himself.

Hawk and I rarely spoke of it. Susan and I did more frequently. But now here we were, and back there.

"You're asking me if the outcome would be the same now?"

"Uh-huh."

"I honestly don't know."

Hawk smiled. "Sho' you do."

I said, "What I do know all this time later is that I couldn't let two innocent people die because of something the two of us had done, something that had nothing to do with them. They only took us to that apartment because they thought we were a couple tricks."

"I offered to do the pimp so you didn't have to," Hawk said.

I let that go, like a batter letting a pitch go by.

"And then," I said, "acting as an agent of the federal government, I took out a different kind of pimp named Jerry Costigan." I swiveled my chair so I was more fully facing him. "Why exactly are we revisiting this today?"

"I'm just curious, on account of we mostly having the same code, you and me," Hawk said. "But we both know I'm willing to do things you can't, or won't, except there was that time with the boy Costigan and his old man you did things I never thought you'd do on account of we had to save Susan."

"Call of duty," I said.

"Ain't that a video game?" Hawk said.

"Not with us."

"Laura Crain ain't Susan."

"She was still my responsibility."

I got up and went into the refrigerator and came out with two more beers. Susan was threatening to cook for all three of us tonight at my apartment, and Hawk and I, without coming right out and saying it, were just fortifying ourselves, almost certainly with stronger stuff later.

"What if you can't find out who the bartender was or where he went?"

"Then we go to Plan B."

"You ain't got no Plan B," Hawk said.

I told him I was hoping he wouldn't notice.

THIRTY-FIVE

I sat at my desk the next afternoon and drank coffee, which usually made me feel better about everything, and wrote out a timeline of everything that happened since Laura Crain had shown up at my office.

Quirk had told me once, a long time ago, while we were working a different case together, how he'd never understood why the line about throwing shit against the wall and hoping some of it stuck had somehow managed to become a cliché.

"Guess what?" Martin Quirk had said. "You do it right, some of it will stick eventually."

"But how do you know if you are doing it right?" I'd asked him.

Quirk had shrugged and said, "Beats the shit out of me."

I put my pen down and made myself another cup of coffee, telling myself I could walk off the caffeine later. I finally got around to reading *The Globe*. I wondered if the man who owned the paper and owned the team even bothered with reading the sports section these days. I wondered if he missed Mookie as much as I did.

I wondered if somebody sent two headbangers after me because they didn't want me nosing around Laura Crain's death, or they didn't want me nosing around her husband's company, and its impending merger with a car company whose name escaped me at the moment?

"We know what we are but know not what we may be," I said aloud.

I knew who'd said that in *Hamlet*. Ophelia. I knew a lot of things. Just not a single one that was helping me solve the murder of a client who'd gone for a walk in the woods in the night.

I looked back down on Berkeley for a few more minutes, then called the number Paul Dockery had given me for Missy Jones, Laura's other roommate at Harvard, which had the Seattle area code 206.

"This better not be another spam call today," she said when she answered. "Or I will find you and beat you."

"You can decide about that later," I told her, then told her who I was and how I'd gotten her number and why I was calling her.

There was a brief pause at her end. I could hear people yelling at each other on a television in the background. I assumed it was either cable news or one of those *Housewives* shows. From my limited knowledge of both, it could have gone either way.

The sounds disappeared suddenly.

"Why did Laura need a private detective?" Missy Jones asked me.

I told her, as succinctly as I could, Laura's concerns about Andrew Crain's increasingly troubling behavior.

There was another pause, not lasting as long as the one before. "Did he hit her, too?"

"You mean the way the old boyfriend did."

"So you know about Rob."

"I do."

"I'm no therapist," Missy Jones said. "But I know about destructive patterns in people's lives. It was a logical question for me to ask."

"I had no indication that he had been abusive in their marriage."

"Do you consider yourself a therapist, Mr. Spenser?"

I knew we needed to get past this.

"A therapist to whom Laura did speak is the one who sent her to me."

"A grasp of who and whom," Missy Jones said. "You don't sound much like a private eye to me."

"Me talk pretty sometimes."

"Okay," she said. "How can I be of assistance to *youse*?"

First indication of a sense of humor. A start.

"I'm trying to find out as much as I can about this Rob."

"Did she tell you about him?"

"Angie is the one who got me up to speed on the bartender boyfriend none of you ever saw."

"I saw him," she said. "It was the night I threatened to kill the sonofabitch."

THIRTY-SIX

Missy Jones asked if I were pressed for time. I told her that presently I had nothing but time.

"There are some things you need to know about me," she said. "First off, I'm a lawyer. My father was also a lawyer. Maybe you've heard of him. His name was Kenneth Jones."

"Oh, ho," I said again.

"You have heard of him."

"Kenneth Jones, the Mob lawyer."

"Dad was resistant to that description. But yes, that's him."

"He was Gino Fish's lawyer when Gino was still with us."

"Yes," she said, "he was."

In my professional career, there had been an All-Star team of Mob bosses in Boston. Tony Marcus. Eddie Lee in

Chinatown. Joe Broz. Jackie DeMarco. Desmond Burke. A handful of others. But the late Gino Fish, in the day, had been as powerful as any of them. I had never actually met his personal lawyer, as many times as Gino's interests and my own had intersected. But Kenneth Jones had been well known in that world, which also meant my world.

"So Big Ken's daughter got into Harvard," I said. "I have to say that was very open-minded of them. Or at least ecumenical."

"I earned it, asshole."

I laughed. "I take it back," I said. "Tell me about your meeting with Rob."

It was, she said, the summer after they all graduated, her and Laura and Angie and Andrew Crain. Missy was living with her boyfriend in Brighton. Laura had a place of her own off Brattle, not far from Harvard, busy with freelance copywriting. Missy and Laura hadn't spoken for a month or so, until Laura called one night from Mount Auburn Hospital and asked Missy to come pick her up.

After the doctors had seen the extent of her injuries, she'd told them that she'd tripped over her dog and fallen down a flight of stairs.

"She didn't have a dog," Missy said. "Unless you counted Rob. She'd finally decided to break it off with him, and this time he'd beaten her within an inch of her life. And told her that if she ever mentioned leaving him again, he'd kill her."

Missy Jones insisted Laura spend the night at her apartment and drove them both to Allston. Laura finally told Missy where Rob worked, a bar called Marino's.

When Laura was asleep, Missy had called her father. Her father called Gino Fish. The next night one of Gino's enforcers, a guy named Mitch, picked up Missy and they drove to Marino's, on Comm Ave in Allston.

"Had Laura told you Rob's last name at this point?"

"I didn't even bother to ask," Missy said, "as I was confident that my relationship with him—and his with Laura—wasn't going to progress past that night."

Rob had closed up that night. Mitch and Missy were waiting for him when he came out the back door and into the alley behind Marino's, where he'd parked his car.

"For what it's worth, he looked a lot like Brad Pitt," she said. "Just not for long."

Mitch pistol-whipped him until Rob's face was what Missy described as a beautiful mess. Then Mitch rolled him over and sat on his stomach and stuck the barrel of his gun in Rob's mouth. Missy knelt down and told him that if he ever went near Laura again, if he even attempted to *contact* her again, the only thing that would change the next time Mitch came looking for him was that he would pull the trigger, something Mitch said he'd done plenty of times before.

"Maybe you get the idea," Missy said. "I had arrived at the 'time's up' point long before the MeToo'ers did."

All Missy ever told Laura was that her father had taken care of her problems with Rob. Laura had asked if that meant killing him. Missy said it hadn't been necessary, and Laura, as best she could recall, had said, "Pity."

A few nights later Missy called Marino's and asked for Rob. The bartender who picked up said Rob had stopped coming to work, wasn't answering his phone, seemed to have disappeared. Missy called a few days later and was told that Rob hadn't come back.

"Laura never heard from him again?" I said.

"If she did, she never mentioned it to me," Missy said.

I told her she had been a good friend. She said she didn't need me to tell her that.

"You're a tough cookie," I said.

"My father's daughter," she said. "What can I tell you? And if you do find out who did this to Laura before the cops do, I think I still have Mitch's number in Florida."

I told her I would keep that in mind.

"And because I *am* my father's daughter?" Missy Jones said. "You can choke on that cookie comment."

I told her I took that back, too.

THIRTY-SEVEN

I went over to the Harbor Health Club in the late afternoon, determined to grind my way through the lingering soreness from the beating I'd caught at Blakely Hoar.

Henry Cimoli watched me from a chair against the wall as I went from the light bag to the contour bag, even skipping rope, something I rarely did, to test my knees. Then over to the old heavy bag. Henry was generous enough to offer a running commentary on my form and my hand speed and my footwork, as if this were some sort of livestream event.

"Jesus H. Santa Claus," Henry said. "No wonder you got your ass handed to you."

"Not to make excuses or point fingers, Henry, but there were two of them, and they jumped me from behind, and one of them had a goddamn Louisville Slugger."

"Whiner," he said.

I took a break. Henry handed me a towel. He remained an ageless wonder, dressed in black boxing leggings and a white HARBOR T-shirt and still looking lean enough and fit enough to go twelve rounds for the featherweight title, something he had thought was within his reach when he was a kid on the way up. Full head of white hair. Bright blue eyes, full of fun and constant eternal mischief. You would have needed Special Forces to find an ounce of fat on him even now. He had been a second father to me for as long as each of us could remember, and to Hawk.

"Shouldn't you be leering at women doing Pilates?" I said.

"We only do Pilates in the mornings, smart guy," Henry said. "Barre method and yoga in the afternoon." He grinned. "And it's not leering. Scouting, is what it is."

"You're a dirty old man, is what you are."

"And proud of it."

I showered and changed there and drove back to my apartment and parked behind my building and then walked back to the office. I knew that Marino's had closed its doors for good during COVID, because I'd looked it up online after speaking with Missy Jones.

So I called another private eye in town I knew, Sunny Randall, a long-standing client of Susan's whom I'd met when Hawk helped her out on a case a couple years ago. Her father, Phil, now retired, had been a legendary detective with the BPD, and longtime friend to Martin Quirk. Her ex-husband, Richie Burke, was the son of Desmond Burke, still the head of the Irish Mob in Boston, and someone powerful enough to have had Gino Fish and all the other All-Stars cross streets to avoid him.

That wasn't as interesting to me, at least not today, as the knowledge that Richie Burke had owned a saloon on Portland Street. And the saloon business, even in a big city like Boston, could feel like as small a world as the one Richie's father inhabited.

"Spenser and Sunny," Sunny Randall said when she answered her phone. "It would be a dream team. I can already see it on the door."

"Do you want to break it to Hawk that I was dumping him for you?" I said.

"It's because I'm a girl, isn't it?"

"You've managed to overcome it," I said, and told her why I was calling and why I needed Richie's number, which she gave to me.

"Weren't you and Richie supposed to be the dream team?"

"Don't be hurtful," she said.

I called Richie Burke and asked him about Marino's and asked if Joe Marino, who'd owned it, was still around. Richie said he'd get back to me. I asked him how things were going with his ex.

He laughed and told me to shut the fuck up and that he'd call me when he knew something.

I was about to call Susan about dinner when there was a single knock on the door and Reggie Smythe came in, followed by Ethan Lowe.

"I think we're in a position to help each other out," Lowe said.

"You first," I said.

THIRTY-EIGHT

I pointed at Reggie Smythe.

"He can wait outside," I said.

"And why is that?" Lowe said.

"I don't know you well enough to know whether or not I can trust you. But I know Reg here well enough to know I don't trust him."

Lowe looked at Smythe and nodded toward the door. Smythe hesitated but left, closing the door a little harder than necessary, I felt.

When it was just the two of us Lowe said, "I'm thinking I might want to hire you."

"Should I thank you now?"

He closed his eyes, then sighed, somewhat theatrically. He hadn't even made me an offer yet, and already I'd disappointed him.

"I'd like to talk to you about doing the same sort of thing you did for Laura, but with me as your client."

"Laura is still my client."

"Laura is also dead."

I shrugged, also theatrically. "I've decided not to hold that against her."

"But as a practical matter, by working for me you'd still be working for her."

I asked if he'd like some coffee. Lowe asked if I had anything stronger on hand. I told him it was too early for whiskey, but there was beer. He said that would be fine. I went to the refrigerator and came back with two cans of Boomsauce.

"You've got good taste in beer," he said.

"Yeah," I said, "but let's face it, as long as it's cold, bad beer is better than none."

We both took healthy swallows from our bottles.

"Andrew has withdrawn even further following Laura's death," he said. "But even though I've always handled the business side of things, he remains the majority shareholder, and the face of Lith around the world. This merger can't go through without his blessing."

"Is he still prepared to withhold it?"

"He hasn't come out and said that," Lowe said. "But no matter how clear I make it to him that this deal only makes our brand stronger, and Lith bigger than it's ever been, he's become more hesitant about it."

"What's the worst that happens to Lith if the merger doesn't happen?" I said. "Smaller Christmas party?"

"It's not as if we're going to suddenly go belly-up," he said. "But there are other people out there looking to make synthetic materials even cheaper and more affordable than ours, while working just as well. The line keeps moving, Mr. Spenser."

He drank more beer. I wouldn't have made him for a beer drinker.

"Are you a sports fan?" he asked.

"Sadly yes."

"Let me offer you an analogy, then," he said. "The Patriots had one kind of brand when they were winning all those championships. Now they're just another team that *used* to win all the championships. Do you understand the distinction?"

"I do," I said. "But don't expect me to be the one who tells *their* owner that."

He took off his glasses, cleaned them with a cloth he pulled out of his pocket, looked through the lenses, put them back on.

"So many people, including consumers, will benefit from this merger," he said. "And in the end, so will so many of Andrew's charities. But if his behavior scares off our potential partners at Prise, then it's not just Lith that gets hurt."

"You practically make this merger sound like a public service," I said.

"I just want to help Andrew through whatever has gotten him off the rails to this extent," Lowe said. "But I can't do it without knowing what it is. It's why Laura came to you and why I've come to you."

"My priority is finding out who killed her, not what might kill your merger," I said. I shrugged. "As another practical matter."

"It doesn't mean our interests can't align here," Lowe said. "And you should know that money is no object."

I smiled again. "Is that ever really true?"

"In my case, almost always."

"Let me ask you something," I said. "Is everybody else at your company on board with this merger?"

He had the bottle almost to his lips, but stopped now and put it down on my desk. "Why do you ask?"

"I'm just curious as to whether someone other than Andrew Crain might be motivated to sabotage the deal from within, whether he's acting like a nutjob or not."

"Sabotage it by killing his wife?" he said. "Now who sounds like a nutjob?"

We sat there in silence then. It seemed to make Ethan Lowe somewhat fidgety, as if not filling any gap in conversation made him somehow negligent. Or less in charge.

Finally I said, "Would you mind if I changed the subject?"

"It's your office."

"What do you know about the bartender Laura dated her senior year at Harvard, and then beyond?"

He frowned.

"That *is* a change of subject."

"Humor me."

"I don't know very much in terms of specific information," he said. "Mostly just that Andrew seemed to hate him more than he hated bin Laden at the time."

"I only bring him up," I said, "because when I discussed him with both of Laura's roommates, they both expressed concern that he might somehow have come back into her life, and been the one to put her at risk."

"I really wouldn't know," he said. "I graduated a semester early, which means I left all of that drama behind me. Then before I knew it, Andrew had gone off to find himself. And when he came back to Boston, he and Laura finally fell in love with each other."

He checked his watch, almost as if he wanted to make me feel as if my office were his now. "Do you honestly think Laura's old boyfriend might have had something to do with her murder?" he asked.

"Somebody once said that what's past is prologue," I said.

He grinned. "I hope it was a Harvard man."

"Shakespeare," I said.

He checked his watch again, and said he needed to be going, he had a late meeting back at Lith. "Name your price," he said.

"I don't want your money," I said.

He looked at me as if I'd suddenly started speaking in tongues.

"Laura gave me a generous retainer," I said. "All I want is some cooperation from you and your partner and Claire and even your lawyer, if I can manage to restrain myself from bouncing him off the nearest wall when I'm next in a room with him."

"I can't make any promises on Andrew, at least not right away, we go day to day with him and occasionally moment to moment," Lowe said. "But the rest of us will be made available to you."

He stood. "I know what you think," he said. "But this is only partially about saving the merger. It's about saving my best friend, or I wouldn't be here."

He was out the door and gone when Reggie Smythe came back through it.

"You rather enjoyed him dismissing me like that, didn't you?" he said.

"Well, I didn't hate it, Reg, put it that way."

"To be continued, then," he said.

"Brilliant," I said.

I tried to make my British accent more subtle than the first time he'd been in my office. But being men of the world, we both knew it was there.

THIRTY-NINE

Susan and I were spending the night together in Cambridge, but our reservation at Oleana wasn't until eight because of another late client for her.

"Waiting that long to eat dinner might make me faint from hunger or pass out or do something along those lines."

"You could eat earlier over on your side of the river and I could sleep alone on my side," she said.

"Meet you at the restaurant or pick you up?" I said.

Richie Burke called and said that Joe Marino had died last year, and hadn't been much of a bookkeeper when he was alive. Richie added that he was still trying to track down an old bartender of his who might have worked at Marino's about the same time Rob had, and would get back to me if he managed to track him down. I told him I appreciated his best efforts in the matter.

"Sunny made me do it," he said. "I think she might have a crush on you."

"I'm too old for her," I said. "How's your father, by the way?"

"Starting to slow down finally."

"Who the hell isn't?"

"Sunny doesn't seem to think you are."

Susan and I took our time at Oleana. It was ten-thirty by the time we paid the check. When we got to her house I told her I would walk Pearl while she prepared herself for yet another trip to the moon on gossamer wings.

"I think it's adorable that you still quote Cole Porter," she said.

"Who am I supposed to quote, Taylor Swift?"

She kissed me on the cheek as she handed me Pearl's leash.

"Only bought this dress so I could take it off," she sang.

"Don't tell me," I said. "Taylor?"

"I try to stay current," Susan said.

Pearl, as always, treated this late-night outing like a jailbreak. I tried to explain to our dog, as patiently as I could, that I needed her to take care of her business. But she pulled me up to Raymond and all the way past the Harvard University Press on Garden.

We had made the turn back on Linnaean and I was trying to see how many lyrics I could still remember from "You're the Top" when Ethan Lowe called to tell me that they had found the body of Claire Megill's assistant, Darius Baker, outside his building in Charlestown.

"They think he threw himself off his balcony," Lowe said.

FORTY

Darius Baker had lived on 1st Ave, an older residential building in what had become one of the most gentrified areas in town over the past several years, his building a few blocks from the old Charlestown Bridge.

It was actually called the North Washington Street Bridge now and had finally been declared structurally deficient about twenty years earlier, which is why they were building a new one next to it. But the original, construction of which dated back to the late eighteenth century, was still open to pedestrian traffic that could take you from the Navy Yard all the way over to the North End.

The police presence stretched up and down 1st. Belson was there when I arrived. So were Lowe and Claire Megill and Clay Whitson.

Andrew Crain was a few yards away from his people, standing next to Reggie Smythe, so close to Smythe I thought he might be leaning against him for support. Smythe nodded at me. I nodded at him. The vacant look on Andrew Crain's face was reflected in the flashing police lights, as if Crain were staring past the USS *Constitution* Museum to infinity, and perhaps beyond.

Belson walked over to me.

"Oh, thank God," he said, "you're finally here."

"What happened?"

"Young couple on their way to walk over the bridge and meet some friends for drinks on the other side of the river hear him land behind them on the sidewalk," Belson said. "He lived on the top floor of 275. Fifth floor." He pointed. "Not a pretty picture."

"I would imagine not."

Belson eyes were fixed on the balcony as he told it. "She gets hysterical, the boyfriend calls nine-one-one, I get the call because the guy worked for Lith and Mrs. Lith was the dead body before this one. Lundquist was rolling up a shooting at a party up in Marblehead, but says he's on his way."

He looked at me.

"You know this guy?" I said.

"I met him just one time, at the Lith offices," I said. "Spoke to him for a minute or so. That was it. He was the assistant to Crain's assistant. She called him a genius."

"His boss says the kid wasn't suicidal," Belson said.

"She'd know better than anyone," I said.

"Your girlfriend's the shrink, not Ms. Megill," Belson said. "A lot of young people are depressed these days and nobody knows it until it's too damn late."

"Andrew Crain's wife gets killed," I said. "Then the assistant to his assistant gets killed. Maybe the universe is trying to tell us something, Frank."

"I'll be sure to keep that in mind," he said.

"You check the cameras at his front door?"

"Aren't any."

"Talk to the people on his floor?"

"Shit!" Belson said, slapping his forehead. "Why didn't I think of that?"

"Phone?"

"Not in the apartment, not on him, not near the body."

"Was the guy seeing someone?"

"Ms. Megill says no."

Belson walked away from me then to talk to Lundquist, who'd just arrived. I went to talk to the upper management of Lith, Inc. about the sudden and violent death of another member of the family.

None of them looked particularly thrilled to see me.

But then, I ran into a lot of that.

FORTY-ONE

Andrew Crain was still keeping some distance from the others, as if in a barely operational state of shock. Reggie Smythe was still at his side. I assumed Smythe had collected Crain and brought him here, from either Beacon Hill or Brookline.

Before I could get to Claire Megill, Clay Whitson saw me.

"What's he doing here?" Whitson said to Ethan Lowe, pointing at me.

"I called him," Lowe said.

"What the hell for?"

Lowe didn't change expression. "Remind me again which one of us is boss, Clay?"

I ignored both of them and motioned with a quick toss of my head for Claire to walk with me. She did. Her eyes were as empty as Andrew Crain's, seeming robotic even in this small movement.

"He wouldn't kill himself," she said. "You have to believe me."

"I do," I said. "But if he didn't, who killed him? And why?"

She lowered her voice.

"He hasn't been to the office since Laura died," she said. "He said he was ill with the flu, but finally called tonight and said he'd been working on something that he couldn't work on at the office, and needed to talk to me about it."

"Working on what?"

"He didn't say. Just that it was important, he'd call back, it might not be safe even talking about it on the phone, it had to be in person."

"Did you tell the police that?"

She shook her head. "I'm telling you," she said.

"Let's keep it that way for now," I said.

Claire Megill started to cry then. No sound came out of her. Her breathing didn't seem to change, nor her posture. There were just the tears. She made no attempt to wipe them away, as if oblivious that they were even there. But they showed no signs of stopping.

Before I could offer her comfort, Ethan Lowe was standing in front of us, as if he'd suddenly felt left out.

"I don't know whether this young man took his own life or not," Lowe said. "But what I do know is that two people connected to our company have died in the past week. So, Mr. Spenser, let me ask you a question: *Now* are you willing to come work for me?"

I told him I wanted to sleep on it, even though I didn't, I didn't want to work for Ethan Lowe or Andrew Crain or Lith, Inc., and not just because I was about as good a fit in any corporate structure or chain of command as an iguana would have been roaming the fiftieth floor at the Hancock.

Laura Crain might have been the first dead client I'd ever had. She was still my client. Even now. And I still owed her.

Belson waved at me from where he and Lundquist now stood in front of Darius Baker's building. I started to head over to them but then Claire Megill yelled, "Mr. Spenser, wait!" and broke away from the others to catch up to me, alert all of a sudden, quickly covering the ground between us.

When she had, she threw her arms around me and pulled me into a fierce hug and in a loud voice said, "You have to find out what happened to this beautiful young man."

Before I could respond she pressed her face into my shoulder.

"Please protect me," she whispered.

I hadn't known any of these people a week ago and now I was suddenly the most popular boy in class.

FORTY-TWO

My knees remained too sore for me to consider our normal run along the Charles, so the next morning Hawk and I were walking the McCurdy Track at Harvard.

"So you know," Hawk said. "We could do this forever and not break a damn sweat."

I said, "There have been multiple studies done on the health benefits of walking if you're able to maintain a brisk pace."

"This," he said, "ain't that."

"What, you *don't* consider this to be a brisk pace?" I asked, trying to sound hurt.

"Maybe at the fucking *home*," Hawk said.

"You just wait. Your heartbeat will be up before you know it."

"Only if I walk to Braintree when we done here."

"Bitch, bitch, bitch," I said.

Hawk snorted. "Man walking like Father Time and calling me the bitch."

"Nevertheless," I said, and we began another lap.

Today Hawk wore a T-shirt that had WOKE THIS on the front of it.

"Claire Megill says that kid knew something, and it was important, and wanted to tell her before he died."

"Kid?" Hawk said. "Shit, you are Father Time."

"Belson said Baker had just turned thirty."

"Stand corrected," Hawk said. "Nobody ought to be thirty." He smiled. "Unless I be dating them."

"If he didn't jump, somebody wanted it to look like he did," I said. "Maybe because of whatever it was he'd found out."

"No suicide note?" Hawk said.

"Nope."

"No sign of no scuffle or whatnot up on that balcony."

"Nope."

The more we walked, the less my knees hurt. But I wasn't going to tell Hawk that. The right one hadn't buckled today, at least not yet.

"You want to keep going?" Hawk said.

"Why not? I'm suddenly feeling fresh as a daisy."

"Or some other kind of delicate flower. First they looking at you as some kind of threat," Hawk said. "Now they falling all over they-selves wanting you on their side."

"Or so they say."

"Uh-huh."

The morning air was cool and clean, as if autumn had

already arrived in Boston, and dropped the temperature more than ten degrees from the day before in the process.

"The kid's boss lady say she wants you to save her," Hawk said, "right after the other boss comes and asks you to go to work for him. Probably on account of two people they know being dead."

"It sounds a lot worse when you put it like that," I said.

Hawk asked when I planned to next talk to Claire Megill. I told him I was meeting her for a drink after she finished work today.

Hawk nodded.

"'Less somebody kill her first," he said.

FORTY-THREE

Martin Quirk showed up at my office an hour or so before I was scheduled to meet Claire Megill at the bar at the Capital Grille, which had moved several years before from Newbury next to Hynes Auditorium on Boylston.

It had begun to rain by then. Quirk took off his ancient Burberry raincoat and hung it on my coatrack, his movements as precise as they were with everything else, as if he were prepared to treat a single drop of water on my rug as some kind of felony.

He was dressed in another of his tweed jackets, another of his knit ties, another blue button-down shirt. I imagined him dressed like this watching a ballgame or playing with his grandchildren or walking his dog.

"Want a drink?" I said when he was seated.

"Thought you'd never ask."

I poured Bushmills for both of us, handed him his

glass. We both drank immediately. The warmth of the whiskey was both immediate and soothing.

"First of the day," Quirk said.

"None better."

"Until the second one."

He slid a coaster close to him and put his glass down.

"You are once again a walking fucking crime wave," he said.

"To be fair," I said, "only one of them was my client. I barely knew the guy they found in Charlestown."

"Tell me everything you know, whether you already told Frank or not. And then tell me everything you think."

"You in a rush?"

"I have a PBA dinner at seven-thirty at the new Ritz, one I would fake *my* death to get out of."

I told him everything, including the parts about Laura Crain's old boyfriend. After a few minutes Quirk held out his empty glass and I refilled it. We were listening to the Bill Evans Trio. Bill on the piano. Chuck Israels on bass. Larry Bunker on drums. All going down as smoothly as the whiskey. Taylor Swift didn't know what she was missing.

Bill Evans was playing "Who Can I Turn To?"

"The media is already having a goddamn field day with this," Quirk said.

He held up his glass and stared at it in the faint light from my desk lamp, now that the early evening outside had grown darker with the rain.

"You think somebody would try to kill this merger by killing two people?" Quirk said.

"Or kill two people to save it."

"How often do we look at either sex or money?" Quirk said.

"So often," I said.

"The commissioner is up my ass already," Quirk said. "So I need you to keep me in the loop on this thing."

"When haven't I?" I said.

I thought he might almost have smiled. "You know," he said, "I could just stay here and finish the bottle and skip the dinner. I got a driver."

"Be my guest," I said. "*Mi casa . . .*"

"Kiss my *casa*."

He finished his whiskey and took the glass over to the sink and rinsed it. He was even tidier than Susan. Almost impossible to fathom.

"How could the wife and the assistant be part of the same problem?" he said as he reached for his coat.

"I don't see a connection. But that doesn't mean there isn't one."

He put on his coat. I could still spot some droplets of moisture on the shoulders. "I don't want this to turn into more of a shitshow than it already is."

Quirk stopped when he got to the door. "You get anything useful out of Ms. Megill tonight, you let me know."

I told him I would.

"Time to head over there," he said.

"Poor bastard."

"Yeah," Quirk said, and then left my office like he was being perp-walked.

FORTY-FOUR

Claire Megill and I sat at a corner table at the Capital Grille. She said the bar had just the proper lack of good lighting, as any good bar should. She had a glass of pinot grigio in front of her. I had a glass of Napa Hills pale ale.

"The one time I met Darius," I said, "he told me to be nice to you, right before I went into your office. When I asked him why he'd say something like that, he said, 'Not everybody is.'"

She drank a healthy amount of her wine.

"You'll find out the truth eventually," she said. "Or maybe have already. I had a relationship, one I'm not very proud of, since we work together, with Clay Whitson."

"I'm shocked," I said. "Shocked, I tell you."

"Don't make fun," she said.

"I take it he wasn't nice to you?"

She stared past me, then brought her eyes back to me. "No," she said.

She drank more wine. "I came in one day, and I hadn't done a good enough job covering a bruise on my chin with my makeup. Darius asked me. I denied it. But I knew that he knew what had happened to his boss."

"But you didn't tell your boss," I said.

"I was too ashamed," she said. "But I think Darius might have."

"If Andrew knew, why wouldn't he just fire Whitson's ass?" I said.

"Because Ethan either believes the merger can't go through without Clay," she said. "Or is afraid that Clay would find a way to sabotage it if he *was* fired."

She moved her glass slightly on the table, as if giving herself something to do with her hands.

"Anything more you'd like to tell me?"

"I've told you too much already," she said. "But as I said, just knowing you a little, I had a feeling you'd find out for yourself sooner or later."

"But it's over now between Whitson and you?"

"As far as I'm concerned it is," she said. "And could we please change the subject?"

The rain had stopped by the time I got to the bar. She wore a short beige linen jacket with a blue T-shirt underneath and white jeans. She said she'd had enough time to stop at her apartment and change after work, and had walked here from there. I told her I would walk her home later. She said it wasn't necessary. I told her that was the plan.

"To walk me to my door?"

"For you to not need saving."

She told me now, in an effort to change topics, if only briefly, that she'd always loved taking her son to the Capital Grille when he'd visit from school.

"Nothing better than watching college boys eat steak," she said.

"They should make it part of their marketing," I said.

Now she ran a finger around the tip of her wineglass. I noticed that her fingernails were the same color as her T-shirt.

"Maybe it's an irrational reaction to what happened to Darius," she said. "But I feel as if I'm in the middle of something and might be next."

"Middle of what?"

"Some toxic mix of family drama and corporate intrigue," she said.

"I'm not sure I understand."

"Andrew is the scientist," she said. "Ethan is the entrepreneur. Because Andrew invented a cheaper way to produce lithium, he has the larger share of the company, as you know. Mr. Inside to Ethan's Mr. Outside. They're both well aware that there is no Lith, Inc. without Andrew's genius. But Ethan believes the company would never have grown to the extent that it has without his business genius. He's always telling Andrew to just keep focusing on the science and let him take care of everything else."

"I got the impression that Laura didn't trust Lowe as completely as her husband did."

"I don't know whether it was simply a lack of trust, or

that she'd just never liked Ethan very much, and got tired of hiding it."

"So Lith isn't everybody's happy place."

"Maybe once. But not for a while. Andrew likes things the way they are," she said. "Ethan, though, he's become increasingly obsessed with the merger."

"His idea?"

"From the beginning," she said. "He wants the company to keep growing, becoming more profitable than it already is. But more and more Andrew is convinced they have enough money, and should use even more of it, for fear of sounding highfalutin, to make the world a better place. That's *his* obsession."

I nodded. I had already gotten the sense from Ethan Lowe why the merger mattered to him the way it did. Now I had heard it from her. I'd finished my beer but was reluctant to order another, as she had barely touched her wine.

"Where would Laura have fit in with the dynamic you're describing?"

"Laura might have been more opposed to the merger than Andrew is," Claire said. "And to be honest, Mr. Spenser, I was quietly cheering her on, because her voice mattered to him a lot more than mine does. And mine matters a lot."

"She called you a bitch," I said.

She sighed. "Laura was always threatened by me, even though she had no reason to be. But on this matter, we were in lockstep."

"Why doesn't Andrew just call a stop to the deal if he doesn't like it?"

"Because he doesn't want to do that to Ethan," she said. "Their relationship can get complicated sometimes, even though they love each other like brothers. But even brothers who do love each other fight."

I'd held out as long as I could, and waved at the bartender now for another beer. Trying to problem-solve made me thirsty. Most everything did, especially at this point in the evening. The bartender put the fresh, chilled glass down in front of me.

"Is your relationship with Clay Whitson really over?" I said when the bartender was gone.

"I just told you it was."

"You also told me you were ashamed of it. Maybe you're ashamed that it's still going on."

"It's not," she said.

"The other day when he was bothering you in front of Equinox, he wanted to know what you'd told someone," I said. "What was he talking about?"

She sighed again. "I'd been questioned by the head of Human Resources about the possibility of an affair with Clay. There had been rumors around the office and they finally made their way to HR. Clay wanted to know what I'd told them."

"Not told anybody he hit you?"

She shook her head.

"I know he has a terrible temper," she said. "And there were times when he did hurt me. But he's not a monster."

"We're going to have to disagree on that," I said. "And any man who ever took a hand to a woman."

"You get into a relationship like that . . ." She forced a smile. "And it's very difficult to get out."

"So I'm told," I said, knowing this was a conversation she should be having with Susan Silverman.

The bar had begun to fill up. Mostly guys. I was picking up a lot of guy chatter, mostly about sports. The universal guy language. Susan had suggested, and not frivolously, that they should teach it in college. But as a Romance language.

"If Darius didn't kill himself, as neither of us believes he did, I'd be a fool not to think someone might come for me next."

"But you don't know what he'd found out before he died."

"Whoever killed him doesn't know that," she said. "Just that he worked closely with me."

"Now you want me to protect you."

She gave me another long look. "Can you?"

"I can't do it alone," I said. "But there are people who can help me help you."

"Are they as good at what you do as you are?" Claire Megill asked.

"One of them is," I said. "But if you tell him I said that, I'll deny it."

FORTY-FIVE

We came out of the restaurant and took a left on Boylston, another left on Dalton, and then another on Belvedere, on our way to Huntington. I asked how she'd come to work for Andrew Crain. She said she was a single mom, raising her son, working for one of Lith's satellite tech companies, another start-up, in Silicon Beach.

"Divorced?" I said. "Widowed?"

"Divorced," she said. "I was young. And stupid. And thought I was madly in love. I got pregnant. He left." She shook her head. "The reason I never talk about it is that it always starts to sound like a bad country song. If it hadn't produced my son, it was as if it never happened."

"Don't they say that if you ran country songs in reverse, they'd all have happy endings?" I said.

"It was my first bad decision with men," she said. "And that is another subject I'd like to change, thank you."

"Done," I said.

She pulled her jacket tighter around her as we waited for the light to change on Huntington with the Colonnade across the street and the shops at the Prudential Center behind us.

"Want to tell me more about how you came to work for your boss?"

"Happily," Claire Megill said.

"Was he around your company a lot, is that how you first met him out there?"

"I was working somewhere else when he hired me," she said. "But a headhunter called one day and asked if I'd be interested in going to work for Andrew Crain. He was out in Southern California and took me to dinner. We talked for a long time that night. He asked how I liked my current job, which was at Apple. I said I liked it fine, but wasn't being challenged, blah, blah, blah. And told him, quite honestly, that I was barely able to support my little boy and me on what I was making. I must have come across pretty well that night, because two weeks later I was working for Lith's tech company out there. Six months after that, I had moved to Boston and became his assistant, with more responsibility, and for more money than I ever thought I'd make in my life."

We passed the Colonnade.

"How can I find out if there's a fox in the henhouse at Lith?" I said.

She smiled for the first time, fully. Almost happily. "Do people still use that expression?"

I smiled back at her. "Only when the wolf is at the door," I said.

"Well, I'm certain I can help you with that," she said. "I just can't have Andrew and Ethan know that I would essentially be spying on my own company. Or have Clay get wind of it, for that matter. So we'll need to be discreet."

"One of my many specialties," I said.

"Do I want to know what the other specialties are?"

"We'd need more time for me to list them all," I said.

We were a couple blocks from her building when we heard the thunder and then saw the lightning over our heads, followed instantly by a violent rain. Neither of us was carrying an umbrella. We just ran. I had promised to keep her safe, just not from the elements.

When we arrived at the walk leading to the front door of her building, both out of breath, she looked up at me, hair matted to her head, drenched as much as I was. She laughed. I laughed, both of us looking as if we'd been thrown fully clothed into a swimming pool as I told her to get the hell inside.

"You really can keep me safe?" she shouted over the roar of the rain.

"Yes," I shouted back. "We start tonight by you not answering your door once you get inside."

"I think I can manage that!" she said.

She found her key in her bag and unlocked the door. I watched through the glass doors as she walked across her lobby and then disappeared into the elevator, giving me a quick wave as she did.

Somehow the rain came even harder then.

I had turned back toward the street, thinking I would run back to Huntington and into the Colonnade and wait for the rain to subside when I slipped in a huge puddle that had formed on her front walk, and my gimpy right knee buckled underneath me, and I went down, cursing myself and the weather gods as I landed hard on my side.

In the next moment I heard a sound that I knew immediately was not lightning, a sound I recognized even underneath the storm, the unmistakable crack of some kind of long gun behind me, an instant before the bullet hit what turned out to be the shatterproof glass of Claire Megill's front door.

FORTY-SIX

I thought I heard a shout from somewhere in the night as I rolled behind the only cover I could find, one of the two huge terra-cotta pots that bracketed the front door, right before a second shot exploded into the top of it and I was showered with pieces of clay.

The rain came harder.

I couldn't pinpoint the place in the park where the shots were coming from as I pulled the nine-millimeter I had brought with me tonight out of the holster I wore at the hip of my jeans. I looked around what was left of the pot and through the driving rain for pedestrians and saw none and fired once in the general direction of where the shots had come from, not expecting to get off a shot of my own at the shooter, but wanting him to know that I was armed, too.

I made out the shape of a man then, running away from me across the park.

Either giving up or not wanting to be seen, or both.

I rolled back out from behind the shattered pot and began to chase him on the bad knee that had likely just saved my life.

There was more light out here in the open, because of the buildings that surrounded the park. If I saw him stop and turn, ready to dive to the ground. He kept running, through the middle of the park, what looked like small gardens fenced on each side of it.

I was not gaining on him.

He was dressed in what looked like some sort of dark slicker and a baseball cap with a long bill and was faster than I was. But just about everybody was these days. His knees were probably stronger and sturdier than Usain Bolt's.

I slipped in the mud and went down again, managing to keep my gun hand high. I liked this gun. But I liked them all, just some more than others.

It was a big, fast man I was chasing, illuminated briefly by a flash of lightning, almost out of sight, on his way out of the park when I was up and after him once again, not just soaked now, but covered in mud.

Underneath another flash of lightning I could clearly see the long gun in his own right hand.

He slowed, but for only a moment, opening the low gate at the far end of the park rather than trying to scale it, and then he was on the street, running to his right. I didn't know the name of the street, but then it didn't matter because he was gone.

I was out of breath. The rain might have begun to subside, but only slightly, as I holstered my gun and began the walk back to Claire Megill's building, my shoes sinking deeper into the mud as I did.

I would have imagined myself as a drowned rat, except that I wasn't the rat out here tonight, a night when the one who needed protecting turned out to be me.

FORTY-SEVEN

Perhaps residents of the building whose apartments faced the park thought the shots fired had been just part of the soundtrack of the storm. Because of the hour, perhaps no one had entered or exited the building after his shots had hit the door, and the pot. As of yet, there were no sirens heading this way, and there might not be unless somebody actually had seen what was happening out a window and called it in.

I called Claire on the number of the phone she carried with her, the one she said she always answered, told her I was still downstairs and what had just happened. She said she could buzz me in and I could come up. I said that wasn't a good idea in my present state. So she came down to the lobby, having already changed into a sweatshirt and jeans and sneakers, though her hair didn't yet look completely dry.

I showed her where the bullet had entered, what I was guessing might be a military-style bullet from the small hole it had left. Perhaps a .223, I told her. She looked at me as if I were speaking Estonian.

"Dear God" is what she said, putting a hand over her mouth.

It was unclear whether she was reacting to the bullet hole or to my appearance. Probably both.

"They weren't after you," I said. "Turns out they were after me."

She said I should really come upstairs and clean up. I said that wasn't likely to happen any time before Veterans Day. I said that I was going to place a call to the police, but that there was no point in having them in her apartment, the guy had been targeting me tonight, not her.

"I only *thought* I was scared before," she said.

"I still have friends in the department, hard as that sometimes is for me to believe," I said. "I'm going to call them now and explain the situation. I'm going to ask them to send a car, and I will wait here in the lobby until it arrives. The car will be out front all night."

"You're sure the shooter won't be back?"

"If anybody approaches that door looking anywhere near as suspicious as I do," I said, "I will shoot them dead."

She produced a tiny, nervous laugh. "I assume you're joking."

"I'm not," I said.

No one came through the door after Claire went back upstairs. No one came down the elevator. So no chance for my appearance to frighten the decent people. The rain finally stopped. When it did I went outside and finally placed a call to Belson.

"They shot at you and missed?" he said.

"Sorry to be the one to have to break it to you, Frank."

He said he'd send some of his people, one of whom would stay outside until morning. It didn't take them long to arrive. Once they did, three cars arrived one after another in quick succession, one carrying the detectives. Claire had contacted the super by now, who lived in a small apartment in the back. I showed everybody the hole in the glass, and where the bullet had hit the wall next to the elevator. One of the detectives extracted the bullet, flattened and misshapen.

"A .223," the taller of the two detectives said. He'd introduced himself as Cohan.

"Nailed it," I said.

"Huh?" he said.

"I know my bullets," I said.

"Happy for you," he said.

The other detective said, "Lieutenant Belson is waiting for you downtown."

I looked back at Cohan. "Bet now you're really happy for me."

He was young. A hard case. Clearly a by-the-book guy. He looked back at me, face impassive. "Next time we should make a night of it," he said.

They didn't ask if I had a car, or needed a ride downtown. I walked back to where I'd managed to find a parking place on Boylston, what felt like a very long time ago. On my way to see Belson, I called Susan and told her about my big night out with Claire Megill.

"You were shot at," she said.

"He turned out to be something less than an expert marksman," I said.

I could hear Pearl working over a squeaky toy in the background. I was pretty sure I knew which toy. It was new. But none of them ever had much of a life expectancy.

"So you dodged another bullet," she said.

"A gift," I said.

"Not funny."

"Hey," I said, "think how I feel."

There was just a brief pause and then she said, "I love you."

It was the same every time she said it, no matter what the circumstances, over the phone or in person, the words making me feel as if I were better than I had been before I heard them, better and more complete and reconnected to the best part of myself.

An hour later I had finished telling it to Belson, and he had typed up his report.

"We take attempted murder seriously around here," he said, "even for hot tickets like you."

We went downstairs then and got into our cars and drove over to Biddy Early's on Pearl Street, which had always advertised itself as the "best damn dive bar in Boston" despite what I knew, just from my own personal experience with dive bars, was extensive competition.

I looked at my watch. I had left the bar at the Capital Grille with Claire Megill well over four hours ago. Much had happened since. Belson ordered Jack Daniel's. I ordered Johnny Walker and soda. We sat at a high-top directly across from the bar. There was a Red Sox "B" prominently displayed above the rows of bottles. In bars like Biddy Early's, it was like displaying a crucifix. Or a picture of the pope.

"So he wasn't after her," Belson said.

"But hiding in the glowing doom," I said.

"It's too late for that shit," he said.

"Thomas Hardy," I said. "I knew you secretly wanted to know."

"Maybe he went there thinking he could take a shot at her when she came home," Belson said, "and changed his mind and decided to clip you instead. Get you out of the way and come for her another time."

"But why try to take me out?"

Belson sipped his drink and very nearly smiled. "Other than for reasons too countless to list?"

"Other than those."

"The wife goes out for a walk in that glowing doom of yours," he said, "and she dies. If you're right about the guy in Charlestown, which my gut tells me you are despite any useful evidence to the contrary, somebody tried to see if he could fly. Now somebody goes after you, in front of the building where the guy from Charlestown's boss lives."

"Three different ways of getting it done," I said. "Or trying to get it done, in my case."

"Not exactly what you'd call a coordinated effort."

"Almost," I said, "as if somebody is making up this shit as they go along."

There were a few diehards at the bar, despite the hour. Or perhaps because of the hour. There was an older guy sitting alone at a table against the wall, studying a glass of whiskey as if it were some kind of math problem he was trying to solve. Late-night ESPN was playing soundlessly on the television. There was no music. Who knew? Maybe it was the best dive bar in Boston after all.

"Somebody must be afraid you know something you shouldn't," Belson said.

"I wish."

"I know the feeling," he said. "I got no leads on Mrs. Crain. Got no physical evidence on the Baker kid."

"But look on the bright side," I said. "Now you've got a bullet from the guy who just tried to assassinate me."

"Assassinate?" Belson said. Hunched over his glass, hands around it, but eyebrows up.

"It just sounds more substantial than 'attempted hit,'" I said.

I knew it was time to go home. The adrenaline had drained out of me long ago. Despite my best efforts in the men's room on Belson's floor at the BPD, I was still filthy enough that he'd found a print edition of *The Globe* for me to sit on in his office. I'd at least had a clean sweatshirt in the backseat that I'd put on when I got downtown, and a dry pair of ancient Adidas sneakers with the three stripes, my favorites, built to last, somewhat like me. Or so I liked to tell myself.

I still liked places like this, this time of night. Even after a night like this one.

Belson got up and walked over to the bartender and handed some cash to him. When he came back I said, "You *paid*? Did I die after all? Is this heaven?"

"You look like shit," Belson said. "Least I could do."

I looked down at what was left of my drink. I had

nursed it well enough that the ice hadn't melted yet. Always a good sign, no matter the hour.

"What the hell is going on with these fucking people?" Belson said as we walked back out to Pearl Street.

I still had no answer for that, so I thanked him for the drink and got into my car and drove home.

When I arrived at my own front door, nobody took a shot at me. I considered that progress as I went upstairs and took a quick, hot shower and threw down a quick shot of whiskey and fell into bed. My knee was throbbing, but I found the feeling comforting, picturing myself going to the ground in front of Claire Megill's front door until I finally fell asleep.

FORTY-EIGHT

Hawk and Vinnie Morris and I were in my apartment the next morning. It was the first time Vinnie had been there since I had moved back to Marlborough Street.

"Sorry I didn't bring a fucking housewarming present," he said.

"Stop before I tear up," I said.

"Gets you right here, don't it?" Hawk said. "Or maybe there."

Vinnie wore a gray summer suit with faint pinstripes, a black shirt underneath, black suede oxfords. If there was a best-dressed list for guys who had once been a shooter for Joe Broz and still dabbled in the field when a lucrative opportunity presented itself, Vinnie would have been on it every single year.

There was more silver to his short, dark hair. He was tan enough that I was not surprised when he told me that the job from which he had just returned had been on Gasparilla Island, on the west coast of Florida.

Because it was Vinnie, there was not much of a report beyond that.

"Lot of rich people on that little island," he said.

"So I've heard."

"They don't like to get braced by somebody trying to make them less rich," he said.

"They don't watch out," Hawk said from where he was stretched out on my couch, "shit like that can throw the radiative equilibrium totally out of whack."

Vinnie stared at him. "Radioactive what?"

Hawk smiled.

"Whatever," Vinnie said. "I got it straightened out and flew back last night, right before you didn't get hit and the storm did."

"Wasn't much of a shootout, all things considered," I said.

"You sure the guy didn't miss on purpose and not because you got lucky and made him miss?" Vinnie said.

"Somebody had already given me a warning at the sanctuary," I said.

"Maybe they think you're slow on the uptake."

"Well," I said, "I can see why someone might think that."

Vinnie was sipping one of the small bottles of regular Coca-Cola. I knew he liked the little bottles, and I had gone out and picked up a six-pack before he and Hawk had arrived.

"You been beat up now and shot at," Vinnie said. "What's next? They try to drown you in your bathtub?"

I had asked him if he'd be willing to keep an eye on Claire Megill for a few days. He said he would, and that he assumed I could afford him. I told him that after what Laura Crain had paid me up front, I was bucks up at the moment.

"So this isn't one of those jobs where you get paid in donuts or some shit like that?" Vinnie said.

"Happily, no."

"She gonna know I'm watching her?" Vinnie asked.

"I will call her after you leave and tell her that you and I will meet her outside the Hancock after work as a way of introducing you."

"She good-looking?" Vinnie said.

"Does it matter?" I said.

"Maybe you are slow on the uptake after all," Vinnie said.

"Man makes a good point," Hawk said, and made a shooting motion at Vinnie with his thumb and forefinger.

I saw Vinnie looking around the living room. "I feel like I got some of that déjà vu going here," he said.

"Because of the way I've managed to artfully reimagine my old apartment?"

"Nah," Vinnie said. "Because here we go again with me watching somebody and Hawk watching you and neither one of you knowing what the fuck is going on here."

"See there," I said, grinning at Hawk. "There is still equilibrium to the universe after all."

FORTY-NINE

"So you're my new nanny," Claire said to Vinnie when we met her at the corner of Clarendon and Stuart.

"Sure," Vinnie said.

It came out *shoo-ah*.

"I meant that in a nice way," Claire said.

"It sounded kind of a-feminist to me," Vinnie said.

I grinned at Vinnie. "This might be a chance for you to be even more metrosexual than you already are," I said.

"Bite me," he said, then nodded at Claire and said, "Pardon my French."

"Seriously?" she said to him. "Thank you for doing this."

"Sure," Vinnie said again.

"I feel as if you'll be walking me home from high school," Claire said to Vinnie.

She turned to me. "Do I even want to know what your next move might be?"

"Only if you want me to tell you," I said.

Belson had told me that he'd cleared it with Quirk to keep a car in front of Claire's building for the next couple nights at least. After that, I would leave the overnight shift to Vinnie. I knew he had people. Who had people. By now I trusted Vinnie Morris the way he trusted me. Susan called it a code that only members of our club understood, and maybe even not all the members.

"Do you really think of it as a club?" I'd asked her.

"Or a secret society," Susan had said. "Except you guys deal in real skulls and bones."

"Yale reference from a Harvard girl?" I said.

"I was making a larger point," Susan said.

I eventually needed to talk to Andrew Crain again, about many things. But Claire said she could not help me with that, that she was more loyal to him than anybody except her own son. If he did not want to meet with me, at least not voluntarily, that was entirely his choice, and she would do nothing to try to change his mind. She told me that she hoped I could respect her choices. I told her that I could. Everybody had codes, whether you were in a club or not.

Andrew Crain, whom Claire said was currently holed up in the town house on Chestnut Street, might know more about his wife's life in college than even he thought he knew. And likely more about the ex-boyfriend than I knew, just because almost everybody did at this point. I was aware that there were other possible links between Laura's death and Darius Baker's. But Crain remained the strongest link between them, as weak as he himself seemed to be these days, a weakness that had brought me into his world in the first place.

For now, though, I wanted to talk to Clay Whitson. I had spoken with Ethan Lowe on the telephone before Vinnie and I had walked over to the Hancock, clearing it with him. Lowe had given me Whitson's cell phone number, which would probably do me no good, and his address at the Seaport, which I suspected probably would.

"Don't tell him you got it from me," Lowe said.

"You're his boss," I said.

"And I do my best to keep him on my side," Lowe said. "It makes my life a lot easier. The old theory about having him inside the tent pissing out."

"Is there any other side for him other than yours?"

"His," Lowe said.

Whitson lived in a high-rise building behind the Boston Harbor Hotel, the view of the water unobstructed by the hotel. Lowe further told me that as part of Whitson's deal with Lith, the company provided Uber rides to and from the office. Whitson's secretary had told Ethan Lowe that he was working late tonight, but that she had booked an UberX for him at seven o'clock to take him back to the Seaport.

I was waiting for him out front when he got out of the black SUV. He was wearing another suit with skinny lapels and what I once would have called pegged pants. Somebody really needed to tell him that he didn't have the body for it, built as he was like a garbage can. He was checking his phone and didn't notice me standing there until he had put the phone away. Reluctantly put it away.

He probably didn't go five minutes without checking it. If that.

He stopped when he did see me.

"You don't get to come to my home," he said.

"And yet, Clay," I said, "here we both are."

"Ethan told me that I had to talk to you, but I assumed you'd make an appointment and come to my office," he said.

"Then I made the executive decision to come here," I said. "I've frankly always thought I had the makings of a first-rate top manager. Not to mention the people skills."

"You really are a smug sonofabitch."

I smiled. "Well, a sonofabitch maybe."

"What do you want to talk about?"

"Your boss."

"Which one."

"Andrew Crain."

He surprised me by barking out a laugh.

"Boss?" he said. "More like the guy who's trying to destroy his own company."

Whitson shook his head, almost sadly.

"You've got this all wrong, Spenser," he said. "I'm not the bad guy here. He is."

FIFTY

We walked around to the dock behind the hotel.

"I could have invited you up to my apartment," Whitson said. "But I don't want you inside my apartment."

"No need to sugarcoat it," I said.

There was a glass-walled gazebo in front of us, a tour boat to our left beginning to board passengers, probably for its last run of the night, smaller boats bobbing in the water. There was a good hard breeze coming from the east. The view from here was timeless, especially at this time of night when the color of the sky seemed to match the color of the water.

I zipped my leather jacket and put the collar up.

"Andrew has never paid much attention to the day-to-day operation of the company, the nuts and bolts of it," Whitson said, leaning over the railing in front of us. "He just thinks of himself as some sort of modern-day Edison.

He invented a better mousetrap and found a way to make the energy from batteries cheaper and more affordable and more friendly to the ecosystem. And away he went."

"When did you start working with him?" I said.

"About five years in," he said. "I've been with him and Ethan ever since."

"So why does a company that was rich beyond avarice even before you came along need this merger so badly?"

"You want the long answer or the short one?"

"Either," I said. "Just promise not to use too many big words."

"Jesus, you really are a horse's ass," Whitson said.

"Well, yeah."

"Okay, here's the short answer," he said. "First of all, he's given away so much money over the past few years, more than ever before, it's like he's got a charity addiction to match any other kind of addiction you want to talk about, including gambling."

"It has to be more than that, even if he has been giving money away with both hands," I said.

"Yeah," he said. "It is. We got hit hard by COVID the way everybody else did, especially in terms of production. And when we were slow coming out of it, along comes some Australian scientists to produce an even cheaper form of synthetic lithium than we are, those Down Under bastards." He shrugged. "So now they're the ones who maybe have built a better mousetrap."

"So is the sixth-richest guy in America still the sixth-richest guy in America?"

"He is, but not for long, the way he's going and the way we're going," Whitson said. "Bottom line? We *do* need this merger. Ethan knows it. I know it. But our looney-tunes founder doesn't want to hear about it."

Whitson turned to face me. "Andrew is constantly talking about the greater good. But now he's about to blow a deal that isn't just good for his company, but might save it."

"Can't Ethan bring him around?"

"He believes he can, he's always been able to keep him in line before," Whitson said. "The problem is that the car people are getting impatient. And if they take their offer off the table, they will sure as shit go running straight to the new kids on the block in Melbourne."

"How did Laura figure into all of this?"

"As far as I can tell, Laura kept telling Andrew that bigger didn't always mean better," Whitson said. "That Lith didn't need this, he didn't need this, *they* didn't need this."

"So she could have been seen as an obstructionist where the merger was concerned."

"Indeed."

"Worth killing because of that?"

"Oh, hell, no," he said. "We may be a dysfunctional family behind the scenes. But we're still family. I've always thought that Ethan loved Laura as much as Andrew did. Maybe more. He's never said anything like that. But I've always had this feeling that he thought he should have been the one to get the girl."

The tour boat, looking as if it had been turned into a party boat on this night, began to slowly ease out into the water.

"What about Darius Baker?" I said.

"What about him?"

"Is there any possibility that he could have been seen as a threat to the merger?"

Whitson turned and leaned his back against the railing, as if the view suddenly bored him.

"Sorry, but Darius didn't matter enough," he said. "Does that make me sound like a prick?"

I smiled, not able to help myself. "You're a lawyer. You probably knew the answer to that before you asked the question."

"I'm trying to help you, and you persist in talking shit at me," he said. "So now we're done here."

"One last thing."

I put a hand on his arm as he started to push off the railing. He looked down at it, but made no move to pull his arm away. It was just the two of us out here. Maybe he could see something in my eyes. Maybe he was worried that if he said or did anything to escalate the moment, I might throw his ass into the water.

"I'm just curious about something," I said, tightening my grip just slightly. "Would Darius have mattered more to you if he knew you were the prick who liked to beat up Claire Megill?"

He jerked his arm back and slid along the railing to create space between us.

"What the hell are you talking about?" he said.

"Just asking a question I might already know the answer to," I said, and left him standing there, proud of myself for not throwing Clay Whitson's sorry ass into the water.

FIFTY-ONE

Hawk and I were at Susan's for a late dinner. She had told me in advance that she was more than willing to cook. I had told her that while I could see that the spirit was willing, the flesh was sadly weak.

"Just out of curiosity?" she'd asked. "*Whose* flesh?"

"Mine and Hawk's."

"In what order?"

"Ordering in," I said.

Hawk had preceded me to Linnaean Street. By the time I arrived from the Seaport, the food from Dumpling House had arrived. From the looks of the bags and containers spread out on the counter in Susan's kitchen, she and Hawk had ordered just about everything: beef with longhorn peppers, General Gao's chicken, string beans with dried shrimp, white and brown rice, plenty of hot mustard on the side. And an order of pork intestines with pickled mustard greens, which I was certain Hawk had ordered just to torture Susan Silverman.

"Pork intestines?" she said when we were all seated at her dining room table.

Hawk rubbed his stomach and smacked his lips. "Hmmmm," he said. "Good and good for you."

Susan used chopsticks. Hawk and I did not. I reminded her again that I was able to use chopsticks, but just chose not to.

As we ate I told them about the time I'd just spent with Clay Whitson.

"Doesn't sound like his interests are aligned with the big boss's," Hawk said.

"No," I said. "They certainly do not."

Susan plucked a single green bean and ate half of it. She looked at me as she did, face serious, all of her focus on me in the moment, making me feel, as always, as if she could look all the way into my soul. I'd mentioned that theory to Hawk once and he'd said, "Always knew somebody'd find it, they looked hard enough."

"But does any of this help you find out what brought Laura Crain to you in the first place?" Susan said. "Or what that might have had to do with her death?"

"Missy here asks a good question," Hawk said.

He was seated next to her. Susan leaned over and kissed him on the cheek. If I didn't know what a hard case he was, I might have thought he was beaming.

"I've often considered asking questions professionally," she said.

"So you're suggesting I go back to the beginning," I said.

"The thought has occurred, yes."

She finished the string bean that had remained firmly in place between her chopsticks, one I thought she had forgotten and might have just stayed where it was indefinitely.

"You still haven't found out what event, or series of events, brought Andrew to his breaking point."

I grinned. "*That* thought has occurred to me, yes," I said.

"So don't you think it might be useful *to* go back to the beginning?" she said.

"Why do I feel as if I'm being shrunk?"

"'Bout damn time," Hawk said.

We both watched as Susan now nibbled on a piece of chicken, though *nibble* might have been a bit of a reach.

"The conclusions to be drawn about Laura's death are limited, just off what I know so far," I said. "One theory would be that it was random, and she really was just at the wrong place at the wrong time, though I can't imagine what she was doing on the trail alone in the night. Or she went there because she knew her killer, a person who might have wished her harm because of what's going on with her husband's company, except that she didn't know he wished her harm."

"Think about something else, since we headed down this path," Hawk said. "How much you know about the girl, really, other than her being married to who she was married to, and that she had herself a boyfriend in college she shouldn't've?"

"Not a lot."

"Is there a chance, and I'm just throwing this out there," Susan said, "that Laura could have had a man on the side, or a woman?"

"She didn't seem like the type," I said.

Susan smiled. "Trust me. There is no type. I've done the research."

Hawk spooned more pork intestines onto his plate, making sure Susan saw him do it.

"Now you're really trying to ruin my appetite," she said.

"What appetite?" Hawk said.

We discussed the conflict between the two partners then, and the obvious drama between Clay Whitson and Claire Megill. And violence. I poured more champagne for Hawk, who was civilized enough tonight to have foregone drinking out of the bottle. I went and got another Boomsauce from the refrigerator.

"Two people are dead, both with strong ties to Lith," Susan said. "Here's my last question before I leave the detecting to the two of you: Is there any connection *between* the two dead people?"

Now I stared at her. "That is an even better question than the other question."

Susan nodded. "I really should consider doing this for a living."

Fifteen minutes later, after we had all cleaned up after dinner, Hawk and I were in his Jaguar and on our way to Charlestown.

FIFTY-TWO

I called Frank Belson on our way to Darius Baker's building. He told me that the tox screen, which he'd fast-tracked, had come back and indicated a high amount of tequila in Baker's system at the time of his death.

"We didn't find tequila in the kid's bar setup," Belson said. "But last time I checked, they do serve it in actual bars."

"Anybody in the area remember serving him that night?" I said.

"We checked," he said. "They didn't. Doesn't mean he couldn't have gotten a load on somewhere else."

"Do we know if he owned a car, Frank?"

"According to his last credit card statement, he was leasing an Audi."

"Where is it?"

"No clue," he said.

"My gut tells me he didn't jump, Frank."

"Prove it."

The next thing I heard was a dial tone.

Hawk told the super at Baker's building that he was Darius's older brother, just by another mother, and had just arrived back in the country from France after having gotten the news about his baby brother. The super, who'd introduced himself as Ramon, said the apartment was supposed to remain sealed, by order of the police.

It was then that I flashed the fake badge that I'd collected from my glove compartment before we'd left Susan's, and said, "I'm unsealing it."

Ramon acted as if I'd pulled a gun on him, said to Hawk, "Very sorry for your loss," and took us upstairs and unlocked the door and we were in.

"Can't believe that badge is still working for you," Hawk said. "Where'd you get it, inside a box of Cracker Jack?"

"I was more worried that Ramon might start to question the lack of family resemblance between you and Darius," I said.

"Wait," Hawk said. "You saying we all *don't* look alike?" It was a young guy's place. The flat screen on the living room wall looked twice the size of my own. On the coffee table was a video-game controller, though I had no idea for which video game. So I asked Hawk. "Xbox," he said. On the wall next to the flat screen was a framed World Series ticket from 2018, Game 2, Red Sox against the Dodgers at Fenway. Those were the days.

Every piece of furniture in the room seemed to have come from Pottery Barn or IKEA or some hybrid of the two. There was a small, well-stocked bar, but without tequila. Combined kitchen and dining area off the living room. You went down a short hallway to the master bedroom, which had a partial view of the water from the balcony where Darius Baker had spent the last moments of his young life.

Hawk stood in the middle of the bedroom. The bed was made. No clothes draped over the one armchair in there, or the chair at his desk.

"Belson's people go over this place good?"

"What do you think?"

"Yeah," he said, nodding. "Frank never been one out there flying on the wings of chance."

He looked around. "We looking for anything in particular?" Hawk said.

"What we're always looking for," I said. "Something that will make us feel smart when we find it."

"Could be here awhile," he said.

Belson said some of his guys had checked out the limited presence Baker'd had on social media. Claire Megill had already told me that Darius did not have a Twitter account, or TikTok, and rarely posted things on Instagram.

"Crazy as it sounds, he was too busy actually living his life to record it," she said.

Until he wasn't.

There were no clues to be found in the drawers of his desk. Some bills that he hadn't paid electronically. One from J.Crew. Another that was from Pottery Barn. A couple unused legal pads, and some gel pens. A small, wallet-sized Red Sox game schedule. No photographs on the desk, or anywhere in the apartment. Maybe he hadn't lived here very long, it would be easy enough to check with Claire, his immediate superior. And probably didn't matter, one way or another. Claire had told me he was a product of the New York City foster-care system but had still managed to earn a scholarship to NYU, majored in economics, after that came an internship at Lith the year before he graduated. Then a full-time job with them. Living the dream.

Hawk found nothing other than clothes in the bureau. There was a floor-to-ceiling bookcase in the living room. I went through the books one by one, hoping that a clue might fall out of one of them. One did not. Most of the books were self-help books, a lot of self-help books on how to become a success in business, a leader of men and women.

I need one of those, I thought.

I went to the closet next. A lot of hanging clothes in there, suits and sports jackets and shirts and jeans. Even his T-shirts were on hangers. A lot of shoes and sneakers on the floor, all neatly arranged. There was an array of baseball caps on hooks, most from New York teams, the heathen.

I began to go through the jackets one by one, meticulously checking the pockets.

The note was in the third blazer from the end, a J. Crew, inside pocket, almost hidden by the flap.

Belson's people had just missed it because everybody missed things. There had been plenty of times when I could have taught a master class in missing things, no matter how hard I looked.

It was actually a personalized note card.

LAURA CRAIN was at the top.
The message was in neat, cursive script.

D:

Didn't want to send anything electronically.
We have to be more careful than ever.
What you've found could change everything.
Love you for caring this much.
Talk soon.
L.

I whistled softly as I stepped out of the closet.
"Oh, ho," I said.

FIFTY-THREE

Claire Megill agreed to meet me the next morning across from the entrance to Trinity Church.

It was one of my favorite landmarks in the city, because of the look of the place, and its history. The original Trinity Church had been built on Summer Street but had burned down in the real Great Boston Fire, the one in 1872. The Public Library was in the distance behind the bench where I waited for her, at the spot on Boylston where the Marathon ended every year. Even though there were taller structures all around the church, it still seemed to dominate Copley Square, with what looked like arms reaching up from both sides to a central tower. I had read somewhere that the Back Bay had originally been a mudflat, and that the church rested now on thousands of wooden piles. But it consistently made the list of the most significant buildings in the entire country. I wasn't sure what that meant, but the old girl had always been significant enough for me.

I had picked up coffee for me and tea for Claire at the Starbucks that was essentially underneath my office on Berkeley. Vinnie walked Claire to the bench on which I was sitting, at the end of a long expanse of well-maintained lawn. I assured Vinnie that I could get Claire safely to her office from here.

"You carrying?" he said.

"If you show me yours, I'll show you mine," I said.

"Okay, then," Vinnie said, and told Claire to call him later, he'd be waiting for her downstairs when she was finished at work.

We both watched him go.

"He's really kind of cute," she said.

"It would be best to keep that between the two of us," I said.

"You don't want him to know I think he's cute?"

"I don't want him to quit," I said.

I got right to it then, asking if she knew of a relationship between Laura Crain and Darius Baker.

Her mouth actually dropped open, in almost an exaggerated movie take.

"A romantic relationship?"

"Any kind of relationship."

"Between the wife of the principal owner of the company and my assistant?" she said. "The people at Human Resources would have been wearing party hats when they fired him. Clay Whitson and I would have seemed like a speed bump."

"But that's what I'm asking you, yes."

She shook her head a few times, slowly, side to side. "If there was something between them or anything between them, it's news to me."

"There was one," I said. "A relationship. Darius and Laura Crain."

She had worn sneakers with her beige pantsuit for her walk to work with Vinnie. Knowing how fashion-conscious Vinnie was with his own attire, I hoped it hadn't offended his sensibilities.

I recited the contents of Laura's note to her, word for word.

"What does that all even mean?" Claire said.

"I was hoping you might be able to tell me," I said. "At the very least, it indicates a shared interest in something. And probably explains why he called you the night he died."

"If there was some kind of shared interest, Darius would have told me."

"Obviously, he didn't."

"This can't be."

"Claire," I said. "We're way past that now. Maybe he kept silent because the boss's wife told him to." I turned slightly on the bench. "You never saw the two of them together in a social setting?"

"Perhaps at the office Christmas party?" she said. "But Laura and I were rarely together in social settings, and when we were, let's just say we kept our distance." She shrugged. "I had long since given up the notion that the two of us were ever going to be friends, even though there was no need for her to be threatened by me."

"It doesn't mean she wasn't," I said.

"And then, what, aligned herself with my assistant on some top-secret mission?" she said.

"Strange bedfellows?"

"Are you suggesting they were sleeping together?"

"Figure of speech," I said. "But I'm not saying they weren't."

She drank some of her tea.

"It's a rather cryptic message," she said.

"Apparently not to them," I said.

We sat in silence then in the morning sun. I watched the foot traffic to our left on Boylston Street, thinking about how many briefcases I would have seen in another time, briefcases replaced by backpacks and leather bags now, or not replaced at all, because everything they all needed was waiting for them inside their desktop computers, or in the slim handheld cases that probably contained their iPads. All I generally carried to work was a .38.

"Is there any chance that Laura could have gone to Darius and asked him to find out why Andrew has been behaving the way he has?" I said.

"But why him?" Claire said. "You're suggesting that she went to the assistant of someone—*me*—she apparently thought was a bitch on wheels?"

"Maybe she knew he was a New York City kid," I said. "Maybe she was looking for street smarts." I raised my shoulders and let them drop. "I'm fumbling here."

Claire placed her cup next to her on the bench, reached into her bag, came out with her phone, checked it, put it back inside the bag.

"But street smarts for what?" she said. "And about what?"

"Something not right about the merger?"

"As closely as I work with Andrew, even I'm not privy to what Andrew and Ethan refer to as 'being in the weeds,'" she said. "He's generally aware of what's going on, of course, he's the major shareholder and will ultimately vote thumbs-up or thumbs-down. But Ethan is the one who's in the barrel on this deal. When Andrew needs to know something, Ethan tells him. When Andrew's got a question, he asks Ethan. When there was some part of the finances I didn't understand, I'd ask Darius."

"But what if it was Laura who wanted to go into the weeds on this thing?" I said. "And didn't want to ask Ethan. It's become pretty clear, at least to me, that she was like her husband in the sense that she liked things the way they are at Lith and saw no need for expansion, or major change."

Claire Megill gave a slight jump as a car horn blared behind us on Dartmouth Street.

"In the end, and despite his misgivings, Andrew will do what's best for the company," she said. "He and Laura never had children. Lith is his baby, and his legacy, and his opportunity to change things he thinks need changing. He calls himself the nerd who conquered the world."

"But seems to be losing himself in the process," I said. "By the way? I met with Clay Whitson last night. And he frankly gave me the impression that if Andrew doesn't get on board with the merger, the walls might come tumbling down."

The mention of Whitson seemed to make her color slightly. Or it could have been a trick of the morning light, I wasn't entirely sure.

"Clay said that?"

"He did."

"The man has no filter."

"There's a lot of things he doesn't have," I said. "But is he right?"

She hesitated, and leaned her head back, and stared up at the tower of the church.

"I swear, he's more dug in on this merger than even Ethan is," she said. "And occasionally acts like he's as much a partner in the firm as either Andrew or Ethan. As if wishing could make it so."

She pulled up the sleeve of her jacket and checked the Apple watch on her wrist. "I need to get to the office."

"Did Darius ask questions recently about the merger or anything that you found odd?" I said.

"No," she said. "But he would have known better than to raise my antennae, if he was poking around where he shouldn't have been."

I took our cups and tossed them into a nearby bin, and told her I would walk her to the Hancock. She said it was called 200 Clarendon now. I told her I knew that, but it was too late for me to change.

"I have the feeling you run into a lot of that," she said, smiling at me.

"Hourly sometimes," I said.

She said it really wasn't necessary for me to bodyguard her in broad daylight. I told her Vinnie would ask if I'd walked her all the way to the door, and I promised that once she was inside, I was confident nobody would take a shot at me.

When we'd made our way over there, she stopped on the sidewalk.

"What I don't understand is why Darius didn't mention his relationship with Laura," she said. "Whether it was personal or professional."

I was about to answer her when I saw the black Lincoln Navigator pulled up. Reggie Smythe, my old pal, got out from behind the wheel and came around and opened the sidewalk-side door and Andrew Crain stepped out.

As he did, Claire Megill turned without saying goodbye and moved as quickly as she could toward the front door without breaking into a sprint.

FIFTY-FOUR

Reggie Smythe, most certainly paid handsomely to see the whole field, picked me out of the morning rush between Clarendon and the entrance to the Hancock before Crain did.

Andrew Crain was just slightly visible behind Smythe, head down, wearing what by now I knew was his uniform: Sweater, lemon-colored today, blue shirt underneath, slightly baggy jeans, loafers that had seen better days.

It was a wide sidewalk, and there were other people on either side of them.

I stepped in front of Reggie Smythe.

He smiled, as if hopeful for some kind of confrontation. Any kind of confrontation.

"I'd like a word," I said.

"I'd like to think not," he said.

I ignored him, took a quick first step past him even on

my bad knee, almost daring Smythe to make the move to stop me.

But I had managed to insinuate myself between him and his boss.

Some bodyguard.

For Smythe to do anything about it, he was going to have to make a scene. In the world of cell phone video and social media, he had to know what a truly bad idea that was.

"Would you prefer I remove him?" Smythe said to Crain.

I said, "You have a better chance of becoming an astronaut, Reg."

Andrew Crain's eyes were everywhere at once, as if trying to find a place to come to rest.

His eyes finally focused directly on me, almost as a last resort. "Please don't embarrass me. Or yourself."

I could feel Smythe's presence close behind me. If he did try to remove me, whatever happened next would happen. And was probably an inevitability between us.

I just didn't want it to happen until I spoke with Andrew Crain, no matter how briefly.

"I'm not trying to embarrass you," I said. "I'm trying to find your wife's killer."

"That's better left to the police," he said. "That's their job."

"And mine," I said. "And yours, if you'll just cooperate with me."

He looked at Smythe and nodded.

"Good day, Mr. Spenser," Andrew Crain said.

I was out of time.

"Are you aware of your wife being involved in a relationship with Darius Baker?" I said.

In the next moment Crain was doing his eye-blink thing again. Maybe this time it was some sort of message in code for Smythe.

"What did you just say?" Crain asked.

"I'm trying to understand why I found a quite personal note from Laura to Darius in his apartment when I was going through his things," I said.

"*Reggie,*" Crain snapped.

His boss voice coming out of him, just like that, as if he'd suddenly remembered he actually *was* the boss.

I detected some movement to my right, out of the corner of my eye. When I turned my head to determine exactly where Smythe was, the sixth-richest man in America, apparently unconcerned about going viral, screamed, "I will not let anybody hurt her ever again!" right before he punched me in the face.

FIFTY-FIVE

"You want me to go over there and beat the bad man up for you?" Hawk said.

We were in my office, in the middle of another morning when we were drinking coffee and eating donuts, Hawk on the couch and me with my feet up on my desk. He had enjoyed the story of what had just happened with Andrew Crain and me immensely.

"Do I have to keep reminding you that it was a sucker punch?" I said.

Hawk snorted. "From the president of the Science Club," he said.

"Go ahead. Have your fun."

"Am trying to look at the bright side, however."

"There's a bright side to me getting tagged?"

"Least the big bully didn't give you another broken nose," Hawk said.

"You done?"

"For now."

At some point we were going to head over to the gym. When we got there, Hawk said, he was going to give me a remedial course in ducking punches.

"I clearly touched a nerve when I asked him about his wife and Darius," I said.

"Though I got to say, touching a nerve with the boy at this point don't seem to me like you had to thread no needles," Hawk said.

He nodded at the open box of donuts. "You plan to eat that last sprinkled?"

"With the pink frosting? It's all yours, you candy ass."

"Look who's talking."

He finished the last donut in two bites. It meant we had gone through the whole box in almost record time, even for the two of us.

Hawk said, "You gonna tell Belson about that note?"

"Eventually."

I drank more coffee, which I had just reheated in the microwave. I didn't fully understand why Dunkin' coffee, cream and sugar, tasted better than fancier and more expensive brands. It just did. Hawk had suggested once that it might have had something to do with them putting enough sugar in it to bake a cake.

"Maybe Belson already found some connection between the two of them by going into her phone or laptop and is waiting to tell *you* eventually."

"I actually asked him about that," I said. "He said Andrew Crain has refused to release either."

"'Scuse me?"

"I happened to place a call to our friend Lieutenant Belson after I stopped at Dunkin'," I said. "And got a very fast and very salty assessment of the Fourth Amendment and privacy rights for the dead and what Lieutenant Belson further described as 'fucking exigency.'"

"You think Crain might've gone into them himself and found out something he didn't want the po-lice to know?" Hawk said.

"Or maybe Andrew Crain doesn't want to know what he doesn't want to know about his late wife."

"But the man just told you, front of God and the world, that he wanted you to stop hurting her," Hawk said, "even now that she gone off to her reward."

"The last time I know of that she was a victim was when she was trapped in an abusive relationship in college," I said.

"Then she come to you because she say her husband was some kind of victim," Hawk said, "even if it was just from all the toys in his attic."

"Unless she went to somebody working for her husband's top assistant first," I said. "Before the two of them both went and got they-selves killed."

I saw Hawk grin. "*They-selves?*"

"Just reading the room."

He took his own last, sad look at the empty donut box and picked it up and dropped it into my wastebasket.

"So the cops don't find Baker's laptop," he said. "And Crain say he ain't giving up his wife's. Or even her old Filofax."

"Correct."

"But maybe it don't matter, since she say in the note she don't want to send anything to the boy electronically."

"Also correct."

By now I knew that Hawk was as good a listener as Susan Silverman was, as observant as Belson or Quirk were at crime scenes, and had a memory like an entire herd of elephants.

"We could break into one of Crain's houses and steal one of his wife's laptops," Hawk said. "Just thinking out loud here."

"And criminally."

"You forget sometimes," he said, "on account of my superior intellect, that I is a career thug."

He asked if I was ready to head over to Henry Cimoli's. I said I was.

"Wait," I said.

"We wait, we never gonna make it over there and just want to go get more donuts."

"No," I said. "I just thought of something."

"Egads, Holmes!" Hawk said. "Enlightened thinking?"

"There's one computer we could check without breaking and entering," I said, and then called Claire Megill, and told her what I needed for her to do, if she was willing.

She called back five minutes later.

"I am now seated at Darius's desk," she said. "I haven't done that since he died."

"Haven't the police been through it?" I said.

"Andrew and Ethan wouldn't let them."

"Do you find that odd?"

"Not for Andrew and Ethan."

She was keeping her voice very low.

"Are you able to get into his files?" I said.

I could barely hear her when she next spoke.

"No," she said.

"No, you can't, or no, you won't?"

"No, I can't," she said, still whispering. "His hard drive is gone."

FIFTY-SIX

I put my phone on my desk between Hawk and me and put it on speaker.

"Somebody removed the hard drive from Darius's desktop," I said to Claire Megill.

"Yes," she said.

"Who could have done that?"

"A lot of people here," she said, "as long as they knew what they were doing, and made sure not to get caught."

She had walked back into her office, she said, and shut the door. She said it had been the first time she had been able to sit at Darius's desk since his death.

"Isn't there a way to get into whatever he stored on the cloud there?" I said.

"How much do you know about how the cloud actually works?" she asked.

I saw Hawk roll his eyes.

"Could you start me off with an easier question?" I said.

"The company doesn't allow the use of a personal cloud for company business," she said. "Ethan thinks information like that is too easy to pirate. So without going all techy on you, any Lith-related business is only backed up here, on a personal cloud for each individual station, all encrypted individually. To access your own stuff, you even have to use your own fingerprint. Like your actual fingerprint."

"So Darius could have had personal stuff on that hard drive, as well as work stuff."

"It works the same way for Andrew, and Ethan, and Clay and me and everybody else in upper management." She paused. "And their assistants."

"Are there any cameras inside the office?"

"No," she said. "As much of a bear as Ethan is for privacy, Andrew won't allow it. The whole 'big brother is watching' thing. But again: Anybody on either the forty-ninth or fiftieth floor who knew what they were doing could have removed the hard drive, most likely after-hours. They'd just have had to pick a time when no one else was around."

"Is it possible to check who might have used their key card or whatever to be around after-hours?" I said.

"An awful lot of people here stay at the office into the night. We're kind of the *home* office for worker bees. Like they're all hoping Andrew or Ethan will walk past their desks and see them still at them."

"So somebody knew that Darius knew something he wasn't supposed to," I said. "Nothing else makes sense."

"And it got him killed?" she asked.

"Put it this way, Claire," I said. "It didn't do very much to keep him alive."

I told her that I would call her later, and that Vinnie would be there when he said he'd be there, because he always did what he said he was going to do. Another part of the code.

I reached over and ended the call.

"All right, all right, all right," Hawk said, lapsing into a Texas drawl now.

"Matthew McConaughey?" I said.

"Got more game than even you know," he said, "accent-wise."

He grabbed his gym bag. My workout clothes were in my locker. Hawk liked to wear something different every time he worked out, the vain bastard.

"Okay," I said. "Was it sex or money that got him killed? Or got both of them killed?"

"You asking me?"

"I saw an opportunity to tap into your superior intellect," I said.

"How come I always got to be the one to figure this shit out?" he said.

"I think of it as the black man's burden," I said.

"Just one more thing to add to the damn list," Hawk said.

FIFTY-SEVEN

Hawk went to Harbor Health without me, as much as I needed to work out. I told him there were some calls I had to make.

"To who?"

"Whom."

He gave me the finger.

"I've put together a list of the committees and boards Laura Crain served on in Boston," I said. "It occurred to me that I know more about the friends she had in college than I do about the friends she might have had when she died, at least apart from Susan."

"And you can't ask her husband 'bout that, on account of he might beat you up again," Hawk said.

Then I gave him the finger.

"Yeah," he said. "I is still number one."

Belson showed up about fifteen minutes later, coming into the office without knocking. He did not look pleased to see me, but then rarely did.

"I keep forgetting to ask how Captain Glass is doing," I said. "She recover okay from COVID?"

"Almost," he said. "When she does, turns out she'll be fully recovered working at Sex Crimes."

"That will probably please Lee Farrell to no end."

Farrell had been transferred to Sex Crimes.

"Glass pissed off Quirk once too often, mostly by acting as if she invented everything except the wording to Miranda."

"You should look happier."

"This *is* happy," he said, and sat down, and then said, "So you and Black Adam lied your way into Baker's apartment."

"Look at you with your pop culture references," I said.

"Eat me."

"You want coffee? I just made a fresh pot."

"No," he said. "Hawk said he was the dead guy's brother?"

"From another mother. Or maybe father. I can't actually recall."

"That super, Ramon? He isn't the sharpest knife in the refrigerator," Belson said.

"But extremely accommodating in light of Hawk's family tragedy," I said.

"You two find anything we didn't?"

"No," I said.

"You lying?"

"Why in the world would you assume that?"

"Why wouldn't I?"

"But I did find out something useful a few minutes ago," I said. "Somebody took the hard drive from Darius Baker's desktop at work."

I fumbled my way through explaining how the computer system at Lith worked, including the part about thumbprints.

"There's ways to get around that. I'd tell you how, but I'd have to kill you, which, by the way, is something I consider from time to time."

I got up and fixed myself another cup of coffee. I'd lost track of how many I'd had today. But this was it. If I didn't stop now, I was going to run to Susan's when it was time to pick her up for dinner.

"I am told," I said when I was back behind my desk, "that our friends at Lith were less than welcoming when you asked for access to Baker's desktop."

"Expectation of privacy," he said. "Even for the deceased."

"Even with a warrant?"

"The lawyer over there, some guy named Whitson, told me what I could do with my warrant when I tried to brace him."

"I've run into Whitson a few times," I said.

"Guy's not exactly a charm offensive."

"Just offensive, mostly."

Belson said he'd take that cup of coffee after all. "You got any donuts stashed in the fridge?"

"Black Adam and me ate them all before you arrived."

When I handed him his mug Belson said, "So this Baker got himself into something."

"Sounds like it."

"The merger?"

"Maybe," I said. "Or maybe he got involved with company secrets that had nothing to do with the merger and got caught and got killed because of it."

"Buying or selling?"

"Be nice to know."

"Be nice to have his hard drive," Belson said. "Or his personal info."

"But we don't."

I considered telling him about Laura's note, but did not. I knew I would at some point. Just not yet. Our relationship had always been transactional, one form or another, case by case, even when we were chasing the same outcome, including justice, as lofty as that sounded. Our roles had remained essentially the same, in all the years we'd known each other, Belson the good cop and me, despite my best intentions, still the bad one.

He put cop eyes on me now, as if able in the moment to read my mind.

"Have you heard anything about Laura Crain having any kind of relationship outside that storybook marriage of hers?" he asked. "I know she was Susan's friend. But I got to ask."

I made sure to keep my eyes on him, mindful, as always, about how little he missed. And saw things that other people did not.

"I had this same conversation with Susan," I said. "When we did, I told her that Laura didn't seem the type for an extramarital affair. And my better half pointed out to me that there is no type."

"She's a lot more than just half," Belson said.

I heard a phone buzz. His, not mine. He ignored it.

"Quirk told me he paid a visit here himself the other day," he said, "to tell you the bosses are up his ass on this. Which, as you know, puts him up mine. You see that, right?"

"Well, Frank, I'm not gonna lie, that's an image I'd actually like to un-see."

"My point being," he continued, "that if you screw around on this, like you do, you have a chance to screw Quirk and me at the same time. Understood?"

"Understood."

"Why'd Crain take a swing at you on Clarendon Street this morning?"

"You heard about that?"

"You'd be amazed the shit I stumble into."

"I basically asked him what you just asked me about his wife perhaps having an affair."

He rubbed a growth of beard around his chin that seemed even darker and heavier than normal.

"That all of it?"

"For now," I said.

He stood.

"I'm going to put this to you another way," he said. "You hold back information that could help us roll this thing up quicker, you might finally cross a line with both of us."

I started to say something back to him, but he pointed a finger as a way of stopping me.

"Don't say something smart, smart guy."

I didn't.

I poured my coffee down the sink, and rinsed the mug, and put it back on its shelf, and then sat in the empty office and wondered, being such a smart guy, if I even knew where the line was anymore.

FIFTY-EIGHT

It took some doing, and experiencing enough rejections on the phone that I started to feel like a telemarketer, but Amanda Levinson, who had served on the board of the Dana-Farber Cancer Institute with Laura Crain, agreed to meet for lunch near her home in Wellesley.

"Are you fond of Middle Eastern food?" she said after she'd returned my call, responding to the lengthy voice message I'd left for her about Laura.

"The answer would have been in the affirmative if you'd asked me about being fond of almost any kind of food," I said.

"Café Mangal," she said, and gave me the address on Washington Street.

She was, I guessed, at the high end of her forties, bordering on being too thin but not quite there, at least not yet, hair dyed a subdued auburn with streaks in it, nice smile, face relatively unlined, perhaps even without chemical or surgical assistance. She wore a black turtleneck that covered a long neck and hardly any jewelry. She was not wearing a wedding ring.

She'd ordered some kind of salad with figs. I'd gone big, electing to go with what was listed as a Yengen sandwich featuring Turkish pepperoni. The larger tables were in the middle of a long dining room. We sat at a smaller one, for two, along one of the walls.

"So Laura hired a private investigator," she said while we waited for our food, having just been served our iced teas.

"She was concerned about Andrew," I said.

"And for quite some time," Amanda Levinson said. "I'd suggested therapy, for him or for both of them. I'm a big believer in therapy, especially since my divorce."

"The girl of my dreams is a therapist," I said.

"So you're married?" she said.

"Not exactly."

"I know the feeling," she said, and smiled. "I just had to ask. But I do that more and more these days when I meet an attractive man."

I let that go by.

"We're very much together," I said. "For a very long time. We just don't choose to live together."

She playfully slapped her forehead. "Why didn't I think of that?" she said.

I had read enough about her to know that she had been married to a hedge-funder named Steve Levinson, the name of his company one I didn't recognize, just because there was no earthly reason why I would have.

Amanda waved at a blond woman seated with another blond woman in the opposite corner of the room. "Oh, goody," she said. "I hope Jenny and Millicent think you're my lunch date."

She offered a half-hearted wave and a fake smile to someone behind me, whispered, "Hello, bitch," then turned back to me and said, "So what can I do for you, Mr. Spenser?"

"I didn't know Laura for very long, or very well," I said. "But now her husband not only doesn't want to talk to me about her, he took a swing at me the other day when I attempted to do that in front of his building."

"Wait," she said. "Andrew *Crain* took a swing at you?"

"I'd say he punched like a girl," I said, "but I make it a policy never to insult women of any age."

"He used to be a lot more fun," she said, "in his nerdy way. But that was before he got so weird."

"I know why Laura was concerned about him," I said. "But what was she like in the time leading up to her death? Was there anything that you found concerning about her behavior? That made you worry about her?"

"I've been thinking a lot about my friend Laura, as you might imagine," she said. She frowned now, producing very few wrinkles in her forehead. Maybe there had been some help with the unlined thing. "You know the expression about a person being an open book? That was never Laura, even though she really was my friend. She had never shared much about her life before Andrew, no matter how hard I pried, and I can be so good at prying I should be the private detective."

She smiled at me. "You don't need a partner, do you?"

"The hours are lousy and the pay is worse," I said.

"Well," she said, "if you ever change your mind, keep *me* in mind."

"Back to Laura," I said. "Did you get the sense that she might have been dealing with some kind of crisis that didn't involve her husband?"

"What kind?"

"Perhaps a relationship with someone other than her husband?"

I wasn't sure what kind of reaction I'd expected, shock or surprise. Or even Amanda Levinson being offended on behalf of her dead friend. But my question elicited none of the above.

"Funny you should ask that," she said. "I'm much more aware of the signs of that than I used to be, mostly because my ex couldn't manage to keep it in his pants, especially toward the end of our marriage. And perhaps well before that." She sighed. "I didn't get the sense that Laura was having an affair, or ever would. But I increasingly got the sense that she thought Andrew might be."

She shrugged.

"He's a nerd," Amanda Levinson said. "But a very, very rich one. You may have noticed with other rich geeks. It makes women ignore certain of their shortcomings."

The waiter showed up with our food then. Café Mangal had gotten far more crowded in the past five or ten minutes, the noise level in the low-ceilinged room rising accordingly.

"So him, not her?"

She nodded. "She told me about a month ago, or thereabouts, that he was spending what she considered even a more disproportionate time than usual with his assistant."

"Claire Megill," I said.

"The one and only," she said. "The sainted Claire."

"Would that be your description of her, or Laura's?"

"Oh, Laura's," she said. "She said that she was convinced Andrew was more invested, I guess that's the word, in Claire's well-being than his own wife's."

I couldn't hold out any longer and took a bite of my sandwich.

"Did Laura think the two of them really were having an affair?"

"She never came right out and said that. But my general sense, just from some of her comments, was that at the very least she thought Andrew and Claire were the ones with the better marriage, whether they were sleeping together or not."

"So she did manage to open up to you about that," I said.

"She finally trusted me enough to do that, at least on this particular subject," she said.

"But I was under the impression that Claire had been seeing someone at Lith," I said.

"Maybe that triggered a form of jealousy in Andrew, and contributed to the weirdness. But if you're right about that, why wouldn't Andrew just fire this Lith person?"

"I've asked the same question," I said. "Maybe because he would have had to fire Claire, too."

"A tangled web," she said. "You're probably good at unraveling those."

"Used to be," I said.

She said, "Would you mind terribly if I ordered a glass of wine?"

I told her to have at it, not wanting to do anything to slow her roll.

"One other thing I should mention," she said, after she'd had her first taste of wine. "Laura vaguely said something once about having a friend looking out for her interests."

"Did *she* mention who that might have been?"

"No," she said. "Wait. She never talked about any of this with you?"

"She wasn't an open book with me, either."

"I can't imagine why," she said. She was smiling again. "You're very easy to talk to."

"They teach it at detective school," I said. "Right after the course on prying."

We ate in silence for a couple minutes. I was more enthusiastic about it than she was. The sandwich was very good. But I rarely encountered a bad one.

"So you didn't get the idea that the friend Laura spoke about wasn't someone with whom she was involved romantically?"

"She wanted to make her marriage work," Amanda said. "As vague as she was about her past, she'd told me more than once about the bad choices she'd made with men before Andrew."

She finished her wine. "And then she died."

I had nothing to add to that. My sandwich was gone, even though she had barely made a dent in her salad. I waved for the check. She said no, this was her treat. I told her to think of this as being on Laura, as she had helped me today more than she knew.

"We aim to please," she said, in a voice I thought had suddenly become huskier.

I'll bet, I thought.

"If you have any more questions, feel free to call anytime," she said.

I told her I would do that.

On my way past Jenny and Millicent's table, I winked at them.

FIFTY-NINE

I went back to my office and saw that I had left my legal pad on top of my desk, with my scribblings about all the players on it, one name on the first page in bigger letters, and circled a couple times:

ROB

Who never left the stage completely, even if I imagined him just standing in the wings sometimes.

The bar at which he had worked was gone. The owner of the bar where he'd worked was dead. According to what Missy Jones had told me, Rob had left town at some point after she and one of Gino's boys had paid him that visit, never to return.

Or so she had hoped.

Missy Jones didn't have a last name. Nobody seemed

to have a last name, not her, not Angie Calabria, not Professor Paul Dockery. Maybe Rob wasn't even his real name. Maybe he had changed his name. Maybe he *had* left town.

Or not.

If not, maybe only Laura had known.

Or maybe, and more likely, it was time for me to move on from him once and for all, and focus on two dead bodies, connected to each other by Lith, and by a note I had found in Darius Baker's pocket, linking him to Laura Crain.

According to Susan, though, I'd always had separation issues in matters like this. She actually called it the dog-with-a-bone syndrome, which I was sure she hadn't been taught at Harvard.

My phone was on the desk next to the legal pad. I reached for it and called Ethan Lowe and asked if he might happen to recall the last name of the guy Laura had dated her last year at Harvard.

"You could have stumped me if you'd asked me for his first name," Lowe said.

"Is there any way you could ask your partner?"

"And tell him what, that I'm asking for a friend?" Lowe said. "How do you think that would go over considering how things went the last time the two of you were together?"

There was a pause.

"Why does it matter, anyway?"

"Not entirely sure that it does, unless he came back into Laura's life and nobody knew it except her," I said.

"If I see an opportunity to casually ask him, say, what

was that asshole's name, I will," Lowe said. "But I can't make any promises."

"I'm rumbling and stumbling here," I said.

"Hey," Lowe said, "everybody's got to be good at something," before quickly adding, "Just kidding."

He didn't sound as if he were kidding.

I next called Richie Burke and asked if he'd found out anything more about Marino's.

"There was a guy," he said, "who went from Marino's to the Five Horses Tavern, over on Columbus. Know it?"

"I know just about all of them," I said. "Does he remember the guy I'm trying to locate?"

"He might've if he hadn't gotten shot at another bar in Somerville a few months ago," Richie said.

"Shot dead?"

"Quite."

I stayed at the office for the rest of the afternoon and accomplished little. Susan and Pearl were coming to the apartment later before Susan and I went for a late dinner at Piccolo Nido in the North End. It was my favorite Italian restaurant in the whole city and Susan's, too. We used to see Larry Lucchino in there sometimes when he was president of the Red Sox. Susan knew him slightly from her work for the Jimmy Fund. I was certain Larry would have never traded Mookie.

When I got back to the apartment I remembered that I'd meant to call Detective Lee Farrell, now of Sex Crimes, and ask him what he'd do if he were trying to find someone whose last name he didn't know and who had left town without a trace twenty years earlier.

So I called and asked him now.

"Is this some kind of trick question?" he said.

"What would you do if you had that little to go on, from that long ago?"

"Let me think on it."

"By the way," I said, "should I congratulate you on Captain Glass coming to work at your shop?"

"Did you really call to ask for help or just to bust my balls?"

"What, I can't do both?"

"I happen to be in the middle of something," he said. "Can this wait until breakfast tomorrow?"

I said it could.

"Before you go, let me ask you something else," I said. "Do you think rumbling and stumbling is one of my strong suits?"

"Maybe your strongest," he said, and then said he'd meet me at the Newbury at eight tomorrow and that he had no intention of buying, he wanted that off the table right now.

I sat on the couch in my living room and pondered whether or not the only structure I had in my life these days was going from restaurant to restaurant, meal to meal. But then concluded that any kind of structure, or semblance of order, was better than none.

Susan called and said she was running late, then told me that she had pushed our reservation to nine o'clock.

"If you can wait and not be tired by waiting," I said.

"Wait," she said.

"I see what you did."

"No," she said, "I meant wait, because I happen to know what the next line is, I've heard you use it before."

"Hit me," I said.

"Or being lied about, don't deal in lies," she said.

"Wow," I said.

"That's what I'm talking about," she said triumphantly.

"Marry me," I said.

"No," she said.

I iced my knee while watching Maria Stephanos read the news on Channel 5, telling myself as always that Maria was speaking directly to me and, further, was ready to leave her family for me if Susan ever dumped me. I had mentioned having these thoughts about Maria to Susan once and she said, "You just keep thinkin', Butch. That's what you're good at."

I ate some cheese and crackers after my shower and drank a Boomsauce and began the cruel wait until our reservation, and remembered what it was like when we were in Paris and Susan insisted that we eat at nine every night the way the goddamn French did. Sometimes later than nine.

I had switched from the news to *SportsCenter* on ESPN when Vinnie called.

"She just buzzed in a visitor," he said.

He was outside Claire Megill's building, about to turn the watch over to one of his young Vinnies for the overnight shift.

"I'm going to assume it's not DoorDash," I said.

By now Belson had informed me that the Boston Police Department would no longer have a car outside the building, there was no point, I had Vinnie.

"It's a guy from one of the pictures you sent me you said I should call about if the guy ever showed up," Vinnie said.

"Don't tell me," I said, "it's Whitson, the lawyer. The one who looks like a bouncer squeezed into a suit."

"Nope."

"Are you going to make me guess?"

"The boss."

"Crain?"

"The other," Vinnie said.

SIXTY

I told Vinnie to have the other Vinnie call me when Ethan Lowe left the building.

"His name is Ronnie, for fuck's sake, how many times do I have to tell you?" Vinnie said.

"I'm terribly sorry," I said. "Have Rocky call me."

"You ain't that funny."

"Am so."

There was no call while Susan and I dined at Piccolo Nido, nor when we were on our way back to Marlborough Street. My phone was with me when I walked Pearl down Commonwealth and back until she performed her nightly duties.

When we were back inside the apartment, Susan said, "I know you might be expecting a call. But would you mind terribly shutting off your phone while I jump your bones?"

She smiled one of her wicked smiles. "I have these urges."

"And the world is a better place for them," I said.

Afterward, once my breathing had returned to normal, I turned the phone back on and saw there was no call from Ronnie, nor would there be one during the night.

Claire Megill knew that either Vinnie or someone working for Vinnie was watching over her, so it wasn't as if she and Lowe were sneaking around, he'd walked right through the front door for what would have been an innocent visit, except for the fact that he had stayed the night.

She'd had more than one opportunity, especially when I'd asked her about Clay Whitson, to tell me that she was in a relationship with one of the owners of the company, if that was in fact what was going on, even if it turned out not to be the owner with whom Laura Crain had suspected her of having one.

I explained all of this to Susan before she headed off to Cambridge in the morning, having rebuffed my last-ditch effort to elicit more urges out of her.

"Maybe the problems of these two little people don't amount to a hill of beans in this crazy world," I said.

"I've asked you to please not do Bogie," she said. "And for your information, the line is 'three little people.'"

Once Susan was gone, I checked with Ronnie.

"Still in there?" I said.

"Sure."

He also pronounced it *shoo-wah*, same as Vinnie.

"I'm on my way," I said, telling him not to leave until I got there.

Ronnie was in an Audi. I waved at him as I came around from the Colonnade and he pulled away. So I was the one standing in front of Claire's building when Lowe came out the front door, one whose glass, I saw, had already been replaced.

No car waiting for him, no driver.

Just me.

He stopped a few feet outside the door when he saw me standing at the end of the walk.

"Aren't you worried about doing the walk of shame at the office?"

"This isn't what it looks like."

"Are you sure?" I said. "Because it sure looks like a sleepover to me."

"It is, but not the way you think."

"You and Claire?" I said. "I gotta say, Ethan, I did *not* see that coming."

"Repeat," he said. "Not what it looks like, not what you think."

"Enlighten me, then."

"Walk with me," he said.

"Okay," I said, "but I hope people at the office aren't going to think I'm the one you spent the night with when they see you in the same clothes you wore yesterday."

"Could you please cut the shit?"

"You first," I said. "Shouldn't Reggie be with you, or one of his guys?"

"I came here alone," he said.

"I thought you were the one always looking over his shoulder," I said.

"Trying to quit."

"Even though two people connected to your company are dead."

"I've decided I can't live my best life thinking I might be next."

"Claire's afraid she might be next," I said. "It's why I've put some people on her."

"I know," he said. "And she has a right to feel that way and you have a right to protect her. I have my people when I need them, as you know."

We were walking up Huntington by then, on our way toward Copley Plaza.

"Claire and I aren't having an affair."

"If you say so."

"I wouldn't put her in that position, and I wouldn't do it to Andrew, knowing how close the two of them are," he said. "I just needed to talk to her away from the office, and once we started talking we got into the wine pretty good. And before I knew it, she was offering to let me sleep on her couch and I accepted."

"Must have been a lot of wine."

"It was, trust me. I haven't felt this hungover in a long time."

I figured it was about a fifteen-minute walk to the Hancock. We were already halfway there, but as Lowe was walking at hangover speed, we might not arrive until lunchtime.

"What did you need to talk to her about?" I said.

"We were talking about the merger, what else?" he said. "I should have had Andrew locked down on this long ago. I still don't. I thought Laura could help me, but she was even more opposed to it than he once was. But now Laura is gone, and I know how much he leans on Claire, maybe now more than ever. So I went there to ask for her help in bringing him around before it's too late, for all of us."

"You're just trying to enlist her now?"

He had picked up his pace just slightly by the time we got to Stuart.

"I've tried this approach before," he said. "But not to the extent that I did last night. This time I offered her a substantial raise, and I do mean substantial, if she could do a better job lobbying Andrew than I have to this point."

"Is she willing to do that?"

Lowe shook his head. "She told me that what I was offering was too big to be a gift and too small to be a bribe. So then I offered to give her a small piece of the merger, as even more of a sweetener."

"You really must have been drunk."

"The money would be a drop in the bucket in the whole grand scheme of things."

"Did she accept?"

"She did not. She told me that her loyalty was, and always will be, to Andrew. He'd given her and her son a future, and a life after her husband left them."

"Hard not to respect that," I said.

We were at Clarendon now, the Hancock dead ahead.

"I begged her one last time before we called it a night to reconsider, that she wouldn't just be saving the company, but Andrew at the same time. Because if we lose the company, if *he* loses the company so soon after Laura, I'm not sure what's going to happen to him."

"'Lose the company' sounds a bit over-the-top."

"There's a lot of plates spinning, Mr. Spenser. I'll just leave it at that."

Lowe turned to face me. His pallor was still gray, his eyes bloodshot. I didn't know how much sleep he'd gotten on Claire's couch. But it clearly hadn't been enough.

"This company is the only child either one of us has ever had," Lowe said. "What would you do if you were faced with losing the thing in the world that mattered the most to you?"

"Fight like hell," I said.

"That's all I'm doing here," he said. "I just want my partner to fight with me, one last time."

Then he said, "Have a good day," in front of the Hancock.

It didn't sound as if his heart was really in it. The part about me having a good day. But at least he hadn't taken a swing at me.

So there was that.

SIXTY-ONE

When I had walked over to my office, I called Lee Farrell and told him that we would have to reschedule breakfast, something had come up.

"We gay men are used to dealing with this sort of heartbreak," he said.

"Better than straight guys?"

"My experience is that we just do the heartbreak way better."

My friend Marty Kaiser was already on his way to my office. Marty described himself as being the world's greatest accountant. When I'd called him, I'd asked if he was still the greatest.

"Of all time," he said.

"Modest much?" I said.

"I have so little reason," Marty said.

He looked as he had always looked, just with more gray in black hair still worn long. He still carried a pigskin attaché case, still wore white shirts with Windsor collars and silk ties, a blood-red one today that matched his pocket square, everything set off nicely against a black pin-striped suit.

"Dress-down day?" I said.

"I continue to dress for success," he said. "You might think about it one of these days."

I was wearing a black T-shirt, jeans, and some old Merrell hiking shoes that I felt were being kinder to my knee lately than regular sneakers.

"What's wrong with my outfit?" I said.

"Nothing," he said, "if you're on your way to bouncer school."

I made us both coffee. He drank some of his and put his mug down on my desk and crossed his legs, smoothing out the crease on the top leg as he did. Unless he'd changed his buying habits, I knew that the wingtips he was wearing came from Tricker's of Jermyn Street, the shirt from Turnbull & Asser.

"So how can the world's greatest accountant be of assistance?" he said.

I told him about my relationship with Laura Crain and my brief interaction with Darius Baker, and my various adventures and misadventures with Andrew Crain and Ethan Lowe and Reggie Smythe and the two men who had jumped me at the sanctuary and another man who had shot at me.

"How closely do you follow Lith?" I said.

"Fairly closely, as a matter of fact," he said. "I think of them as one of our hometown teams, and have always wanted them to succeed for that reason alone."

"Okay, then," I said. "I'm going to ask you some money questions, and feel free to treat me like an idiot."

"You told me once that as long as I did that with you I would never be disappointed," Marty said. "And I never have been."

"What is the most fundamental difference between a privately owned company and a public one?" I said. "Start there."

"Well, the most obvious one is the most fundamental one," he said. "A privately held company doesn't trade on the stock exchange, and doesn't have to disclose financial information to the public."

"So it would be easier for market analysts, say, to value a public company as opposed to a private one."

"Much," Marty said.

"But you can obviously track how a private company is doing, correct?"

He nodded. "There are several ways," he said. "Comparable company analysis is one. Capital market transactions is another, and discounted cash flow, provided you could get the data. There's a longer list than that." He grinned and raised bushy Groucho black eyebrows. "Am I going too fast?"

"Much," I said.

Marty said, "We could continue with this tutorial, and I could continue to show off, or you could ask me what you got me over here to ask me." He drank more coffee.

"I can't even remember the last time you enlisted my services."

I could. I had forced a white-collar criminal named Bob Cooper to open the books of a private company called Kinergy, which only people on the inside knew had become a house of cards in an almost Madoffian way. When Marty had gone through the books, he had discovered that the accounting there was more fun than a theme park.

I reminded him of those heady times. "Some of my best work," he said. "Thanks for reminding me." He whistled. "And those *pishers* nearly got away with it. And murder, as I recall."

I asked him if he'd heard about the prospective merger between Lith and the Canadian electric-car company. Marty said it wasn't as if anybody were keeping it a secret, even though he hadn't read much about it lately.

"Ethan Lowe has indicated that they badly need the merger to go through," I said. "Why would that possibly be?"

Marty nodded. "If it is," he said, "it's probably because of Aahil."

He spelled it out for me.

"It nearly turned into a hill to die on for our friends at Lith," he said.

Marty explained that it had all gone down right before COVID, and much of what he was about to tell me was thirdhand and largely anecdotal. But what he'd heard, from sources he considered to be good ones, was that Lowe had thrown a lot of Lith money behind a proposed golf and gambling resort empire called Aahil.

"Paradise in the desert, that was the theme," Marty said. "Qatar, Abu Dhabi, Dubai, Riyadh. If I'm not mistaken, I believe the bulk of the money came from Qatar. They were going crazy for sports at the time because they'd gotten the World Cup. As that man used to say, it was all going to be huuuuuuge. But then along came the pandemic and the world closed down, and all of a sudden the rich guys that Lowe was partnering with decided they didn't want to play in that particular sandbox, literally and figuratively—2019, 2020, in there. Long story short? Lowe, who I know to be a very savvy guy, got caught holding the bag. Or with his pants down. You pick. But he ended up highly leveraged, with no equity cushion."

"I know that he and Crain were diversifying at that point," I said. "So Lowe must have thought it was a sure thing."

"But when it turned out to not be a sure thing, Lowe ended up in the worst place you can be, whether you think you're too big to fail or not."

"Which is where?"

"The place where the debt is due, and to guys who don't deal well with disappointment."

"Was this widely known at the time?"

"Let us go back to the beginning of our conversation, my friend," Marty Kaiser said. "They're not on the market. But again, just going off what I heard from people who would know better than me, Lowe suddenly found himself in a position where the world he and Crain had built for themselves wasn't nearly as battery-powered as it once had been, put it that way. It needed a boost."

"Meaning he needed cash."

"Lots."

"But he's still here and Lith is still here, which means he found a way to get it," I said.

"And Lith is once again a business that the car people want to do business *with*," Marty said. "And because the world's greatest accountant keeps his ear to the ground when money is about to change hands, what I am hearing is that Lowe might be looking to cash out once this deal goes through."

"But not Crain?"

Marty shook his head. "Not sure about Crain. Just Lowe. I think what happened in the Middle East made him feel as if his balls were in a lockbox somewhere, and he might be ready to go off and count the money he already has before things go *plotz* the next time, as we say in the faith."

"So does he want this merger more, or need it?"

"Maybe both," Marty said.

He stood then, checked himself for wrinkles or lint or both, picked up his ancient attaché case, the kind you don't see much of anymore. But then you don't see a lot of accountants who were larger-than-life characters the way Marty Kaiser was.

"There's one more thing I heard," he said. "It's that the electric-car people from Canada aren't just looking to merge with Lith. They're looking to *acquire* it."

"Be interesting to know if that's true," I said. "And how Lowe managed to save their collective asses along the way, starting with his own."

"Not my department," Marty said. "You're the one who's supposed to be the world's greatest detective."

SIXTY-TWO

Ethan Lowe didn't return my calls the rest of the day. Maybe we hadn't done as much male bonding as I thought we had. But when we did next speak, whenever that was, I wanted to hear from him, at least in general terms, about what Marty Kaiser had heard.

I called Hawk then and told him this case really was starting to make my head hurt something awful, and he said what did I mean *starting* to make it hurt? So we decided to meet at Parker's Bar at the Omni Parker House and do the only sensible thing and discuss it over a drink. Or perhaps drinks, plural, as the case might be. Which was almost always the case for Hawk and me.

I stopped at the apartment and put on a blue shirt and blazer and loafers. When I got to the bar I saw that Hawk wore a double-breasted charcoal blazer and black jeans and a white shirt.

"You didn't have to clean up for me," I said.

"Got a dinner date," he said.

"Do I know her?"

"No."

"Might I ever?"

"Too early to tell."

We both ordered martinis. I told him about Marty and what he knew and what I now wanted to know from, and about, Ethan Lowe.

"Maybe you just ought to hold your little friend up and shake him till he tells you what you want to know, and stop fucking around," Hawk said. "Because it sure sounds to me as if he knows a lot more than he's told you so far. And you don't know how much he *has* told you is true."

"I don't think we're there quite yet," I said. "The shaking part."

"You sure?"

Our drinks were delivered, in martini glasses that looked bigger than normal, which nearly made my heart skip a beat. We had both gone with lemon peels this time around. The vodka was as cold as vodka in a martini was supposed to be, tiny beads of ice still visible on the outside of the glasses.

I drank and Hawk drank.

"God*damn*," Hawk said. "Something this good could make a man change his religious persuasion."

"You don't have a religious persuasion."

"If I did," he said.

"Where were we?" I said.

Hawk smiled and took another sip of his drink and said, "Who gives a shit?"

There had been a time when the Parker House had been one of the best hotels in Boston. Then came the Four Seasons and Ritz, the new one on Avery Street, and Mandarin, and the hotels that had sprung up at the Seaport. But the Omni people had come along to fix up the old girl, including the bar. The gilded entrance outside, though, looked the same to me as it always had, just with OMNI now written above the front doors underneath the green awnings adorning the windows of the second floor.

"Ask you something?" Hawk said.

"Anything," I said. "I am in a very happy place right now."

"Who you trust over there at Lith for real?" he said.

Normally he would have finished his first martini by now. But he appeared to be pacing himself. I would've thought that he might be wanting to present his *best* self to his date, whomever she was, except that Hawk had only one self.

"At this point," I said, "I'm not sure I'd trust the receptionist."

"You can't trust either of the damn owners for shit," Hawk said. "You can't trust the lawyer."

"Not as far as I could throw him."

"Not even off a balcony."

"Wow," I said.

Hawk shrugged. "Too soon?"

"Little bit."

"What about Claire Megill?"

"What about her?"

"You trust her to be, ah, forthcoming?"

"Yeah," I said. "But maybe only to a point."

"What point would that be?"

"The one where she'd be afraid of compromising her boss."

"The boss Crain."

"Uh-huh."

"So they could all be lying they asses off to you." He grinned.

"We going somewhere with this?" I said.

"Seems to me the best you can hope for right now is figure out who's lying to you the least," he said. "And decide if somebody over there really might think this merger is worth killing over."

My martini was less cold than it had been, but still delicious. I drank more of it.

"What time you got?" Hawk said.

I told him.

"Gots to go," he said.

"I still don't know what happened to Laura Crain's old boyfriend."

Hawk said, "I'm working on that, matter of fact."

"Now you tell me?"

"Not there yet."

"By the way? I'd still *like* to know who sent those two stooges after me."

"And who tried to shoot you up, don't forget that."

"Marty Kaiser called me the world's greatest detective."

"Easy for him to say," Hawk said.

I told him I'd pick up the check, and to have a good time.

He smiled again. "Hope it's as good as the one she's gonna have," he said. "If such a thing even be possible."

I paid the check and sadly finished my martini. I took my time walking home. When I got there I fried some onions. Then I cooked up a burger in the air fryer Susan had given me last Christmas after convincing me that using it wasn't a form of cheating.

The literature with the fryer had promised burgers both tender and juicy and so far had delivered every time.

And did tonight.

I then set up a tray and forced myself to watch the Red Sox game, telling myself that it was all going to be over soon. There were losing to the Orioles in the fifth when I called Missy Jones in Seattle.

"You better be calling to tell me that you or somebody else caught Laura's killer," she said.

I could once again hear a television in the background, this time with the sound of baseball announcers, excitement in their voices about something in the game they were broadcasting.

"Is that the Mariners I hear?" I said.

"It is," she said. "And even though I know you didn't call to talk baseball with me, I might point out that my team is better than your team this season."

"Hold on," I said. "You're from here. How come my team isn't still your team?"

"Not after those clowns traded Mookie," she said.

"Got a question about Laura," I said.

"I didn't think you were calling to talk baseball," she said.

"Is there any chance that Rob might not have left town when you thought he had?" I said.

There was a long pause at her end and then I heard the ballgame noise disappear.

"In a relationship like the one that they had, there's a form of madness that takes over, on both sides. It's why abused women stay in them long after they should have run for the hills, and even end up defending their accusers. So maybe it was a form of madness for her to still keep secrets from me about this guy even after I tried to save her from him."

"So it wasn't verifiable for you that Rob left Boston after Gino's guy gave him that beating," I said.

"No," she said. "It was not."

"You just made the assumption that he beat it, after catching that kind of beating from your guy and not going back to work."

"Technically Gino's guy. But yes."

"So we don't know if he stayed or came back," I said. "And might never."

"Sounds like a Spenser problem to me."

"Damn it," I said. "I was afraid of that. Here's maybe the best question of all. How the hell did Laura end up with a guy like this prick in the first place?"

"There's something about bad boys, what can I tell you," she said. "Always has been, always will be. Even for good girls."

"Are you speaking from experience?"

"Whoever said I was a good girl?" Missy Jones said.

SIXTY-THREE

September turned into October in Boston. The leaves began to change and the baseball playoffs began without the Red Sox, and without me. And Lee Farrell called one morning to tell me he had some information on Joe Marino's bar.

"It seems Joe was averse to paying his taxes," Lee said.

"Isn't our government averse to a practice like that?"

"Very much so," Lee said. "I'm now thinking that if a heart attack hadn't gotten Joe, the Feds would have."

"So nobody with a name like Rob on the books?"

"Are you listening to me?" Lee said. "They weren't any books! I think Marino's was like some cozy little Mob hideaway. I asked a couple vets from Organized Crime Control, and they told me that the joint had a relatively young clientele. College kids who wanted to take a little walk on the wild side. They also told me at OCC that Joe might have had some of the boys behind the bar dealing some drugs. Coke, grass, like that. Nothing major."

"Thanks for trying," I said.

"You know what they say. No medals for trying."

"Well, there should be," I said.

"Speaking from personal experience?"

"Very much so," I said.

I no longer needed Vinnie Morris to watch Claire, because she had flown to California on business with Andrew Crain a few days earlier, telling me before they left she wasn't sure when they'd be back. At least they knew where they were going.

That night I had cooked risotto with seafood for Susan and me at her place, having picked up shrimp and mussels and scallops and oysters from the New Deal Fish Market on Cambridge Street. When we were in bed later, she asked if I had made any progress, with either Laura Crain or Darius Baker. I asked her to define *progress*. She asked then if it might be time to piss on the fire and call in the dogs.

"Did I just hear you say that?"

"A client of mine from Texas said it to me the other day."

"It would be better than pissing on the dogs."

"Hush," she said. "The baby might hear you."

We had not yet let Pearl back into the bedroom after our recently concluded lovemaking.

"I don't quit," I said.

She tucked herself more firmly into my side. I could

feel the heat coming off her, if not as much as there had been a few minutes ago.

"Not exactly breaking news," she said.

"There's still so much I don't know," I said. "But what I do know is that Laura and Darius knew something."

"And who knows," she said, "maybe when you find out what that was, it will help you finally solve the riddle of Andrew Crain."

"*When* I find out?"

"My money's still on you, big boy."

She got up and walked naked to the door. Pearl must have been right behind it, because she was in the bed before Susan was.

"Laura Crain's old roommate says that there's just something about bad boys," I said. "Do you concur?"

"Oh, God yes," Dr. Susan Silverman said in a husky voice.

SIXTY-FOUR

The young woman was waiting for me outside my office when I got back from Henry's gym the next morning.

"I probably shouldn't be here," she said as her opening line.

"I often bring that out in people," I said.

Even at a time when young women kept looking younger and younger to me, she seemed as if she had stopped in on her way to her nine o'clock class.

Her name was Cindy Patton. She informed me that she worked as one of Clay Whitson's assistants at Lith, describing herself as a "forty-niner." Meaning she worked on the forty-ninth floor. She had blond hair cut short, a shirt cut almost as short, a slate-blue sweater that in a less enlightened time—and a less evolved time for me, certainly—I would have thought accentuated the positive and eliminated the negatives entirely.

I had been at the Harbor Health Club at seven-thirty. I was glad I had showered there and changed out of my workout clothes, even if I still wasn't dressed for success.

"So why *are* you here even though you don't think you should be?" I said.

I had just fixed myself my first cup of coffee of the day. She declined when I offered her one.

"Darius told me about you after you came to the office that time," she said. "He'd never met a real live private detective. And knew that Mrs. Crain had hired you."

"How did he seem?"

"He had become very mysterious lately," she said. "All he told me then was that he was working on a project. I asked if it was a project for work and he smiled and said, 'Kind of.'"

"But gave you no indication of what the project might be?"

She shook her head.

"Did you ever hear him talking about Mrs. Crain?" I asked.

I was walking a fine line with this young woman, and knew it. I had met her only a few minutes ago. Even though she seemed quite sincere, she still worked for Whitson. Whom I did not like, and trusted even less. I didn't think she was here because he had sent her on a fishing expedition, but I couldn't rule out that possibility, either.

"Every so often he'd mention how much he admired her," she said. "I joked with him one time that he sounded as if he had a crush on her."

"A lot to admire about Laura Crain."

"I know I did," she said, "just as a woman. She could

have just sat back and counted her husband's money when she wasn't off spending it. But she wanted to make a difference, the same as Mr. Crain does."

She folded her hands in her lap. For some reason she suddenly seemed even more nervous than she was when she'd arrived. For the first time I noticed a small tattoo, of three birds, inside her right wrist.

"You don't believe Darius killed himself, do you?" I said.

"One hundred percent he didn't!"

She seemed embarrassed that the words had come out as heated as they had.

"I tend to get a little worked up when I'm talking about Darius."

"You *are* aware that somebody removed the hard drive from his work computer, right?" I said.

She nodded. "You hear things about the fiftieth floor even when you're still just a forty-niner."

She leaned forward. "That's why I'm here, Mr. Spenser. I did hear about the hard drive. But nobody at Lith seems to be doing anything about that. I finally screwed up my courage and asked Mr. Whitson if there was going to be some kind of internal investigation or anything. He just brushed me off. He's good at that, by the way, brushing people off, and not just me. He said they had done an investigation and just concluded that Darius had removed it himself, for some unknown reason, before he died."

"Can't they find out internally the last time he accessed it?"

"I believe they can."

"Did they?"

"I believe they did not."

"Did Whitson have a reason why Darius would have done something like that? Removed his own hard drive?"

"That's the thing," she said. "Darius would never have done something like that, unless he had a very good reason. Or was afraid of somebody."

"Somebody capable of killing him?"

"Yes," she said without hesitation.

She crossed her legs. It was impossible not to notice that they were very good legs, despite all of my best intentions about being evolved, and even if I felt like her lecherous old uncle looking at them. My rationalization was that if she weren't proud of those legs herself, she would have worn a longer skirt.

Or pants.

Weak, I knew.

All I had.

I forced myself to stop looking at her legs.

"Nobody seems to care about Darius over there, that's the bottom line," she said. "It's like he's been gone a few years and not just a few weeks. Like everybody has moved on, and just accepts that he threw himself off his balcony, without leaving a note or showing any signs of depression. Anyone who had ever been around him for five minutes would have known he wasn't depressed."

"You know that doesn't mean he *wasn't* depressed."

"I know," she said. "But he wasn't."

"So how can I help you, really?"

"My boss can't know I'm here," she said. "He can't *ever* know I was here."

"Okay," I said.

"O*kay?*" she said. "That's it?"

"I can tell you my word is my bond, if that will make you feel any better," I said.

"Sorry," she said. "I didn't come over here to insult you."

"Easier for a camel to pass through the eye of a needle than to insult me," I said. "And all the other stuff that came after the needle part about the Kingdom of God."

"The truth is, I came here to help *you*, Mr. Spenser."

"And how exactly do you plan to do that?" I said.

She smiled. It was a very good smile to go with the very good rest of Ms. Cindy Patton.

"By getting my head in a cloud," she said. "Specifically, Darius's cloud."

SIXTY-FIVE

Cindy Patton didn't have time to explain all of what she planned to do, or at least wanted to do, before she had to leave my office for her own. But she said she was hopeful that this was going to be the beginning of a longer conversation, which she hoped would be a fruitful one.

"By the way?" she said. "Fruitful to me means I don't get fired at the end of this."

"You won't get fired," I said.

"How can you sound so sure?"

"Because if anybody over there tries to do that," I said, "I will beat them up."

"You don't know Mr. Whitson," she said.

"The first one I beat up would be him," I said.

"Do you have a general knowledge of how data is stored?" she said.

"I do," I said. "But it's my understanding there was no way to get at Darius's personal data once the hard drive was gone, at least not the way things work at Lith."

"See, that's where you're wrong," she said. "There's always a way in." Now she grinned. "Either through a side door or a back door. Or maybe a window somebody left open."

"Do tell," I said, and she did, quickly, explaining about bonded software companies and corporate accounts and the ability for the bonded company to back up a firm's information in case of cyberattacks.

"What software companies are basically saying is that nothing is foolproof," she said, "no matter how hard they make it to find a way in."

"Are you talking about Darius's office computer or his personal one?" I said.

"He worked on both at the office," she said. "A lot of people bring laptops from home at Lith. I'd come up to visit him on the fiftieth floor and he'd have his MacBook Air set up right next to the beast that Lith set him up with. Like he was trying to see which one could come up with information he needed the fastest."

"You know that the police couldn't find a laptop at his apartment and neither could I," I said.

"I didn't know that," she said. "But I'm not surprised. If somebody would take his hard drive, why wouldn't they take his laptop, too?"

"Listen, I can't be sure that the killer, or killers, took it," I said. "There's no proof of that, at least not yet. But if it wasn't in his desk at the office and wasn't at his home, where was it?"

"The same person who has his hard drive took it," she said. "I'd bet anything on that."

"So how are you going to find a way into his information?" I said.

"I know someone at Proscape," she said. "That's the name of the software company that has the Lith account. It's a guy I used to date. And if he'll help me, which I think he will, I can get to somebody with the key—and the code—to Darius's personal accounts."

"I heard you need a fingerprint," I said.

She smiled more fully. "Not if you find a side door."

"Or back door," I said.

"I am going to need a little time and probably a lot of conniving. And perhaps some flirtatiousness thrown in. But I think I can get us to where we want to go."

"You really think you can pull this off?" I said.

"You think I'm only counting on luck to get me to the fiftieth floor someday?"

She and her smile and her legs left my office then. She actually had made me feel hopeful, even if she'd made me feel older than Paul Revere's House at the same time.

SIXTY-SIX

Hawk and I were in my office. Me behind my desk. Him on the couch. Our default positions. He said that if it was true that drugs were being dealt at Joe Marino's bar, even in a small-time way, it might be worthwhile to talk to Tony Marcus about that.

"I'm trying to limit my interactions with Tony to one a year," I said. "And I already had mine for this year, as well as it worked out for me."

"Well, it got to be you and not me," Hawk said.

"You can't make me."

"Got to," Hawk said. "Tony even still got a hard-on for me about a thing happened between the two of us year *before* this one. And you know how the man is when it comes to grudges."

"He stores them up like squirrels store nuts," I said.

"Till he sees a chance to grab you by yours," Hawk said.

"Not so easy to do with you," I said. "Or me, for that matter."

"Tony don't think so."

"So you think he may have had a hand in over at Marino's?"

"Nothing's changed," Hawk said. "Dope or girls, he wants both hands in. Sometimes he don't even care about the amount of money involved. His mind, it's the principle of the damn thing, not having nobody put nothing over on him."

"You think it's worth it for me to talk to him?"

Hawk smiled. "Ask yourself what you got to lose at this point."

"You think I should call him first, or just surprise him?"

"Tony never much for surprises," Hawk said, "unless you looking for Ty-Bop to shoot you."

Ty-Bop, who was Tony's gunnie, had been with Tony Marcus for as long as I'd known him. Junior was Tony's body man. Except that in Junior's case, it appeared to be a lot more than just one body. He was built like half of the Patriots' offensive line. Or all of it.

"Admit it," I said when Tony Marcus answered his phone. "You missed me."

"Like missing the clap," he said.

"You speaking from experience?" I said.

"Heard you might call," he said. "My lucky damn day."

I offered to meet him at Buddy's Fox, the restaurant where he still kept his office.

"Like I was going to come to you," he said.

"I was just being polite."

"And don't bring Hawk," Tony said.

I said, "He told me the two of you were having relationship issues."

"Fuck Hawk," Tony said, and told me when to stop by, and to leave my piece in the car, it annoyed Junior when he had to pat me down.

There was a decent lunchtime crowd at Buddy's Fox. Tony had once renamed it Ebony and Ivory, which is what he used to call Hawk and me when it was a far more topical musical reference.

But now it was back to being Buddy's Fox. When I came through the door I noticed that the clientele was exclusively black, as it usually was, and that all conversation stopped, as if a pink flamingo had just come walking into the place.

Junior was waiting for me at the other end of the room, at the hallway that led back to Tony's office.

"Junior," I said. "You're looking well."

He gave me a bored shake of the head. "You know the drill," he said.

"I was told by the owner to leave my piece in the car and did," I said.

"Boss don't trust you for shit."

"I'm not going to lie, Junior," I said. "That hurts."

But raised my hands above my head.

"No inappropriate touching," I said. "And no tickling, I mean it."

Tony was behind his desk. Ty-Bop leaned against the wall next to the door, wearing a white Celtics jersey with Jayson Tatum's number 0 in front and a knit stocking cap on his head despite unseasonably warm weather outside. He nodded to a beat only he could hear, whether he had buds in his ears or not.

Tony was wearing what I thought was a very sporty jacket of charcoal gray with a purple plaid to it, which I was sure was part of a suit, mostly because I had rarely ever seen Tony Marcus, gentleman gangster, not wearing a suit. There was a tea setup in front of him.

"'Sup, mother*fucker*," he said, putting all his weight on the second half of the word, like he usually did.

I nodded at him. "Are you wearing your hair that short as a fashion statement, or because you're starting to lose it?"

He nodded at Ty-Bop. "Go ahead and shoot him, Ty. You know you always wanted to."

I sat down.

"I hear you been looking for intel on Joe Marino's old place," Tony said.

"And where did you hear something like that?"

He closed his eyes and sighed. "You really want us to do it like that?" he said. "You got to know by now I hear everything, and see everything and pretty much know everything, leastways most of the time. Why I'm still me, talking like this here to you."

"I'm looking for someone who tended bar there about twenty years ago," I said. "All I got is the name Rob."

He frowned. "Don't think I ever had the pleasure."

"Of meeting that particular bartender, or gracing Marino's with your presence?"

"Neither nor," Tony said.

"How much do you remember about the place?" I said.

"What's in it for me, something comes up if it turns out you goosed up my memory?"

I smiled, as I often did at Tony's distinctive use of the language.

"My undying gratitude?" I said.

He sipped some tea. "Lot of college kids back in the day," he said. "Weed being dealt, way, *way* before the shit was legal. Some coke. No heavy shit. Compared to what else I had going, nickel-and-dime stuff. Like a mom-pop."

He shrugged. "I got a piece of the action anyways, Joe got a bigger one, it being his place and all. What I recall, more girls in there than boys, Joe was smart enough to hire some pretty boys to work the bar. The movie business started to pick up in Boston 'round that time, and he'd get guys happy to work cheap between, ah, engagements."

I turned to look at Ty-Bop. Head still bopping. It looked as if his eyes were closed. I knew better. Hawk said that of everybody we'd ever known, the only better shooter than him was Vinnie. I didn't know how old Ty-Bop was, or even what his real name was. But considering his profession, he was older than he should have been.

"I think the guy I'm looking for might have been one of the pretty boys," I said, "whether he was in the movies or not."

"I do something for you, you know how this-all works, you got to do more for me in return."

"You have something in mind?"

"Let you know when it pops in my mind," Tony said.

He poured more tea then. The porcelain pot matched his cup and looked expensive. Tony liked nice things and could afford them.

"Why you need to find him?"

"He might help me solve something I'm in on."

"The Crain woman," he said.

"It turns out she used to go around with this Rob guy who worked there," I said. "And he used to hit her."

"She sure traded up after that," Tony said.

"Didn't help her at the end."

"I got no use for that, man taking a hand to a woman."

"At last," I said, "some common ground."

Now Tony smiled. "Now get the fuck out my office."

As I passed Ty-Bop I said, "We should double-date at a Celts game one of these days."

His lizard eyes opened, but just briefly.

I put my hand to my ear as if I had a phone in it, mouthed "Call me," and left. There were even more people in the front room than there had been before. Oh, the places I'd go.

SIXTY-SEVEN

Cindy Patton called the next morning and told me she was going to need a few more days, her contact at Pro-scape was out of the country.

I just reminded her to be careful, knowing she really didn't need reminding after what had happened to her friend Darius.

"You wouldn't have come to me if you didn't think that Darius had found out something that got him killed," I said. "And if that's true, the threat might be one floor above you."

"I'm being careful, I promise," she said. "I'm not trusting anybody except you right now."

"Words to live by," I said. "And quite literally, by the way."

"This place is starting to scare me," she said.

"*Starting* to scare you?" I said.

I hadn't heard back from Tony Marcus but wasn't expecting to, certainly not right away. As fluid as our relationship truly was, he had never forgotten that I had once been responsible for putting him in jail, though I had done favors for him since, including one involving his daughter and the meathead she had married.

I knew he might make me wait, even if he did get the information I needed, just because he was Tony.

Hawk and I had taken a late-afternoon walk along the river after my visit to Buddy's Fox. "Tony's just another old dog licks himself on account of he can," Hawk said.

I asked him what he'd done this time to get himself sideways with Tony.

"Some shit he thought I did that I didn't," Hawk said. "He'll get himself over it."

"You sure about that?"

"Yeah," Hawk said. "Because if he don't, he'll be the one got himself sideways. With *me*."

"And who in his right mind would ever want that?"

"Tony knows enough to take his dickery with me just so far," Hawk said. "And not one damn step past that."

We were nearing the end of the path when Hawk told me he had another date with the new woman. I told him I was always excited to get relationship intel from him.

"Is this the second or third?" I said.

"Don't worry about it."

"You know you're not always the giver you say you are," I said.

"Not what she says," he said.

Susan was having dinner in Swampscott with an old high school friend. After Hawk was gone, I stayed in my office, telling myself I would order takeout at some point, but not until I read up on Ethan Lowe's participation in the Aahil project before it went belly-up.

When I finally couldn't wait, and had gotten lost in *Wall Street Journal* stories about Aahil that made as much sense to me as reading about cricket, I ordered a large pizza, green peppers and onions, from Upper Crust.

Before it arrived, I forced myself to read one more story from the *Financial Times*, one that recounted all the fanfare that had accompanied the announcement of the Aahil project, and quoted Lowe proclaiming how expansion like this could only enhance Lith's global brand.

And corporate autonomy.

They were bears for corporate autonomy in the world of big money, something else I had discovered in my reading.

It turned out there was far less fanfare when the project was abandoned. Both sides combined to issue a press release, proclaiming their undying love for each other. There was nothing in the story to indicate that Lith's viability had been compromised in any way, or diminished.

But it *was* a private company, I kept reminding myself.

After that was a long stretch when the only coverage of Lith involved Andrew Crain's charity work around the world. Some of it was in Africa. He had invested a ton of money in various human rights issues, and seemed more passionate about the plight of oppressed women, no matter where he found them.

My pizza was eventually delivered. I ate all of it and drank two beers. When I finished eating I put the empty Upper Crust box into a tall kitchen garbage bag and brought it downstairs to the trash area in the basement, just as a way of getting the smell of peppers and onions out of my office, as pleasant as the smell had been about a half-hour before.

Just to make sure, I lit a jar candle that Susan had bought me, partially, I was sure, because of its name:

Last Call.

Susan said the scent was sandalwood. But she knew better than anyone that you could stump me on most fragrances, and she could easily have told me it was something else and gotten by with it.

"Pretty sure Sam Spade didn't have a scented candle," I had said after she had given it to me.

"He probably could have used one," she said. "I'll bet he opened his window and let fresh air in even less often than you do."

I had to admit the smell, whatever it was, wasn't displeasing. The candle was still lit when there was a single rap on my door and Martin Quirk walked in.

"How'd you know I was here?" I said.

"Had 'em ping your phone," he said.

"Isn't that an invasion of my privacy?"

"Hell, yes," Quirk said.

"I should call the cops," I said.

"Whiskey?" Quirk said.

We both knew he wasn't asking if I had any, because he knew I did. I went and got out my bottle of Midleton Very Rare. The good stuff. I had been spoiling myself a lot lately. Johnny Walker Blue and now Midleton. But Martin Quirk was well worth it the same as I was.

He nodded at the candle.

"We going to meditate?" he said.

He held up his glass. I held up mine. We drank. The first taste of it, the feeling as it went down, made me want to burst into song.

"Maybe meditating would be helpful," I said.

"Or maybe we just drink," he said. "But first, blow out the fucking candle."

I did. Now the only light in the room came from my small desk lamp.

"You ever feel as if you stayed at this too long?" Quirk said.

I knew him well enough to know it was not a frivolous question. Quirk was not now, nor ever had been, a frivolous man.

"When I get that feeling," I said, "I usually just lie down until it passes."

"Laura Crain was like royalty in this city," he said. He took another sip of whiskey. The highball glass looked like a shot glass in his big hand.

"I can't let whoever did it get away with murder," he said. "And I know you feel the same way."

"Goes without saying."

"Problem is, I got no evidence," he said. "And no motive."

"I assume you are speaking for both you and Frank," I said.

"The literary *we* can be used with *I* in narration," he said. "I assumed you knew that."

"Why, you literate bastard, you."

"Goddamn right," he said.

Somehow the dim light of the office made the hour seem later than it was.

"Frank thinks you might have a thought or two you haven't shared about a possible motive," he said.

"I'm aware that he thinks that, mostly because he continues to remind me every few days."

"Do you?" Quirk said.

"There may have been some bad business going on with the big business of Lith, Inc.," I said. "But if there is, I haven't found it yet."

"Because of this merger," Quirk said.

"Or something else going on over there," I said. "Just because there always seems to be something going on over there, hardly ever good."

"But what would Crain's wife have to do with any of that?"

"She never came right out and told me," I said, "but I think she might have taken more of an interest in her husband's company than most people knew. Including him. He has a history of his head being in the clouds."

I thought of Cindy Patton, her talking about a different kind of cloud.

"And that might have gotten her killed?" Quirk said.

"I'm not sure it even rises to the level of working theory," I said. "But what I am sure of is that nobody ever compared any business as big as Lith to church."

"I'm Catholic," Quirk said. "Even church isn't church anymore. Probably never was."

I got up and refilled his glass. I knew he had a driver

downstairs waiting for him. And I knew I was walking home from here.

"I'm working close with Frank on this," he said. "You need to know that."

"The bosses still up your ass?"

"They are," he said. "But it's not just that. I'm not going out with one last goddamn case I couldn't close."

The Midleton was going down easier, for both of us, I assumed.

"You tried to retire before," I said. "You were no good at it."

"I'm putting in my papers at the end of the year," he said. "And I'm fuckin' ay going out with a win, and you're gonna help me. Or else."

"You ever wonder what 'or else' might actually entail?" I said.

"All the time." He grinned. "Still sounds good."

"You know I'll help any way I can."

"Where is Crain on this merger?" he said.

"He was against it before he was for it."

"But his wife might have died still being against it," Quirk said.

"The way to bet," I said.

Quirk nodded. "You probably have noticed that money, especially a lot of money, can make normally sane people lose their freaking minds. So let me ask you something: Can you see the other partner killing his best friend's wife, or having it done, over money?"

"He could," I said. "I just don't see it."

"And maybe that guy in Charlestown jumped."

"Don't see that, either."

"You're still dug in on that?"

"Yes, sir."

Quirk smiled then. "I'm off-duty," he said. "You can call me Martin."

I smiled back at him. "Too soon in our relationship for me to be that informal."

We sat in silence. I heard a siren, coming either up Boylston or across Berkeley, before it was gone.

"You think the wife's death and the jumper's death are connected," Quirk said.

"Yeah," I said. "I do. I just can't prove it, at least not yet."

"Have you had a case of your own lately felt like this much of a shitshow?"

"It's not like you didn't warn me."

He finished his drink. I pointed to his glass. He shook his head.

"I need this," he said.

I knew he wasn't talking about the whiskey.

There was a longer quiet between us then, before I reached into the middle drawer of my desk and pulled out Laura Crain's note to Darius Baker, the one I'd found in his jacket, and slid it across the desk to Quirk.

He held it close to the desk lamp as he read it, then slid it back to me.

"Now you give this up?"

"Maybe my own Catholic guilt?"

"You're not Catholic," Quirk said.

"Imagine my surprise at the guilt, then."

"This all you got that we don't?"

I nodded.

"Not much to go on," he said.

"Not yet, anyway," I said.

"You got a much better chance to get inside this thing than we do," he said. "So maybe going forward you can act like a team player."

"No *i* in *team*," I said.

"But two in Martin Quirk, hotshot," he said.

When he was gone I stood in my window and saw him standing next to the unmarked on the street, its motor running. Before he got in, Quirk looked up at my window and nodded. There was no way for him to see me nod back.

The car pulled away. I rinsed our glasses and put them away and then I walked home, thinking about what Quirk had said about needing the win.

Maybe I needed a win even more than he did, whether he was really moving toward the door or not. It wasn't my fault that Laura and Baker were dead. I still felt guilt about both of them, Catholic or otherwise.

I had walked along Arlington Street even though it was slightly out of my way. I liked walking past the park, even at night. Especially at night sometimes.

Reggie Smythe was waiting for me outside my building again, leaning against the Navigator.

"Mr. Lowe says I should suggest you stop talking to his people without his permission," Smythe said.

"I don't need his permission to talk to his people," I said. "That's one thing. And as I recall, it was Mr. Lowe who came to me asking for help."

"I watch over Mr. Lowe," Reggie Smythe said. "He doesn't watch over me."

He casually moved away from the car, as if he were about to walk me to my door.

"So you, as one of his people, have still taken it upon yourself to tell me to stop talking to *other* of his people?"

"Your grasp of the obvious," Smythe said, "continues to be almost breathtaking."

"And if I don't, ah, accede to your wishes?" I said. "Or his?"

"Cindy Patton is a very nice young woman," he said.

He was smiling as he said it.

"Blimey, Reg," I said. "Was that a threat?"

"Perhaps think of it more as an observation," he said.

He was still smiling.

"You bring anybody with you?" I said, looking around. There could have been someone in the Navigator, but somehow I doubted it. He wasn't the type.

"What in the world for?" he said.

He was probably good. Just not as good as me, even if he had size on me, and probably reach, or not. I smiled back at him then, before I took a quick first step toward him with my right leg and hit him with a short left hook whose force, even in close quarters, surprised even me. He had a hard body, as I expected him to. I could feel it when the punch landed, but I still could hear air come out of him before following up with the straight overhand right I'd been working on lately at Henry's and of which I was now pretty proud. It didn't put Reggie Smythe down, but nearly did, knocking him back a couple steps before he managed to gather himself.

He didn't swing back, taking a couple more steps backward instead, reaching inside his jacket as he did. But

I was on him before he could come out with the gun for which he had to be reaching. Then I pressed the .38 I was carrying tonight right above his nose. It all happened to Smythe with the speed of the combination with which he'd just been hit.

The right hand I'd thrown already had his left eye starting to close. But he was trying to remain cool, even now. Hard to do with a gun between your eyes. But he had forgotten the first rule of being a tough guy, the one about never letting the other guy get the first punch in.

"Nothing is going to happen to Cindy Patton, now or ever," I said softly. "Nod your head if you understand me, so I don't have to blow it off."

He hesitated, but then complied.

Then I was behind him, my gun in his back, shoving him hard toward his Navigator with it, then opening the driver's-side door with my free hand.

"*Now* buzz off," I said.

I had the gun pointed at his window until the Navigator slowly pulled onto Marlborough. I watched until its taillights were gone into the night.

Martin Quirk might be worried about the game passing him by.

I was not.

SIXTY-EIGHT

I called Cindy Patton and she answered right away.

"Are you okay?" I said.

"I'm fine," she said. "Eating Skinny Pop and watching *White Lotus* again. Why?"

I didn't know what *White Lotus* was, but chose to move on, telling her that Reggie Smythe had just paid me a visit that had not ended well.

"For him, I hope," she said. "That man scares me. I don't know why they keep him around."

"I'm starting to get the idea that it actually takes more than Reggie Smythe to make you want to hide under your desk," I said.

I told her then what he said about her and what I'd proceeded to do about it.

"You pulled your gun?" she said. "On *Marlborough* Street?"

"It was just the two of us at the moment," I said, "so as not to scare any of my neighbors."

"It's creepy that he mentioned my name," Cindy said.

"Just another way of calling him a creep," I said.

"What should I do?"

I was resting my right hand, which had started to throb and swell slightly, in a bowl of ice and water. I tried to remember if I used this much ice when I was still boxing.

"Somehow Smythe knew you had come to see me," I said, "or there would have been no reason for him to bring up your name."

"He was having me followed," she said, and I could hear the ripple of alarm in her voice.

"Maybe by tracking your phone."

"You're making me feel like I'm in some sort of spy movie."

I took my hand out of the ice and dried it on my jeans.

"Starting to think even bad spy movies make more sense than ours."

"Maybe ours will turn out to make more sense than we think."

"Listen, Cindy," I said. "You can walk away from this right now. Go in to the office in the morning and tell your boss that you only came to see me because Darius had been your friend, and you wanted to help me in any way you could."

She didn't answer right away. Maybe she was considering her options.

Finally she said, "No."

"Are you sure?"

"I *am* scared, Mr. Spenser. But I'm not going to let that creep make me quit. If I can help you find out what might have happened to my friend, I'm going to."

"You could be putting yourself into even more danger going forward," I said. "And you're talking to somebody who didn't do much of a job keeping your friend safe."

"You didn't know that you had to," she said.

I asked for her address and she gave it to me, North Washington Street in Brighton. I asked her what kind of building it was. She said it was a doorman building, her parents had insisted on one when she'd moved from Ohio. Then I told her to go out in the morning when the stores opened and buy herself a burner phone she was to use only when she was contacting me or I was contacting her.

"Wow," she said, "this is a spy movie."

I told her that if Clay Whitson did ask her about coming to see me, to tell him the story I'd just given her, that she'd simply acted out of loyalty and friendship and didn't think she was doing anything wrong.

Before I ended the call, I told her I would protect her, no matter how we moved forward.

Then I called Hawk.

"Middle of something here," he said, though he did answer his phone, maybe because he'd seen it was me.

"It's important," I said.

"So is what I'm in the middle of," he said.

I told him, as succinctly as I could, about Smythe and

Cindy Patton and that I needed him to watch her for a couple days.

Hawk said he would, and then told me he'd try to wrap things up in his present circumstances much sooner than he'd planned.

"See," he said, "I am a damn giver after all."

SIXTY-NINE

I knew from Claire Megill that Ethan Lowe owned a town house of his own on Beacon Hill, even bigger and more lavish than Andrew Crain's, with a tonier address at Louisburg Square. His weekend place, she had also informed me, was in Marblehead.

I was up at seven the next morning and walked over to the address she'd given me for Lowe, stopping along the way at the Starbucks on Charles Street. The largest size coffee they had was a "trenta." I asked the kid serving me if he knew that meant thirty.

"Yeah," he said, running my credit card. "My parents are pretty proud that I majored in speaking barista at UMass."

I made my way over to Revere and then W. Cedar and then Mount Vernon after that, before hanging a left at

Louisburg Square. The red-brick homes here, set back from fences and small, well-kept lawns, always made me feel as if I should be looking at them in black-and-white, imagining that they had looked largely the same a hundred and fifty years ago.

I knew better than to loiter in front of Lowe's building and risk being executed on the spot by someone behind the wheel of a private security vehicle.

So I walked around the small park across the street from where Lowe lived, and then did that again, as if part of my morning routine, finishing my trenta and regretting that I hadn't brought a couple blueberry scones with me. But then I told myself, thinking ahead, that I had something to look forward to on the walk home.

There was no black Navigator in sight, at least not yet. Maybe Lowe walked to work from here, I knew it could be only a mile or so, if that, to the Hancock. Maybe he was less and less afraid of the bogeyman, for reasons known only to him. I was hoping he would walk to work, having no enthusiasm for Round 2 with Reggie Smythe if he happened to show up, not in Louisburg Square, it would have been an insult to everything good and holy about old Boston.

Lowe came out of his front door about fifteen minutes after eight o'clock. Khakis, white T-shirt showing over the top of a dark v-neck sweater. I saw him put his earbuds in, and then check his phone before putting it away.

He was making his way toward Mount Vernon when I fell into step alongside him. If I'd startled him, it had been only slightly.

He sighed and took the bud out of his left ear.

"You don't need to call security," I said.

"It wouldn't do me much good, from what I heard happened to my security last evening," he said.

He took out the other earbud and stuffed them both into his pocket.

"I thought I'd made it clear that I'm not trying to make trouble with you," Ethan Lowe said. "And that we ought to be on the same side here."

"Then why'd you send your guy Reggie after me?"

It hadn't taken us long to get to Mount Vernon. Lowe was walking briskly and I was gamely keeping up, even on a sore knee. I assumed we were headed for the Public Garden.

"I didn't send Reggie."

"Gonna need to call bullshit on that one," I said.

"Clay sent him," Lowe said. "I didn't find out until afterward. He wanted to know why his assistant had come to see you."

"And how did Clay know that she had?" I said.

I wondered if he and Smythe had their stories straight. If necessary, I knew I could brace Whitson at a later date, just for the sheer joy of it.

"Reggie likes to keep track of people."

"Big brother watching?" I said. "I mean, he *is* a big brother, after all."

"Clever," Lowe said.

"It's both my blessing and my curse."

We had made our way to Charles.

"During the course of my conversation with Reggie," I said, "he threatened a young woman who'd only come to me because she'd cared as much as she had for Darius Baker."

"Reggie's version is that all he'd said was what a nice person she was," Lowe said. "And that you then overreacted and sucker-punched him."

"Twice," I said. "But who's really counting?"

"Then pulled a gun on him."

"Not to make too fine a point of things," I said, "but he was reaching for his own at the time."

"Well, after you'd sucker-punched him twice."

The conversation was as casual as if he were discussing how the Japanese markets had opened.

"Let's not chase each other around more bullshit," I said. "His threat to Cindy Patton was implied, and overt, at the same goddamn time. But here's a threat that's neither: If he goes anywhere near her again, I will be coming for you first, then Whitson, then him."

"And beat me up, too? I'm sure that you could."

"Nah," I said. "But I will find a way to beat up your company."

"Don't flatter yourself."

We'd crossed Beacon and were in the park, angling toward either Newbury or Boylston. It was already an almost perfect autumn morning in the city. I was spending it with Ethan Lowe, who had now officially annoyed me. I found as I grew older it took less and less.

"I have a dear old friend named Wayne Cosgrove, who is a bigger deal than ever at *The Globe*," I said. "And I'm thinking that if he suddenly had people from that *Globe* Spotlight team they made that movie about attach themselves to you like deer ticks, there might be an interesting tale to be told about events that led to this merger being so important to you. And even about how you came up with the capital you needed after that Aahil deal turned into this year's Red Sox."

He stopped walking then. We were in front of the duckling statues inspired by "Make Way for Ducklings," but whose beauty seemed completely lost on Ethan Lowe at the moment.

He stared at me, but said nothing, as if a bogeyman finally had just jumped out in front of him.

"I know," I said. "The story almost takes my breath away, too."

"You don't know what you don't know, Mr. Spenser," he said. "We should just leave it at that, and go our separate ways."

"No," I said.

"To which part?"

"We have no separate ways now," I said. "We just have me wanting to know if Darius Baker's hard drive having gone missing has something to do with your merger, and his death."

"You're obviously a very smart guy," Lowe said. "And a very persistent guy. And you seem to be loyal as hell. But you're out of your depth here. And it's not just going to be one person who gets hurt if you don't leave my company alone, it will be a lot of people."

I was going to point out that it was really Andrew Crain's company, but didn't. And likewise didn't tell him that I was having a difficult time deciding whether it was him or Darius, when he was still with us, who was trying to hide something. Instead I told him that I'd be in touch, and then the two of us did go our separate ways, at least for the time being.

I was on my way to my office with a box full of Dunkin' donuts, just in case I had guests, when I received the following heartfelt text from Tony Marcus:

> Maybe got a name for you, bitch.

SEVENTY

He followed it up with a phone call, telling me he happened to be in my hood, and would come to me this time.

"'Hood,' Tony?" I said.

"Cultural expression," he said, "from bygone days, even though I took this boy out the hood a long time ago."

"To what do I owe the honor?"

"Got a girl I put up at the Newbury," he said. "She's not my primary, understand, my primary is the one I got living with me presently. But the one at the hotel, she's worked her way up through the farm system. I'm right around the corner, is my point."

"I was starting to worry there might not be a point coming along anytime soon. Or ever."

"You want my fucking help or not?" he said.

I asked what kind of tea he liked. He said he didn't

need any damn tea, but if a woman identifying herself as Shirelle happened to check in with me later, I was to tell her that Tony and I had been working together on something all night and into this morning.

"You do that, we square."

"Seriously?"

"I still got a lot to live for," he said. "And Shirelle can be a bad sport."

He came into the office without either Junior or Ty-Bop. I assumed that Junior had driven and Ty-Bop had walked Tony from the car into my building. Now the two of them were probably downstairs arguing about the president's tax plan.

I would have thought Tony would be once again dressed to the nines, but with him the number always seemed on the low side. Navy suit today, perfectly tailored, a big-knotted tie whose brand I knew I should know but didn't. Whatever had happened last night with the woman at the Ritz who wasn't his primary, Tony still looked as fresh as freshly cut flowers. There was suddenly a scent in the room that reminded me of my candle.

"Troy Robinson," Tony said when he was seated.

"Tell me more," I said.

"Ain't much more to tell," he said. "Worked part-time at the bar. Did some TV and movie work on the side, couple movies shooting here, and some lawyer show. Or maybe was a cop show. Pretty-boy background actor, or so I was told."

"Told by whom?"

"Don't ask, don't tell," Tony said.

"Pretty sure you stole that," I said.

"We done?" Tony said. "Other than you handling that business with Shirelle, it ever comes up."

"The person with whom you spoke," I said. "Did they have any idea whatever happened to Robinson? I heard he left town suddenly when he left."

"Catch me up on this here," Tony said. "Who's the damn detective here, me or you?"

He stood up. His way of telling me we were done.

"What if Shirelle doesn't call?" I said.

Tony was looking at his reflection in my window, frowning, leaning slightly forward. I saw him square himself up then, adjusting a knot in his tie that really was as big as my fist. When he was satisfied, he walked over to the door, put his hand on the knob, and stopped.

"Oh, she'll call, sooner or later," Tony said. "Girl got herself some serious trust issues."

"I can't imagine why," I said.

When he was gone, I called Zebulon Sixkill in Los Angeles and asked him how good his contacts were in the world of TV and movies.

"Let me count the ways, paleface," Z said.

SEVENTY-ONE

Z informed me, rather proudly, I thought, that he'd already been to the gym and had just finished an energy shake he'd made for himself, from scratch.

"What color?" I said.

"You don't want to know. But think mint."

We got the small talk out of the way both quickly and efficiently, as we usually did. Business for his own private detective agency was good. Things were also good with Jen Yoon, a computer savant who'd become his partner both in business and in life, the longest relationship he'd had with anybody except me since we'd met.

"She's not sick of you yet?" I said.

"Susan's not sick of you yet?" he said.

I asked about Mattie. He said she kept tabling the discussion of becoming a cop, mostly because she was having too much of a blast, he said, working with him and Jen.

"She's got nearly enough hours with us to get her PI license," Z said.

"She got any plans to get a place of her own?"

"Not unless she moves in with this new guy she's been seeing."

"I thought there was a new guy the last time I spoke with her."

"That was a new guy right before this one," Z said. "He's like the third lead in some zombie cop show on Hulu."

"You like him?"

"For an actor."

"Low bar."

"Tell me about it. I live here, remember?"

"What's his name?"

"Brick something."

"*Brick?* You're joking."

"I wish."

I then told him what I was working on, in as organized a way as I could manage, even knowing as I did that I still sounded as if I were wrestling myself to the ground. But, I told Z, I now had a lead, if you could call it that, on Laura Crain's old boyfriend, who might not figure into the case but might.

"I got the name from Tony Marcus," I said.

"Always a reliable source."

"When he wants something from me, he is."

"What's he want this time?"

"As far as I could tell, for his current love interest not

to kill him in his sleep when he's not sleeping around on her."

I told Z that all I had was that Troy Robinson might have worked in the industry here about twenty years ago, which meant there might be some kind of union record on him out there. Extra or background actor or event stunt man, I really had no idea. Z knew better than I did about the inner workings of Tinsel Town.

"Tinsel Town? You're getting old."

"I may be, but irony never does," I said. "So could you or Jen or even Mattie help me out."

"If it's important to you, you know I will."

"He may be important, or somebody I turned into a red herring all by myself," I said. "I just want to know one way or another how he might figure into this thing, if he does."

"Wait," Z said. "*Now* you're worrying about tying up loose ends."

"You're pretty funny for a Cree."

"Guy walks into a reservation," he said.

"The only thing I've got other than a name is that somebody said he might've looked like Brad Pitt."

"Half the town used to," Z said. "No more. Word is that blond guys aren't dangerous enough."

"But you are."

"Hell, yeah. But I was taught by the best."

He said he'd worked on a case one time that involved an actor who'd started out in the Screen Extras Guild, before it was absorbed into SAG. He would see what history he could find from what had been the Screen Extras Guild, but that if the Robinson guy had worked on independent shoots in Boston, we might be screwed checking back on him, because it was likely a non-union operation. But there might be a chance, if he was trying to get into the business, that he might have worked in Los Angeles before he went east.

"It was probably a long shot from the start," I said. "I just had this feeling."

"Give me a few days," Z said.

"I'm the one starting to feel like a zombie," I said.

"Maybe you could find background work with Brick," Z said.

SEVENTY-TWO

I called Hawk with the good news that I was on my way to relieve him, as I was taking Cindy Patton to dinner.

"I ain't sleeping in my car, in case you were thinking about asking me after you had dinner," Hawk said. "Jag's built for a lot of things. Not that."

"I've got one of the Vinnies covering the overnight shift," I said.

"You make it sound like a singing group."

There was a pause. "What kind of tab you running, even though you no longer have a client?" Hawk said.

"There's a price to pay for speaking the truth," I said. "A bigger price for living a lie."

"I know you want to tell me who said that."

"Cornell West."

"Figured it was so smart, had to be a brother."

When I arrived at Cindy Patton's building, the Jag was parked right in front on North Washington, only standing out in the neighborhood the way an armored tank would have.

"Thank you for your service," I said to Hawk.

"Gonna be out of pocket the next few hours," he said, "now that my evening opened up like this."

"Don't do anything I wouldn't do."

"Think you mean to say *couldn't* do."

Cindy and I walked to the Brighton Bodega and settled into a booth. I asked if she'd ever been here before. She said she had not. I told her she was about to find out what she had been missing, and ordered the equivalent of a tasting menu for both of us.

Tacos carnitas. Peking ravioli pork dumplings. Korean BBQ short ribs. Crispy Sichuan pepper wings. We each had a glass of True North Ale.

While we waited for our food to be delivered, after I'd told the waitress she could bring dishes out whenever they were ready, I asked Cindy how she was doing, really, with all the sudden drama in her life.

"It probably won't surprise you to know I've never required a bodyguard before," she said. "But I have to say, the one I have is *very* impressive."

"All you have to do is ask him," I said.

I smiled at her and drank some beer. It was local, from Ipswich, and very good.

"He must be the best," she said.

"Definitely in the top two."

She said it had been an odd day at work. Clay Whitson had come downstairs and *he'd* asked how she was doing.

"I take it that's not a normal occurrence?"

"Asking me to do extra work, that's a normal occurrence," Cindy said. "Acting as if he cares about me as a person happens about as often as a change of seasons."

"Maybe me kicking Reggie Smythe's ass got his attention."

"I really wish I'd seen that," she said.

"Have you had any further conversations with your friend from Proscape?"

"I'm having a drink with him tomorrow night, as a matter of fact," she said. "Does Hawk have to be my plus-one?"

"Only from a respectful distance, so as not to cramp your style."

Vinnie texted me when we were finishing up with our feast to tell me that Ronnie was on his way to Cindy's apartment. I told him we were just about to leave the restaurant and walk back.

"I feel like your dad walking you home," I said as we made our way back up North Washington.

"But a very cool dad," she said.

I saw Ronnie had arrived as I walked Cindy to her front door, as any cool dad would have.

"I want this to be over," she said. "And when it is finally over, I still want to have my job."

"You will," I said.

"I wish I were as confident as you are," I said.

"Who doesn't?"

She thanked me for dinner then, and got up on her toes and gave me a quick peck on the cheek.

"I'm not as young as you think I am," she said.

"Yeah, kid," I said, "you are."

"I'll tell you one thing," she said. "I'm old enough to remember when I still thought I was working for the good guys."

SEVENTY-THREE

Susan and I were with Pearl the next day at Raymond Park in Cambridge on a rare afternoon off for her. We had walked there from Linnaean Street.

"I forgot to ask," she said. "How was date night?"

"Very funny."

"The two of you have any common interests besides the case?" she said.

"A quest for justice?"

"Oh," Susan said. "That old thing."

I was throwing a tennis ball and Pearl was retrieving it and seemed, as always, to be willing to do that until the end of days.

We finally found an empty bench and Susan brought out the small plastic dish she had in her Pearl bag and poured water into it. Pearl drank loudly and thirstily and plopped down in the grass at last.

It was my first chance to brief Susan on having spoken to Z, and Mattie's new love interest, and Cindy Patton's conviction that our accessing Darius Baker's information was imminent.

"Believe in yourself and you can achieve," Susan said.

"Is that from a poem?" I asked.

"If it's not, it should be."

I leaned over and kissed her. She kissed me back, with vigor, and then asked, in what I felt was a less-than-poetic way, if I would be interested in heading back to her place for a matinee.

She was in bed reading much later and I was watching the Amazon series about Harry Bosch when Claire Megill called.

"You're back," I said.

"I need to see you," she said.

There was something wrong with her voice, as if she were afraid to raise it. She said she was at her apartment and asked how long it would take me to get there. I told her I was in Cambridge, which meant not terribly long.

"Claire," I said. "What's wrong?"

"Andrew," she said. "I'm worried about Andrew."

So I was all the way back to the beginning.

"Has something happened to him?" I said. "Has he done something?"

"I'm afraid he might do something," she said.

She hesitated.

"To Clay," she said.

Then she was crying.

"Clay hit me," she said, before adding, "Again."

SEVENTY-FOUR

The bruise was around her left eye, in the same general area where I had clocked Reggie Smythe.

"I should have called you first and not Andrew," she said.

I thought she might start crying again, though it looked as if she hadn't really stopped since we'd ended our call. Perhaps she was finally cried out about Clay Whitson. I put an arm around her and walked her to her couch and took a seat across from her.

"Tell me what happened," I said.

Since returning from California, she said, she had been thinking a lot about her relationship with Clay Whitson, and the choice she'd originally made with him, and the choice to stay with him longer after she knew she shouldn't. And keeping largely silent about the abuse for as long as she had. Eventually she made the decision to tell him that she was stopping her own destructive pattern once and for all.

"I just finally decided I deserved better," she said. "That I *am* better."

She nodded like a child who had been caught misbehaving, even though she had done nothing wrong, the way Laura Crain had not done anything wrong back in college.

"It was always the same," she said. "He would hit me, and then be remorseful, and I would take him back."

"Did you try therapy?"

"Repeatedly."

"But you'd take him back, anyway."

"Madness," she said.

The same word Missy Jones had used about Laura. Maybe the word all abused women used about themselves sooner or later. Just because it was madness that they couldn't see a way out.

"Perhaps what got me across the line at last was seeing my son on this trip, seeing the strong woman he thinks I am. The *person* I want to be. Clay was still calling, and texting, and begging me to give him another chance. But tonight I screwed up stupid courage and decided to tell him in person that I was never going to take him back, and never planned to see his face outside the office ever again.

"And ended up with *this* face," she said.

She took in a lot of air.

"He snapped," she said. "Worse than I'd ever seen him."

She lightly touched her fingers to the area next to her eye.

"I locked myself in the bathroom and told him I was going to call nine-one-one if he didn't leave," she said. "I had the ability to track him on his phone, and finally saw that he had left the building. I just had to talk to someone who I knew did care about me, and called Andrew." She put her head in her hands. "God, I have such awful taste in men!"

Her voice broke again. "Andrew was the one who snapped when he got here," she said. "He said he was going after him."

"Where is he now, and where is Whitson?" I said.

"Andrew is at the Brookline house," she said. "I can track him on my phone as well."

"What about Whitson?"

"I'm afraid he's there, too," she said.

She took more deep breaths then, as if trying to calm herself, even though it was clear that was a lost cause at this point.

"Andrew does care for me, very deeply," she said. "Not in the way that Laura thought. But he does." One more deep breath, deepest yet. "He just might care too much in this case."

"What are you saying, Claire?"

"When he left here he said he was going to kill him," she said.

SEVENTY-FIVE

The gate was open when I arrived at his house.

No floodlights came on as I stepped through it.

No alarms sounded.

As I made my way along the tree line toward the house, I finally saw a silver Mercedes parked in front.

Perhaps Crain's own car was in the garage next to the house.

I kept waiting for floodlights, or for an alarm, for something, the closer I got to the house, but nothing happened. I pressed myself against the outside walls, ducking down when I came to one of the first-floor windows.

I kept inching along, eventually making my way to the front door.

I reached over and gently tried the knob.

The door, like the gate, was unlocked.

When I silently opened it a crack, I could clearly hear Andrew Crain's voice.

"You really left me no choice," Crain was saying. "I had to save Claire from you."

Then, as if a switch had been thrown, he was shouting, like a different kind of alarm sounding.

"You can only let so much go!" Crain yelled.

When he stopped yelling, I heard Clay Whitson.

"You don't have to do this, Andrew," he said.

I knew they were in the living room, on the other side of the foyer from the front door. It meant a fair amount of distance between me and them, I just couldn't remember exactly how much.

I had no way of knowing if it was just the two of them.

I had worn sneakers to Claire Megill's, still having them on after Susan and I had been to the park. I opened the door a few inches more and was into the foyer then. The sneakers made no noise. The fog, on little cat's feet. Sandburg. The things in my head.

"Getting you away from her once and for all," Crain said, "is the right thing to do. Then you can't hurt her ever again. Or anybody else."

I pressed myself against the wall to my left, passing in front of art I knew had to be worth millions, and finally got close enough to the living room to see Crain standing in the middle of the room, pointing what I didn't have to get any closer to know was a .357 Magnum.

"It's funny, Clay," Crain said, lowering his voice. "I hate guns. But as hard as it might be for you to believe, I've always known how to use them."

Whitson was on the couch, the Magnum pointed directly at him, the entire left side of his face bloody and swollen, as if Crain had already used his gun on him without firing it.

Yet.

I stuck mine in the back pocket of my jeans and stepped out into the entranceway, my hands in the air, not wanting to spook him.

"Don't shoot, Andrew," I said quietly, trying to remember the last time I'd said that to anyone.

He turned his head slightly, but kept the gun pointed at Whitson, and remained surprisingly calm in the moment.

"You need to leave, Mr. Spenser," he said. "This doesn't involve you. This is between Clay and me now. It really should have been long before this."

"I'm not leaving," I said.

I calculated the distance between us and how quickly I might be able to cover it.

No way to rush him.

And no way of knowing what he might do if I did.

"Then you need to slowly and carefully walk over and take a seat next to him," Crain said.

"And if I refuse?" I said.

"Then you can just stand there and watch while I shoot him," Crain said.

He stepped back a few feet, expanding his field of vision as I slowly walked to the couch, keeping my hands in the air.

"He told me he wanted to talk about the merger," Whitson said. "That he was officially onboard, he knew how hard I'd worked on it, and he wanted me to know. I was fixing myself a drink when he hit me in the face with his gun and kept hitting me until I finally passed out. When I woke up, I was sitting where I am right now."

"Stop talking, please," Crain said. *"Both of you."*

"Andrew," I said. "I know what Whitson did to Claire. If you hadn't gotten him here, I would have gone looking for him myself. But doing it like this, that's not you."

Crain's voice was amazingly calm then.

"Actually," he said, "it is."

"You can't throw away everything you've built and everything you've done," I said. "You don't want to be remembered for killing a man in cold blood."

"I'll change," Whitson said.

"No, you won't," Crain said. "That's the problem. Men like you never change."

"Even Claire isn't worth this," I said. "Not *like* this."

I did not want to set him off further. I did want him to keep talking.

"They're all worth it!" Crain yelled.

There was an antique coffee table between us, looking as old as one of the maple trees outside. I didn't think I could turn it over if I tried to rush him from here. And I knew I didn't want to shoot Andrew Crain, even if he turned his gun on me.

"Laura wouldn't want you to do this," I said.

He turned slightly, maybe a quarter of a turn, and now the gun was pointed at me. It had been a long time since someone had shot me. I hoped this time it wouldn't be the husband of my former client putting one in me because I made the wrong move, or said the wrong thing.

But Crain was back to focusing on Whitson then. I

knew all about the gun in his hand. Knew there was no safety. If the hammer came back, it would mean the balloon had already gone up.

"Did you think treating her like that, *violating her like that*, wouldn't catch up with you eventually?" Crain said to Whitson. "That someday a bill wouldn't be presented to you?"

"I'll get help," Whitson said.

His own eyes were fixed on the gun. One of his eyes was already swollen shut. Crain hitting him with the Magnum must have felt as if he was hitting Whitson with a hammer.

"It's too late for that!" Crain said.

Yelling again.

"Claire knew that you and Whitson were here together," I said. "She sent me here."

Crain had said that he knew how to use the gun. I had no way of knowing whether he did or not. And did not want to find out.

"It's the only way," Crain said, almost as if he were talking to himself, reasoning with himself. "I should have done this with my father, to save my mother from *him*."

He cocked the gun then and I shoved Whitson to the side and dove across the table as the first bullet went into the couch where Whitson had been sitting, keeping myself underneath the barrel of the gun, which he fired again, the sound of it like an explosion in the small world that included only Crain and Whitson and me.

I heard something shatter behind me as I drove my shoulder into Crain's midsection, my full force taking him into the chair behind him, and then to the ground.

He still had the gun in his hand.

Even with all of my weight on him, he tried to roll out from underneath me, away from me, before I finally got the gun away from him.

"I need this to be over!" he shouted.

"It is," I said.

I lifted him to his feet with my free hand and shoved him into the chair that was still in place. As I did, I saw Whitson out of the corner of my eye, running for the front door.

"Whitson!"

I was the one shouting.

He stopped and turned and saw me pointing Andrew Crain's gun at him.

"Sit the fuck down," I said, "before I'm the one who shoots you."

SEVENTY-SIX

Hawk said, "Your boy Crain sounds like the damn buffet at the psychiatrists' convention."

"At least it sounds as if he's going to get that kind of help now," I said.

"He doesn't need some fancy place in California," Hawk said. "All he needs to do is go see Susan."

"I'm here," Susan said, smiling at Hawk from the other side of the table.

"Just paying you a compliment, missy," Hawk said, and smiled back.

The three of us were having dinner a few nights later at the Atlantic Fish Company on Boylston. Before making the reservation I had asked Hawk if he wanted to bring along his current paramour. He had declined, saying she had elected to break things off.

"She told me she wanted to play the long game with me," Hawk had said. "And I had to tell her that unfortunately for her, I *got* no long game."

Andrew Crain had checked into a place in Pacific Palisades called Groves. Claire had flown out there with him on the company jet. They had managed to do this without leaks of any kind. If someone did question where Crain was this close to the merger with the Prise people, the cover story was that he had gone to California for back surgery, not because of the breakdown that had finally culminated with him threatening to shoot Clay Whitson.

Ethan Lowe was now running all facets of the company, the Prise deal scheduled to be officially consummated in a week or so. There had been only one condition from Crain before he left for California: Lowe had finally agreed to terminate Whitson, after nondisclosure agreements on both sides. Claire Megill assured me that they were more comprehensive, and binding, than a nuclear arms treaty.

"So much of this with Clay was my fault," she told me on the phone.

"Said the victim," I said.

"Maybe when I'm out there with Andrew I should talk to somebody at Groves myself," she said.

"Maybe you should," I said.

I had dragged Whitson to his car when he was leaving Crain's house that night. Before he'd gotten in, I told him that if he ever sent Claire Megill so much as another email, then what had just happened to him inside would seem like something you could set to music.

We were almost finished with our appetizers. Susan had barely touched her wine, but sipped some of it now, as if suddenly remembering it was there.

"Andrew himself was probably abused by his father, too, along with his mother," she said. "It's as if he hasn't been able to stop the cycle of abuse since he was a little boy."

"Don't forget that he told me he thought his wife might have killed her abuser," I said. "Maybe in the end he saw Clay Whitson as being all of them."

"Why he *should've* shot his ass," Hawk said.

He pointed at Susan's shrimp cocktail with his fork. "You gonna eat that last one," he said. "Or just try to stare it into your stomach?"

Susan forked the shrimp now and put it on Hawk's plate. "At least *you* ask, Hawk," she said.

"I only take food off your plate when it's clear it's going to be wasted," I said. "I'm actually doing you a favor."

We were finishing up with dessert later—New York Cheesecake for me, Crème de la Boston for Hawk, decaf cappuccino for Susan—when Hawk said to me, "We both know what a bear you are for putting a bow on things. But maybe you got to consider that if you and Quirk and Belson can't roll this thing all the way up, maybe this is one *can't* be rolled up."

Susan put her hand over mine. "Maybe not even by you."

Hawk grinned. "You know what Drake says."

"As a matter of fact, I don't."

"Say you're moving on," Hawk said.

"Screw Drake," I said.

Now Susan squeezed my hand. "Thank you for not saying 'fuck,' dear."

Hawk went off into the night. Susan and I decided to walk back to my apartment, having Ubered to the restaurant. We were debating whether or not to have a nightcap at The Newbury when Cindy Patton called.

"I think I might have something," she said. "My friend from Proscape came through for me. And it looks like my friend Darius knew plenty about getting into other people's clouds, before someone basically tried to steal his."

"And found what?"

"Company financial records," she said, lowering her voice as if she had somehow found the holy grail.

"Private records, I take it."

"And private codes," she said. "I don't know how he did it. But he did. Some of it was on his personal computer, some on his one at work."

She paused. "But we may need some kind of forensic accountant to sort it all out."

I told her I happened to know someone who fit that bill, though he would have been resistant to "forensic," thinking it redundant.

Then I told her what I wanted her to do.

"Old school," she said.

"I went to that school before they closed it down," I said.

SEVENTY-SEVEN

The press conference that would announce the merger between Lith and the Canadian car company was scheduled for the following morning. Over the weekend, Marty Kaiser had turned my office into his office, and a bit of a war room, his laptop and mine. Marty worked off the old-school thumb drive that I'd had him pick up from Cindy Patton's apartment, not wanting to go anywhere near there myself, just in case she was still being watched, or I was being watched, or both of us were being watched.

"Are we getting near the end of our movie?" she said, still using the burner phone I'd made her buy, and calling me on the landline at my office.

"Jesus," I said, "I hope so."

Now it was Monday night, and I was on my way to Ethan Lowe's waterfront home on Marblehead Neck. I had called to tell him I needed to see him in person. I wanted to apologize to his face for having misjudged him, that it was time for me to man up and admit I'd been wrong about him, and about a lot of things.

He lived on the eastern side of Ocean Ave Parkway. I'd Googled his purchase of the home, and read that he had as much waterfront exposure as any home on the North Shore.

When I arrived, I saw a Tesla parked out front. I hoped his new business partners didn't find out.

It was the only car in front of the main house, whose size and architecture made me wonder where the West Wing was. There was a huge garage to the side, and in the distance, I could make out what looked to be some kind of guesthouse.

Good being Ethan Lowe.

He was waiting for me on his porch when I got out of my car. He stepped back after shaking my hand and made a sweeping gesture with his own that took in his house, the property, maybe the stars in the sky and the waves I could hear in the distance.

"Annoying, isn't it?" he said, and ushered me inside.

There was less art, at least in the living room, than what adorned the walls of his partner's home in Brookline. It was all more modern in here, glass and steel and a lot of white, including a double-sided sofa, one side facing the water, the other facing a flat screen that was as big as any I'd ever seen in my life.

Lowe asked if I wanted a drink. I told him I'd pass, the drive up had taken longer than I'd thought it would. He asked if I minded if he fixed himself one and I told him to have at it, I'd drink vicariously.

When he'd settled into an armchair across from me he said, "Okay, I'm ready for the big reveal."

"Let me tell it in the form of a story," I said.

"Who doesn't like a good story?" Lowe said.

Now we were bonding.

"Claire Megill once told me she hired Darius Baker because he knew more about modern finance than she and Andrew Crain combined," I said. "Following the money at Lith wasn't Andrew's primary skill. He was a science guy at heart. Claire said that from the time she'd first gone to work for him he'd talked about his money guys as if they were neuroscientists. And then, as you know, he set out to save the world. So Claire thought it was almost like checks and balances, trying to stay aware of where the checks were going."

"There was no need," Lowe said. "I was always transparent with Andrew about what was coming in and what was going out."

"Of course you were!" I said, worried that I sounded too enthusiastic, or eager to please.

I had seen him pour himself tequila. He drank some now. I was aware that in a fitness-crazed world, tequila had become a drink of choice because of the low sugar content. I just thought it made grown men and women whoop.

"Anyway," I continued, "it turns out that things got complicated when Laura Crain got suspicious about how you'd pulled the rabbit out of the hat during that period when it looked as if Lith might go under."

"Don't be stupid," Lowe said. "That was never going to happen."

I grinned. "Be that as it may," I said. "But while maybe you had certainty about that, Laura didn't. She didn't like Claire very much, so she couldn't go to her. But her husband must have told her what a sharp kid Darius was. So she trusted him with the task of, well, following the money for real. More Andrew's than yours."

I was taking some big leaps, at least with some of this. But believed this version of things to be accurate, around what Marty Kaiser had intuited.

"And you think you know all of this . . . *how*?" Lowe said.

"As it happens," I said, "I am now in possession of the information on Darius's cloud, and what a lucky boy am I because of it."

I didn't tell him that I had also gotten into Laura Crain's personal information, after breaking into the Brookline house and actually finding passwords inside her old-fashioned Filofax. But there was no point. And I really didn't need her information once I had Darius Baker's, thanks to Cindy Patton's friend from Proscape, who had gotten me all the way to this meeting with Ethan Lowe.

"Somehow Darius accessed the 'Sources and Users' reports for the two partners. Yours and Andrew's," I said. "I guess that's as good a place to pick up as any."

I could hear Marty Kaiser's voice inside my head, even though he had occasionally lost me talking about superusers and off-site storage and the kind of history on the cloud, because he was a bit of a computer geek himself.

"I frankly don't know how Darius figured out how to access the files from you," I said. "But he did, probably because of some inspired hacking on his part. And from his own records, he analyzed money going in and money going out over the past few years, and how it just didn't seem to add up."

I told him the rest of it then the way Marty had told it to me, just not nearly as well.

"In the last month of his life, Darius Baker somehow managed to access the codes for money coming in from off-site storage of company files, from the period when Lith was in big trouble that you'd frankly created. Only during that period, the money suddenly wasn't coming through JPMorgan the way it usually did. It was coming from a different bank. UBS. Lots and lots of money." I shrugged again, and smiled, what I hoped was sheepishly. "But I'm not telling you anything you don't know."

"It's called diversifying, Mr. Spenser," Lowe said, a bit dismissively, I thought. "And nothing I did was illegal, though you probably wouldn't know anything about that."

"What I *do* know," I said, "is how strict UBS's policies are about privacy for their clients."

I actually hadn't known that. But the world's greatest accountant sure had.

"Even Hitler had a Swiss bank account," I added. "Did you know that?"

Lowe's tequila had gone untouched now.

"Long story short?" I said. "What we found in Darius's history, as well as he tried to cover his tracks, was that the money you needed to keep the big wheel turning and maybe even Proud Mary to keep on burning had come from Saudi Arabia. Of all places." I shook my head slowly from time to time, like I was the one explaining things to a slow kid in class. "Oh, Ethan," I said. "You've been a very bad boy."

Lowe stared at me, maybe blinking a little more rapidly, the way his partner did under stress.

"Because you went panhandling to the country that is your partner's sworn enemy because of the truly shitty way it treats women," I said. "Now Darius knew, and he told Laura what he had. Then she knew. The one thing I'll never know is why she confronted you when she found out. Maybe she wanted to give you the chance to deny it, or at least explain it, before she went to her husband. Maybe she didn't want to believe it was true. Or didn't want to send her husband any further around the bend than he already was. But she knew that if it *was* true, you were fucked, because of language she knew existed in the partners' agreement giving her husband the right to buy your forty percent, as long as he had cause. And Saudi Arabia sure as shit would have been enough cause for Andrew Crain, whether he was in a diminished mental state at the time or not."

I breathed in deeply through my nose, out through my mouth, loudly, and largely for effect.

"And all of this, Ethan, just to put a bow on things," I said, "is why I believe you had to have Laura and Darius killed."

I shook my head from side to side, more slowly than before, and more sadly.

"Funny how things turn out, really," I said. "Laura Crain came to me because she thought her husband had gone crazy. But the crazy partner turned out to be you."

SEVENTY-EIGHT

"No wonder you didn't want a drink," Lowe finally said. "Clearly you're already drunk."

"Only with power," I said.

He got up now and walked over to his bar and poured more tequila, came back and sat down.

"You've literally taken numbers out of thin air, *out* of the clouds, and convinced yourself that they're facts," he said.

"Here's a fact," I said. "I've got your ass. And as soon as the cops figure out a way to get DNA from your pal Reggie and I match it to what it turns out they ultimately found on Laura Crain's body, I'm going to have his ass, too." This wasn't entirely true—there had been no DNA on Laura's body—but Ethan didn't have to know that.

It wouldn't have happened without Cindy Patton. Or

her friend from Proscape, who had become a super-provider in more ways than one. All because Cindy had convinced him to do the right thing. People still did that, whether there was anything in it for them or not.

Something I was certain Lowe would never understand.

"You need to go now," Lowe said. "But before you do, just be aware that if you try to take this fever dream of yours to your friend at *The Globe* or anybody else, I will have *your* ass in litigation when hell freezes over with you in it."

I stood.

"Take your best shot," I said. "Forget about *The Globe* or *The Wall Street Journal* or CNBC. What I'm wondering is how you're going to explain taking that blood money to your partner."

"Oh, spare me your woke bullshit about blood money, Spenser," he said. "Take a look at the real world, and at how much business this country does with the Saudis, and how many other American businesses do the same goddamn thing."

"I thought you and Andrew were supposed to be brothers," I said.

"We are," he said. "I'm Cain. He's Abel."

"What *are* you going to tell Andrew?"

"I don't have to tell Andrew shit," Lowe said. "Andrew wouldn't still have a company if it wasn't for me. He was more interested in saving whales and women. Fuck him. You can tell him that the next time you see him."

I walked over to Lowe and moved the pocket square I was wearing to the side, and showed him the tiny camera that my high-tech thief, by the name of Ghost Garrity, had outfitted me with after he'd helped get me into the Crains' house.

Now I was the science guy, helping the science guy.

"You just told him," I said.

My phone sounded then. I took it out of my pocket and put it on speaker and held it up between Ethan Lowe and me.

The voice was Andrew Crain's.

"Remember that TV show, Ethan?" Crain said, his voice sounding tinny, the way speakerphone calls always did.

Lowe hesitated, then seemed to find his own voice.

"What show is that?" he said.

"The 'you're fired' show," Crain said.

Lowe was staring at the phone in my hand as if it might go off like a grenade.

There was a pause.

"Fuck *me*, Ethan?" Crain said. "No. Fuck *you*."

SEVENTY-NINE

I had flown to Los Angeles, but not to visit Andrew Crain and Claire Megill at Groves. Now I was back, and so were the two of them.

"So who's minding the store now that the big boss bought out the weasel boss?" Hawk said.

Maybe it had been the L.A. weather while I was away. Maybe it had been Z's trainer, and the combination of runs and walks Z and I took along the boardwalk in Santa Monica every morning. But my knee felt as sturdy as it has been since I'd been assaulted that night.

Hawk and I had finished our own morning run, and were walking the last half-mile along the Charles.

"The public version is that Andrew Crain is back in charge," I said. "But it is my belief that Claire Megill, who is probably more qualified than Crain or Ethan Lowe at this point, is the real point person."

We stopped and sat on the bench that was just a few yards past the head statue of Arthur Fiedler. The old boy was still looking good.

"How's it hanging, Pops," Hawk had said, rubbing the head for luck.

"I see what you did there with Pops," I said.

"'Course you did."

I leaned back and felt the morning sun on my face.

"So the merger's dead," Hawk said.

"Deader than the Sox."

"Where's Lowe at?"

"Claire says the Maldives," I said.

"No extradition, it ever comes to that. Least the boy did something smart."

"Just to give you a heads-up?" I said. "I'm not giving up on tying him to the murders, even if he ends up living on the moon."

"Murders you believe got committed by the badass Brit brother," Hawk said. "And where's the brother at, by the way?"

"Parts unknown," I said. "But if I have anything to say about it, not for long. I'll get to him eventually, same as I'm going to get to Lowe."

"Take me with you," Hawk said.

"I assumed that was understood."

"Crain sounds like he's as sure Lowe got Smythe to do it as you are," Hawk said.

"Which is why Crain wants to hire me now the way his wife did," I said. "She wanted to find out what was wrong with him. Now he wants me to find the guy he believes killed her."

"On account of he can't get to Lowe," Hawk said.

Hawk leaned his own head back. It was like watching the sun reflect off a smooth black stone gem.

"You think Crain can really put his Humpty Dumpty self back together?" Hawk said.

"Esoteric language like that, I can't believe you weren't the one treating him out there."

"*Do* you think he can get put back together?" Hawk asked.

"Guy's pretty damaged," I said. "But Susan doesn't think beyond repair. And would be ready to help, if he ever asked her for it."

"Susan gives up on people about as easy as you do," Hawk said.

Hawk turned his head to admire two young women in impossibly tight running pants and tighter tops, if such a thing were even sartorially possible given the way their pants fit them, until they disappeared up the path. Being a good friend, I joined him with my own laserlike focus just to keep him company.

"Couldn't understand why you went out to L.A. when you went," he said.

"But now you do."

"Uh-huh."

"I was right, just not the way I thought."

"No law got passed that you got to tell him," Hawk said. "Or tell her."

"I've given that some consideration," I said. "But then decided that I can't help myself, I am just one transparent sonofabitch."

It had taken a substantial amount of old-fashioned

legwork from Zebulon Sixkill and me, around what turned out to be a pleasant visit with him, and Mattie, in our spare time. I had even met Mattie's zombie actor. And while I didn't love the guy, I also didn't feel the urge to rearrange his disgustingly perfect features.

Maybe Cindy Patton had been right.

Maybe I was the cool dad.

"So you gonna tell them what you went and found out?" Hawk said.

I nodded.

"Forthwith?" he said.

I nodded again.

"Was gonna go with 'anon,'" Hawk said. "But I decided in this case bigger was better."

He smiled and further brightened the day,

"Something you wouldn't know nothing about," Hawk said.

EIGHTY

Claire Megill was once again conducting regular hours at her office. She'd informed me that Andrew Crain was not, but was at least showing up for a couple hours every day, so that people on the fiftieth floor could see him back at work, and the people down on the forty-ninth would hear about him being back at work.

Claire's office looked the same. But so much had changed, for both of us, since I'd first been inside it.

I previously hadn't taken any notice of the small display of framed photographs near the big window behind her, but did now.

She sat at her desk. I sat across from her, as if I were the one in the client chair now.

"How's he doing?" I said.

"A little better every day," she said. "For the time being

I've moved into the house on Chestnut with him." She smiled. "As a friend."

"I don't judge," I said.

"The hell you don't," she said.

She really did have beautiful eyes.

"So have you decided to come work for Andrew?" she said. "He continues to be of the belief that only you, and you alone, can prove that Ethan really was behind those murders."

"If I do decide to stay with it," I said, "it would be on the house. I still feel as if I owe it to Laura and to Darius."

"I doubt Andrew would agree to it."

"It won't be up to him."

"You really are exceptionally stubborn."

I winked at her. "Don't judge," I said.

She spoke of the intense treatment he'd gotten in California, and how she'd been a participant in some of it, almost as if it were an Al-Anon meeting for a family member, now that she was all the family he had.

"Such endless abuse in his life," she said, "starting with his parents and extending all the way to me."

"I wouldn't have ever known about his father if he hadn't blurted it out the night he threatened to shoot Whitson," I said.

She sighed. It was almost a mournful sound. "His primary doctor believes that what Clay did to me was a trigger for the way he has been acting." She shook her head. "It's amazing that he's been able to function as well as he has as an adult, and be as successful. His father treated his mother the way he did. The woman he would marry was abused after that. Then me."

"But he wasn't the only one in a cycle of abuse, was he?" I said.

Claire Megill looked puzzled. "I'm not sure I understand."

"I'm not entirely sure I do, either, to tell you the truth," I said.

I reached for the inside pocket of my blazer and took out the photograph that Z had come up with, and slid it across the desk to her.

The head shot of a young man who really did look a little like Brad Pitt.

She reacted as if she'd seen a ghost, mostly because she had.

"That's a picture of . . . That's my husband," she said.

"Troy Robinson," I said. "But Laura called him Rob."

EIGHTY-ONE

She started to reach for the photo from the Screen Extras Guild that had finally been discovered, though Troy Robinson hadn't joined SAG before he left Claire Megill and left Los Angeles and headed east.

Then it had taken most of the week I was out in L.A. to finally trace him to the address at which Claire had still been living with her young son when she went to work for Andrew Crain, at one of the businesses that Crain and Ethan Lowe had acquired about five years after the start-up of Lith.

Claire's hand, shaking slightly, hovered over the photograph like a drone, as if she were afraid to touch it.

She looked at me. "Did you find out . . . Do you know what happened to him?"

The view behind her was as clear and perfect and every bit as thrilling as it had been the first time I had been on this floor, and in this office. What looked like a graduation picture of her son, either high school or college, was on that table next to her. He had some of his mother in his face. But even from a few feet away, I could see that he was the spitting image of his father, what his father had looked like at that age. Same dirty blond hair. If I looked closer, I was sure I would see the same blue eyes.

"No," I said. "As a matter of fact, I don't know what happened to him."

"But I do," Andrew Crain said from behind me.

I hadn't heard him come into her office. I'm not sure she had even seen him, as fixed as she was on the photograph of Troy Robinson, as clearly knocked back as she was by her husband being in this room with us.

Crain shut the door quietly behind him, came around the desk, stood next to Claire Megill, putting a hand on her shoulder.

She looked up at him. But Crain was looking directly at me.

"I killed him," he said.

EIGHTY-TWO

He took us down the hall to his own office.

When we arrived there and he'd shut the door he said, "I'm going to assume you're not wearing another of your recording devices, Mr. Spenser."

"I'm not," I said. "And that's not why I'm here, you must know that."

The office was at least three or four times the size of Claire Megill's. The three of us sat in a corner that was like the small living room of a hotel suite. Crain and Claire were on a small silk sofa. I sat in a matching chair across from them.

The view in here was even better. More windows.

Claire Megill had not spoken since we'd left her office. Now she did.

"How, Andrew?" she said.

He told us both about Troy, who his wife had known

as Rob, putting Laura Mason in the hospital, and Missy Jones telling Crain about that, but how Laura was going to be safe after Missy had literally taken matters into her own hands. Or her father had.

"But he didn't leave town the way he said he would," Crain said. "He came back. Missy Jones didn't know that. I did."

He turned to face Claire Megill.

"I went to see Laura one night later that summer," he said. "He had beaten her again. Not badly enough to put her in the hospital this time. But badly enough. And Rob told her that if she told anybody this time, if anybody came after him, he was going to kill her."

I said to Claire Megill, "Did he hit you? Your husband?"

She shook her head. "At the end," she said. Then in a whisper she said, "Maybe he didn't love me as much as he loved Laura."

She put quotes around "loved."

"He blamed me for the pregnancy," she said.

Crain said he stayed with Laura that night, taking the couch in her apartment. When she was finally asleep, he snuck in and got her phone and texted the man he knew only as Rob, texting just starting to become popular at the time. Crain told Troy Robinson, using Laura's phone, that she still loved him, and wanted to meet him and just talk.

"Where?" I said.

"It doesn't matter where."

"How did you kill him?"

"I shot him," he said. "I really am a very good shot when someone like you isn't rushing me."

"What did you do with the body?"

"I disposed of it." He shrugged. "I'm a scientist, remember?"

He seemed quite composed, and clear-eyed, in light of the story he was telling.

"Then I went away for a couple years, to deal with what I'd done," he said. "Like I was trying to escape myself. When I came back, Laura and I were finally together and Ethan and I hit it big with Lith. And I have been trying to bury what I did ever since underneath good works."

No one spoke. Claire Megill was still turned to him, but staring vacantly past him at the same time, as if in a mild state of shock. I had come here expecting some sort of reaction from her.

Not from him.

And not this.

"For all of these years," he said, "it's been like that Poe story, about the telltale heart. No matter what I did and no matter where I went, what I'd done was there. Finally I became obsessed with the man I'd killed, wanting to know more about him other than what he'd done to Laura. I did what Mr. Spenser did, and finally traced him back to you. But I had one advantage that Mr. Spenser didn't. I'd taken his California driver's license, the night I killed him."

"You found Claire and her son," I said.

"She was working at Apple at the time," Crain said, "but she and her son were just scraping by."

"Then one day I got the call from the headhunter," she said, shifting her head slightly and looking at me, as if picking up the story.

"The headhunter called because I told him to call, and

to offer you a much better job, at much higher compensation," Crain said. "After that, the law of unintended consequences took over. Because you weren't some charity case, you turned out to be brilliant. And ultimately, for me, indispensable. Now more than ever."

He took her hands in his now.

"I wanted to save you both," he said to her. "That night with Whitson, I was ready to kill again, as much as I'd fought the urge to do that, for as long as I had."

Claire Megill started to say something, didn't.

"You can't escape your own past forever," Andrew Crain said. "I realize that now."

I didn't have anything to add to that, for either one of them, so I headed for the elevators. Forthwith.

EIGHTY-THREE

"So both the partners at Lith, Inc. get away with murder," Susan Silverman said.

"I hadn't thought of it precisely that way, but I suppose you're right, Doctor," I said.

It was Sunday at her house. We were in her kitchen, and I was about to prepare brunch.

"His break with reality obviously came when he wanted to kill again," she said. "Whitson, in this case. He had fought the urge as long as he could. To kill Whitson the way he had killed the man he knew as Rob."

"Claire was being abused the way Laura had been," I said. "But he didn't want to kill again."

"Who does?" Susan said.

"Only then Whitson went after her again, and he went after Whitson, and I stopped him," I said.

"And my hero became his," Susan said. "It is almost a festival of symmetry."

"And you call me a poet."

"No," she said, "you call yourself a poet."

I was preparing Belgian waffles, doing them up big, from scratch, flour and sugar and milk and baking powder and too much butter, three large eggs, freshly sliced strawberries on the side, Vermont maple syrup, and, wait for it, even freshly whipped cream. Susan called the whole thing the Triple Bypass. She was still in her favorite white robe. I was in a LARAMIE WYOMING T-shirt she ordered from The Knothole in Laramie, and sweatpants. She sat at the butcher-block table while I cooked. At some point after we ate we would walk Pearl and then, if all went according to plan, be back in her bed for yet another matinee.

I liked Sundays with Susan very much.

I poured more Dunkin' coffee for both of us.

"So in the end we are talking about an otherwise good and moral man committing a terrible and immoral act," Susan said.

"We are."

"A terrible and immoral act for which you have given him a full pardon," she said.

"He'll never fully pardon himself," I said. "I think of it more as clemency. For a crime, incidentally, I could never prove."

She held her mug in elegant fingers and stared at me over it with eyes dark and deep. It was past noon and she had not yet done her face. She was still the most beautiful woman I had ever known. I told her something then I told her often: If she ever left me, she just needed to give me time to pack a bag, because I was going with her.

She got up then and came around the table and got behind me and got up on her toes and kissed me behind my ear.

"I love you," she said.

"I loved you first."

"I'm not sure that is verifiable," Susan said. "But I'll take it."

She kept her arms around me.

"Everything you now know," she said. "Is it enough?"

"I'm afraid it's going to have to be," I said. "In the words of the philosopher Dirty Harry, man's got to know his limitations."

"As I recall from all the times you made me watch that movie, he said that right before he blew up Hal Holbrook's car."

"Boy," I said, "those were the days."

I told her to sit down and prepare herself, if she possibly could, for the brunch of her dreams.

"It's funny," I said. "I couldn't get it out of my head that Troy Robinson was a part of this. It just wasn't the way I ever could have imagined."

"Even you're not that smart, big boy," she said.

We ate. And walked Pearl. And made love in the big bed in the middle of the afternoon. She was leaving in a few hours for New York, a two-day psychotherapy conference. When it was time, I drove her to Logan Airport, Pearl in the backseat. I always hated saying goodbye to Susan, even when she was leaving for just a couple days. A week in Los Angeles had seemed like a couple lifetimes for me.

When she had disappeared into the terminal, Pearl and I drove back to Marlborough Street and I threw one of her old tennis balls until I thought my arm would detach from my shoulder, then let her frolic for a while with a golden retriever, the other dog seeming to have as much energy as my own. We went back to the apartment and I fed her and fed myself with huevos rancheros, which I ate while watching, but paying scant attention to, *Sunday Night Football.*

When the game was over I felt the same sort of restlessness I had been feeling the past few days. Susan had asked if knowing what I knew was enough for me. I had told her it would have to be. But knew in my heart it never would be. Because I would never know for sure exactly how two innocent people had died. Or be able to prove that Ethan Lowe and Reggie Smythe were behind it, though I knew they were.

I had taken Frank Belson to lunch the day before and finally laid out everything I knew, excluding only what Andrew Crain had told me about Troy Robinson, because that got Belson nowhere on either Laura Crain or Darius Baker.

"I did everything I could, Frank," I told him.

"I'll tell Quirk," Belson said. "He'll probably want to give you a participation trophy."

I stared out my window. The nights were getting longer, and the temperature had dropped, and, combined with the rain that had started to fall when Pearl and I were back in the apartment, blanketed the Back Bay in fog.

"A foggy day . . ." I crooned.

Pearl was underneath the TV. She briefly picked up her head as I began to sing, but then put it right back down, realizing the song wasn't about food.

I had found out more than I had bargained for, a lot more, and it wasn't unreasonable to think of that as a form of closure.

But was closure without justice enough?

Z had joked about me and loose ends, but we both knew loose ends were no joke, not for me.

I put on my leather jacket, the old thing impervious by now to rain, and went outside and walked past the river, the lights of Cambridge on the other side dimmed mightily by the fog.

"Take the damn win," Hawk had said.

"Even if it feels like a tie?" I said.

I passed Arthur Fiedler and began walking toward Mass Ave. Somehow the fog made the city and the water and even the traffic seem more quiet. I wasn't looking for peace out here. Just less restlessness.

I turned up the collar of my jacket and told myself it would be a short walk tonight because Susan was probably at her hotel in Midtown Manhattan by now and I wanted to call her.

I was the only one out here.

Or thought so.

"Spenser," I heard from behind me.

I recognized both the voice and the accent.

When I turned I saw only the outline of him, twenty or so yards away.

I could see his arm outstretched.

"Even with you," Reggie Smythe said, "I felt it wouldn't be sporting to shoot you in the back. But get those hands nice and high, you darling boy. Because I can guarantee you that I won't miss this time."

"Not that *you* asked, Reg," I said, "but I'm unarmed."

"I don't care," he said.

He did miss with the first bullet, as it turned out.

Just not the second, which hit me high up on the left side, just below my shoulder, and spun me half around and staggered me off the path and down toward the water.

EIGHTY-FOUR

The feeling of being shot was as I remembered it, because you never forget. I could still vividly and painfully recall being shot by the Gray Man, going into the Charles River by choice that time, my only chance I had at self-preservation, and the Gray Man thinking that he had fired kill shots when he had not.

My left shoulder felt as if someone had set fire to it.

But I was not all the way in the river this time, just in wet grass and mud at the water's edge, turning myself enough to see Smythe jogging to cover the distance between us.

I knew by now he had a suppressor.

He fired again into the fog, this bullet missing me but splattering mud I felt hit me in the face.

I screamed as if the bullet had hit me and thrashed around briefly and then lay still.

"I told our Mr. Lowe he couldn't scare you off with a couple of bully boys, you weren't the type," Smythe said. "And then I told him to let me finish the job after I missed, but he said he'd thought it was over and he was too close to getting everything he wanted."

I heard him sigh. He was very close by now.

"You really did kill them both, didn't you?"

He ignored the question.

"Even though everything has now been buggered up beyond belief, I still can't take the chance that what you told him about my DNA was true," he said softly.

He was down off the walking path then, slipping slightly as he made his way to me, righting himself. The moon was hidden by the night. I couldn't make out his face.

I didn't know how much blood I was losing, but had to assume it was a lot. My left arm had gone numb. He had made his way back to me then, and was raising his gun, for what I knew would be the last time.

"May I say one last thing?" I said.

"I'd make it fast."

"I lied about the DNA," I said. "And I also lied about being unarmed, you dumb bastard."

Then came up with the gun I'd told him I didn't have and shot him in the chest, center mass, and then again, and saw him stumble and go into the Charles River, face-first into it, arms and legs extended.

Dead man's float.

EIGHTY-FIVE

Somehow it was the week before Thanksgiving.

The stitches underneath the front of my left shoulder had been removed, and I had stopped wearing a sling, but was still in the early stages of rebuilding my left hook at Henry Cimoli's gym. Day at a time.

Claire Megill had stopped by my office, and was seated in the same chair where it had all begun with Laura Crain.

"I don't know if you've heard," she said. "But Ethan Lowe seems to have disappeared from the home he was renting in the Maldives."

"Is that so?" I said.

"He was last seen hiking near Mount Villingili," she said. "It's the highest point there, though not all that high."

"Good to know," I said.

"Maybe Andrew was right," I said. "That day in his office. Maybe in the end you can't escape your past."

I smiled. She smiled.

"Anyway," she said, "I just thought you should know, and wanted to thank you again for caring as much as you did. And do."

"I'm curious about something," I said.

"Curious to the end."

"Do you plan to tell your son about what really happened to his father?" I said. "Who his father really was."

She stopped smiling, and shook her head, and looked quite sad. Still beautiful. But sad.

"Some things *should* stay buried," she said.

Before she left, she told me that Crain had entered into negotiations with the Prise car people, not for a merger this time, but to sell them his company. And that she and Crain were planning a trip around the world once everything was in place, like some sort of tour of his good causes.

"What about Saudi Arabia?" I said.

"It will be our first stop," she said. She paused and said, "On our way to wherever the two of us are going to end up, and whatever we're going to be."

She hugged me before walking out the door. Hawk and I were meeting for a drink at the Rowes Wharf Bar in an hour or so.

It gave me just enough time.

When he opened the door, after I had bluffed my way past his doorman with almost breathtaking ease, and knowing my left was nothing these days, I hit him with the right hand that had only gotten better since I'd used it on Reggie Smythe in front of my building that night.

I was almost certain, just from the sound and the feeling in my knuckles when I connected, that I had broken Clay Whitson's nose.

He was already bleeding all over his white shirt and onto his off-white carpet as he managed to get himself into a sitting position.

But he was still a smart lawyer, even now. It meant smart enough to not even consider getting to his feet, and then trying to come at me.

"What was that for?" he said.

"For every woman who ever got hit by somebody like you," I said.

Then I went to meet Hawk at the bar.

Acknowledgments

As always, I must first acknowledge David and Daniel Parker, who continue to give me the high honor of continuing their father's characters.

My agent, Esther Newberg, is the one who got me into the game in the first place, telling me one summer day to write a sample chapter in the voice of Sunny Randall, and now here we are.

You simply cannot ask for a better or more supportive boss than I have with Ivan Held, the capo di tutti capi at Putnam.

One final and heartfelt thanks to a wonderful editor named Danielle Dieterich, literally my partner in crime on so many books in the Parker-sphere.

And last, but certainly not least, my gratitude once again to Capt. John Fisher of the Bedford (Mass.) Police Deparment; the great Ziggy Alderman, still giving me the business; and Peter Gethers, spitballer supreme.